MARITIMEA

ABOVE AND BENEATH THE WAVES

MARITIMEA

ABOVE AND BENEATH THE WAVES

Foreword
Philippe Cousteau

Chief Consultant
Charles F. Gritzner

MILLENNIUM HOUSE

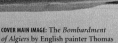

First published in 2009 by
Millennium House Pty Ltd
52 Bolwarra Road, Elanora Heights
NSW, 2101, Australia

ISBN: 978-1-921209-62-8

SALES
For all sales, please contact:
Millennium House Pty Ltd
52 Bolwarra Road, Elanora Heights
NSW, 2101, Australia
Ph: (612) 9970 6850 Fax: (612) 9913 3500
Email: info@millenniumhouse.com.au
Website: www.millenniumhouse.com.au

Printed in China by Sing Cheong Printing Co Ltd
Color Separation by Pica Digital Pte Ltd, Singapore

AUTHORS
Millennium House would be happy to receive
submissions from authors. Please send brief
submissions to:
editor@millenniumhouse.com.au

PHOTOGRAPHERS AND ILLUSTRATORS
Millennium House would be happy to receive
submissions from photographers or illustrators.
Please send submissions to:
editor@millenniumhouse.com.au

PUBLISHER
Gordon Cheers

ASSOCIATE PUBLISHER
Janet Parker

ART DIRECTOR
Stan Lamond

PROJECT MANAGERS
Loretta Barnard, Janet Parker

CHIEF CONSULTANT
Charles F. Gritzner

CONTRIBUTORS
Gary Aguiar, Donald J. Berg, Roland Boer,
Robert Coenraads, Adam Clulow, Roman
Cybriwsky, Alan Edenborough, David W.
Greenfield, Charles F. Gritzner, Jeffrey Gritzner,
David Hamper, James Inglis, Nicholas Irving,
Thomas Lewis, Bruce V. Millett, Jonathan Nally,
Tanya Patrick, Zoran Pavlovic, Richard Pelvin,
Douglas A. Phillips, Robyn Stutchbury, Aswin
Subanthore, Noel Tait, H. Jesse Walker

COVER DESIGN
Stan Lamond

DESIGNER
Avril Makula

EDITORS
Loretta Barnard, Helen Cooney, Kate
Etherington, James Inglis, Heather Jackson,
Carol Jacobson, Dannielle Viera, Jan Watson

PICTURE RESEARCH
Carol Jacobson, Kathy Lamond, Chantal
MacClelland, Tracy Tucker, Michael van Ewijk

ILLUSTRATORS
Andrew Davies, Glen Vause

CARTOGRAPHIC CONSULTANT
Damien Demaj

CARTOGRAPHERS
Marion Byass, Warwick Jacobson

INDEX
Di Harriman

PRODUCTION
Simone Russell

PUBLISHING ASSISTANT
Michelle Di Stefano

COVER MAIN IMAGE: The *Bombardment of Algiers* by English painter Thomas Luny (1759–1837).

FRONT COVER INSETS (LEFT TO RIGHT): Golden butterflyfish, lyretail, and coral reef in the Red Sea; *The Death of Captain Cook*, painted in 1781 by George Carter (1737–1794); the great white shark (*Carcharodon carcharias*), one of the largest marine predators; detail from a 1599 map of the Pacific, China, and America by Abraham Ortelius (1527–1598). The *Queen Victoria* joined the Cunard Line's cruise ship fleet in 2007.

PAGE 1: An early nineteenth-century print of a giant octopus attacking a galleon.

PAGES 2–3: *The Act of Sacrifice by Captain Desse toward the Dutch ship 'Columbus'* by J.A. Theodore Gudin (1802–1880).

PAGES 4–5: Scientists descend an ice breaker research ship to study Arctic waters.

PAGES 6–7: Dolphins (*Delphinus delphis*) and northern anchovies (*Engraulis mordax*) off the coast of Mexico.

PAGES 8–9: Fishing boats moored at Rupen, a fishing village on India's west coast.

PAGES 12–13: The mantle around the edge of a giant clam (*Tridacna sp.*).

PAGE 20–21: A NASA image of Earth's ocean floor from space.

PAGE 28–29: The Phare d'Ar-Men lighthouse, Brittany, France.

PAGE 44–45: Chinstrap penguins (*Pygoscelis antarcticus*) on an iceberg in Antarctica.

PAGE 138–139: The Great Barrier Reef, Queensland, Australia.

PAGE 154–155: A marbled stargazer (*Uranoscopus bicinctus*) hiding under the sand.

PAGE 226–227: *The Death of Captain Cook* by George Carter (1737–1794).

PAGE 296–297: *A Sea Battle with Sardinian and Venetian Warships* by Luca Carlevariis (1663–1729).

PAGE 342–343: *The Rainbow* by Russian artist Ivan Aivazovsky (1817–1900).

PAGE 386–387: The port of Marseille, France, by eighteenth-century artist Claude Joseph Vernet (1714–1789).

PAGE 398–399: Four new liquid natural gas (LNG) carriers docked at Goje Island, Republic of Korea, in February 2009.

PAGE 414–415: The SuperAviator, a one-atmosphere two-person submarine designed for deep-sea exploration.

Foreword

As the author Arthur C. Clarke once wrote, "How inappropriate to call this planet Earth, when clearly it is planet Ocean."

Our history with the oceans is long and complex, from ancient Phoenician mariners who spent their lives plying the waters of the Mediterranean to the giant cruise ships that cross the Atlantic in mere days. The oceans have had a defining influence on our cultural, political, and economic development since *Homo sapiens* first stood upright on the shores of East Africa and stared out upon her vast expanse.

And yet, despite the fact that over two-thirds of our planet is covered by water, more than 90 percent of the oceans remain unexplored. From mountain ranges that stretch 31,000 miles (50,000 km) in length—four times longer than the Andes, Rockies, and Himalayas combined—to the Mariana Trench, which, at more than a mile deeper than Mount Everest is tall, is the lowest known point on Earth; and from coral reefs that are more diverse than tropical rainforests to the tiny box jellyfish, which carries enough poison in each tentacle to kill 60 grown men, the oceans are full of wonders that can hardly be imagined. Perhaps even more amazingly, the oceans nurture all life on our planet, providing up to 70 percent of our oxygen, regulating our climate, and providing the majority of protein to over 1 billion people.

My own travels have brought me to all the oceans from the Arctic to the Southern Ocean. While I have witnessed incredible wonders, I have also seen tremendous changes. Between 70 and 100 million sharks a year are killed, mostly to supply the shark fin soup trade; 25 percent of coral reefs are gone and another 25 percent are in desperate peril; fishery after fishery is collapsing; shifting ocean currents are melting ice caps and destroying kelp forests; the list goes on and on. However, the key to a sustainable planet is simple—humans armed with knowledge and passion. *Maritimea* is an inspiring exploration of the beauty and majesty of our oceans, a fascinating collection of what we know. It reminds us of the vital role that oceans play on this planet and arms us with the knowledge necessary to recognize the critical responsibility we all have to protect and restore what my father once called "our water planet."

PHILIPPE COUSTEAU

EARTH is an epic publishing feat never to be repeated, proudly created by Millennium House

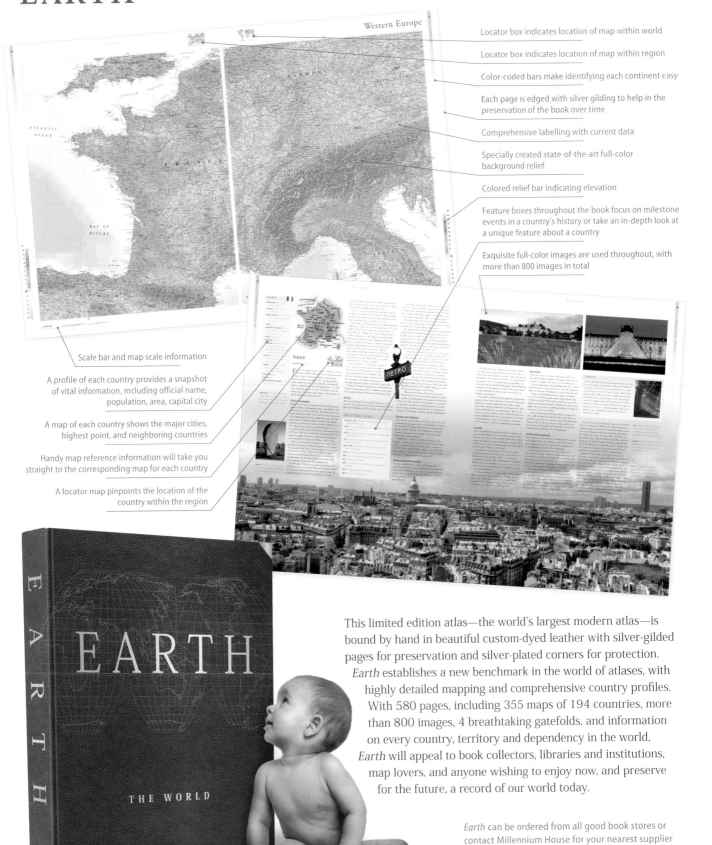

Western Europe

Locator box indicates location of map within world

Locator box indicates location of map within region

Color-coded bars make identifying each continent easy

Each page is edged with silver gilding to help in the preservation of the book over time

Comprehensive labelling with current data

Specially created state-of-the-art full-color background relief

Colored relief bar indicating elevation

Feature boxes throughout the book focus on milestone events in a country's history or take an in-depth look at a unique feature about a country

Exquisite full-color images are used throughout, with more than 800 images in total

Scale bar and map scale information

A profile of each country provides a snapshot of vital information, including official name, population, area, capital city

A map of each country shows the major cities, highest point, and neighboring countries

Handy map reference information will take you straight to the corresponding map for each country

A locator map pinpoints the location of the country within the region

This limited edition atlas—the world's largest modern atlas—is bound by hand in beautiful custom-dyed leather with silver-gilded pages for preservation and silver-plated corners for protection. *Earth* establishes a new benchmark in the world of atlases, with highly detailed mapping and comprehensive country profiles. With 580 pages, including 355 maps of 194 countries, more than 800 images, 4 breathtaking gatefolds, and information on every country, territory and dependency in the world, *Earth* will appeal to book collectors, libraries and institutions, map lovers, and anyone wishing to enjoy now, and preserve for the future, a record of our world today.

Earth can be ordered from all good book stores or contact Millennium House for your nearest supplier

www.millenniumhouse.com.au

Contents

Contributors

CHIEF CONSULTANT

CHARLES F. GRITZNER

Charles F. "Fritz" Gritzner is a Distinguished Professor of Geography at South Dakota State University in Brookings, South Dakota, USA. He is now in his fifth decade of college teaching and research. In addition to teaching, he enjoys travel, research, working with teachers, and writing to share his passion for geography with readers. As a contributor to this volume, he has a wonderful opportunity to combine each of these "hobbies." Professor Gritzner has served as both president and executive director of the National Council for Geographic Education and has received the Council's highest honor—the George J. Miller Award for Distinguished Services to Geographic Education—as well as numerous other honors for teaching and research from the NCGE, the Association of American Geographers, and a number of other organizations.

CONTRIBUTORS

GARY AGUIAR

Gary Aguiar, an Associate Professor of Political Science at South Dakota State University since 1999, teaches courses in American politics. His primary research interest is local politics, including rural politics and policy. He was born and raised in Hilo, Hawaii, where he worked as a tour guide, hotel clerk, and educator. He is active in town politics in Brookings, South Dakota. He earned his PhD from Indiana University–Bloomington.

DONALD J. BERG

Donald J. Berg is Professor of Geography at South Dakota State University, USA. He was born in Fargo, North Dakota, and received his BA (History) and MA (History) from North Dakota State University, and his MA (Geography) and PhD (Geography) from University of California at Berkeley. He served in the United States Army from 1966–1969. Professor Berg has been teaching at South Dakota State University since 1969. He was a contributor to the *Encyclopedia of Global Warming and Climate Change* (SAGE, 2008), the *Encyclopedia of Race, Ethnicity, and Society* (SAGE, 2008), and *Earth* (Millennium House, 2009).

ROLAND BOER

Roland Boer is Research Professor at the University of Newcastle, Australia. He has written 13 books and more than 200 articles on various topics, including politics, culture, history, religion, and travel. His works have been translated into eight languages. Apart from cycling as far as he can, he loves to journey by ship.

ADAM CLULOW

Adam Clulow completed his PhD at Columbia University, USA, and now teaches in the School of Historical Studies at Monash University, Australia. His academic research focuses on the history of piracy and maritime violence in East Asia. Dr Clulow is currently working on a book manuscript that examines the interaction between the Tokugawa state and the Dutch East India Company in early modern Japan.

ROBERT R. COENRAADS

Dr Robert R. Coenraads is a geoscientist and author of many books and scientific publications. He has been an avid explorer of the undersea world since becoming certified with the Professional Association of Diving Instructors (PADI) in 1975. Highlights include diving the sacred Mayan cenotes or limestone sinkholes during archeological expeditions to Mexico's Yucatan Peninsula. During his 30-year career, travel to some of the world's poorest regions has sparked a strong humanitarian interest. Dr Coenraads is President of FreeSchools World Literacy–Australia, and has established a support network providing free education for underprivileged children in India and Thailand. It is his firm belief that education for all, not just a privileged few, is key to solving the world's major problems such as overpopulation and poverty. The privilege of helping write quality educational books, such as *Maritimea*, is a step in this direction.

ROMAN CYBRIWSKY

Roman Cybriwsky is Professor of Geography and Urban Studies at Temple University in Philadelphia, USA. He has lived for many years in Tokyo, Japan, and is an expert on the geography of East and Southeast Asia. His major publications include books and periodical articles about Tokyo, Singapore, Jakarta, Phnom Penh, and other cities. He is a photographer and professional writer as well, working now on a book of photographs about Tokyo with text in Ukrainian and Russian, and the screenplay for *Makarenko Sisters*, a murder mystery set in Tokyo and Kyiv.

ALAN EDENBOROUGH

Alan Edenborough has been involved with maritime heritage, and more particularly, ship restoration, for some 40 years. In the early 1970s, he discovered and salvaged the 1874 barque *James Craig*, now fully restored, which sails again from Sydney, Australia. He now works as a specialist consultant to the Sydney Heritage Fleet and is also editor of the Fleet's quarterly magazine *Australian Sea Heritage*: www.shf.org.au. Alan is a member of the Steering Committee and the Council of the Australian Register of Historic Vessels, a major maritime heritage project of the Australian National Maritime Museum in association with Sydney Heritage Fleet: www.anmm.gov.au/arhv.

DAVID W. GREENFIELD

David W. Greenfield is a Research Associate in the Department of Ichthyology at the California Academy of Sciences in San Francisco and an Emeritus Professor at the University of Hawaii, where he taught ichthyology. Dr Greenfield is also a Research Associate at the Bernice P. Bishop Museum in Honolulu, the Field Museum in Chicago, and the Moss Landing Marine Laboratories in California. He has published over 100 scientific papers on fishes and a book, *Fishes of the Continental Waters of Belize*. He has conducted extensive fieldwork on both freshwater and marine fishes in Northern, Central, and South America. His current research is on the systematics of coral-reef fishes, particularly in the Hawaiian and Fiji Islands, where he has described a number of species new to science.

JEFFREY ALLMAN GRITZNER

Dr Gritzner is a Professor in the Department of Geography at the University of Montana, USA, and executive director of the Earth Restoration Project. He is the author of numerous books, monographs, and articles concerned chiefly with economic development, energy, agro–sylvo–pastoral systems, environmental history, linkages between economic activity and environmental rehabilitation, the drylands of the Islamic World, and New World prehistory. Among the many administrative and executive positions he has held are Vice-Chairman, Commission on Environmental, Economic, and Social Policy, IUCN; Primary Coordinator, Montana Geographic Alliance; International Coordinator, Drynet South Institute; Director, Program on Threatened and Endangered Cultures; Director of Public Policy Research Institute at the University of Montana; Chairman of Great Plains/Rocky Mountain Division of the Association of American Geographers. He is a member of the International Union for Conservation of Nature and Natural Resources (IUCN); the Commission on Ecology; the Ethnozoölogy Specialist Group (SSC); and the World Alliance of Mobile Indigenous Peoples. He has served on the International Editorial Board, Global Environmental Change: Human and Policy Dimensions (1990–2004); the Editorial Board of *The Montana Professor* (1990–present); and the International Editorial Advisory Board, *The Arab World Geographer* (2003–present). Dr Gritzner's work has been recognized in the *International Directory of Distinguished Leadership*, *Who's Who in American Education*, *Who's Who in Science and Engineering*, *Who's Who in the World*, and *World Who's Who in Environment and Conservation*.

DAVID HAMPER

David Hamper is an experienced author and educator. He is currently the Assistant Principal Staff at the International Grammar School, Sydney, Australia. For a number of years, David has been involved in curriculum development in Geography and he has considerable experience in the education and professional development of Geography teachers. David has authored and co-authored many texts on a diverse range of topics including physical and human geography, human rights, ecosystem management, and international relations and agreements. He has also contributed to several atlas projects, including *Earth*, published by Millennium House, and has had numerous articles published in professional journals. David is a passionate traveler and amateur photographer.

JAMES INGLIS

James Inglis is an Australian editor and writer based in Melbourne. He has been published in various national and state newspapers and periodicals, and contributes to books on history, and other humanities and sciences. His book *Fighting Talk* was published in 2008. James is a keen analyst of language, particularly where it is abused for ulterior motives.

NICK IRVING

Nick Irving completed his Bachelor of Arts with Honours in History, and is currently working on a PhD in history at the University of Sydney, Australia. His research interests include military history, the history of peace, and the Cold War.

TOM LEWIS

Dr Tom Lewis is a military and maritime historian who has worked as a naval officer, divemaster, and as a high school teacher. The author of seven books, he holds a PhD in Strategic Studies and an MA in Literature and Politics. Tom has published some 1,100 articles over the last 25 years, mostly in the areas of history and literacy. He has won eight literary prizes and is the editor of two magazines, the popular *Warship*, and *Headmark*, the Journal of the Australian Naval Institute. In 2003, he was awarded the Medal in the Military Division of the Order of Australia for services to naval history.

BRUCE V. MILLETT

Dr Bruce V. Millett specializes in climatology, Geographic Information Systems (GIS), wetland ecology, and remote sensing. He is an Assistant Professor in the Department of Geography at South Dakota State University, USA. He teaches courses in Atmospheric Science, Climate Change, Physical Geography, GIS, and Aerial Photo Interpretation. His research is focused on ecological modeling of northern prairie wetlands in North America. There are three aspects to Dr Millett's work. He reconstructs historic data sets, conducts field surveys, and constructs digital elevation models for use in wetland model simulations. In addition, Dr Millett uses aerial photographs and satellite imagery to map and delineate the physical features of northern prairie wetlands on local and regional scales.

JONATHAN NALLY

Jonathan Nally is an award-winning Australian author, scriptwriter, and broadcaster who specializes in the fields of science and militaria. He has founded and edited several magazines, and is production manager, designer, and contributor to Australian *Warship* magazine. He has also been a regular on Australian radio and television since the early 1990s, appearing on every format from children's television to live news coverage of major technology and science events. These days, he concentrates full time on writing for television, radio, print, and the Internet.

TANYA PATRICK

Tanya Patrick is the editor of the popular children's science magazine *Scientriffic* published by the Australian Commonwealth Scientific and Industrial Research Organisation (CSIRO), and the author of *Polar Eyes—an Antarctic Journey*, an interactive book about Antarctica. Tanya has a background in science and graphic design, and is passionate about making science engaging and accessible. Since becoming editor of *Scientriffic* in 2004, she has written and edited hundreds of stories ranging from dispelling some myths about sharks and backyard biodiversity, to asking readers to count the millipedes marauding their gardens. She was awarded an Australian Antarctic Division Arts fellowship in 2006–2007. The resulting photographs and articles from her journey have been published around the world.

ZORAN "ZOK" PAVLOVIĆ

Zoran "Zok" Pavlović is a geographer who resides and works in Eagan, Minnesota, and teaches at the University of Wisconsin–Barron County. His areas of professional interest and research are traditional cultural geography, primarily the landscape change in geography of viticulture, the evolution of geographic thought, and geographic education. He completed his bachelor's and master's degrees at South Dakota State University and is currently a doctoral candidate in geography at the University

of Minnesota. Since 2001, he has worked as a contributing author to the Chelsea House Publishers/Facts on File's series *Modern World Nations*, *Modern World Cultures*, and *Global Connections*. Most recently, he served on a selected panel that created the *Why Geography is Important* brochure, sponsored by the National Geographic Society and Gilbert M. Grosvenor Center for Geographic Education. He also contributed to Millennium House's *Earth*.

RICHARD PELVIN

Richard Pelvin worked in the Australian Department of Defence and the Australian War Memorial before he became an independent military history researcher and writer. He has published a number of articles and papers on military, naval, and aviation history. He is the author *of ANZAC, An Illustrated History 1914–1918*; *Second World War, A Generation of Australian Heroes*; and *Vietnam, Australia's Ten Year War 1962–1972*. He is currently a research assistant for the Defence Honours and Awards Tribunal and is working on a book on the Royal Australian Navy's Mediterranean operations during World War II.

DOUGLAS A. PHILLIPS

Doug Phillips is a life-long educator who worked in public education for 26 years and has provided over 3,500 trainings and presentations at the local, state, national, and international levels. Doug's specializations are in civic education, geography, history, the other social sciences, and in curriculum development. As a curriculum developer, he has facilitated and helped to write over 100 curricula including post-war national efforts in Macedonia and Bosnia and Herzegovina. He has worked in education at a variety of levels, including elementary and secondary levels, college and university, and at the state department of education level. He started as a classroom teacher and has served in many administrative and leadership positions. He has been President of the National Council for Geographic Education and is the founder of the South Dakota and Alaska Councils for the Social Studies in the United States. Among the many awards he has received is the Outstanding Service Award from the National Council for the Social Studies. He has also received numerous awards in geography, economics, civics, social studies and American history, and has been recognized by the US Congress for his contributions. Doug Phillips was also designated as Mr Social Studies by the Alaska Council for the Social Studies.

ROBYN STUTCHBURY

Robyn Stutchbury has a deep passion for all things natural. After teaching biology for some years, she completed a degree in geology and believes that together, these have given her an exceptional understanding of Earth and its processes. A later graduate qualification in science communication set her on the path of freelance writing. For *Maritimea*, she wrote How the Oceans and Seas were formed; Ocean Floor Dynamics; Basins, Toughs and Trenches; Reefs; The Great Barrier Reef (including notes on Ningaloo Reef); Pacific Ocean Reefs and Atolls, and Other Major Reefs around the World. She was also a contributor to Millennium House's *Natural Disasters* and *Geologica*. Her other writing includes the book *Exploring Nature in Lakes, Rivers and Creeks*,

co-authored with her husband, Dr Noel Tait, and various articles for scientific publications through their company, Peripatus Productions Pty Limited.

ASWIN SUBANTHORE

Aswin Subanthore is a cultural geographer from Chennai, India. Presently he is completing his doctorate at the University of Wisconsin—Milwaukee, USA. Aswin's research investigates the geography of new immigrants on American urban areas, with specific attention to South Asians from post-colonial India. In addition, Aswin Subanthore has contributed to books on Egypt and Saudi Arabia with Chelsea House Publishers in New York as well as a peer-reviewed article on the 2004 Indian Ocean tsunami. On the teaching front, Aswin has instructed cultural and regional geography courses across two American universities for over five years.

NOEL TAIT

While Dr Noel Tait spent his childhood fossicking in rock pools near his home in Sydney, Australia, it was not until he had left school that he realized he could combine his passion for natural history with an academic career. He gained his BSc at the University of Sydney and an MSc and PhD at the Australian National University. He joined the academic staff of the fledgling Macquarie University, Sydney, in 1969. Noel's interest in teaching and research has always centered on the invertebrates for a variety of reasons, not the least of which is their diversity of form and way of life. After all they make up 99 percent of the animal world. They also present their greatest diversity in the oceans and so these same rock pools that first sparked his imagination became his living laboratory. During his teaching career, Noel regularly conducted field excursions to Heron Island at the southern end of the Great Barrier Reef. Here he exposed students to the wonders of the largest and most complex structure ever created by living organisms. In retirement, he has maintained these contacts with students and has also continued collaborative research with colleagues in Australia and overseas. A new and challenging venture has been the production of books on natural history for children with the hope of nurturing this life-long passion for natural history.

H. JESSE WALKER

Harley Jesse Walker, born in Michigan, USA, in 1921, grew up in California, and attended the University of California, Berkeley, where he received his BA and MA degrees. His doctorate is from the Department of Geography and Anthropology at the Louisiana State University (LSU) in the USA. He has been with LSU since 1960, where he is currently Boyd Professor Emeritus. His teaching and research have mainly dealt with coastal geomorphology, hydrology, near-shore oceanography, the cryosphere, and coastal engineering. Research has carried him to all the continents, although Arctic deltas and eastern Asiatic coasts have commanded the most attention. He has been involved with several national and international geomorphology organizations and has written over 150 publications. He was awarded an honorary doctorate from the University of Uppsala, Sweden, the Patron's Royal Gold Medal from the Royal Geographical Society of England, and the Lauréat d'honneur from the International Geographical Union.

Our Water Planet

Oceans—that vast interconnected "global sea"—are Earth's most dominant feature, covering 71 percent of its surface. Yet in many respects this vast body of salt water is the planet's last remaining frontier to reveal its long held secrets. Even though we know much more about the "Blue Planet" today than in times past, many mysteries remain. *Maritimea* represents a bold attempt to summarize and present a comprehensive "state of the art" overview of contemporary knowledge pertaining to the marine environment. Because of the ocean's extreme complexity, this volume has involved the expertise of scholars from many fields of study.

Much of what is known about the marine environment is quite recent. For example, it was not until the mid-twentieth century that scientists began to grasp the concept of plate tectonics, the key to understanding the origin of ocean basins. Many gaps continue to exist in our knowledge of tides, currents, and waves. Only recently has the finite nature of most marine resources been recognized. It was long believed that the ocean was a veritable cornucopia of wealth that could provide food and other resources indefinitely. We now know that this is not the case. Many species already are in sharp decline. The same holds true for using the ocean as a dump for terrestrial refuse. In recent decades, vast garbage patches—some the size of the United States—have been discovered in the mid-Pacific and mid-Atlantic oceans. And waters of the global sea are becoming so polluted that deadly red tides and other dead zones have become common in many coastal areas.

Since humans first gazed upon the seemingly endless expanses of the sea, they have been both

ABOVE Water pollution is a major threat to marine environments. Pollution comes from industrial waste, oil leaking from ships, and countless other forms of garbage. All contribute to the decline in numbers of certain marine species.

BELOW Coral reefs are places of great beauty and biodiversity. Here a school of surgeonfish (*Acanthurus sp.*) swim across a reef in their never-ending search for food.

attracted to and repelled by the ocean. To some populations, both ancient and contemporary, the marine environment offered a wealth of opportunity. Some scholars, for example, have suggested that the seashore of equatorial Africa's Indian Ocean may have been the early home of *Homo sapiens*. There, early humans would have found an abundance of marine life to sustain them. Today, millions of people flock to the coast for recreation, to witness its ever-changing moods, to harvest its riches, to use its waters for recreational purposes, or to use its surface as a far-reaching pathway. In many coastal locations, a narrow ribbon of dense settlement clings along the coastal zone, offering even further evidence of our ongoing attraction to the sea.

Yet to many others, as is suggested by "Here there be monsters" warnings on some early maps, the ocean can also be an ominous and foreboding place—one to be feared and avoided at all costs.

To most early Mediterranean peoples, the Pillars of Hercules (Strait of Gibraltar) was the very end of the known world, beyond which few dared to venture. In the waters beyond, horrible sea monsters, fields of seaweed from which ships could not be freed, and other dreaded obstacles were believed to await those who ventured into the Atlantic. With these and countless other negative images of the marine environment guiding their behavior, it is little wonder that Europeans were among the very last of coastal peoples to venture into the global sea. After all, when Magellan made his epic voyage across the Pacific, the vast ocean already had been crossed thousands of years earlier and by people of numerous cultures.

OCEANIC EXTREMES

The global sea is an environment of superlatives! In nearly every respect, its features dwarf those of their terrestrial counterparts. Were Earth a perfect sphere with a smooth surface, the entire planet would be covered by seawater to a depth of nearly 2 miles (3 km). The world's tallest (bottom-to-top) mountains, deepest gorges, longest mountain ranges, and greatest plateaux and plains are found in the sea, not on dry land. If Mt Everest (the world's highest point above mean sea level) rose from the floor of the deepest ocean trench, its peak would be about 1 mile (1.6 km) below sea level.

Oceans contain a large percentage of the world's biomass and may be home to a majority of the planet's floral and faunal species. The blue whale is the largest animal that ever lived. Full grown, these monsters can reach a length of 105 ft (32 m) and weigh up to 419,000 lbs (190 tonnes). Five of the world's ten deadliest creatures lurk in the marine environment, including the most deadly—the box jellyfish (the most deadly variety being the tiny irukandji).

From a human perspective, the ocean also holds great significance. About half the human population, for example, lives within several hundred miles of salt water. And many of the world's great cities were founded and grew as seaports. A number of thallocracies (sea powers) became the most powerful civilizations of their time. Some of history's greatest battles

ABOVE A sixteenth-century illustration of some imaginary sea monsters from *Cosmographia* by German cartographer Sebastian Münster (1488–1552). The work contained details of both the known and the unknown world.

ABOVE RIGHT The box jellyfish (*Chironex fleckeri*) is found in tropical waters of northern Australia. Venom from just one of these jellyfish can kill more than 50 adult humans.

have been fought on the sea, and the sea has been the venue for some of history's greatest adventures.

DYNAMIC OCEANIC ENVIRONMENT

In many respects, the ocean is kaleidoscopic—it is always changing. Salinity, water temperature, hydrostatic pressure, and other properties change from place to place and time to time. Seawater averages around 3.5 percent salinity, but the figure varies considerably depending upon location. Oceanic temperatures also vary greatly. Water temperature can reach nearly 90°F (32.2° C) in shallow tropical pools, or plunge to 28.9°F (−1.7°C) before turning to ice in cold locations. Water pressure changes vertically, as any swimmer knows. In the Challenger Deep, with almost 7 miles (11 km) of water overhead, hydrostatic pressure reaches 16,000 lbs per square inch (1,125 kg per cm^2)!

The sea is always in motion. Waves gently caress the seashore, or violently crash against the coast and savagely gnaw away land and property. Tides rise and fall like clockwork, in some locations twice a day, and in others but once during the "tidal day" of 24 hours and 50 minutes. In some locations, tidal variations are hardly measurable; in others, such as Canada's Bay of Fundy, they reach extremes of more than 50 ft (15 m). Currents resemble wide rivers of water that flow across the ocean's surface. Those that flow from the equatorial zone transport warm water toward the poles, whereas those that originate in the high latitudes bring colder water to the mid-latitudes. In this way, they greatly affect the climate in many locations. Counter currents also flow deep within the ocean basins. Nature, after all, attempts to maintain equilibrium of sea level.

ABOVE An ocean wave by iconic Japanese artist Hokusai (1760–1849). Ocean waves are caused by the friction of wind at the interface of water and air.

BELOW Waves caused by the El Niño weather phenomenon pummel houses on Laguna Beach, California, USA, in 1983.

SEA–LAND INFLUENCES

The global sea and Earth's terrestrial environments interact with one another in many ways. Such reciprocal influences can be as simple as silt from land erosion entering the sea and being reworked into coastal dunes, beaches, barrier islands, sand spits, or other features resulting from the action of waves, currents, and tides. Or they can be extremely complex, such as the possible link between land temperatures, pressure systems, wind velocity and direction, the formation of an El Niño or La Niña phenomenon, and global temperature and precipitation conditions.

According to most scientific accounts, life began in the sea and some forms eventually adapted to terrestrial conditions. Even humans possess physical characteristics that suggest an ancient marine origin. During our embryonic stage (and in some instances after birth), we have vestigial gill structures, and our blood, minus hemoglobin, very closely resembles the make-up of seawater. It even has been suggested that our erect stance can be attributed to the need to stand erect when walking in shallow coastal water.

The most apparent sea–land influence is atmospheric. Through a process known as the hydrologic cycle, moisture evaporates from the sea, is transported by air currents over land, and then can be precipitated in the form of rain, snow, hail, or sleet. Precipitation, in turn, influences climate, vegetation, animal life habitat, soils, and obviously water features. Temperatures, too, are strongly influenced by marine conditions. The sea itself maintains a fairly constant temperature, so land locations proximate to a large water body experience warmer winters and cooler summers than inland locations at similar latitudes. Water currents, too, can strongly affect temperatures. Because of warm Atlantic currents and prevailing westerly winds, much

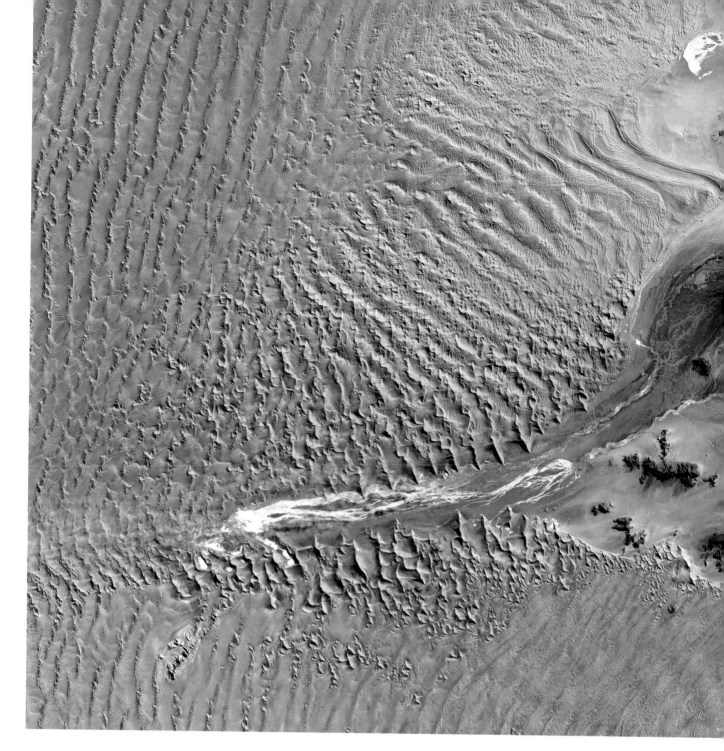

of Western Europe, for example, is much warmer than places located at similar latitudes far inland. Many storms also have all or part of their origin in the sea. Hurricanes form over and feed upon warm tropical waters. Even tornadoes require warm, moist air—in the United States, off the Gulf of Mexico—clashing with cooler dry air in order to form.

LAND–SEA IMPACT

What happens on land also can have a profound impact on marine conditions. Mention already has been made of the oceanic garbage patches in the Pacific and Atlantic oceans. Plastic objects, styrofoam, various

ABOVE Coastal winds in the Namib Desert, Namibia, have created the tallest sand dunes in the world—some dunes are 980 ft (300 m) high. This NASA image was taken in 2000.

wooden objects, and virtually anything that floats can find its way from land to sea and become a pollutant.

Agricultural effluent and nutrient rich run-off from other sources reach the sea where they contribute to the creation of red tides and other dead zones. Oceanic salinity is higher in areas of high evaporation and lower in places where rivers discharge large amounts of fresh water into the ocean. Because it is less dense, fresh water "floats" as a lens atop salt water resulting, for example, in the presence of fresh surface water several hundred miles off the mouth of the Amazon River.

Icebergs—a potential threat to shipping in the North Atlantic—are huge masses of ice calved from

terrestrial glaciers. A small number of marine species are anadromous, able to live in both salt and fresh water. The best-known example is the Pacific salmon. It spends its life at sea, but returns to the stream in which it was born so it can spawn. Certain types of eels and sharks also pass freely between saline and freshwater environments.

HUMANS AND THE SEA

It is a uniquely human characteristic to classify, label, and occasionally imbue features with mystical significance. The results can be mystifying. For example, such varied features as inland saltwater bodies (such as Salton, Galilee, Azov), a large portion of the central North Atlantic Ocean (Sargasso), and the waters that occupy many coastal indentations all bear the name "Sea." Simple perusal of a world map, however, will reveal numerous examples of very similar marine features that bear generic toponyms (place names) Sea, Gulf, or Bay. In antiquity, the number of seas, first in the Mediterranean Basin and ultimately the world oceans, were classified to conform to the mystical number "7." Many early maps identify seven oceans (and most continue to identify seven continents, as well). *Maritimea* follows the lead of the International

ABOVE Icebergs are large pieces of ice that have calved from glaciers. The largest icebergs recorded have been in Antarctic waters, particularly around the Ross Ice Shelf.

BELOW A whirlwind above the sea. These swirling, sometimes very destructive columns of air are often formed over the sea.

Hydrographic Organization in recognizing five oceans: Arctic, Atlantic, Indian, Pacific, and the Southern Ocean (oceanic waters south of 60°S).

Through history, human dependence upon the sea has grown in many ways. This importance is evident in the number of scientists from many different fields of study who have developed marine-oriented specializations. Most directly, study of the global sea involves the science of oceanography, within which there are many subfields. But, as the diverse backgrounds of authors who contributed to this volume attest, scholars from many fields also study ocean-related features, conditions, and uses. They include marine biologists, geographers, and historians. Coastal morphologists, engineers, climatologists, and geologists also study various aspects of the sea. So do economists, political scientists, and military strategists.

There are many others, each of whom contributes to our growing knowledge of "maritimea" and its human importance us all.

MARITIMEA IN PERSPECTIVE

The ocean has been romanticized in prose, poetry, and song. Who in Western culture is unaware of Ernest Hemingway's *The Old Man and the Sea*, or is not

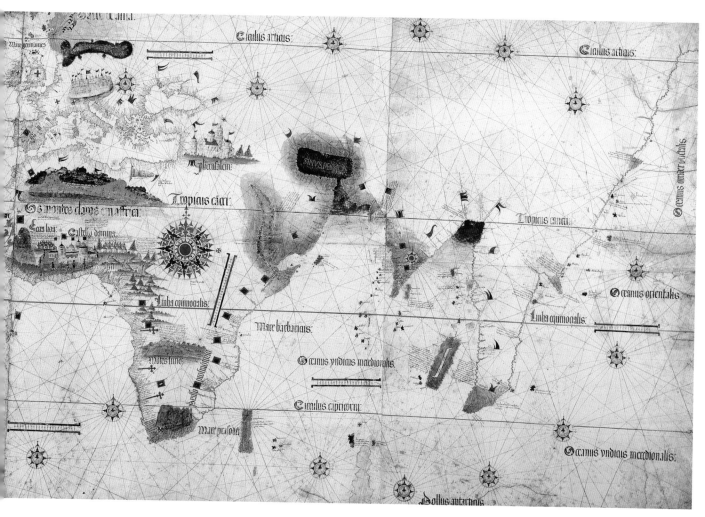

familiar with at least some passages from Samuel Taylor Coleridge's famous poem, *The Rime of the Ancient Mariner*:

> *Day after day, day after day,*
> *We stuck, nor breath nor motion;*
> *As idle as a painted ship*
> *Upon a painted ocean.*
> *Water, water, everywhere,*
> *And all the boards did shrink;*
> *Water, water, everywhere,*
> *Nor any drop to drink.*

"Sea shanties"—shipboard working songs—have provided scholars and other listeners with vivid details of a seaman's life at sea. Popular motion pictures, such as *Titanic* and *The Perfect Storm*, and television programs including *The Deadliest Catch*, attest to our ongoing fascination with the ocean. Esthetically, many artists have turned to the sea—waves, beaches, ships, and other themes—as inspiration for their works.

Those involved in the production of *Maritimea* join countless others who have attempted to capture and portray the excitement, romance, moods, importance, and vagaries of the restless sea.

Charles F. Gritzner

ABOVE The Cantino planisphere of 1502 depicting the meridian designated by the Treaty of Tordesillas, which came into effect in 1494. The treaty divided the "newly discovered" lands outside Europe between Spain and Portugal along a north–south meridian.

RIGHT The sea is a source of endless fascination for humans. Sailing across the seven seas has even been the subject of a Christmas carol.

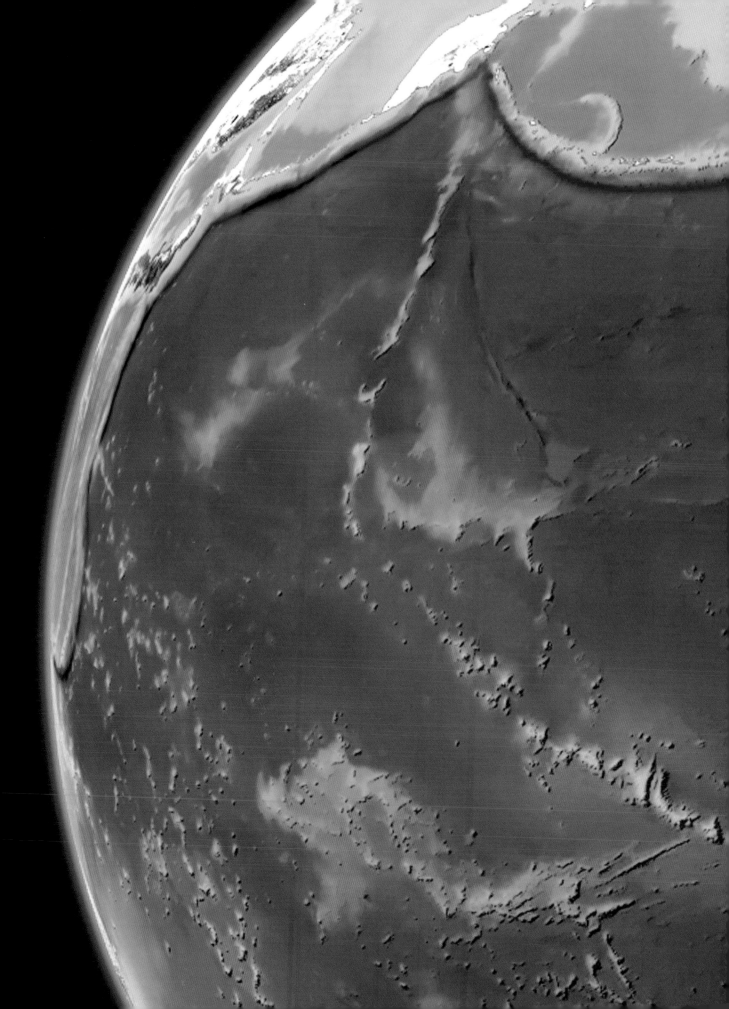

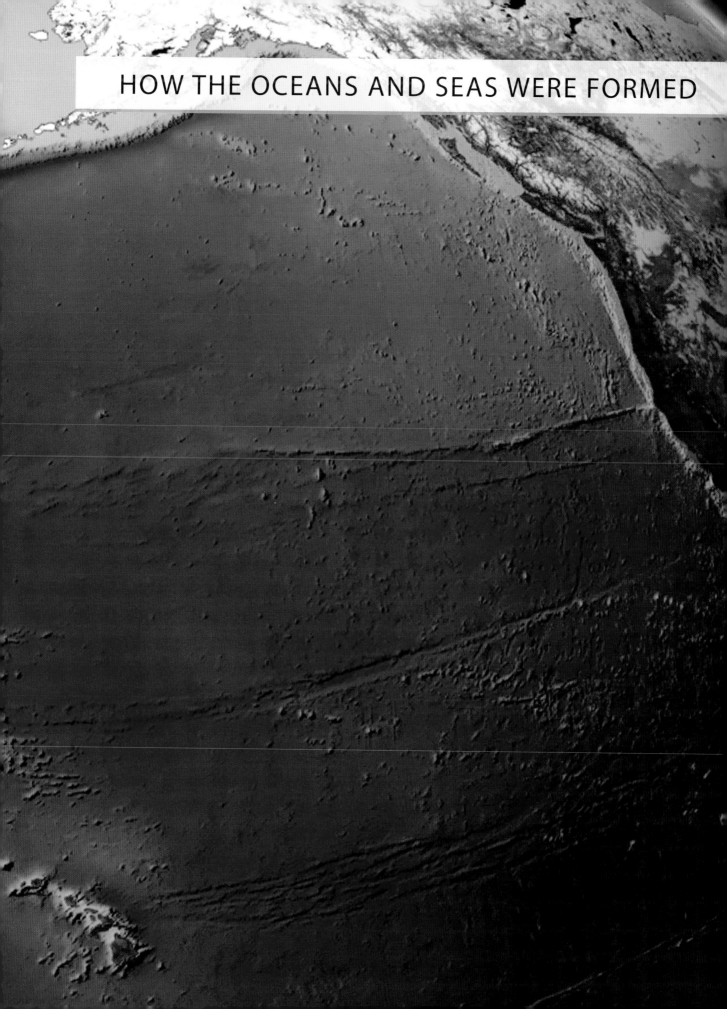

HOW THE OCEANS AND SEAS WERE FORMED

Oceans of the Earth

E arth is the only planet in the solar system with surface water. How would it look without water? Perhaps it might look like the red planet, Mars, where some landscapes appear to have been shaped by water erosion. Where is the Martian water now? Where did ours come from? These questions are the stuff of speculation and science fiction.

Oceans, seas, and lakes cover more than 71 percent of Earth's surface. To understand where water might have come from, we need to consider Earth's formation around five billion years ago. In the beginning, Earth was a mass of extremely hot molten material with no gaseous atmosphere, constantly bombarded by metallic meteorites and icy comets. Water may have been delivered by these comets or other icy masses.

Some water may have reached Earth after being blown from the inner planets, Mercury and Venus. Perhaps the water of Mars is still present, but frozen beneath the planet's surface. Very little is known of the origin of water on Earth and other planets.

As the young Earth cooled, molten rock began to form a solid crust. Gravity forced the denser material to the center of the Earth, leaving the lighter rock to "float" to the surface, where it slowly cooled, over a period of about 200 million years, to form Earth's first crust about 4.4 billion years ago. This was the very first continental crust. As the mantle gradually solidified, it formed the rocks of the ocean floor—the oceanic crust.

During this time, water vapor was released into the developing atmosphere. Further cooling caused it to condense into clouds and eventually fall as rain, which flowed along water courses through the cooling crust, eroding the rocky surface as it ran into deep depressions formed by early tectonic processes. These depressions formed the first ocean basins.

HAVE THE OCEANS ALWAYS BEEN THE SAME?

Geologically speaking, the ocean is relatively young. The oldest oceanic crust was formed "only" around

RIGHT By about 250 million years ago, the supercontinent Pangea had formed and all lands on Earth were joined as a single entity. About 240 million years ago, Pangea began to rift, creating Laurasia and Gondwana. Around 180 million years ago, Gondwana began to separate into the continents of today.

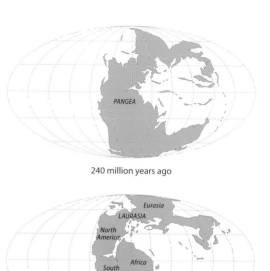

240 million years ago

200 million years ago

120 million years ago

170 million years ago, while the oldest continental crust is more than four billion years old. Ocean crust is being created at the mid-ocean ridges, from where it spreads toward the plate margin, and is then destroyed by subduction into the mantle. This means that oceanic crust is oldest at the edge of the subduction zone. So what became of the oceans that existed more than 170 million years ago? To answer this, we must consider the supercontinents of the geologic past.

A   B   C

SUPERCONTINENTS AND SUPER OCEANS

The shape, position, and depth of ocean basins have changed dramatically over the eons. Supercontinents formed—then were rifted apart—by cyclic tectonic processes, changing the distribution of land, and the shape and size of the oceans.

Convection currents in the mantle pull blocks of continental crust apart. They also cause them to collide. There have been times when blocks of continental crust came together to form a massive single continent—a supercontinent. Over the past three billion years, at least four supercontinents have formed; rifted to form smaller continents; re-formed, accompanied by ocean creation and redistribution, in cycles of 250 million years or so. Continental collision results in fewer, larger continents; rifting makes more, smaller continents.

The oldest supercontinent—Rodinia—formed between 1.3 and 1.1 billion years ago. Surrounded by a "super ocean" known as Mirovia (from *mir*, Russian for "globe"), Rodinia broke up over the period from 830 to 745 million years ago. Around 300 million years ago, the Rodinian fragments re-formed to create the next supercontinent, Pangea (Greek for "all lands"). It was surrounded by a global ocean known as Panthalassa (Greek for "all sea").

About 200 million years ago, Pangea began to break apart, forming Laurasia to the north, and Gondwana to the south. This split saw the opening of what would become the Pacific Ocean.

When eastern North America and northwest Africa broke apart, the Atlantic Ocean was formed. Gondwana was made up of the modern landmasses of South America, Africa (including Madagascar), India, Antarctica, Australia, and New Zealand. Australia was the last continent to separate from the remnants of Gondwana, starting its move northward when it split from Antarctica about 90 million years ago. By this time, all of today's major oceans had formed, and the rifting between Antarctica and Australia created the Southern Ocean, the Earth's youngest ocean.

What was happening to sea levels over this period? In general, sea level is low when continents are joined,

ABOVE Mt Erebus on Ross Island, is the most active volcano in Antarctica. Geologists estimate that this volcano is less than one million years old.

and high when they are fragmented, because if the global ocean is young, the seafloor will be comparatively shallow, resulting in higher sea levels and greater flooding of the continents. If the global ocean is older, the seafloor will be relatively deep, causing a drop in sea levels and exposing more of the continents.

At the time of Pangea, the sea level was low; as it broke up, sea levels rose.

PLATE TECTONICS

There was early recognition of the apparent "jigsaw" fit of some continents, such as Africa and South America, but no understanding of how they could have come apart. The German scientist Alfred Wegener suggested the theory of continental drift in 1915, but scientists dismissed the idea on the basis that no known force could move continents over such vast distances.

But in the late 1960s, scientists discovered that the continents are actually "floating" on plates that are moved by convection currents within the hot molten layers of the Earth. These tectonic plates are usually

Plate Tectonics in Action

The illustration below shows how convection currents rising and falling in Earth's interior drive the movement of its surface plates creating all of the landforms around us.

A. **Collision** When light thick continents collide, their edges buckle and fold, pushing up tall mountain ranges, such as the Himalayas and the Alps.

B. **Hotspots** Enormous volcanic islands grow on the seafloor above deep mantle hotspots until they are moved from their source by the continual movement of the tectonic plate. As each volcano dies and sinks, new islands grow.

C. **Subduction volcanic islands** Denser and thinner ocean crust pushes beneath lighter crust, such as younger ocean. The descending and melting oceanic plate gives rise to magma that rises to form arcs of volcanic islands, such as Indonesia and the Philippines.

D. **Mid-Oceanic Ridge** New basaltic crust forms along the mid-oceanic ridges. Here, magma intrudes into the widening cracks and solidifies as the tectonic plates move apart.

E. **Subduction volcanic mountain ranges** Continental crust easily overrides oceanic crust, which is forced to descend and melt. Molten magma rises to form chains of volcanoes like those of the Andes Mountains.

F. **Rifting** Rifting occurs in the middle of large continents sitting on top of rising convection plumes. The land is put under tension, which causes it to crack and move apart.

D　　　　　　　　　　　　E　　　　　　　　　　　　F

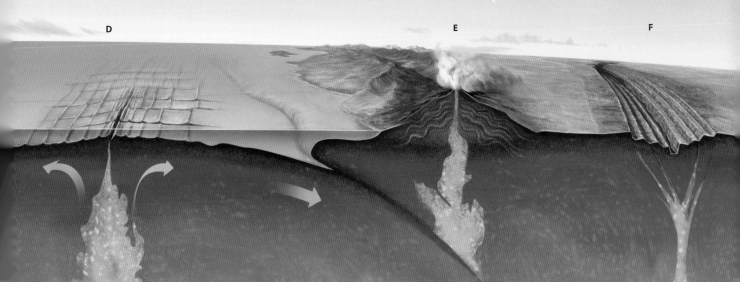

ABOVE The San Andreas Fault is part of the Pacific "Ring of Fire," a massive seismic belt that rings the Pacific Ocean.

BELOW Mt Bromo in east Java, Indonesia, erupts, spewing forth ash and lava. Bromo, on the Pacific rim, is a stratovolcano. This type of volcano erupts along plate edges.

made up of continental crust and oceanic crust. The Earth's surface currently comprises about 12 major plates and a number of smaller ones. All are interlocking and all, apart from the Antarctic Plate, are in motion. Knowledge of plate tectonics revolutionized our understanding of the Earth's processes, just as the theory of evolution transformed our understanding of life. There are three discrete types of plate margin. Convergent margins occur where two plates come together or collide. The Himalayas formed (and are still growing) as a result of the Indo–Australian Plate diving beneath the Eurasian Plate and "squeezing" the subduction zone in an upward direction.

The advent of highly-accurate satellite cameras has allowed us to precisely measure tectonic movements. Divergent margins move apart as the ocean floor spreads—the Australian Plate is moving northward, away from the Antarctic Plate at around 2.6 in (66 mm) per year. At that rate, we can predict that one million years hence, Australia will be 42 miles (67 km) closer to Asia, and 420 miles (675 km) closer after 10 million years. Ten million years is a mere blink in the vast geological time scale.

The third type of margin is the transform margin, where two plates slide past each other (such as the famous San Andreas fault in western North America.)

Many transform margins occur at right angles to the axis associated with seafloor spreading, resulting in powerful and destructive earthquakes.

PACIFIC RING OF FIRE

When migrating oceanic crust collides with the active margin of another plate, a subduction zone forms. The Pacific Ocean is surrounded by the active margins of the western coasts of North and South America, the Aleutian and Kuril Islands, Japan, the Philippines, and the Indo–Australian Plate. Subduction causes intense geologic activity in the form of earthquakes, volcanoes, and mountain formation. The Pacific rim experiences more volcanic eruptions and earthquakes than anywhere else on Earth—80 percent of the world's largest earthquakes occur in the region—and is known as the Pacific "Ring of Fire."

TODAY'S OCEANS AND SEAS

There is really only one ocean on our planet. That ocean stretches from pole to pole and encircles the globe as a continuous body of salty water. However, it is divided for convenience into five geographical areas; from largest to smallest they are the Pacific, Atlantic, Indian, Southern (or Antarctic), and Arctic Oceans. Ocean boundaries are defined by continental margins,

archipelagos, and other physical features. The Pacific and Atlantic Oceans are divided into North and South sections by the Equator.

The term "sea" is used very broadly. Generally speaking, it refers to a body of salt water surrounded by land on all (or most) sides. The Caspian Sea is a salt lake that is surrounded by land; the Mediterranean Sea is surrounded by the lands of Europe, North Africa, and the Middle East, but is open to the Atlantic Ocean. The "Sea" of Galilee is a freshwater lake. A sea can also be part of an ocean; the Tasman Sea, between Australia and New Zealand, is part of the Pacific; the Sargasso Sea is surrounded by ocean currents (but no land) in the North Atlantic Ocean.

Tectonic forces driven by convection currents within the mantle cause cracks in the continental crust and pull it apart. When a continent begins to break up or rift, pressure from the convection currents produces a dome in the crust, forming a vast upland. Eventually the rifting creates huge tensional cracks or faults that pull apart to form deep flat-bottomed valleys, called rift valleys. Blocks of crust slide down the faults as the rift valley widens. Molten material from the mantle wells into the faults as basaltic magma, erupting at the surface to form volcanoes and islands.

Further rifting causes the valley to widen and deepen. It is fed by molten mantle material that forms basaltic oceanic crust as it cools. Eventually the rift valley breaches the edge of the separating continent so that seawater enters, either gradually or as a raging torrent. The walls of the widening valley become the new continents on either side of the developing ocean.

The Atlantic has a mid-ocean ridge—one of the world's longest mountain ranges—extending from north of Greenland to its southern junction with the Antarctic Plate. The ridge preserves the shape of the original rift, and the continental coasts are those that were once the sides of the rift valley. Spreading continues on either side of the mid-ocean ridge as new crust is formed, and continents are pulled further and further apart. However, if a continental coast is at a tectonically active margin, the density difference causes the spreading oceanic crust to dive below the less dense continental crust. The oceanic crust is then subducted back into the mantle where it melts.

These processes occur over millions of years, and are accompanied by significant seismic and volcanic activity. The great East African Rift and Lake Baikal in eastern Russia, among others, are rifting today. At some time in the future, the African continent will split in half from north to south, and Lake Baikal will become a fully-fledged ocean.

ABOVE A panoramic image of Earth by day. Sophisticated satellite technology has helped scientists to discover more about how Earth and its oceans were formed.

BELOW LEFT A NASA image of Lake Baikal in eastern Russia. Estimated at 25 million years old, Lake Baikal is the world's deepest lake. Rifting over millions of years is expected to eventually turn it into an ocean.

FOLLOWING PAGES The outermost part of Earth is made up of two layers: the lithosphere—the crust and rigid uppermost part of the mantle—and the asthenosphere, which flows like a liquid on geological time scales. The lithosphere is broken up into seven major and many minor tectonic plates. These plates move around the globe, jostling one another at convergent or collision boundaries, divergent or spreading boundaries, and transform boundaries, all of which are major locations for earthquakes, volcanic activity, mountain-building, and oceanic trench formation.

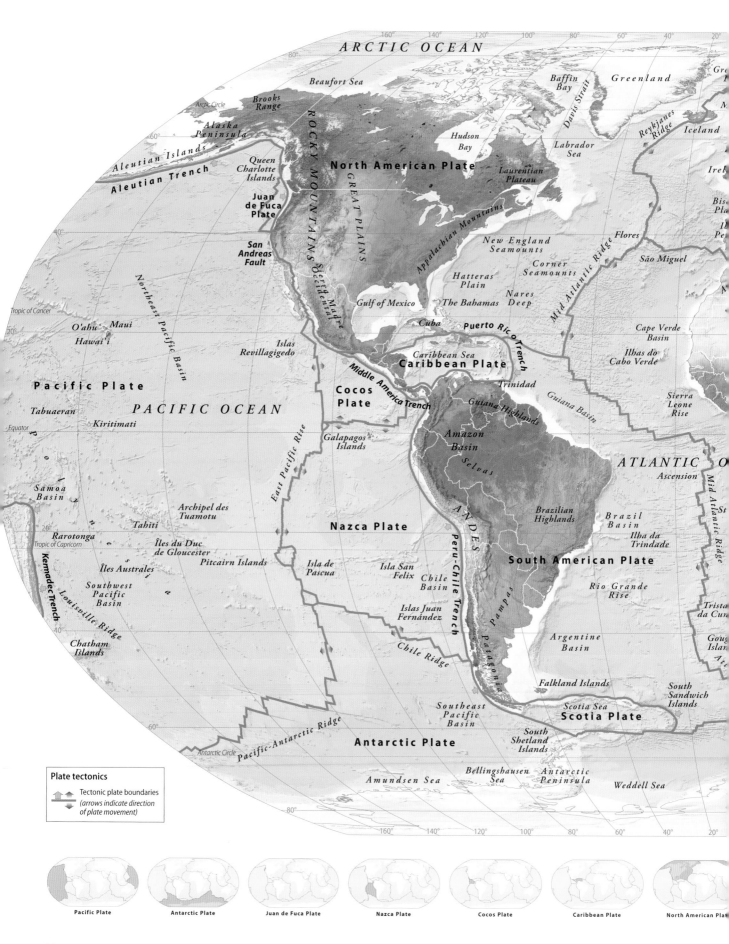

Plate tectonics

Tectonic plate boundaries
*(arrows indicate direction
of plate movement)*

Pacific Plate   Antarctic Plate   Juan de Fuca Plate   Nazca Plate   Cocos Plate   Caribbean Plate   North American Plate

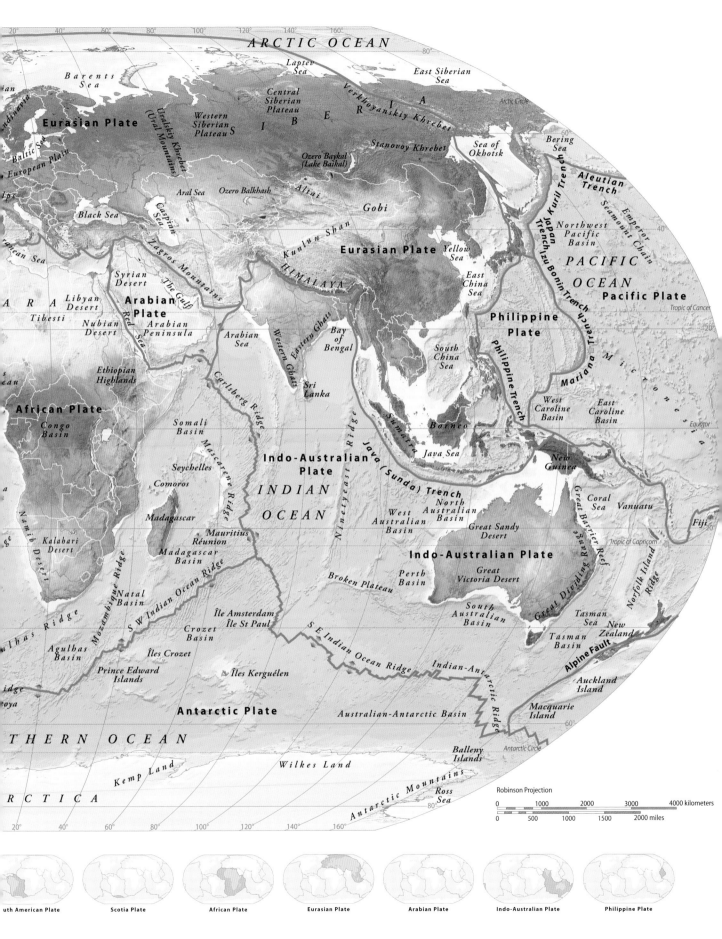

ARCTIC OCEAN

Barents
Sea

Laptev
Sea

East Siberian
Sea

Arctic Circle

Eurasian Plate

Western
Siberian
Plateau

Central
Siberian
Plateau

Verkhoyanskiy Khrebet

S I B E R I A

Bering
Sea

Aleutian
Trench

Baltic Sea

European Plain

Uralskiy Khrebet
(Ural Mountains)

Stanovoy Khrebet

Sea of
Okhotsk

Emperor
Seamount Chain

Aral Sea

Ozero Balkhash

Ozero Baykal
(Lake Baikal)

Altai

Kuril Trench

Northwest
Pacific
Basin

Black Sea

Caspian
Sea

Gobi

Japan Trench

PACIFIC

OCEAN

...nean Sea

Zagros Mountains

Kunlun Shan

Eurasian Plate

Yellow
Sea

Izu Bonin Trench

Pacific Plate

Tropic of Cancer

A R A

Libyan
Desert

Syrian
Desert

Arabian
Plate

The Gulf

HIMALAYA

East
China
Sea

Philippine
Plate

Tibesti

Nubian
Desert

Red Sea

Arabian
Peninsula

Arabian
Sea

Western Ghats

Eastern Ghats

Bay
of
Bengal

South
China
Sea

Mariana Trench

Micronesia

...eau

Ethiopian
Highlands

Carlsberg Ridge

Sri
Lanka

Philippine Trench

West
Caroline
Basin

East
Caroline
Basin

Equator

African Plate

Congo
Basin

Somali
Basin

Sumatra

Borneo

Seychelles

Mascarene Ridge

Ninetyeast Ridge

Java (Sunda) Trench

Java Sea

New
Guinea

Comoros

Indo-Australian
Plate

North
Australian
Basin

Coral
Sea

Vanuatu

Madagascar

INDIAN

OCEAN

West
Australian
Basin

Great Sandy
Desert

Great Barrier Reef

Fiji

Namib Desert

Mauritius
Réunion

Madagascar
Basin

Broken Plateau

Perth
Basin

Indo-Australian Plate

Great
Victoria Desert

Great Dividing Range

Tropic of Capricorn

Kalahari
Desert

SW Indian Ocean Ridge

Natal
Basin

Mozambique Ridge

Crozet
Basin

Île Amsterdam
Île St Paul

South
Australian
Basin

Tasman
Sea

Norfolk Island Ridge

...ulhas Ridge

Agulhas
Basin

Îles Crozet

SE Indian Ocean Ridge

Tasman
Basin

New
Zealand

Prince Edward
Islands

Îles Kerguélen

Indian-Antarctic Ridge

Indian-Antarctic Ridge

Alpine Fault

...ridge

...oya

Antarctic Plate

Australian-Antarctic Basin

Auckland
Island

Macquarie
Island

...THERN   OCEAN

Balleny
Islands

Antarctic Circle

Kemp Land

Wilkes Land

...RCTICA

Antarctic Mountains

Ross
Sea

Robinson Projection

0   1000   2000   3000   4000 kilometers

0   500   1000   1500   2000 miles

...uth American Plate   Scotia Plate   African Plate   Eurasian Plate   Arabian Plate   Indo-Australian Plate   Philippine Plate

THE DYNAMIC OCEAN

The Ocean's Shifting Moods

When Spanish explorer Ferdinand Magellan reached the Southern Ocean (as it was named when first seen by Vasco Núñez de Balboa in 1513), he renamed it Mare Pacificum, Latin for "Peaceful Sea." But neither the Pacific Ocean nor most of the world's other seas warrant such a placid-sounding title. In fact, the sea is often just as dynamic, variable, and treacherous as terrestrial environments.

PROPERTIES OF OCEAN WATER

There is considerable truth in English poet Samuel Coleridge's statement from his epic poem, *The Rime of the Ancient Mariner*, "Water, water everywhere, nor any drop to drink." Water dominates the surface of Earth, yet 97.6 percent of it is saline. Unless salt is removed by the costly process of desalination, it is useless for drinking, irrigation, and most industrial purposes.

The global sea averages 3.5 percent (35 parts per thousand) salinity. In the semi-enclosed Red Sea, which receives almost no fresh water inflow and experiences very high evaporation, the salt content is in excess of 4 percent. In the Baltic Sea, with many inflowing rivers and very little evaporation, salinity drops to less than 2 percent. If all minerals were precipitated out of the global sea, they would cover the Earth's surface to a depth of 400 ft (120 m)!

Worldwide, oceanic surface temperatures average 63°F (17°C). At 3.5 percent salinity, seawater freezes at 28.9°F (−1.7°C). Such temperatures are found in Arctic and Antarctic waters, and result in large expanses of sea ice. In shallow tropical waters, temperatures can reach

BELOW This NASA translunar coast photograph, taken by *Apollo 17* astronauts, shows ocean cover from the Mediterranean Sea area south to the polar ice cap of Antarctica.

BELOW The ocean is a place of many moods. Depending on the prevailing conditions, its waves can be invitingly gentle and caressing, or wildly turbulent, pounding the shore with unremitting energy.

88°F (31°C). The weight of overlying water creates huge vertical differences in hydrostatic pressure. At a depth of 3,280 ft (1,000 m) the pressure is 1,000 times greater than it is at sea level. This pressure causes our eardrums to hurt if we swim at great depths, and means that deepwater divers must slowly adjust to changes in pressure as they return to the surface. Aquatic life forms have, of course, adapted to the various oceanic depths—if deepwater species rose to the surface, they would explode; if surface organisms descended, they would be crushed.

WATER MOVEMENT

The sea is restless, constantly in motion as waves create oscillations. As they break on the shore, their force causes erosion and other damage. Tides raise and lower the water's surface twice a day. Currents transfer water, heat, icebergs, and assorted debris over large distances. Coastal-dwelling humans have taken advantage of these movements since the dawn of history. Indeed, the geographer Carl Sauer believed that the shore of eastern equatorial Africa was the earliest home of humankind because low tides exposed pools that offered an abundant and easily collected food supply.

In locations with large tidal variations, coastal fishing and gathering, navigation, recreation, and other activities need to be coordinated with tidal changes. As the tide rises in estuaries, water rushes upstream, often as a potentially dangerous tidal bore. Waves, particularly when generated by storms, can cause huge damage to coastal areas, but are sought after by recreational

surfers. Giant waves, including tsunamis (often incorrectly named "tidal waves"), wreak widespread havoc on life, land, and property. Today's technology can harness tides, waves, currents, and even differences in water temperature, to produce electrical power.

OCEANS AND CLIMATE

If the Sun is the fuel source that powers most of Earth's systems, it can be said that the oceans are the engine—at least in regard to weather and climate. Much of our planet's precipitation, temperature, pressure, and wind is influenced by the oceans. The hydrologic cycle is an endless process of evaporation from the sea, then precipitation over land and water. Water bodies do not heat or cool as rapidly (nor to such great extremes) as landmasses. This is why coastal regions experience

ABOVE Deep Rover submersibles have revolutionized deep ocean exploration. Divers are even able to perform jobs such as welding while underwater.

ABOVE RIGHT People in Mumbai, India, come to the shore during monsoon season to watch the huge waves caused by high tide.

RIGHT Recreational activities associated with the ocean and its shores are legion. People across the globe enjoy boating, surfing, diving, and swimming.

warmer winters and cooler summers. Warm and cold currents also transfer vast amounts of water that influence climatic conditions far from their sources. Cold water currents are responsible for many of the world's most arid desert regions. Many wind systems, including Asia's monsoons, are influenced by barometric pressure conditions that form over oceans.

The Properties of Ocean Water

The chemical formula for a water molecule, H_2O, shows that water consists of two hydrogen atoms and one oxygen atom. The hydrogen atoms are bonded to the oxygen atom at an angle of almost 105°. This geometry makes the water molecule asymmetrical, causing one end to have a positive electrical charge, and the other a negative charge.

THE WATER MOLECULE

Hydrogen atoms have single electrons that spend a great deal of time near the oxygen atom, leaving the outside portions positively charged. The oxygen atom has eight electrons, most of them on the side facing away from the hydrogen atoms, making this side of the atom negatively charged. When water molecules are close together, their positive and negative regions are attracted to the oppositely charged regions of nearby molecules. These weak bonds are called hydrogen bonds. Water molecules are continually pushed or pulled in several directions, which causes the weak hydrogen bonds to break, and then attach to other water molecules. The attraction of one water molecule to another is called cohesion—this gives water a high surface tension. Hydrogen bonds hold the molecules of water together, forming a surface that is capable of supporting small water-walking insects, or filling a glass slightly above the rim.

Hydrogen bonds also cause the water to form a sphere, the shape with the smallest surface area, as can be seen when a water droplet falls from a faucet.

SPECIFIC HEAT CAPACITY

Oceans gain and lose heat very slowly compared with landmasses. This helps to regulate Earth's temperature by reducing the temperature variation between night and day, and from season to season. Heat and temperature are similar, though slightly different concepts. Heat is the energy produced by vibration of atoms or molecules. Objects with slowly vibrating molecules produce less energy than those that vibrate rapidly. Temperature measures the molecular kinetic energy of a substance, that is, how rapidly the molecules are vibrating. The amount of heat required to raise the temperature of one gram of a substance by 1.8°F (1°C) is called its specific heat. The specific heat of water is about five times greater than that of granite. As a result, one gram of water requires five times more energy to raise its temperature 1.8°F (1°C) than does one gram of granite (see table below). Another consequence of water's high specific heat is that ocean water maintains its temperature over long distances.

BELOW Seawater contains hundreds of viruses. By adding dye to seawater samples (right), researchers isolate and study them to better understand the complex interactions of viruses with living creatures.

RIGHT The structure of a water molecule in different states. The hydrogen atoms are colored white and the oxygen atoms are colored red.

Specific Heat Capacity

SUBSTANCE	PHASE	SPECIFIC HEAT JOULES/GRAM °C
Ammonia 0°C	Liquid	4.600
Water	Liquid	4.186
Seawater	Liquid	3.930
Alcohol (ethyl) 0°C	Liquid	2.400
Olive oil	Liquid	1.960
Wood	Solid	1.700
Asphalt	Solid	0.920
Aluminum	Solid	0.900
Quartz sand	Solid	0.830
Granite	Solid	0.790
Graphite	Solid	0.720
Mercury	Liquid	0.140
Gold	Solid	0.129

THE THREE STATES OF WATER

Earth is unique in the solar system in that its temperature range allows water to exist in three different states. Below 32°F (0°C) water is solid, forming ice or snow. Between 32°F (0°C) and 212°F (100°C), water is liquid, and above 212°F (100°C), it forms gas—in the form of water vapor or steam. The transition from solid to liquid is called melting; from liquid to solid is called freezing. Water changing from liquid to gas is called evaporation; the reverse is condensation.

Water can also change directly from solid to gas (sublimation) and from a gas to a solid (deposition). In the gaseous state, water molecules are very energetic. The molecules do not bond with one another, but remain separate. Water molecules have less energy; the bonds between them continually break and re-form. Ice forms hexagonal crystals in which water molecules are locked together and vibrate only weakly, with far less energy than water or vapor.

One unusual property of ice is that it is around 9 percent less dense than water. Water is most dense at 39°F (4°C) and becomes less dense as its molecules form ice crystals. This is why ice floats on water, and is the characteristic that makes aquatic life possible. If ice were denser than water, it would sink to the ocean floor and cause it to freeze from the bottom upward. But because ice floats, it is exposed to solar radiation and melts, keeping most of the ocean in a liquid state.

SALINITY

Most of the oceans' dissolved chemicals come from the land. There are approximately 72 chemical elements in the oceans, most in extremely small amounts.

One of the most important elements is sodium chloride (NaCl, or salt). Salinity is a measure of the quantity of dissolved salts in seawater and is expressed by the amount of salt found per 1,000 grams of water. If one gram of salt is dissolved in 1,000 grams of water, the salinity is one part per thousand (1 ppt).

Ocean salinity mostly varies between around 28 ppt and 40 ppt, with a global average of 35 ppt. Fresh water from rainfall and rivers causes a reduction in salinity, while evaporation and ice formation increase salinity. Polar regions bear lower salinity—between 28 ppt and 32 ppt—because as the sea ice melts, it "freshens" the water. Temperate regions of the ocean typically show higher salinities of approximately 35 ppt. This is because evaporation is high and precipitation is low.

In equatorial regions, ocean salinity tends to be somewhat lower as a result of increased rainfall. In the drier regions of the tropics however, salinity can reach around 35 ppt to 37 ppt. The salinity values tend to vary greatly in those seas that are almost land-locked. Due to the very high evaporation rates, locations like the Red Sea and The Gulf average 40 ppt, while the Black Sea, which is fed by a number of rivers, has salinity of less than 20 ppt.

ABOVE A salt harvest from the Hon Khoi salt factory, Vietnam. Shallow ponds are flooded with seawater and then allowed to evaporate in the sunlight. The salt is then gathered by workers.

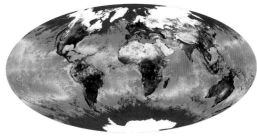

ABOVE A diver enters a decompression chamber, where the atmospheric pressure is raised or lowered gradually, giving divers time to adjust to normal atmospheric pressure.

ABOVE RIGHT A NASA image showing a global composite of land surface reflectance and sea surface temperature.

OPPOSITE A safety diver, suspended on an ascent line, carries a spare bottle of mixed gas to lend support as needed to fellow divers who are coming up from a deep dive.

RIGHT A deep ocean sampling device is lowered into the North Pacific from the research vessel *Thomas G. Thompson*. Such devices allow scientists to study deep ocean samples in situ.

TEMPERATURE

Approximately 71 percent of Earth's surface is covered by oceans and seas. Solar heat is absorbed into surface water, and retained for much longer than on land or in the atmosphere. The oceans operate like a giant heat reservoir, with a temperature range from the equator to the poles of 61°F (34°C), whereas the land temperature range is over 250°F (140°C).

Sea Surface Temperature (SST) recordings are usually taken within a few feet of the surface. They are gathered from buoys, on ships at the depth of the engine water intakes, or remotely by satellites. Long-term study of SST data has shown that annual variation fluctuates from the tropics to the poles. Tropical and polar waters experience less than 9°F (5°C) variation, while temperate waters experience the greatest seasonal change, around 18°F (10°C). Sea surface temperature measurements have led to a better

understanding of currents, seasonal weather patterns, and long-term climate shifts. One example is El Niño, an oscillation of the ocean–atmosphere system in the tropical Pacific with important consequences for worldwide weather. In some regions, El Niño causes destructive flooding, while other regions suffer severe drought. Sea surface temperatures are also a critical factor in tropical cyclone formation. When the SST reaches 80°F (27°C) or more, tropical depressions often transform into cyclones.

Just below the surface is the mixed layer, which fluctuates seasonally as waters are churned by wind and wave action. The temperature is relatively uniform to a depth of around 330 ft (100 m). Below this layer lies the thermocline, where the temperature decreases more rapidly. Below the thermocline lies the deep water, which makes up about 90 percent of the volume of oceans. Temperatures slowly decrease to about 37°F (3°C). The deepest and coldest water—ranging from 30.5 to 32°F (−0.8 to 0°C)—originates near Antarctica and flows northward.

PRESSURE

It is very useful to compare ocean pressure with atmospheric pressure—which is highest at sea level and decreases rapidly with height. Gravity concentrates and compresses air molecules in the lower atmosphere. At sea level, air exerts 14.7 lbs per square inch (psi) (1.03 kg per cm^2). Our bodies compensate for this weight by pushing outward with the same force. For all practical purposes, water molecules in the ocean are already as close together as possible, so water pressure increases with depth at a constant rate. Water is heavier than air and for every 33 ft (10 m) in depth there is an increase of one atmosphere. At 66 ft (20 m), the pressure equals 44.1 psi (3.1 kg per cm^2), and at 100 ft (30 m), the pressure equals 58.8 psi (4.13 kg per cm^2).

Unprotected divers can safely descend to three or four atmospheres, but must undergo decompression after a long or deep dive to avoid decompression sickness, or "the bends." Body tissue absorbs nitrogen as a diver descends. If a diver ascends too quickly, nitrogen bubbles form in body tissue instead of being exhaled. Symptoms of "the bends" include itching, rashes, joint pain, sensory system failure, paralysis, and death. Many marine organisms however, have adapted to living at crushing ocean depths by keeping their internal pressure equal to the pressure exerted on them.

Tides and Waves

Ocean tides are rhythmic rises and falls of sea level that affect coastlines. They are long-period waves caused by Earth's rotation, and by the gravitational attraction of the Moon and Sun. The Moon has the stronger gravitational pull because it is closer to Earth. Changing water levels set off horizontal movements of water, and create tidal currents. These can be especially strong along coastlines with narrow passages.

Accurate tidal measurements have been taken in many ports for centuries. Knowing the range of tides and tidal currents allows us to monitor the health of coastal ecosystems, improve coastal navigation for shipping, and fine-tune engineering requirements for shoreline buildings and structures.

The periodic rise and fall of ocean waters is caused by the changing gravitational forces of the Moon and Sun as Earth rotates on its axis. The magnitude of gravitational attraction is dependent on distance and mass. The Sun is the largest object in our solar system, 27 million times more massive than the Moon. The Moon, however, is 390 times closer to Earth. It has an average distance of 238,857 miles (384,403 km) from Earth, while the distance to the Sun averages 93 million miles (150 million km). Gravitational attraction

is affected more by the distance between two objects than by their masses. The Sun's gravitational attraction is about half that of the Moon.

The Moon's gravitational pull causes two bulges on Earth's surface, one located on the side facing the Moon, the other on the opposite side. The bulges are caused by differential gravitational forces. The Moon pulls on the water nearest to it and creates a high tide bulge of water. On the opposite side, the Moon's pull is weakest and forms another high tide bulge. Between the two high tide bulges are two low tides. The Earth and Moon orbit around a common center of mass located about 3,000 miles (4,800 km) from Earth's center. It takes 24 hours and 50 minutes to complete a lunar day, making it 54 minutes longer than a solar day. The additional minutes occur because the Earth

BELOW Waves crashing onto boulders in the Hawaiian Islands dwarf this adventurous surfer. Waves occur when the wind blows over the surface of the water. The resulting friction causes a wave to be formed.

and Moon revolve around each other in the same direction that the Earth rotates on its axis.

The rotating Earth produces two high and two low tides every 24 hours and 50 minutes. On average, high tides occur every 12 hours and 25 minutes. Low tides follow high tides by 6 hours and 12.5 minutes. The difference in height between high and low tide is known as the tidal range. The Bay of Fundy on the Atlantic border between Canada and the United States experiences a very large tidal range of 56 ft (17 m). In many other locations, tidal ranges are barely perceptible.

MONTHLY CYCLES OF SPRING AND NEAP TIDES

Lunar phases are the result of different illumination angles of the Moon's surface. Although the Moon's illumination cycles repeat every 29.5 days, there are four distinct phases that are important to tides. These are the Full Moon (complete illumination facing Earth), the New Moon (illuminated half facing away from Earth), first Quarter Moon (half of the Moon's surface is illuminated), and last Quarter Moon (the other half of the Moon is illuminated). Neap (small) tides occur during Quarter Moons, while spring tides occur during Full and New Moon periods. Spring tides (the largest tides) occur when Earth, Sun, and Moon are in alignment. Neap tides produce the smallest tidal range. This is because the perpendicular positions of the Sun and Moon offset each other's gravitational attraction.

TIDAL CURRENTS

The vertical movement of water generates horizontal movements known as tidal currents. During high tides, a flood tide or flood current flows into coastal margins. As it flows out again it is called an ebb tide, or ebb current. The currents are greatest soon after the onset of the low and high tides. The speed of tidal currents can reach up to several knots near narrow straits and inlets. "Slack water" occurs when there is virtually no tidal current, just before and after the tide reverses direction.

WAVES

Ocean waves are caused by the friction of wind at the air and water interface. Waves can travel thousands of miles across the ocean, ranging in size from a mere ripple to over 90 ft (27 m) in height. Interestingly, there is little or no forward motion of individual water particles within a wave until it breaks. Water is simply the medium through which kinetic energy passes.

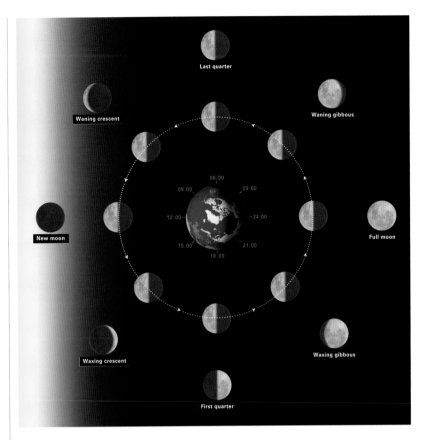

ABOVE The phases of the Moon. The inner ring shows the Moon as it would appear from above. From Earth we see only the part that is facing toward us (the near side). This is the lit part of the Moon that is shown inside the white circle.

LEFT Low tides have caused these fishing boats in Portugal to be beached. There are two high and two low tides each day.

There are several parts to a series of waves. The crest is the highest point on a wave. The trough, or valley between two crests, is the lowest point. The wavelength is the horizontal distance between the crests of two consecutive waves. Wave height is the vertical distance between a wave's crest and trough. Wave period is the time that elapses between the passage of two successive wave crests past a fixed point. A wave period can be measured by picking a stationary point or a floating object and counting the seconds it takes for two consecutive crests to pass. Wave periods can range from 0.5 seconds for small ripples, to over 12 hours for tides.

ABOVE The prow of a ship cuts through massive waves, produced by gale-force winds. In these conditions, waves can be up to 20 ft (6 m) high.

OPPOSITE Omaha Beach, Calvados, France. Waves and tidal action play a huge part in the formation of beaches—they are responsible for erosion and the deposition of sediments.

WAVE FORMATION

Waves are influenced by four factors—wind speed, fetch, duration, and water depth. Wind in contact with the surface causes changes in pressure, and frictional forces on the water. Faster wind speeds increase these effects and increase the wave height. Fetch is the un-interrupted distance over which a steady wind travels without a significant change of direction. Steady winds blowing over a long distance create a large fetch area. Duration is the length of time the ocean surface is exposed to sustained winds. Water depth affects wave height because energy is also carried in deeper water. When the water depth is greater than one-half of the wavelength, the wave is classified as a deepwater wave, and water does not move forward. In shallow water, a wave cannot dissipate its energy downward, so the wave becomes top-heavy and eventually collapses.

TYPES OF WAVES

Several types of wave are produced by surface winds. Wind waves are formed in the area in which the wind is blowing. When winds come from several different directions over a short period of time, standing waves are formed, then they collide, and there is no definite direction of movement. A standardized method of describing wave size was developed in 1805 by Englishman Sir Francis Beaufort, and is still used today (see box, opposite). Swell waves occur as wave energy travels away from the generation area, and gradually transforms into swell. These appear as uniformly symmetrical waves and travel over vast areas.

BREAKING WAVES

A wave breaks when its base can no longer support the top, causing it to collapse, such as when it moves from deep to shallow water near the shoreline. There are three types of breaking waves; their type is dependent on the steepness of the near-shore slope. Spilling breakers are formed along relatively flat shorelines where the peak of the crest gently slips down the face of the wave. Plunging breakers occur when the shoreline has a moderate slope, creating a thunderous sound as the air that is trapped in the curl is released. Surging breakers are found along shorelines with very steep slopes. The base of these waves keeps pace with the top, so the wave does not curl over.

ROGUE WAVES

Rogue waves are gigantic waves, much higher than wind waves, and with a different shape. The face tends to be very steep and the preceding trough very deep. Many scientists questioned eyewitness accounts of these waves, until measurements confirmed a rogue wave at the Draupner oil platform in the North Sea on January 1, 1995. It had a maximum wave height of 84 ft (25.6 m) and a peak elevation of 61 ft (18.6 m).

The Beaufort Scale

FORCE (Knots)	WIND (WMO*)	CLASSIFICATION	APPEARANCE OF WIND EFFECTS ON THE WATER
0	Less than 1	Calm	Sea surface smooth and mirror-like
1	1–3	Light Air	Scaly ripples, no foam crests
2	4–6	Light Breeze	Small wavelets, crests glassy, no breaking
3	7–10	Gentle Breeze	Large wavelets, crests begin to break, scattered whitecaps
4	11–16	Moderate Breeze	Small waves 1–4 ft (90 cm–1.2 m) becoming longer, numerous whitecaps
5	17–21	Fresh Breeze	Moderate waves 4–8 ft (1.2–2.4 m) taking longer form, many whitecaps, some spray
6	22–27	Strong Breeze	Larger waves 8–13 ft (2.4–4 m), whitecaps common, more spray
7	28–33	Near Gale	Sea heaps up, waves 13–20 ft (4–6 m), white foam streaks off breakers
8	34–40	Gale	Moderately high waves (13–20 ft/4–6 m) of greater length, edges of crests break into spindrift, foam blown in streaks
9	41–47	Strong Gale	High waves (20 ft/6 m), sea begins to roll, dense streaks of foam, spray may reduce visibility
10	48–55	Storm	Very high waves (20–30 ft/6–9 m), overhanging crests, sea white with dense foam, heavy rolling, lowered visibility
11	56–63	Violent Storm	Exceptionally high waves (30–45 ft/9–14 m) , foam patches cover sea, visibility more reduced
12	64+	Hurricane	Air filled with foam, waves over 45 ft (14 m), sea completely white with driving spray, visibility greatly reduced

*World Meteorological Organization

Currents

Water in the oceans is constantly moving and ocean currents are the transport systems that move water from one location to another. Currents have significant influences on the climate as well as marine and terrestrial ecosystems. Ocean currents are divided into surface currents and deep water currents.

BELOW Norwegian explorer Fridtjof Nansen's observations of polar tides and drifts inspired Swedish physicist V. Walfrid Ekman's studies on the effect on water of wind blowing across the ocean. This is now known as the Ekman spiral.

BOTTOM A feather starfish on a branch of whip coral sway in the surface currents of the Red Sea.

Surface currents are primarily driven by wind flow and occur in the upper 1,310 ft (400 m) of the ocean. They make up about 10 percent of all the water in the ocean. Deep water currents are driven by density forces and make up the other 90 percent of the ocean. Both types circulate huge amounts of heat energy globally.

SURFACE CURRENTS

Surface currents are primarily driven by the wind from large atmospheric circulation patterns. The speed of a wind-driven current is about 2 percent of the wind speed, as long as wind

speeds have been consistent over an extended period of time. For example, a wind blowing steadily for 12 hours at 20 knots (37 km/h) would produce a current speed of 0.4 knots (0.75 km/h). Currents vary in direction and speed because other forces, such as wind and tidal influences, are constantly changing.

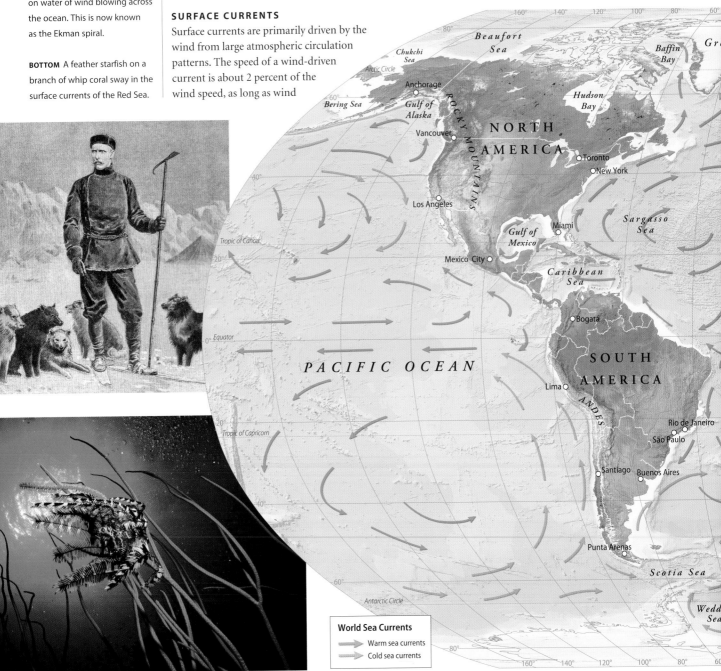

World Sea Currents

➡ Warm sea currents

➡ Cold sea currents

CORIOLIS EFFECT

Another influence on ocean currents is the Coriolis effect. First described in 1835 by the French engineer Gaspard-Gustave de Coriolis (1792–1843), it is an apparent deflection of a freely moving object caused by Earth's rotation. In the Northern Hemisphere, objects are deflected to the right (clockwise direction) and in the Southern Hemisphere, objects are deflected to the left (counter-clockwise direction). The deflecting force of the Coriolis effect is greater at high latitudes.

EKMAN SPIRAL AND EKMAN TRANSPORT

The combined influences of wind and the Coriolis effect cause ocean currents to move at an angle to the prevailing wind direction. This is called the Ekman spiral and was named for the Swedish physicist V. Walfrid Ekman (1874–1954) who, in 1905, was the scientist who described the phenomenon.

Generally speaking, the angular difference in direction between the wind and the surface current is 45° in the deep ocean. The angle can be as little as 10° in shallow coastal areas. Each layer of moving water sets the layer below in motion. The layer below is also deflected by the Coriolis effect. This forms a spiral flow pattern that descends from the surface layer into successively deeper layers. Deeper layers move far more slowly. This is because energy is lost in each transfer between the layers of moving water. As the

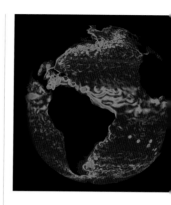

ABOVE This image from NASA shows the movement of ocean currents. The lighter green areas indicate fast moving currents. The blue areas indicate slower-moving currents.

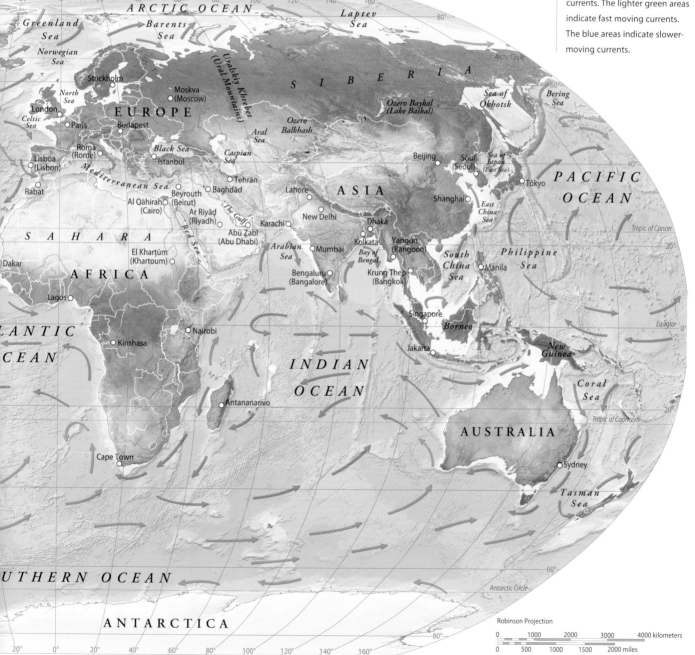

in the oceans called gyres. There are five major subtropical gyres—two in the Pacific Ocean, two in the Atlantic Ocean, and one in the Indian Ocean. Ocean currents flow along the boundaries of these gyres. Some of these currents are relatively warm, whereas others are cold.

The western boundary currents are the fastest and deepest. These currents transport warm water from the equatorial regions toward the poles. The five warm currents are the Gulf Stream (in the North Atlantic), the Kuroshio Current (in the North Pacific), the Brazil Current (in the South Atlantic), the Agulhas Current (in the Indian Ocean), and the East Australian Current (in the South Pacific Ocean). The largest and strongest of these is the Gulf Stream. It moves at about 4 knots (4½ mph; 7.4 km/h) and transports 300 times as much water as the Amazon River.

There are also five eastern boundary currents. These currents transport cold water from higher latitudes toward the tropics and equatorial regions. The five cold currents are the Canary Current (in the North Atlantic), the Benguela Current (in the South Atlantic), the California Current (in the North Pacific), the Peru or Humboldt Current (in the South Pacific), and the West Australian Current (in the Indian Ocean). These currents tend to be shallower and their total flow is less than western boundary currents.

Transverse currents flow from east to west or from west to east. Currents that flow east to west transport water along the equatorial portions of the gyres and are driven by the trade winds. There are six equatorial currents and these are divided into North Equatorial Currents and South Equatorial Currents for the Atlantic, Pacific, and Indian oceans. There are six currents that flow along the northern edges of the gyres and move water from west to east. These are driven by the prevailing westerly winds, which are not as reliable as the trade winds—this makes them wider and slower than the equatorial currents.

The West Wind Drift, or Antarctic Circumpolar Current, has the ocean's greatest water flow. This current flows eastward around Antarctica at about 60°S. Driven by nearly continuous westerly winds, the current encircles the Antarctic continent instead of being a rotating ocean gyre, so it keeps warm ocean waters away from Antarctica, and helps to maintain Antarctica's huge ice sheet. This is only possible in the

ABOVE Strong tidal currents sweep water from the North Sea and the Atlantic Ocean through the narrow Strait of Dover. Fast-moving water is shown as white streaks in this image, taken by the Advanced Spaceborne Thermal Emission and Reflection Radiometer (ASTER) on NASA's Terra Satellite on March 14, 2001.

current flow angle increases with the depth, it may flow in the opposite direction from that of the surface.

The Ekman transport (the net transport of water) tends to pile up surface water in the western and center portions of oceans. This causes changes in the height of the sea surface. The Ekman transport also moves surface waters away from the coast when surface winds blow in the same direction as the coastal current. This causes upwelling along the coast as warmer surface waters are replaced by colder water that moves upward from below. This upwelling is an important source of nutrients for many marine ecosystems, and marine populations die off when it fails. The ocean warming episodes in the tropical Pacific—known as El Niño—are a famous example of this event.

OCEAN GYRES AND CURRENTS

The long-term average pattern of ocean surface currents shows that they create large circular patterns

Southern Ocean because continents in the Northern Hemisphere interrupt the east–west currents.

Large continental landmasses in the Northern Hemisphere prevent the formation of a large current like the West Wind Drift. Instead smaller sub-polar gyres are formed around seasonal circulation patterns like the Aleutian and the Icelandic Lows near 60°N. These systems rotate in the opposite direction (clockwise in the Northern Hemisphere) from the subtropical gyres. This causes the Ekman spiral circulation to transport surface waters away from the central region. The circulation moves nutrient-rich waters from deeper in the ocean toward the surface.

DEEP WATER CURRENTS

Deep water currents are driven by density and the forces of gravity. The currents are actually one interconnected, massive, slow-moving deep current that involves the entire world ocean. The density difference is the result of changes in temperatures and salinity—it is known as thermohaline circulation from the Greek words "therme," meaning heat, and "halos," meaning salt. It is sometimes called the ocean conveyor belt, the great ocean conveyor, or the global conveyor belt.

THE GULF STREAM AND CLIMATE

Density is increased if water temperature is decreased and/or salinity is increased. Both processes occur in the North Atlantic and the Southern Ocean. In the North Atlantic, warm water from the Gulf Stream flows poleward and gradually becomes colder. Cold dry winds from Canada, Greenland, and Iceland chill sea surface temperatures to about 28°F (–2°C). As the water freezes into ice, salts are precipitated out, creating ice composed of fresh water and leaving water that is high in salinity. This increased salinity makes the water column denser than the surrounding waters, and it begins then to sink slowly down toward the abyssal plain. From here, it gradually spreads out and travels throughout the world ocean. Along its path, some of the water comes to the surface in the Indian Ocean and the rest surfaces in the Pacific Ocean. Once at the surface it travels back to the polar regions. The entire journey takes about 1,000 years to complete.

The continued flow of the ocean conveyor belt is essential for the global climate system. The Gulf Stream flows northeastward and moderates Western Europe's temperatures. If the conveyor were to slow or shut down, the Gulf Stream could slow or its flow could be redirected. Temperatures in Europe would be much colder and this could potentially lead to a shortened growing season and overall reductions in agricultural production.

While there are many parts of the thermohaline circulation system, the North Atlantic is a critical component. Evidence from paleoclimate studies suggest that the ocean conveyor has been shut down in the past. The most prominent event occurred about

LEFT This image, taken from the space shuttle *Endeavour* in 1994, shows sunlight shining on an eddy in the Gulf Stream in the North Atlantic Ocean. An eddy moves in the opposite direction to the prevailing current.

12,000 years ago during the brief cooling period known as the Younger Dryas. Temperatures were warming after the last Ice Age, but then suddenly cooled in the North Atlantic region for a period of about 1,000 years. Climate scientists believe that the rapid influx of fresh water from melting glaciers, glacial lakes, and icebergs desalinated the water and decreased its density. This event showed that climate can change very abruptly.

Many of today's conditions are, however, very different from those that existed 12,000 years ago. The change in Earth's orbital relationship to the Sun and increased levels of carbon dioxide make it unclear as to how the thermohaline circulation would respond to a sudden increase of fresh water from the melting of the Greenland ice sheet.

BELOW An aerial view, taken in 2006, of meltwater lakes and streams on the surface of the Greenland ice sheet. There are concerns that global warming is speeding up the melting of the this, the world's second-largest ice sheet. Such an event would lead to sharp rises in sea levels.

UNIQUE MARINE ENVIRONMENTS

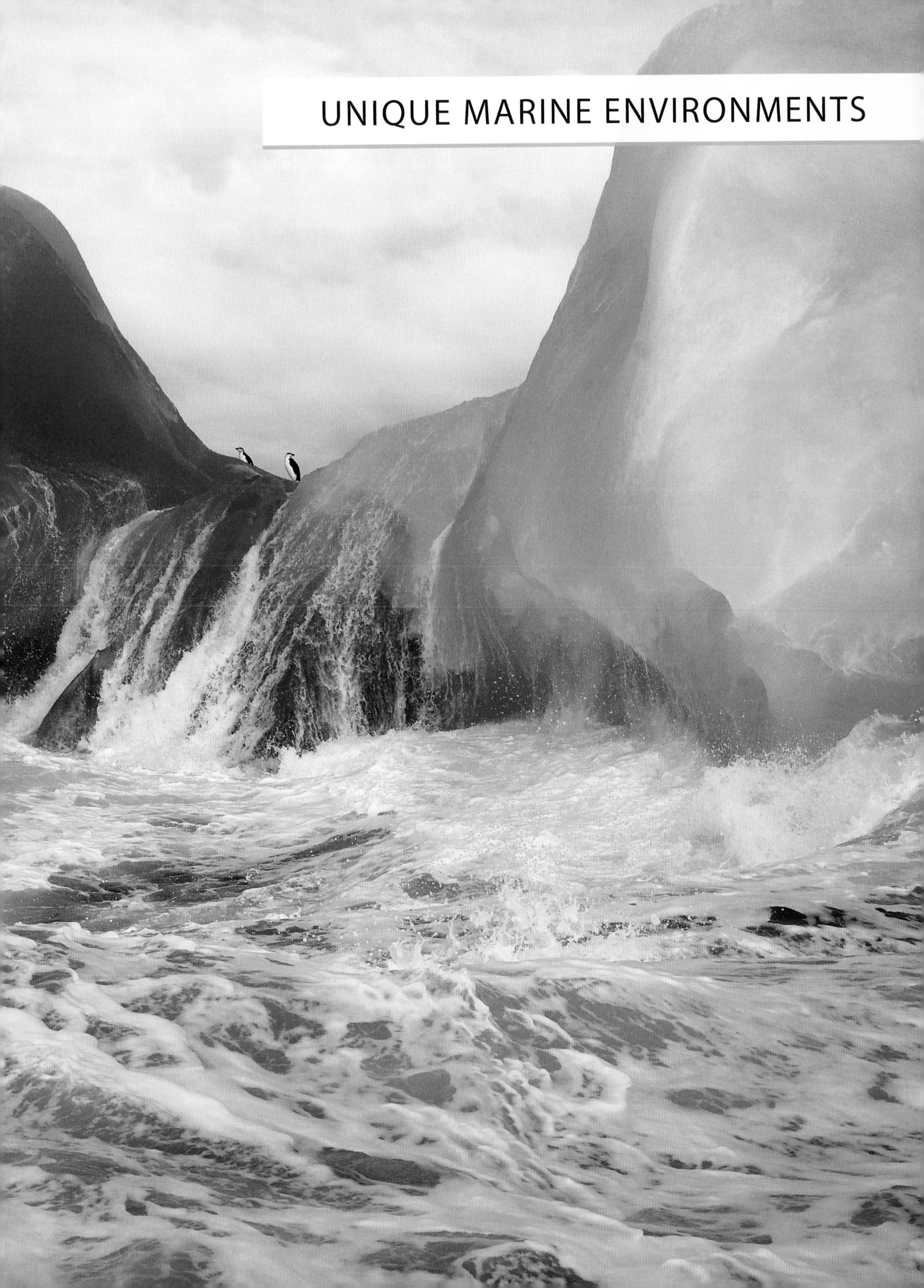

Myth of the "Seven Seas"

The 71 percent of the Earth's surface covered by the sea has been arbitrarily divided into oceans, seas, gulfs, and bays. Their number, definitions, and names, however, have long been the subject of dispute. Each of the world's cultures had its own perception of, and name(s) for, the waters with which it was familiar. Early civilizations in the eastern Mediterranean, for example, believed Earth was a dish-shaped object with land surrounded by an ocean river (much like a wheel and tire).

SEVEN SEAS

Within Western civilization, controversy has existed since ancient Greeks associated the known major water bodies with the mystical number seven. In ancient times, sailors who traveled widely could boast that they had "sailed the seven seas." Early Greek sailors recognized the seven seas as being the *Mare Internum* (Mediterranean), Euxine (Black Sea), Ionian Sea, Aegean Sea, Caspian Sea, and two parts of the Erythraean Sea (Indian Ocean)—the Red Sea and The Gulf (Persian Gulf). In the minds of later Mediterranean navigators, the seven became the Mediterranean, Black, Caspian, Adriatic, and Red seas; The Gulf; and the Indian Ocean. As Europeans' knowledge expanded, they also defined seven oceans. In addition to the Arctic and Indian oceans, the Atlantic and Pacific were divided into northern and southern sectors, with the southernmost waters labeled the Antarctic Ocean.

ABOVE Hiding in wait for prey, clownfishes form a kind of symbiotic relationship with sea anemones, digesting any material that could harm the anemone and providing nutrients in return.

BELOW At low tide, seastacks covered in seaweed are visible along the length of Seal Beach in Oregon, USA. The peaks of the taller stacks are just visible at high tide.

SOUTHERN WATERS

During the twentieth century, most maps and globes showed only four oceans—the Atlantic, Pacific, Indian, and Arctic. Some continued to add an Antarctic Ocean. "Antarctic" has largely given way to "Southern Ocean," with its northern limit variously placed between latitudes 35°S and 60°S.

However, this designation limit is not universally accepted and remains unofficial. The International Hydrographic Organization identifies the Southern Ocean—also Great Southern Ocean, South Polar Ocean, or Antarctic Ocean—as those waters lying south of latitude 60°S. Most geographers, however, continue to recognize only four oceans.

SURFACE AREA

The global sea is vast, occupying 41 million square miles (106 million km^2) of the planet's 57.9-million-square-mile (150 million km^2) surface area. The Pacific Basin alone is larger in area than all of Earth's continents and islands combined.

Many divisions between oceans remain vague and contested, as do their number and name. When seas, gulfs, and bays are added to the mix, definitions and nomenclature become even more confusing.

The physical properties of seawater, such as the temperature and salinity, vary greatly depending upon their location. So does water depth and resulting pressure in various seas and oceans.

UNDERWATER TERRAIN

Geologically, the terrain of the ocean floor features great diversity and many extremes. The world's highest mountains, longest mountain ranges, deepest canyons, and largest plateaus all lie beneath the ocean's surface.

Structurally, the same tectonic agents that create terrestrial landforms are at work on the ocean floor, although the agents of weathering and erosion are considerably different.

FLORA AND FAUNA

As on land, oceanic flora and fauna vary with environmental conditions. Coral reefs, forests of seaweed, and coastal tidal pools offer diverse marine environments. Although oceans occupy less than three-quarters of the Earth's surface, they contain around 300 times more habitable space than the terrestrial biosphere. Specific numbers are unknown, but a majority of Earth's life forms are believed to exist in the sea.

CONTINENTAL SHELF

Coastal environments vary greatly in their physical nature and utility to humans. Some coastal zones, such as the Pacific Coast of the United States, feature a very narrow continental shelf; uplifted, cliffed coasts; and excellent deep harbors.

In other regions, such as the Gulf of Mexico and the North Atlantic coastal plain, the shallow continental shelf is wide and coasts are subsiding. In such regions, sandy barrier islands are common, and most ports are built around shallow estuaries, or river mouths as within the Mississippi delta.

RIGHT Whitehaven Beach, situated on Whitsunday Island, the largest island in the Whitsunday Group off North Queensland, Australia, has some of the whitest sand of any beach in the world.

ABOVE An Adélie penguin *(Pygoscelis adeliae)* watches a leopard seal from its perch on an iceberg in Antarctica. The penguins mainly feed on the abundant supply of krill.

Atlantic Ocean

The Atlantic Ocean is the earth's second largest body of water, after the Pacific. Covering one-fifth of the earth's surface, the S-shaped Atlantic covers the vast area between the western coasts of Europe and Africa, and the eastern shores of the Americas. The Arctic Ocean and the Southern (or Antarctic) Ocean border the Atlantic to the north and south respectively. It is the world's busiest ocean for shipping.

ABOVE This satellite image shows Hurricane Isabel churning across the tropical center of the Atlantic Ocean in September 2003. It was located 1,265 miles (2,036 km) east of the Leeward Islands, traveling west-northwest at 14 mph (22 km/h).

BELOW This unusual coastal feature along the coast of Brazil has a river curving along the sand dunes of a beach before turning a bend and emptying into the Atlantic Ocean.

SEA OF ATLAS

The Atlantic is named for Atlas, the god who held up the heavens in ancient Greek mythology. Herodotus, the father of history, first used the term "Sea of Atlas" in his fifth-century BCE book *The Histories*.

The Atlantic covers an area of approximately 29,637,974 square miles (76,762,000 km^2), making it more than 7½ times larger than the United States, and 10 times the size of Australia.

FORM AND FEATURES

The Atlantic is the world's second youngest ocean. It was formed by the breakup of the prehistoric supercontinent Pangea that existed during the Mesozoic Era. About 100 million years ago, a rift appeared in Pangea, and Africa and South America began to slowly separate. That continental drift continues today, widening the Atlantic by several inches each year.

The average depth of the Atlantic is approximately 12,881 ft (3,926 m). If one includes adjacent waters such as the Black, Baltic, Caribbean, Labrador, Mediterranean, North, and Norwegian seas, the average depth is some 10,936 ft (3,333 m). The deepest point is at Milwaukee Deep in the Puerto Rico Trench, northeast of the island of Puerto Rico in the north Caribbean, where the ocean floor plunges to 28,232 ft (8,605 m).

The topography of the ocean floor is marked by the Mid-Atlantic Ridge. This rugged mountain range is 930 miles (1,500 km) wide and nearly 4,500 miles (7,200 km) long. It runs from Iceland in the north to the southernmost point of South America.

Atlantic currents flow clockwise in the Northern Hemisphere, and counterclockwise in the Southern Hemisphere. In the North Atlantic, inward spiral currents affect a large portion of the Sargasso Sea, preventing any flotsam that enters from escaping. This marine "black hole" has always been marked by massive amounts of seaweed flotsam; it is now an ever-increasing garbage repository for human waste, mostly plastics.

The Atlantic features far fewer islands than the Pacific. These include Greenland —arguably the world's largest island— Great Britain, Ireland, Iceland, Bermuda, Newfoundland, Ascension, the Falklands, Madeira, the Canary Islands, and Cape Verde, as well as numerous small Caribbean islands.

PEOPLE AND THE ATLANTIC

The Atlantic has long been traversed by seafarers. From the early Phoenician and Viking explorers to modern passengers on cruise ships, the ocean has always provided adventure and wonder. Norse explorer Leif Ericson is believed to be the first European to land in North America, arriving in Newfoundland around 1000 CE after crossing the Atlantic. Over the next five and a half centuries, Columbus, Vespucci, Cabral, Verrazano, and many others followed.

The North Atlantic captured worldwide headlines when the enormous, "unsinkable," luxury liner *Titanic* sank after it hit an iceberg on its maiden voyage in 1912. Many ships and aircraft have since mysteriously disappeared in the Bermuda (or Devil's) Triangle in the Caribbean. Other Atlantic hazards include fog that can appear instantly, and hurricanes that generate enormous waves across the ocean.

Economic activity dominates modern maritime traffic on the Atlantic, as sea trade is the most cost-effective means of connecting ports in Europe, Africa, and America. Mining is also prevalent, as crude oil and natural gas are extracted from offshore locations.

LIFE BELOW

Aquatic life in the Atlantic is abundant and diverse, ranging from whales and seals to many types of seaweed. Fish species such as cod, flounder, herring, sardine, perch, mackerel, haddock, eel, tuna, and lobster were once plentiful, but overfishing has drastically reduced their numbers in many areas.

ABOVE Manhattan, New York, boasts one of the largest passenger ship terminals in the world. Here a cruise ship enters the terminal on the Hudson River, which flows into the Atlantic Ocean.

LEFT Namibia, on the east coast of Africa, borders the Atlantic Ocean. This aerial view shows a huge colony of Cape Fur Seals playing in the surf at Cape Frio, Namibia.

ASIA

EUROPE

AFRICA

NORTH AMERICA

ARCTIC OCEAN

ATLANTIC OCEAN

MID-ATLANTIC RIDGE

KARA SEA

BARENTS SEA

WHITE SEA

NORTH SEA

Baltic Sea

BLACK SEA

AEGEAN SEA

MEDITERRANEAN SEA

ADRIATIC SEA

Ionian Sea

Tyrrhenian Sea

British Isles

CELTIC SEA

Norwegian Basin

Greenland

Iceland

Reykjanes Ridge

Denmark Strait

Charlie-Gibbs Fracture Zone

Oceanographer Fracture Zone

Atlantis Fracture Zone

Kane Fracture Zone

Cape Verde Fracture Zone

Vema Fracture Zone

Doldrums Fracture Zone

CAPE VERDE ABYSSAL PLAIN

Gambia Plain

GUIANA BASIN

Iberian Peninsula

Iberian Plain

Porcupine Abyssal Plain

Biscay Plain

Nansen Basin

Gakkel Ridge

Lomonosov Ridge

Mendeleyev Ridge

Alpha Ridge

Canada Basin

Makarov Basin

Baffin Bay

Baffin Island

Davis Strait

LABRADOR SEA

Newfoundland

Grand Banks of Newfoundland

Flemish Cap

Newfoundland Basin

Corner Seamounts

New England Seamounts

Bermuda Rise

Hatteras Abyssal Plain

SARGASSO SEA

Nares Deep

Puerto Rico Trench

Lesser Antilles

Greater Antilles

CARIBBEAN SEA

Venezuelan Basin

Colombian Basin

Demerara Abyssal Plain

Demerara Plateau

Queen Elizabeth Islands

Parry Islands

Victoria Island

Beaufort Sea

Amundsen Gulf

Chukchi Plateau

BERING SEA

Aleutian Islands

Aleutian Trench

Gulf of Alaska

Tufts Plain

Anchorage

HUDSON BAY

James Bay

Great Bear Lake

Great Slave Lake

Lake Athabasca

Lake Winnipeg

L. Superior

L. Michigan

L. Huron

L. Ontario

L. Erie

Gulf of St. Lawrence

Gulf of Maine

George Bank

Boston

New York

Philadelphia

Washington DC

Wilmington

Cape Hatteras

Charleston

Savannah

Blake Plateau

Bahama Ridge

Bahama Islands

Miami

Straits of Florida

Tampa

New Orleans

GULF OF MEXICO

Mexico Basin

Campeche Bank

Yucatan Channel

Cayman Trench

Houston

Veracruz

Rio Grande

Middle America Trench

Guatemala Basin

Vancouver

Halifax

Cape Sable

Cape Breton Island

Saint John's

1:41,300,000
Lambert Azimuthal Equal Area Projection

Meters	Feet
	LAND
0	BELOW SEA LEVEL
100	328
200	656
1000	3281
2000	6562
4000	13123
6000	19685

Scale:
0 — 750 — 1500 — 2250 — 3000 kilometers
0 — 500 — 1000 — 1500 — 2000 miles

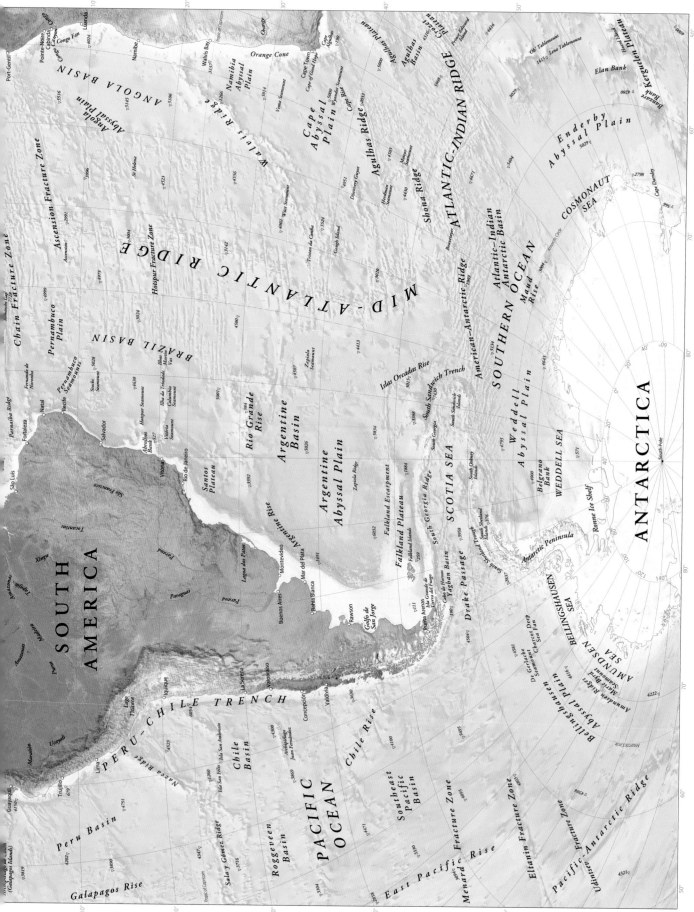

Pacific Ocean

The Pacific Ocean is a definite misnomer. The ocean was designated *Mare Pacificum* by Portuguese explorer Ferdinand Magellan in 1520, Latin for "peaceful sea." But in stark contrast to its name, the ocean is marked by violent seas, typhoons, earthquakes, and tsunamis, giving the ocean a character that is definitely not calm or peaceful.

ABOVE The beautiful and rugged central coast of California—Big Sur—is where the Santa Lucia mountains rise out of the Pacific Ocean. The beaches, bays, and cliffs formed by the ravages of the Pacific's waves have created some of the most stunning scenery in the United States. The area runs roughly from just north of Los Angeles to just south of San Francisco.

WORLD'S LARGEST OCEAN

The multi-personality Pacific is the world's largest ocean, covering around 60 million square miles (155,400,000 km²)—15 times the area of the United States—and occupying approximately one-third of the Earth's surface.

The Pacific Ocean extends from the Arctic in the north to Antarctica in the south. North and South America form its eastern boundaries, with Asia and Australia bordering the west.

The immense Pacific Basin is the world's oldest ocean basin. Over 30,000 islands, collectively referred to as Oceania, are found in the Pacific—more than in all the other oceans combined. The largest of these islands is New Guinea. Nearly 40 countries touch or are located within the Pacific Rim. They include the world's smallest island nation, Nauru, and five of the six largest countries—Russia, China, Canada, Australia, and the United States.

FORMATION

The Pacific floor is subject to very active plate tectonics, leading to the description "Ring of Fire," as violent earthquakes and volcanic eruptions feature in many areas of the basin. Volcanic activity has created many Pacific islands, including the Hawaiian Islands that are moving rapidly—in tectonic terms—northward toward Alaska. Earthquakes in the Pacific region often devastate human enclaves. Plate activity has also created the world's deepest point, the Mariana Trench where the bottom plunges to 35,800 ft (10,911 m) at Challenger Deep, 190 miles (300 km) southwest of Guam.

MYSTERIES OF THE DEEP

Beneath the surface of the ocean many mysteries are being unravelled. Sea currents generally move clockwise in the Northern Hemisphere and counterclockwise in the Southern Hemisphere. The Pacific hosts abundant life forms, from the tiny krill and plankton

that form the foundation of the food chain, to the largest creature in world history, the blue whale, that can exceed 110 feet (34 m) and 200 tons (180 tonnes).

PEOPLE OF THE PACIFIC

The Pacific Ocean served as an immense and almost impenetrable barrier to human activity for most of prehistory. The ocean was simply too vast and hostile for early humans with their limited technology. This began to change with early migrations of the Polynesians, who expanded their reach across the sea to Tahiti, Hawaii, New Zealand, and Easter Island. Portuguese navigator Ferdinand Magellan was the first to circumnavigate the globe (1519–1521) on his ultimately ill-fated trip to find a westward route to the Spice Islands—Indonesia. He was killed by natives in the Philippines in 1521, but his voyage inspired other Europeans to venture across the Pacific in search of adventure, trade, and treasures.

Explorers, fortune seekers, entrepreneurs, settlers, missionaries, and others followed, colonizing many Pacific lands. The sea was still a constant threat to travelers, but ever-improving technology reduced the risks over succeeding centuries.

In an ironic twist, although the Pacific was once a mortal threat to humans, today humans have become a threat to the ocean. Overfishing, waste dumping, and other pollution are now affecting life in the Pacific. Most pollution comes from land, where pesticides, plastics, and other waste materials are generated and the waste run off into the ocean. Pollution such as this threatens life forms, and creates ecological "dead zones."

The Pacific holds plentiful rich resources that we use for daily life, including minerals, oil, gas, sand, and gravel. It provides nearly 60 percent of the world's fish catch. Our challenge for the future of the Pacific—and the other oceans of the world—is to find a balance between exploitation and sustainability.

ABOVE Bora Bora, a major island of French Polynesia, boasts Mt Otemanu rising from its center. Romanticized in movies, Bora Bora is surrounded by a massive lagoon protected by a coral reef. French Polynesia is situated in the southeast of the Pacific Ocean and is a protectorate of France.

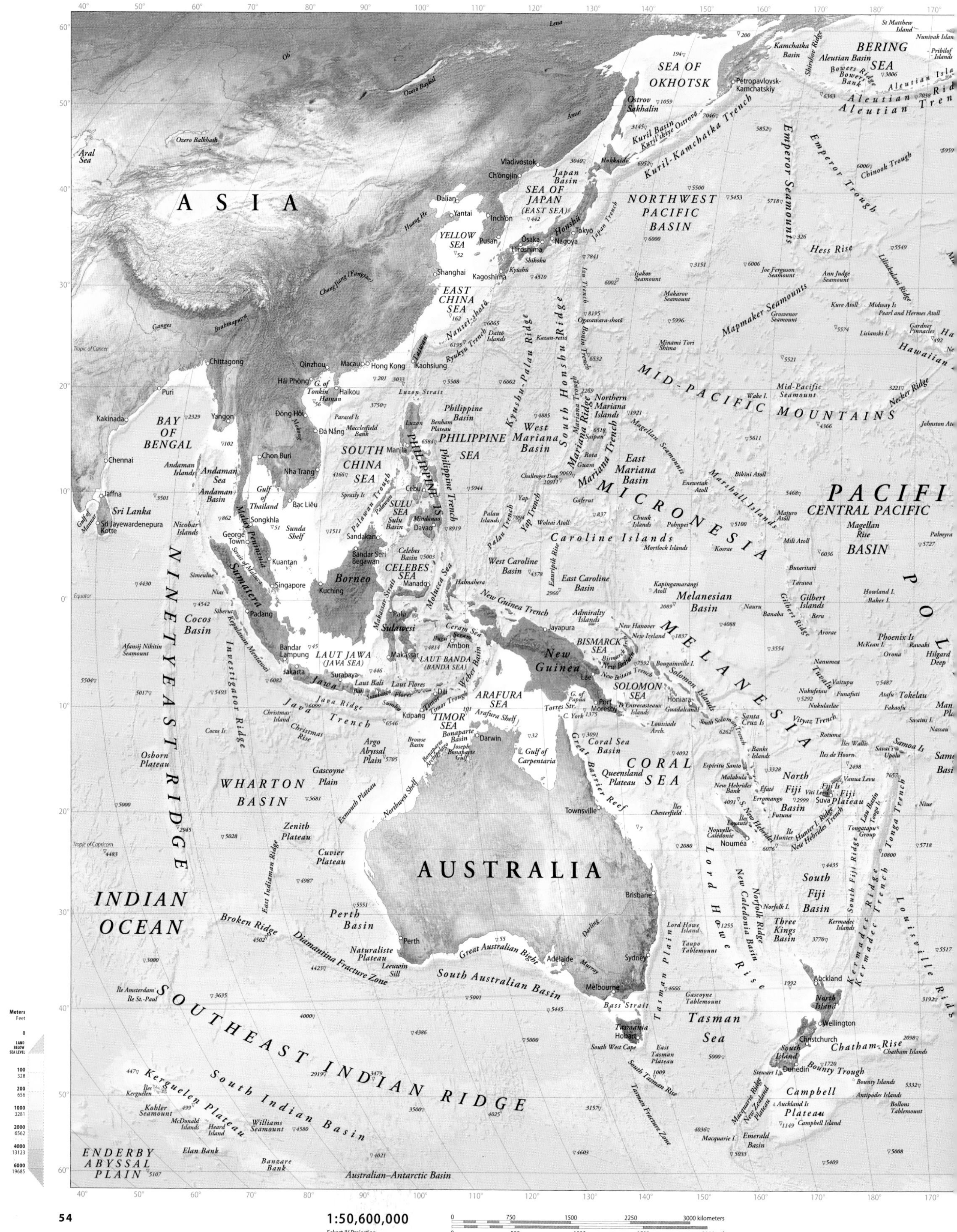

ASIA

AUSTRALIA

INDIAN
OCEAN

PACIFIC

BERING
SEA

SEA OF
OKHOTSK

NORTHWEST
PACIFIC
BASIN

SEA OF
JAPAN
(EAST SEA)

YELLOW
SEA

EAST
CHINA
SEA

SOUTH
CHINA
SEA

BAY
OF
BENGAL

Andaman
Sea

Andaman
Basin

PHILIPPINE
SEA

West
Mariana
Basin

East
Mariana
Basin

Philippine
Basin

SULU
SEA

Sulu
Basin

CELEBES
SEA

Celebes
Basin

Molucca Sea

LAUT JAWA
(JAVA SEA)

LAUT BANDA
(BANDA SEA)

ARAFURA
SEA

TIMOR
SEA

New
Guinea

BISMARCK
SEA

SOLOMON
SEA

CORAL
SEA

MICRONESIA

Caroline Islands

West Caroline
Basin

East Caroline
Basin

Melanesian
Basin

MELANESIA

CENTRAL PACIFIC
BASIN

POLY

MID-PACIFIC MOUNTAINS

Hawaiian

NINETYEAST RIDGE

WHARTON
BASIN

Perth
Basin

Cocos
Basin

SOUTHEAST INDIAN RIDGE

South Indian Basin

South Australian Basin

Tasman
Sea

South
Fiji
Basin

North
Fiji
Basin

New Caledonia Basin

ENDERBY
ABYSSAL
PLAIN

Australian–Antarctic Basin

New Zealand

Chatham Rise

Campbell
Plateau

Meters
Feet

0
LAND
BELOW
SEA LEVEL

100
328

200
656

1000
3281

2000
6562

4000
13123

6000
19685

54

1:50,600,000
Eckert IV Projection

0   750   1500   2250   3000 kilometers
0   500   1000   1500   2000 miles

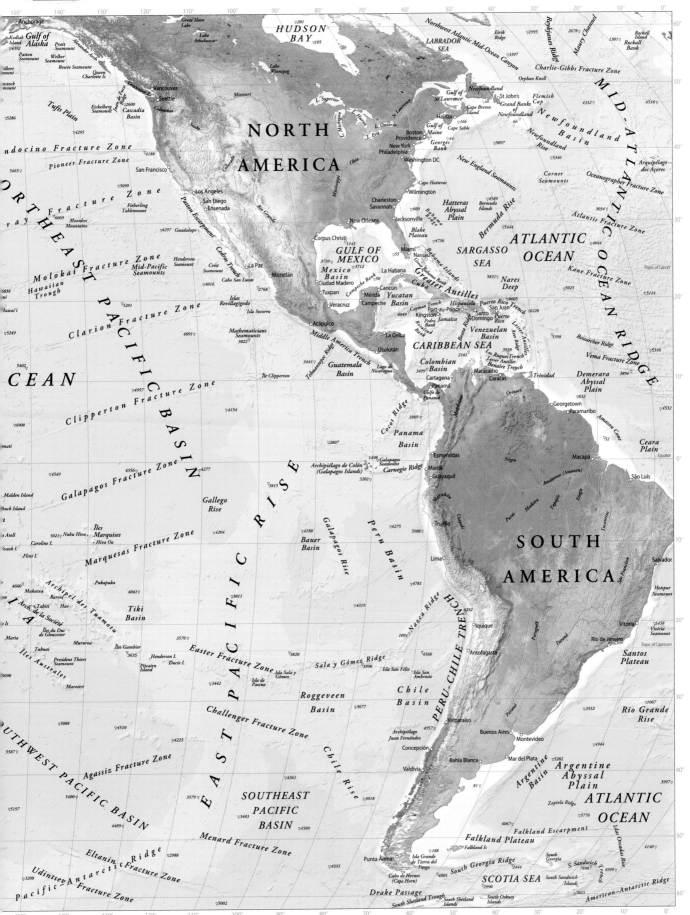

Indian Ocean

Containing over 20 percent of the world's ocean water, covering an area of 26 million square miles (67.5 million km²), and adjoining coastline of more than 41,300 miles (66,500 km), the Indian Ocean is the world's third largest ocean. It is bounded by Africa, Asia, and Australia.

CLIMATE AND CURRENTS

The Indian Ocean extends from latitudes 30°N to 60°S, and longitudes 20°E to 147°E. The climatic conditions of all nations that border the Indian Ocean are greatly affected by its current systems and temperature. Its surface is marked by a system of currents that run in a counterclockwise direction in the south, and clockwise in the north and near the Equator.

These simultaneous, opposing currents have greatly assisted maritime traders, explorers, and civilizations for millennia, while maintaining an ecosystem populated by numerous species. However, not all climate related to the Indian Ocean is regulated by the ocean currents. Wind systems or monsoons—derived from

the Arabic word *mausam*, or "seasons"—have helped maintain agricultural systems for millions of people since the dawn of humanity. High pressure systems developing over hot summer air in southwest Asia create the southwestern monsoon winds that flow across south Asia in a northeasterly direction.

During the winter period, low pressure systems over cold northern Asia create the northeastern monsoon system. These seasonal wind movements bring valuable precipitation to farmers and fishers around the coast.

But not all of the Indian Ocean's manifestations are beneficial to those who live on or around it. Marked by very low pressure centers, storm systems, thunderstorms, and tropical cyclones—called typhoons in the

BELOW An iconic image along the south coast of Sri Lanka, these fishermen swim out in waist-deep water and climb on stilts they have set into the mud. Here they fish, protected from the Atlantic Ocean by a breakwater.

north—are common in and around the Indian Ocean, and often bring disastrous amounts of rainfall, especially along the Asian coast. Southeastern China and southern Asia are especially vulnerable during the months of April to December. In 2008, Typhoon Kalmaegi—"seagull" in Korean—affected much of China, North and South Korea, and Japan, and featured winds of up to 75 miles per hour (120 km/h). One of the biggest disasters in recorded history was the killer tsunami, or tidal wave, that was set off on December 26, 2004, by a sub-oceanic earthquake off the Indonesian island of Sumatra. More than 225,000 people perished, from Indonesia to the East African coast.

CULTURE

No other ocean has contributed as much to the rich tapestry of human history as the Indian Ocean. Numerous civilizations have emerged and perished around its shores, and the travels of brave warriors and merchants have been documented for more than 5,000 years. From Egyptian kingdoms to the Indus Valley cultures in South Asia, the Indian Ocean has been the scene of some of the world's oldest cultures. Five thousand year-old Indian teak has been found in the ancient Sumerian city of Ur, in present-day southeast Iraq, while ancient Roman coins have been found in southeastern India.

PEOPLE AND RELIGION

The story of the peoples of the Indian Ocean basin is the story of great explorations and voyages. Western and eastern civilizations traveled and colonized the shores around the ocean's great expanses thousands of years before the explorations of the Vikings into southern Europe and Asia Minor, or the Europeans into the New World of the Americas. Around 510 BCE, the Greek marine captain, Scylax of Caryanda, sailed

down the Indus River in present-day Pakistan, then across the Indian Ocean to the Red Sea. Voyagers used the ocean currents as their natural navigation and propulsion system, with the assistance of the monsoon winds that filled their sails.

The world's great religions flourished in new lands as travelers and colonizers brought their faith with them. Voyages of Arab merchants across the Arabian Sea to the Indian Ocean added Islam to the Hinduism and Buddhism found in southern and southeastern Asia, adding another layer to the area's already rich religious and cultural mosaic.

The missionary travels of Saint Thomas the Apostle in early years of the first century CE, and the more recent Portuguese, British, Dutch, and French colonial expansions, introduced Christianity to the surrounding regions of the Indian Ocean, and helped shape trade routes between coastal cities.

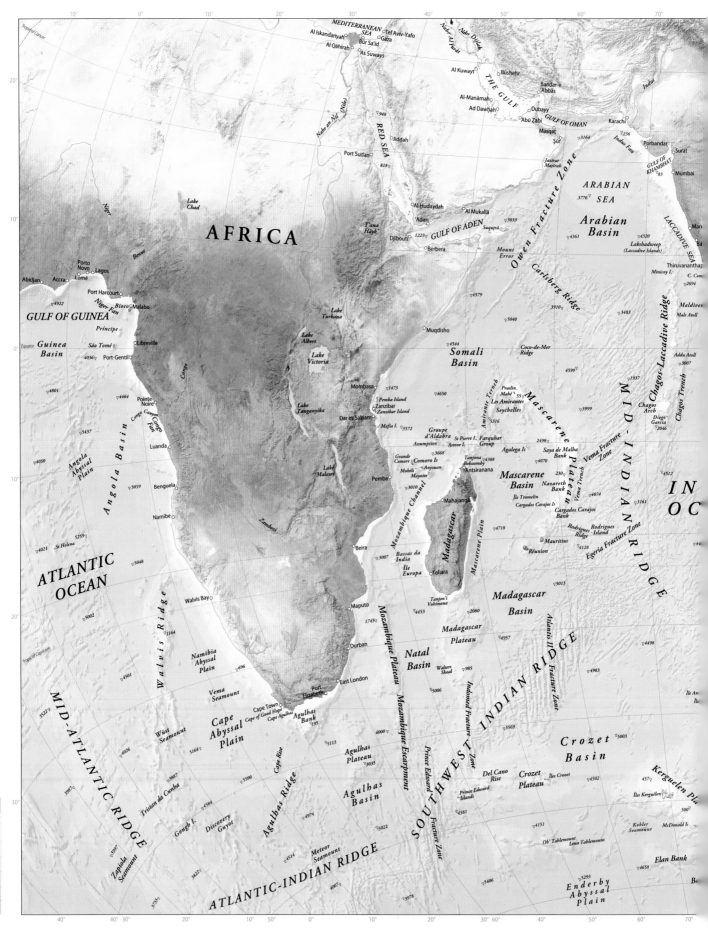

Tropic of Cancer

MEDITERRANEAN
SEA
Al Iskandariyah   Tel Aviv-Yafo
Gaza
Al Qāhirah   Būr Sa'īd
As Suways   Al Kuwayt   Būshehr
                                                              Bandar-e
▽948   Ad Dawḥah   Dubayy Abbās
RED SEA   Abū Zabi   Masqaṭ   Karachi
                            Jiddah   Ṣūr ▽3164
Port Sudan   Jazīrat   ▽236
▽818*   Majīrah   Indus Fan   Porbandar
                                                                          GULF OF   Surat
                                                                          KHAMBHAT
                                      ARABIAN   ▽83
                              ▽3776   SEA
Lake   Arabian
Chad   Al Ḥudaydah   Basin   ▽4320   Man
                  'Adan GULF OF ADEN Suquṭrā ▽3033   Lakshadweep
AFRICA   Djibouti 1223*   ▽4361   (Laccadive Islands)
          Berbera   Mount   Thiruvananthap
          T'ana   Error   Carlsberg Ridge Minicoy I.   C. Com
          Hāyk'   3910   ▽2694
Porto   ▽4579   ▽3483 Maldives
Novo Lagos Benue   Male Atoll
Abidjan Accra Tomé   Lake   ▽5040
      Port Harcourt Bioco Malabo Turkana   ▽4544   Coco-de-Mer
▽4922   Somali   Ridge
GULF OF GUINEA Niger Fan   Lake   Basin   4599   Addu Atoll
      Principe   Lake Albert   ▽3007
Guinea São Tomé Principe Victoria   Praslin ▽1937
Basin   Les Amirantes Mahé
      4036 Port-Gentil   Mombasa ▽1473   Seychelles ▽3999 Chagos
Equator   Pemba Island   5316   Arch
      ▽4801   Lake Zanzibar   ▽4650   Diego
            Pointe- Tanganyika Zanzibar Island   2498   Garcia
            Noire   Dar es Salaam   Groupe   ▽4070 2046
▽5437 Congo Canyon   Mafia I. ▽3572 d'Aldabra St Pierre I. Farquhar
      Congo Fan   Assumption Astove I. Group
      Fan   ▽3668   Saya de Malha
Luanda   Bank
      Angola   Lake   Grande Comoro Is Tanjona ▽4388 Nazareth
      Abyssal   Malawi   Comore Anjouan Bobaomby   Bank
Benguela Plain ▽5059   Mohéli Mayotte Antsiranana Mascarene Cargados Carajos
                        Pemba   ▽3010   Basin   Bank
Namibe   Île Tromelin Cargados Carajos
▽4050   Zambezi   Mahajanga Rodrigues Bank
      5259 ▽4021 St Helena   ▽4718   Ridge Rodrigues
ATLANTIC   Mascarene ▽4128 Island
OCEAN   ▽5048   Beira   Mauritius
                                    ▽3007 Bassas da   Réunion
                              Walvis Bay   India
                                        Île
Tropic of Capricorn   Europa Toliara   Madagascar
                                                      Basin
            ▽5002   Maputo   Tanjon'i
            ▽1164   Vohimena ▽2080
      Namibia   1745 ▽4453   Madagascar
      Abyssal   ▽696   Walters Plateau ▽4957
      Plain   Durban   Shoal
      Vema   Natal   ▽985
      Seamount   East London   Basin
MID-ATLANTIC   Cape Town Port   ▽5006
                        Cape of Good Hope Elizabeth 4000
                  Cape   Cape Agulhas Agulhas   ▽3569
            ▽3521 Abyssal   Bank 195
            Wüst Plain   Agulhas   ▽5013
            Seamount   Plateau   Crozet
      ▽4026   Agulhas 3035   Basin ▽5003
            5164   Basin
                        Cape Rise ▽5113   Del Cano Crozet Îles Crozet
            Discovery   3887   Rise Plateau   ▽4502
            Guyot   ▽3500   Prince Edward 457
      ▽3997 Tristan da Cunha ▽4584   Islands Prince Edward Îles Kerguélen
MID-ATLANTIC RIDGE   ▽4974   ▽4581 Islands
      Gough I. Discovery   ▽4151   Kohler
            3822 Zapiola   ▽5022   Seamount McDonald I.
            Seamount ▽4514 Meteor   Ob' Tablemount Lena Tablemount
                        Seamount ATLANTIC-INDIAN RIDGE   Elan Bank
            573v ▽5978   ▽5406 ▽5293   ▽4658
                        4007   Enderby
                                          Abyssal
                                          Plain

Owen Fracture Zone

Chagos-Laccadive Ridge

Chagos Trench

LACCADIVE SEA

Mascarene Plateau

MID-INDIAN RIDGE

Vema Fracture Zone

IN
OC

▽4512

▽3161

▽4074

Atlantis II Fracture Zone

▽4983

▽4498

SOUTHWEST INDIAN RIDGE

Indomed Fracture Zone

Prince Edward Fracture Zone

Mozambique Plateau

Mozambique Escarpment

Mozambique Channel

Madagascar

Walvis Ridge

Agulhas Ridge

Meters
Feet

0

LAND
BELOW
SEA LEVEL

100
328

200
656

1000
3281

2000
6562

4000
13123

6000
19685

1:37,500,000
Lambert Azimuthal Equal Area

0   500   1000   1500   2000 kilometers
0   250   500   750   1000 miles

Indian Ocean

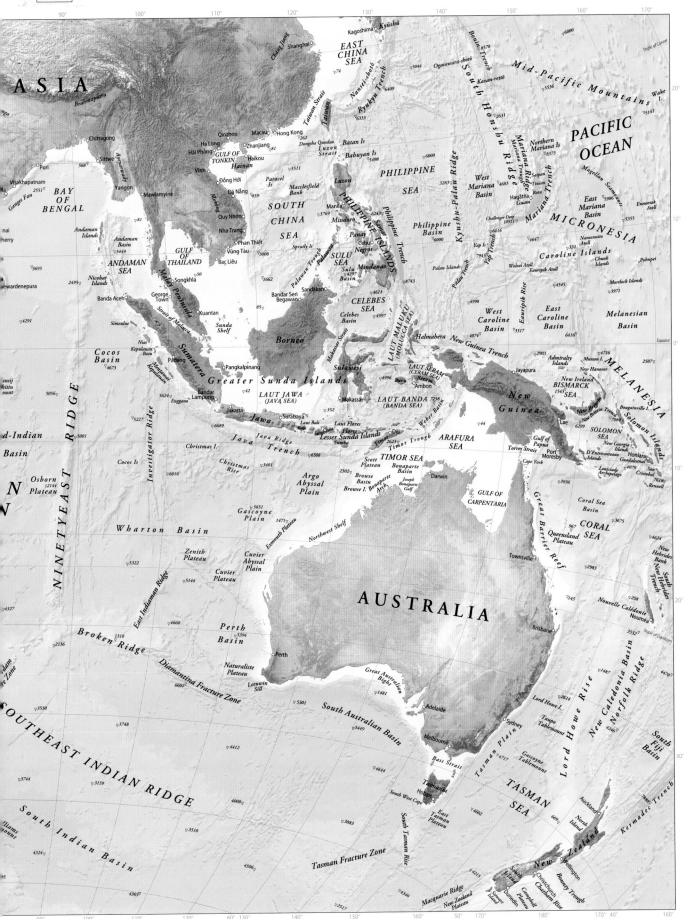

Southern Ocean

The Southern Ocean lies in the region between latitude 60°S and Antarctica. It covers an area of more than 780,000 square miles (20 million km²) and includes a number of smaller seas and bodies of water. Geologically, it is the world's youngest ocean.

ABOVE Named after its favorite habitat, the Weddell Sea, the Weddell seal (Leptonychotes weddellii) is born with a thin light coat that darkens and becomes mottled at maturity.

BELOW A diver swims with a group of crabeater seal (Lobodon carcinophaga) under the ice off Signy Island, Antarctica.

ANTARCTIC CONVERGENCE

A key feature of the Southern Ocean is the Antarctic Circumpolar Current (ACC) that transports vast quantities of water around the Antarctic continent. Driven by strong westerly winds, this slow-moving current flows from the ocean surface to a depth of 10,000 ft (3,000 m), and carries more water than any other on Earth.

Marine scientists have recently discovered that the ACC has a great influence on global ocean circulation. Its frigid waters are bounded by warmer waters on the northern edge of the current, creating a very distinct boundary known as the Antarctic Convergence. This border prompted the International Hydrographic Organization to officially create the Southern Ocean in 2000. Before this, the region was considered part of the Atlantic, Pacific, and Indian Oceans.

ICY DEPTHS

The Southern Ocean is very deep, ranging between 13,000–16,400 ft (4,000–5,000 m). There are few shallow areas; even the Antarctic continental shelf is unusually deep. A feature of the ocean is its ice packs, which cover around 1.3 million square miles (3.4 million km²) in late summer—January to March, and up to 7.2 million square miles (18.7 million km²) in the depth of winter.

ROARING FORTIES

For centuries, mariners have feared the Southern Ocean's enormous seas and intense winter storms, which are exacerbated by the temperature difference between the warmer ocean waters to the north, and the waters drifting northward from the frozen ice sheets of Antarctica.

The region south of the line of latitude 40°S, known as the "roaring forties," has stronger winds than anywhere else on the world's oceans. When ships were powered only by the wind, mariners would nevertheless often sail in this region, risking the obvious danger in order to take advantage of the powerful winds. Enormous icebergs that have broken off ice sheets, some of them hundreds of square miles in size, litter the ocean. These, along with solid sea ice that can suddenly form in inclement weather, further endanger shipping in the ocean.

COLDEST WATERS ON EARTH

Sea temperatures within the ocean range from around 50°F (10°C) to 29°F (−2°C), making these the coldest waters on Earth. Antarctica is covered by a permanent ice sheet more than 650 ft (200 m) thick in places. Nevertheless, the Southern Ocean is highly productive with plentiful fishing grounds. During the warmer summer months, December to March, productivity is as high as in the seas and oceans of the temperate zone.

FRIGID DWELLERS

Some marine animals have become perfectly adapted to the frigid environment. Of the world's more than 20,000 fish species, less than 150 are found in the Southern Ocean, and almost all are endemic to the region. Most are bottom-dwellers, living on the continental shelf. Their body fluids contain an anti-freeze-like substance.

In spring, ocean currents create upwellings that brings vast amounts of nutrients toward the surface of the ocean. Tiny plankton and krill start to increase

in numbers, attracting baleen whales such as hump-backs, minkes, and elusive blue whales—the largest animal to have ever lived on Earth. They consume vast numbers of the minuscule animals. Toothed whales, such as sperm whales also appear, and feed mainly on the abundant squid.

ICY HABITATS

In summer, the floating ice sheets break up, creating ice floes and pockets of calm water. The algae population at the very base of the food chain explodes under the light of the long summer days, supporting even more plankton and krill.

Four species of seal are found within the waters of the Southern Ocean—the crabeater seal, the world's most prolific seal; the leopard seal; the Antarctic fur seal; and the Weddell seal. The sea ice provides a perfect habitat for these seals, which hunt off the ice floes. Penguins also use the ice floes as a home base, breeding and feeding off the abundant krill and small fish, and in turn being preyed upon by leopard seals and killer whales. The killer whale, the largest member of the dolphin family, has no natural predators.

MARINE SUPERMARKET

Despite its remoteness, the Southern Ocean faces numerous environmental challenges. More than 110 tons (100,000 tonnes) of seafood are harvested annually, including enormous amounts of krill. In 1982, the Convention for the Conservation of Antarctic Marine Living Resources was ratified in order to protect the Southern Ocean, but extensive illegal fishing is endangering many Antarctic species, including commercial varieties such as the Patagonian tooth fish.

ABOVE The ravages of wind and waves have formed this fantastic ice arch through a massive iceberg found floating off the western Antarctic Peninsula, in the Southern Ocean.

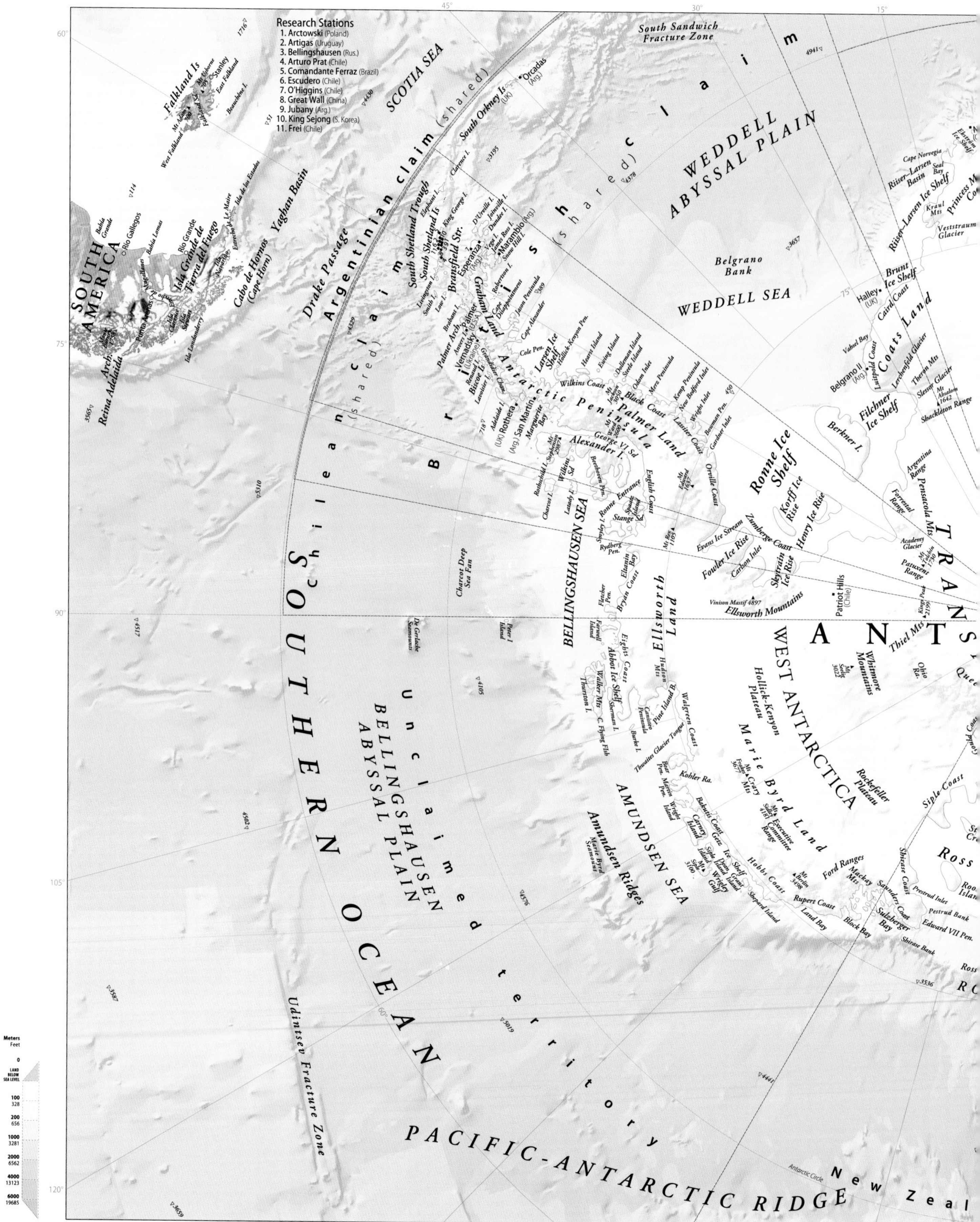

Research Stations
1. Arctowski (Poland)
2. Artigas (Uruguay)
3. Bellingshausen (Rus.)
4. Arturo Prat (Chile)
5. Comandante Ferraz (Brazil)
6. Escudero (Chile)
7. O'Higgins (Chile)
8. Great Wall (China)
9. Jubany (Arg.)
10. King Sejong (S. Korea)
11. Frei (Chile)

South Sandwich
Fracture Zone

WEDDELL
ABYSSAL PLAIN

SCOTIA SEA

South Orkney Is.
(UK)
•Orcadas
(Arg.)

Belgrano
Bank

WEDDELL SEA

Cape Norvegia

Riiser-Larsen
Sea
Seal
Bay

Princess M

Krawl
Coast

Veststraum
Glacier

Halley
(UK)

Brunt
Ice Shelf

Caird Coast

Coats Land

Vahsel Bay

Belgrano II
(Arg.)

Luitpold Coast

Rechefield Glacier

Theron Mts

Filchner
Ice Shelf

Ronne Ice
Shelf

Berkner I.

Ronne
Ice

Korff Ice
Rise

Henry Ice Rise

Pensacola Mts

Argentina
Range

Forrestal
Range

Academy
Glacier

Patuxent
Range

Thiel
Mts

Ohio
Ra.

WEST ANTARCTICA

Marie Byrd Land

Hollick-Kenyon
Plateau

Whitmore
Mountains

Ellsworth Mountains

Vinson Massif 4897

Patriot Hills
(Chile)

FALKLAND Is

SOUTH AMERICA

Drake Passage

Antarctic Peninsula

Graham Land

Palmer Land

Alexander I.

George VI Sd.

BELLINGSHAUSEN SEA

Ellsworth
Land

AMUNDSEN
SEA

Amundsen Ridges

Ford Ranges

Ross

SOUTHERN OCEAN

unclaimed territory

BELLINGSHAUSEN
ABYSSAL PLAIN

Peter I
Island

Udintsev Fracture Zone

PACIFIC-ANTARCTIC RIDGE

Antarctic Circle

New Zeal

Argentinian claim (shared)

Chilean claim (shared)

Chilean claim

Meters Feet
0
LAND
BELOW
SEA LEVEL
100 328
200 656
1000 3281
2000 6562
4000 13123
6000 19685

62

1:18,700,000
Polar Stereographic Projection

0   250   500   750   1000 kilometers
0 125 miles 250 miles 375 miles 500 miles

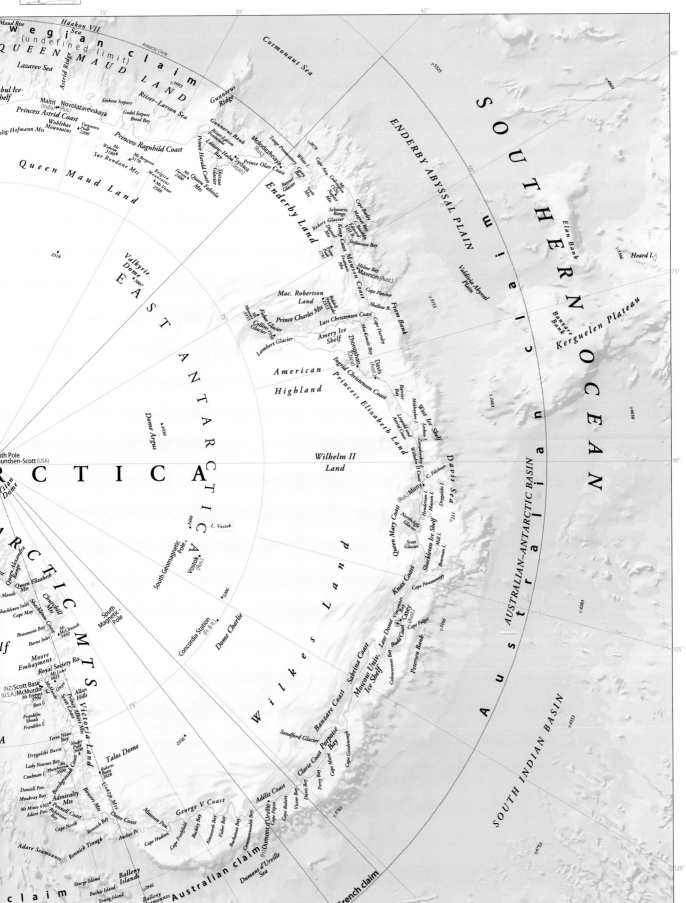

Arctic Ocean

The smallest of the world's oceans, the Arctic is one of the least navigated bodies of water on Earth. The majority of the ocean lies north of the Arctic Circle and it encompasses an area of approximately 5,428,000 square miles (14,060,000 km²). Canada, Alaska, Russia, and Greenland all have coasts on the Arctic. Thus, land almost entirely encircles the ocean with the only significant outlet lying between Greenland and Scandinavia. In total, the ocean's coastline exceeds 28,000 miles (45,000 km).

GEOGRAPHY

A number of seas lie off the Arctic Ocean, including the Beaufort Sea of the Alaskan and Canadian coasts, Barents Sea in the east of the Scandinavian coast, the East Siberian Sea, and the Kara Sea adjacent to Russia. Depths within the ocean are highly variable with the shallowest part—approximately 500 ft (150 m)—in the southeast, off the Scandinavian coast.

Off the coast of Alaska, where the continental shelf is at its narrowest, depths are greatest, plunging to a maximum depth of 18,050 ft (5,502 m) in the Fram Basin. Average depths within the ocean are 3,240 ft (987 m). Numerous sizable islands are found in the Arctic Ocean, generally hugging the coastlines. Most notable of these are the Queen Elizabeth Islands that lie close to the Canadian coastline.

BOWLS OF STAGNANT WATER

The ocean is divided into two distinct regions, the Eurasian Basin in the east and the North American Basin in the west, with the Lomonosov Ridge dividing the two. Spurs of the extensive Atlantic submarine ridges also protrude into the Arctic. The sea floor is therefore highly dissected, which serves to cause a slowing of water in the bottom of the ocean, making it almost stagnant. In addition, waters at depth within the Arctic have a considerably higher salt content than the surface waters. This increases the density of the water, causing a further reduction in flow. This large body of stagnating water is extremely cold.

The surface waters that extend to a depth of around 150 ft (46 m), circulate in a clockwise direction around the polar ice cap. This rotating pattern is referred to as

BELOW Standing precariously over a rocky outcrop, these fishermens' cabins on Vestvagoy in Norway, are painted to contrast with the cold environment of the Arctic Ocean.

LEFT The Arctic National Wildlife Refuge in Alaska on the fringe of the Arctic Ocean. The area has no roads, although a settlement of Inupiat people on the northern edge and Gwich'in people on the southern boundary do exist. The walking passage between the two villages is a popular wilderness route.

the gyre and is the result of the prevailing clockwise rotating winds in the region. Two principal rotating currents are found within the ocean—the Beaufort Gyre, which rotates around the North American Basin, and the Barents Gyre, which is the dominant current within the Eurasian Basin. Surface water also moves out of the Arctic via the Labrador Current that flows down into the Labrador Sea through the narrow Davis Strait via Baffin Bay between Baffin Island and Greenland. A smaller current also flows through the extremely narrow Roes Welcome Sound into Hudson Bay.

ENVIRONMENT

Located so far north, the Arctic Ocean is subject to polar climatic conditions characterized by constant cold temperatures with only a slight warming in the summer months. The waters of the Arctic have a covering of perennial ice, although global warming associated with the greenhouse effect is beginning to limit the extent and persistence of this ice. During the coldest parts of the year, the sea ice has an average thickness of around 10 ft (3 m), although in parts this can exceed 33 ft (10 m) more than doubling the sea ice and virtually connecting all the land areas to each other.

Icebergs are a common feature of the Arctic and present a significant threat to shipping in and around the ocean. The icebergs are generally calved from the huge glaciers of Greenland and far northern Canada. In recent years, enormous ice islands have also began to break off the ice shelf on Ellesmere Island, which lies to the north of Greenland.

In 2005, a massive 41 square-mile (66 km²) ice island broke away from the Ayles Ice Shelf and floated around the Arctic, slowly melting for more than three

years. Climatologists have pointed to such massive breakups of the ice shelves as further evidence of the effects of global warming.

WILDLIFE

The extremely cold waters of the Arctic would appear to be amongst the least hospitable environments on Earth and yet the ocean supports a surprising variety of life. At the base of the food chain, ice diatoms—single-celled algae—form the basis of further life within the ecosystem. The most iconic of the Arctic creatures is the polar bear, the region's top predator. Living on the edge of the sea ice, the bear, which is highly endangered, lives on seals in the region, such as the sleepy ringed seal and the northern fur seal.

ABOVE The influx of eco-tourism throughout the world has brought a variety of different pursuits for the adventurous. Here a woman takes a swim in the frigid waters of the Artic Ocean at the North Pole, watched by sensibly-dressed fellow travelers from the Russian icebreaker *Yamai*.

A S I A

SEA OF OKHOTSK

POLUOSTROV KAMCHATKA

Kuril'skye Ostrova

Kuril-Kamchatka Trench

Aleutian Trench

Aleutian Islands

Shirshov Ridge

Kamchatka Basin

Bowers Bank

Bowers Ridge

Aleutian Basin

BERING SEA

Zaliv Shelikhova

Penzhinskaya Guba

Karaginskiy Zaliv

Olyutorskiy Zaliv

Anadyr

Anadyrskiy Zaliv

Zaliv Kresta

Chukotskiy Poluostrov

St. Matthew I.

St. Lawrence I.

Kolyuchinskaya Guba

Nunivak Island

Bering Strait

Pribilof Islands

Etolin Strait

Norton Sound

Kuskokwim Bay

Kotzebue Sound

Seward Peninsula

Prince of Wales

CHUKCHI SEA

VOSTOCHNO-SIBIRSKOYE MORE
(East Siberian Sea)

Proliv Dmitriya Lapteva

Ostrova Anzhu

Novaya Sibir'

Novosibirskiye Ostrova

Ostrov Kotel'nyy

Yanskiy Zaliv

MORE LAPTEVYKH
(Laptev Sea)

Lyakhovskiye Ostrova

Proliv Longa

Ostrov Vrangelya

Kucherov Terrace

Wrangel Abyssal Plain

Pole Abyssal Pl

Lomonos

MAKAROV BAS

NANS

ARCTIC OCEA

Mendeleyev Ridge

Mendeleyev Abyssal Plain

Chukchi Abyssal Plain

Chukchi Plateau

Northwind Abyssal Plain

Northwind Ridge

Northwind Escarpment

Canada Abyssal Plain

CANADA BASIN

BEAUFORT SEA

Point Barrow

Mackenzie Bay

Amundsen Gulf

Amundsen Trough

Banks Island

Prince of Wales Str.

Prince Albert Peninsula

Victoria Island

Prince Albert Sd.

Wollaston Peninsula

Dolphin and Union Str.

Coronation G.

Dease Str.

Great Bear L.

Queen Maud Gulf

Mackenzie

NORTH AM

Melville I.

M'Clure Strait

Viscount

Melville Sd.

Parry Is

Prince Patrick Island

Eli

Banks Island

Q

Sve

Adolf I.

Borden Island

Mackenzie King I.

Ellef Ringnes I.

Hazen Strait

Lougheed I.

Prince of Wales Island

Stefansson Island

Victoria Island

King William Island

M'Clintock Chan.

Larsen Sound

Queen Maud Gulf

NORTH AMERICA

Aleutian Islands

Fox Islands

Aleutian Trench

Aleutian Ridge

Unimak Island

Unalaska Island

Alaska Peninsula

Bristol Bay

Shumagin Islands

Trinity Islands

Shelikof Strait

Cook Inlet

Kodiak I.

Kenai Peninsula

Gulf of Alaska

PACIFIC OCEAN

Patton Seamount

Gilbert Seamount

Pratt Seamount

Chirikof Island

Kodiak-Bowie Seamount

1:18,700,000

Lambert Conic Conformal Projection

Meters
Feet

0

LAND BELOW SEA LEVEL

100 / 328

200 / 656

1000 / 3281

2000 / 6562

4000 / 13123

6000 / 19685

0   200   400   600   800 kilometers
0   100   200   300   400 miles

150°   135°   120°   105°

165°

EUROPE

ASIA

Gydanskiy
Poluostrov

Ob'

Yenisey

Yenisey

Poluostrov Yamal

Obskaya Guba

Khrebet Pay-Khoy

Bol'shezemel'skaya
Gaba

Ostrov
Vaygach

Pechorskoye
More

Proliv Karskiye Vorota

Ostrov
Belyy

Cheshskaya Guba

Pechora

Arkhangel'sk

Severnaya Dvina

Volga

Rybinskoye

Vodokhranilishche

Onezhskoye
Ozero

Belove
Ozero

Ladozhskoye
Ozero

Osero
Imara

Cludskoy
Osera

Peipus
Jar.

G. of
Rīga

Saaremaa

Gulf of Finland

Hiiumaa

Väind

Gulf of Bothnia

BALTIC SEA

Bornholm

Gotland

Öland

København

Skälland

Fyn
Odense

Århus

KARSKOYE MORE
(Kara Sea)

Novaya Zemlya Trough

Novaya Zemlya

Gusinaya
Bank

North Kanin
Basin

Murmansk Rise

Belove More
White Sea

Kandalakshskiy
Zaliv

Onezhskaya
Guba

Kol'skiy
Poluostrov

Murmansk

BARENTS
SEA

Kattegat

Göteborg

Skagerrak

NORTH
SEA

Rost Bank

Traena
Bank

Halten
Bank

Trondheim

Stavanger

Bergen

Oslo

Vänern

Vättern

SCANDINAVIA

Central Kara
Plateau

Svyataya Anna Trough

Zemlya Frantsa-Iosifa

Svyataya Anna
Fan

Olga Basin

Edgeøya

Spitsbergen
Bank

Spitsbergen

Svalbard

Nordaustlandet

Yermak
Plateau

Spitsbergen
Fracture Zone

Voronin Plateau

Murray Jeep Rise

BASIN

Abyssal plain

Ridge

am Basin

Nansen Basin

Belgica
Bank

Boreas
Abyssal
Plain

Hovgaard Ridge

GREENLAND
SEA

Mohns Ridge

GREENLAND Fracture Zone

Greenland Abyssal Plain

Jan Mayen Fracture Zone

Jan Mayen Ridge

Icelandic
Plateau

Kolbeinsey Ridge

Norwegian
Abyssal
Plain

NORWEGIAN SEA
Basin

Aegir Ridge

Vøring
Plateau

Damshaf

Faroe-Iceland
Ridge

Faroe
Islands

Bill Bailey's
Bank

Outer
Bailey

Wyville-Thomson
Ridge

Faroe
Bank

Rockall Rise

George Bligh
Bank

Rockall
Island

Rockall Bank

Shetland
Islands

Orkney
Islands

Outer Hebrides

Inner Hebrides

Aberdeen

Edinburgh

Blackpool

British
Isles

Londonderry

Belfast

Isle of
Man

Irish Sea

ATLANTIC
OCEAN

Greenland

Independence Fjord

Denmark
Fjord

Dove Bugt

Victoria Fjord

Lincoln Sea

Robeson Chan.

Nares Str.

North Geomagnetic Pole

Kane
Basin

Hayes

Smith Bay

Halvo

Qimusseriarsuaq

Ellesmere Island

Gredy Sd.

Smith Sd.

Foster Bay

Kong Oscar Fjord

Scoresby
Sund

Denmark Strait

Reykjavik

Iceland

Greenland-Iceland
Rise

Reykjanes Ridge

MAURY CHANNEL

IMARSSUAK CHANNEL

Arctic Circle

Uummannaq Fjord

Qeqertarsuaq

Qeqertarsuup
Tunua

Baffin
Bay

Davis Strait

Home
Bay

Nuuk

Nanny Jensu
(Cape Farewell)

Eirik
Ridge

Charlie-Gibbs Fracture Zone

AMERICA

Jones Sound

von Island

Lancaster Sound

Baffin Island

Bylot
Island

Eclipse
Sound

Borden
Peninsula

Brodeur Peninsula

Admiralty Inlet

Commitee Bay

Melville
Peninsula

Rowley I.

Prince
Charles
Islands

Spicer
Islands

Air
Force I.

Wales I.

Foxe
Basin

Cumberland
Peninsula

Cumberland Sd.

Meters	
Feet	
0	LAND
	BELOW
	SEA LEVEL
100	328
200	656
1000	3281
2000	6562
4000	13123
6000	19685

SEAS, GULFS, AND BAYS

Seas, gulfs, and bays are generally located at the edge of oceans, which makes their coastlines very expedient for human settlement and exploitation. Worldwide, there are thousands of seas, gulfs, and bays, many without names. As is true of all place names, a direct relationship exists between the importance of a place, and whether it is actually given a name.

NAMING FEATURES

In heavily navigated waters, many names exist—for example, a map of the Mediterranean Sea shows more than 24 seas, gulfs, and bays. But a more detailed map of a smaller portion of this highly populated and historically important water body discloses many more such named features. Similarly, around the relatively small but populous Aegean Sea, around 30 such features have been given names. In the USA, a map of Washington's relatively small Puget Sound reveals more than 24 named subfeatures. Areas of lower economic importance and navigation, such as around the Southern and Arctic oceans, generally feature fewer names. However, some exceptions do exist—for example, along the sparsely populated coasts of southern Chile and Argentina.

CONFUSING DISPARITY

"Maps," said naturalist and writer Peter Steinhart in 1986, "are a way of organizing wonder." This certainly holds very true in regard to the naming of seas, bays, gulfs, and related features such as sounds, inlets, fjords, harbors, ports, estuaries, and lakes. One wonders how the nomenclature relating to these similar features could possibly be so inconsistent and confusing! Even a cursory scan of an ocean map discloses the apparently haphazard and contradictory way in which they are named. As with all toponymy (for example, "hill" and "mountain"), names were based upon the discoverer's original perceptions.

Even small-scale maps—showing greater detail—reveal confusing disparities. For example, the Sargasso Sea occupies the mid-northern Atlantic Ocean and has no coastline at all, whereas the Dead, Caspian, and Aral Seas are totally surrounded by land.

Southern California's Salton Sea is actually a landlocked saline lake in the Colorado Desert, whereas Utah's larger and much saltier water body is named Great Salt Lake.

In terms of physical characteristics, little difference—other than size—exists between the Red Sea, The Gulf, Hudson Bay, and Venezuela's Lake Maracaibo. There is little significant difference between the configuration of the Gulf of Mexico and the Caribbean Sea. The same is true for the Arabian Sea and the Bay of Bengal, which both flank the Indian subcontinent.

It's All in the Name

The following definitions help to distinguish the use of the respective names.

SEA: A tract of water within an ocean; any of the various bodies of salt water smaller than an ocean; a smaller body of water attached to the oceans

GULF: A large area of sea or ocean partially enclosed by land; a large area of ocean reaching into the land; an inlet of the sea, especially large inlets that are relatively deep

BAY: A body of water partly enclosed by land but with a wide outlet to the sea; a wide inlet of a sea or lake along the shore; an indentation of the sea into the land, especially one with a wide opening, or greater in width than in depth

SAFE HARBORS

Coastal areas of the sea assume considerable importance in settled areas. Waters that offer protection from storms, waves, and strong currents make excellent harbors. Many of the world's largest cities are located on gulfs or bays—by whatever local name. Because they tend to be shallow and protected, seas, gulfs, and bays also allow us to harvest a wide variety of seafood including fishes, crabs, lobsters, and various shellfishes. Many also offer amenities such as scenery and recreational areas. In many locations around the world, their shallow waters are becoming increasingly dotted with oil rigs as the oil extraction industry continues to move offshore.

LEFT Crossing the Bay of Bengal can be hazardous, particularly in a small boat with handmade sails. The Bay of Bengal is the largest bay by area in the world.

RIGHT White cliffs contrast with the blue of the Mediterranean Sea on Zakynthos Island in Greece. Zakynthos Island is home to the loggerhead sea turtle *(Caretta caretta)*, an endangered species.

BELOW Isla San Francisco in the Sea of Cortez, is a safe anchorage for yachts cruising the west coast of North America. The Sea of Cortez is another name for the Gulf of California.

Seas of the Arctic Region

The waters contained within the Arctic region—north of the Arctic Circle—are made up of many small seas that are almost completely covered in ice. Because the area is around the North Pole, at the top of the world, the seas are within the territories of countries that extend into the region—Canada, Denmark, Russia, USA, Iceland, Norway, Sweden, and Finland.

BEAUFORT SEA

The Beaufort Sea extends beyond its relatively narrow continental shelf, to the continental slope and deeper waters. Its seaward boundary extends from Prince Patrick Island to Point Barrow, giving it a triangular shape. The sea covers an area of around 185,000 square miles (480,000 km²). To the northwest, depths in the sea exceed 12,100 ft (3,700 m), making the Beaufort the deepest of the Arctic seas. Although the shelf area is small, it is rich in petroleum reserves. It is named for Irish hydrographer Sir Francis Beaufort, who devised the wind scale used by mariners around the world.

CHUKCHI SEA

The Chukchi Sea shares a boundary with the Beaufort Sea, and stretches west across Bering Strait to Wrangel Island. It covers an area of around 224,000 square miles (580,000 km²) and its average depth is around 250 ft (75 m). Its seaward limit is the edge of the continental shelf, between latitudes 72°N and 75°N. Fresh water flows in from northwestern Alaska and eastern Siberia. It also receives relatively warm Pacific water from the Bering Sea, resulting in a comparatively long ice-free period of five months. The sea is named for the Chukchi people of northeastern Siberia.

EAST SIBERIAN SEA

The East Siberian Sea, with an average depth of just over 165 ft (50 m), is the shallowest of the Russian Arctic seas. It covers an area of 361,000 square miles (935,000 km²) and extends from the Chukchi Sea in the east to the New Siberian Islands in the west. Its

BELOW A polar bear *(Ursus maritimus)* mother and spring cub travel over the sea ice formed where the Bering Sea meets the Chukchi Sea, just 20 miles (32 km) from the Arctic village of Barrow, Alaska.

northern boundary is defined by an arc that runs from Wrangel Island to De Long Island. It is covered in ice for most of the year. Even during the short summer, icebergs trouble shipping. The population density along the coast is very low, with just a few settlements near river mouths.

LAPTEV SEA

The Laptev Sea, north of central Siberia, lies between the New Siberian Islands to the east, and the Taymyr Peninsula and the Severnaya Zemlya Islands to the west. Covering 260,000 square miles (670,000 km²), the Laptev is the smallest of the central Siberian seas. More than half its depth is less than 165 ft (50 m). The coastline of the Laptev Sea features many bays, inlets, and islands. Large inflows from the mainland reduce its salinity, and provide a large amount of mineral and organic material.

KARA SEA

The Kara Sea is bordered to the northeast by the Severnaya Zemlya Islands, and to the southwest by Novaya Zemlya. It is rectangular in shape and features many islands. It covers around 340,000 square miles (880,000 km²), and has an average depth of around 360 ft (110 m). Two of the world's longest rivers, the Ob and Yenisey, flow into the sea, which remains frozen for about nine months of the year.

WHITE SEA

The White Sea is a small inlet of the Barents Sea. It is almost completely surrounded by land, and is connected to the Baltic Sea to the south by the White Sea Canal. With an average depth of around 310 ft (95 m), the sea covers an area of 35,000 square miles (90,000 km²). It supports six important ports, a major fishing industry, and several other essential industries including shipbuilding.

LABRADOR SEA

The Labrador Sea is separated from Baffin Bay to the north by the Davis Strait, which straddles the Arctic Circle. It is bound by Labrador to the west and a small portion of Greenland to the northeast. It covers around 540,000 square miles (1,400,000 km²) and ranges in depth from 2,300 ft (700 m) to more than 10,000 ft (3,000 m). Shipping is affected by numerous icebergs, calved from the Greenland, Ellesmere, and Baffin Island glaciers. The warm Gulf Stream keeps most of the sea free of ice, but in the northwest, the cold Labrador Current causes freezes in the winter.

BAFFIN BAY

Baffin Bay, which is connected to the Arctic Ocean by the narrow Nares Strait between Greenland and Ellesmere Island, and to the Labrador Sea and Atlantic Ocean by the much wider Davis Strait, covers around 270,000 square miles (690,000 km²). It lies between

Greenland and Baffin Island, and has an average depth of 2,400 ft (725 m). Located at the center of one of the Arctic's most geologically active areas, Baffin Bay is covered in ice for about eight months of the year.

LINCOLN SEA

The small Lincoln Sea covers only 4,600 square miles (12,000 km²). It lies between northwestern Greenland and northeastern Ellesmere Island. To the south, the Nares Strait links it to Baffin Bay. Frozen for most of the year, the Lincoln Sea boasts the thickest ice cover of any Arctic sea.

ABOVE Exquisite architecture can be seen in this tiny Russian Orthodox chapel sitting on the edge of Solovetsky Island in the White Sea.

Waters of the North Pacific

The Bering Sea, the Gulf of Alaska, and the Sea of Okhotsk are all located in the far north of the grand Pacific Ocean. Having little in common with the temperate and tropical areas most associated with the Pacific, these three beautiful bodies of deep, crisp, clear water attract crabs and salmon that in turn bring sea lions, seals, and polar bears to feast.

ABOVE The harsh climate of the Bering Sea attracts tourists who enjoy the extreme views within the luxury of a cruise ship. The Amutka Volcano on the Aleutian Islands forms a spectacular backdrop for the cruise ship *World Discover*.

OPPOSITE The true size of this massive iceberg in Prince William Sound can be seen underwater, where its bulk is evident. Ninety percent of an iceberg is underwater.

BERING SEA

Separating the continents of North America and Asia, the Bering Sea lies at the northernmost extremity of the Pacific Ocean. It covers an area of approximately 890,000 square miles (2,304,000 km²). At its narrowest point, the Bering Strait is only 53 miles (85 km) wide. The east coast of Siberia forms the western edge of the sea, while the eastern boundary is Alaska's west coast. The Alaska Peninsula lies along the southeast of the sea.

Depths within the Bering Sea range considerably, the shallowest being the Bering Straits where average depths are around 130 ft (40 m). The sea's deepest point is 13,442 ft (4,100 m) in the Bowers Basin.

Currents within the sea tend to flow in a northwest direction. The main current is the Transverse Current, which draws in waters from the Pacific Ocean through channels in the Fox Islands to the south of the Alaska Peninsula. The Kamchatka Current then carries the waters south along the Siberian coastline. Sea ice forms in coastal waters, creating a habitat for polar bears. In summer the world's largest creature, the blue whale, migrates through on its way to the Arctic Ocean.

GULF OF ALASKA

Lying off the south coast of the US state of Alaska, the Gulf of Alaska is a significant inlet of the North Pacific Ocean. It covers an area of some 592,000 square miles (1,533,000 km²) and contains numerous fjords and other deep inlets, including Cook Inlet and Prince William Sound. Sizable icebergs that have detached from glaciers float across the gulf before being carried out into the Pacific by the Alaska Current, which moves in a counterclockwise direction around the gulf. Vast amounts of fresh water also enter the gulf from the Susitna and Copper rivers.

A number of islands lie within the gulf, the most significant being Kodiak Island that is separated from the Alaska Peninsula by the deep Shelikof Strait.

The sea floor of the Gulf of Alaska is dotted with hundreds of seamounts. Some of these reach heights of close to 10,000 ft (3,000 m), rising above the sea surface to form islands. They have been formed by tectonic movement of the Pacific Plate moving over hotspots, or weaknesses in the earth's crust. Many are millions of years old and are no longer active.

SEA OF OKHOTSK

Located off the North Pacific Ocean, the Sea of Okhotsk covers an area of 611,000 square miles (1,580,000 km²). The southern edge of the sea is bounded by Hokkaido, the northernmost Japanese island. To the east lies the Russian Kamchatka Peninsula. Stretching southwest in a long arch toward Hokkaido, the Kuril Islands chain forms the eastern border of the sea. To the west lies continental Russia.

The sea has an average depth of around 2,920 ft (890 m). The northern part of the sea is quite shallow; depths are generally less than 650 ft (200 m). Depths increase toward the south and east; the deepest regions are located on the eastern edge of the sea near the Kuril Islands, where the Kuril Basin plunges to approximately 8,200 ft (2,500 m).

Currents within the sea tend to move in a counterclockwise direction. Warmer water flows in from the Sea of Japan and the La Perouse Strait. Another current carries water from the Pacific through the various straits between the northern Kuril Islands.

The sea is covered with sea ice during the winter months, reaching its greatest thickness by March. During the summer, all but the far north of the sea is ice-free. The Sea of Okhotsk features rich biodiversity, with abundant stocks of cod, herring, flounder, salmon, and pollock attracting seals, sea lions, dolphins, and humans. Orcas (killer whales) are also found within the sea.

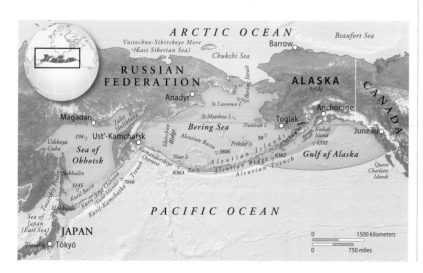

Hudson Bay

Located in eastern Canada, Hudson Bay is a large inland sea covering an area of around 316,000 square miles (819,000 km²). The bay is surrounded by land on all sides, with the exception of a few straits and channels between a series of islands in the north. Hudson Strait connects the bay to the North Atlantic Ocean in the northeast. To the north, the Foxe Channel winds its way through myriad narrow straits to provide a passage through to the Arctic Ocean via the Gulf of Boothia and the Parry Channel.

ABOVE The willow ptarmigan (*Lagopus lagopus)* is a member of the grouse family. During winter, their plumage turns white, blending with the snowy backdrop of the Hudson Bay region. The birds' range extends across northern Canada.

SCATTERED WITH ISLANDS

Hudson Bay is a shallow sea with an average depth of around 410 ft (125 m), the deepest point being around 820 ft (250 m). Depths are greater in the channels to the north that link the bay to the Hudson Strait. A number of significant islands are found within the bay; the largest, Southampton Island, is located in the northwest corner. Along with Coats Island, Mansel Island, and Nottingham Island, it forms the northern boundary of Hudson Bay. The Belcher Island group lies off the coast of Quebec in the east. Akimiski Island is a large island to the south, in James Bay, Hudson Bay's largest inlet.

Surface currents within the bay generally flow in an anticlockwise direction. However, the islands, bays, and inlets within Hudson Bay disrupt this pattern to some extent. Water is drawn in from the Atlantic through Hudson Strait, entering through Evans Strait on the eastern side of Southampton Island. Another current draws in cold water from the Arctic Ocean via the extremely narrow Roes Welcome Sound located between the mainland and Southampton Island.

LONG WINTER FREEZE

Hudson Bay is located above 50°N latitude and sea ice covers much of its surface for up to nine months of the year. In April the ice is at its thickest, at an average depth of around of 5 ft (1.6 m). This sea ice also complicates the water movement around the Bay; the heavier colder waters from the Arctic tend to circulate at greater depths.

The vast expanse of Hudson Bay has a significant effect on the climate of northeastern North America. In summer, the water moderates temperatures in the lowlands to the south, but the existence of sea ice in the autumn and winter months reduces the bay's ability to moderate winter temperatures. During the summer months, water temperatures range between 54°F and 61°F (12°C to 16°C), while in winter the temperature can plunge to as low as −13°F (−25°C).

RUGGED COASTLINE

The coastal areas surrounding Hudson Bay are inconsistent in form. The northern coastline contains areas of permafrost, with large lowland lakes surrounded by marshes. The northern and eastern shores feature high cliffs but the majority of the coastline is relatively flat. In the south, particularly at James Bay, coniferous forests are found. Around the rest of the bay, stands of willow, aspen, and small bushes are widespread.

MARINE MAMMAL MIGRATION

Hudson Bay is a highly productive environment, supporting significant populations of seals and other animals. Estimates place the number of ringed seals at more than half a million. It was the presence of seals that first attracted humans to the waters of the bay in the late seventeenth century, when the Hudson Bay

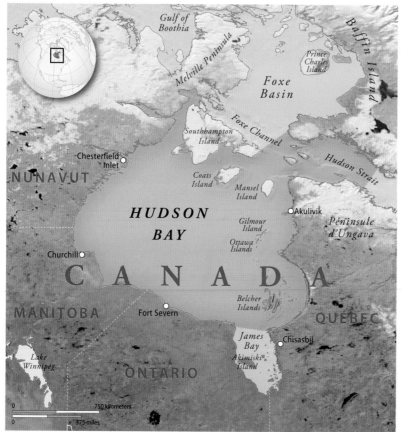

Company began to operate in the area. Around 2,000 walrus migrate into the northern part of the bay each summer, forming colonies on the southern areas of Southampton Island and Coats Island. Polar bears are also found along the northern coastlines in the summer and autumn. An estimated 9,000 beluga whales may be found within the bay. The highly-endangered bowhead whale is also found in small numbers to the north. More than 60 species of fish are found. The lake sturgeon—a large, bottom-dwelling fish—has been hunted almost to extinction and although its numbers are increasing, it remains threatened.

ANCIENT INHABITANTS

Humans have long occupied the coastal regions around Hudson Bay. The Inuit and Cree people have inhabited the area for thousands of years, and the waters and lands of the bay are important traditional areas that hold great spiritual significance for them. The lucrative fur trade attracted significant European populations to the bay during the eighteenth and nineteenth centuries.

ABOVE The harsh environment of the Hudson Bay area requires adaptation by flora and fauna species. Even these hardy spruce trees have suffered from constant high winds in the region.

LEFT This satellite image shows ice melting on Hudson Bay. During winter, much of the surface is frozen, allowing passage by only the toughest ice-breaker craft, before warmer temperatures thaw the thick icy surface.

Gulf of California

The Gulf of California—also known as the Sea of Cortez—is a long, narrow arm of the Pacific Ocean that separates Mexico's mainland from the Baja California peninsula. Geologists believe the gulf began to form around five million years ago in a trench created by a southward extension of the San Andreas Fault.

The Gulf of California covers an area of approximately 60,000 square miles (155,000 km^2). Alluvial deposits of the Colorado River delta block the gulf's northward extension into Southern California's Salton Trough. The Imperial and Coachella valleys, and the shore of the Salton Sea, reach elevations as low as 235 ft (72 m) below sea level. Some evidence suggests that the gulf may still have been connected to the Salton Trough in 1538 when Francisco de Ulloa explored the region.

ENVIRONMENT

The gulf waters vary greatly in depth. In its northern regions the trench is relatively shallow, filling over the ages to a depth of several thousand feet with deltaic silt from the Colorado River. In its southern regions the floor drops to a depth of about 12,000 ft (3,600 m). More than 900 islands, most of which are quite small, dot the gulf's surface. They offer nesting sites for millions of marine birds and a temporary refuge for migrating species. The largest islands are Tiburón, once inhabited by turtle-hunting Seri Indians, and Ángel de la Guarda. Small Isla Tortuga, the gulf's only volcano, is home to the Tortuga Island diamond rattlesnake—*Crotalus tortugensis*.

BELOW This popular mooring ground in the Gulf of California gives small craft protection from the rolling waves of the Pacific Ocean.

UNIQUE ECOSYSTEM

The Gulf of California offers a unique ecosystem rich in assorted marine life, both endemic and migratory. Seasonal visitors include humpback, California gray, killer, and blue whales; manta rays; and leatherback sea turtles. Gulf waters have long been fished commercially and for sport, sardines and anchovies being the principal commercial species. They have also seen a number of sport-fishing world records, including the Pacific amberjack, Pacific bonito, Pacific jack, roosterfish, and wahoo. Many gulf communities depend upon sport fishing as a mainstay of their economy. They include La Paz, Guaymas, and Mazatlán. Years of over-fishing have greatly reduced the populations of all fish species.

Gulf of Panama

The Gulf of Panama—Golfo de Panamá—occupies a 900-square-mile (2,300-km²) area of the Pacific Ocean off the southeast coast of Panama in Central America. Within it lie the Gulf of Paria to the west, Panama Bay to the north, and the Gulf of San Miguel to the east.

TIDAL FLOW

The Gulf of Panama is a shallow water body perched entirely on the continental shelf, with a maximum depth of around 700 ft (220 m). Many islands dot the gulf, the largest group being the Pearl Islands archipelago which includes more than 220 islands and islets, fewer than half of which are named.

On the Pacific side of the isthmus, where the sea level is 7–16 in (18–40 cm) lower than on the eastern—Caribbean—side, the Panama Canal reaches the gulf at Panama City. The prevailing northeast trade winds blow water toward the Caribbean side of Panama and away from the Pacific coast. Additionally, the tidal range on the Caribbean side is about 27 in (69 cm), whereas the Gulf of Panama experiences a high-to-low variation of nearly 23 ft (7 m). Canal designers faced the huge engineering challenge of extreme tidal conditions as the difference in water level between its two ends can reach up to 20 ft (6 m).

ENVIRONMENT

Fisheries are extremely important to the local economy. Shrimp and prawns are plentiful, and are now farmed in large quantities. Deep sea fishing attracts both commercial and sport fishermen from the United States and other countries.

BELOW The Panama Canal is a series of locks and man-made lakes that enable shipping to move from the Pacific Ocean to the Caribbean Sea. The three-stage Gatun locks shown here drop the ships back to sea level.

Pearl Islands

When Vasco Nuñez de Balboa became the first European to see the eastern shore of the Pacific Ocean in 1513 from a vantage point overlooking the Gulf of Panama, he encountered indigenous people wearing beautiful pearls. The Pearl Islands, around 30 miles (50 km) off the Panama coast, have since been one of the world's major sources of these precious gems. The region's most celebrated pearl is the 31-carat "La Peregrina," discovered in the sixteenth century. At various times it has been owned by King Phillip II of Spain, Queen Mary I of England, the Bonaparte family of France, and actor Richard Burton, who presented it to his wife, actor Elizabeth Taylor.

Sargasso Sea

The Sargasso is unique among the world's seas. It is a huge gyre—spiral—of slowly rotating, relatively calm water, seaweed, and assorted debris located in the mid-North Atlantic Ocean. Surrounded by ocean rather than land, the 1.5 million-square-mile (3,900,000-km²) Sargasso holds the distinction of being the only "sea" without a shore.

BELOW In September 2003, Hurricane Fabian passed over the Sargasso Sea. Bermuda can be seen as a tiny green island in the upper left. The large central island in the bottom left is the Republic of Haiti and the Dominican Republic. Cuba is to the left and Puerto Rico to the right.

OCEAN WHIRLPOOL

This unusual pool of ocean water owes its existence to the combined action of four major ocean currents in the North Atlantic that create a gigantic "whirl" with a relatively calm center—the Sargasso Sea. The North Equatorial Current forms the southern flank; warm waters of the Gulf Stream and North Atlantic Current form the western and northern sections of the gyre; while the cold Canary Current borders the Sargasso on its eastern margin. The Coriolis force causes the wind-driven currents to veer to the right, resulting in a permanent spiral that rotates in a clockwise direction.

UNIQUE ENVIRONMENT

The Sargasso Sea takes its name from prolific seaweed, *Sargassum natans*, which floats in huge mats on its surface. In addition to its aquatic "forest," the sea is a unique environment in several other ways. Although formed by swiftly flowing ocean currents, the Sargasso experiences very little horizontal surface water motion. If it were a land area, the Sargasso would be classified as a desert. The mid-North Atlantic lies beneath a huge system of high pressure that contributes to year-round atmospheric stability. Annual rainfall amounts to less than 10 in (250 mm), and winds are generally very

calm. Because of the sea's subtropical location and cloudless skies, temperatures are quite high throughout the year. High evaporation and low rainfall combine to make the Sargasso Sea much saltier than surrounding waters.

SPAWNING GROUND

Scientists believed that the Sargasso Sea, apart from its ubiquitous seaweed, was an oceanic desert in terms of life. Recently, however, they have discovered vertically flowing eddies that bring nutrient-rich water to the surface from deep within the ocean. These nutrients, in turn, support the growth of phytoplankton, upon which zooplankton and other life forms further up the food chain thrive. Nonetheless, because of its high salinity, the Sargasso Sea is inhospitable to many oceanic species. Eels are one exception.

Both European and North American eels, including the sea lamprey that has nearly destroyed fishing in the North American Great Lakes, spawn in the Sargasso Sea. After laying their eggs they die. As one of the few anadromous species, the young eels grow to maturity in the Sargasso's protective environment then migrate to freshwater bodies in North America and Europe. Eventually, they return to the Sargasso, spawn, and die, thereby completing their amazing life cycle.

The loggerhead sea turtle is another species that thrives in this unusual environment. After birth, the young turtles are carried by the Gulf Stream and other currents and deposited in the Sargasso Sea's sargassum-sheltered environment. Once they mature, the turtles return to the distant waters where they will spend the rest of their lives.

GARBAGE DUMP

Because the Sargasso Sea occupies the giant North Atlantic Subtropical Gyre, objects drift into the sea, but are unable to drift out. As a result, over time the sea has become a huge garbage dump. Debris includes flotsam and jetsam, driftwood, styrofoam and other plastics, remnants of vessels, and other assorted wastes, many of them non-biodegradable.

Of particular threat to the Sargasso Sea's fragile aquatic environment is a sharp increase in tar balls, blobs that form when oil congeals after an oceanic spill. These blobs are transported by ocean currents and deposited in the Sargasso Sea, where they accumulate and float indefinitely.

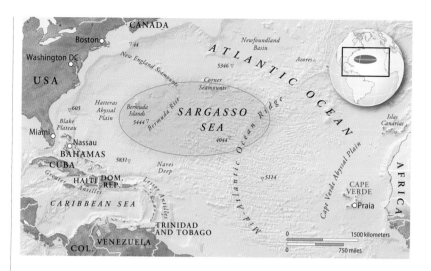

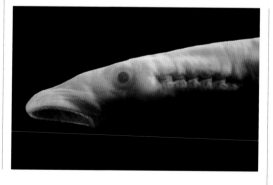

ABOVE Mats of sargassum weed float around the area of the Sargasso Sea. This free-floating seaweed is a crucial habitat for a wide variety of marine animals.

LEFT Sea lamprey, a variety of eel and a curse to other fish, spawn in the Sargasso Sea. In their parasite phase, they feed on other fish by rasping through their skin.

Horse Latitudes

There is evidence that Phoenicians and Greeks were aware of the Sargasso's unique and often treacherous waters more than 2,000 years ago. Through time, the Sargasso earned the nickname the "Sea of Lost Ships." During the era of sailing vessels, the expanse was dreaded by seafarers because of the deadly calms and floating sargassum that could conspire to ensnare ships. Early Spanish sailors, following the reliable trade winds to the Americas, often veered off track and found their ships stranded in the Sargasso's calm waters for weeks at a time. When water ran short, horses were thrown overboard. This practice gave rise to the popular name "Horse Latitudes" for this high-pressure zone and its calm sea.

Caribbean Sea

Situated east of Mexico, the Caribbean Sea is almost 90 percent enclosed by continental or large island landmasses. The sea covers an area of approximately 1,063,000 square miles (2,753,000 km²), and is connected to the Atlantic Ocean by numerous channels that thread through its many islands. The most significant of these is the Yucatan Channel that separates Mexico's Yucatan province from Cuba.

OPPOSITE The Caribbean Sea is a haven for scuba divers wishing to explore the magnificent corals and marine life that inhabit the sea. Here an underwater photographer snaps a picture of a Nassau grouper *(Epinephelus striatus)* as it heads out of its cave.

ISLANDS IN THE SUN

Significant Caribbean islands include Hispaniola, on which lie the countries of Haiti and the Dominican Republic; and Jamaica, which along with Cuba, Puerto Rico, and the Virgin Islands form the Greater Antilles group. The Lesser Antilles, made up of the Leeward and Windward Island groups, lie in the eastern part of the Caribbean Sea and stretch south toward continental South America. The Greater and Lesser Antilles form a sweeping arch that divides the sea from the western Atlantic Ocean.

TRENCHES AND CURRENTS

The Caribbean Sea is generally deep, with most areas having a depth greater than 5,900 ft (1,800 m). The Cayman Trench, which runs for 478 miles (770 km) in a northeast to southwest direction, and separates the island of Jamaica from the Cayman Islands, is the deepest part of the sea, exceeding 24,500 ft (7,500 m). This area is geologically unstable, with considerable tectonic activity. This instability creates an ever-present threat of tsunamis. An extensive shelf off the coast of Nicaragua in the southwest is relatively shallow.

Currents within the sea tend to move in a northwesterly direction. The most important of these is the Caribbean Current, formed by waters drawn into the sea from the Atlantic through the islands of the Lesser Antilles in the southeast, between the Grenada, St Lucia, and St Vincent channels. The current hugs the coastlines of Venezuela and Colombia before heading northeast and exiting the sea through the Yucatan Channel. A significant reverse current also circulates in a counterclockwise direction in the large inlet that forms the northern coastlines of Panama and Costa Rica and the eastern coast of Nicaragua. Significant local currents also flow through the numerous channels that separate the islands of the Lesser Antilles.

ENVIRONMENT

Despite lying entirely within the tropical zone, the climate across the Caribbean is highly variable. Annual rainfalls range from just 1 in (25 mm) on the island of Bonaire in the Netherland Antilles in the southeast, to more than 335 in (8,500 mm) in Dominica, part of the Leeward Islands in the eastern region of the sea. Such variations are caused by local factors such as mountain ranges and ocean currents.

The diversity in climate is, in turn, reflected in the wide variety of environments found throughout the Caribbean. Significant reef systems, formed by more than 70 species of coral, have developed near the coast. The waters off Belize include the longest reef system in the Northern Hemisphere, second only in size to Australia's Great Barrier Reef. The once-flourishing reefs of the Caribbean are now in significant decline, with extensive bleaching caused by pollution destroying vast areas of coral. Sizable sea-grass beds provide an important habitat for the endangered West Indian manatee, or sea cow. Many unique species of seabirds, reptiles, and frogs are also found on the many islands of the Caribbean.

HUMAN FOOTPRINT

More than 230 million people live in 36 countries bordering the Caribbean Sea. The Caribbean islander population numbers more than 38 million, and much of this population relies directly on the sea for survival.

The fragile environments of the sea are under considerable threat from climate change, which is posing risks to low-lying island and coastal environments. Global warming will also raise the frequency and intensity of hurricanes, causing massive storms

ABOVE A green sea turtle *(Chelonia mydas)* swims up the side of a coral pinnacle in the Caribbean Sea. Green turtles are in danger from the deterioration of the coral reefs due to pollution and overuse.

RIGHT Oil refineries such as this one in Venezuela are the source of increased shipping through the Caribbean Sea, bringing oil spills and bleaching of coral due to pollution.

that will inflict ever-increasing damage on human and biophysical environments across the Caribbean region.

Declining water quality is another issue within the Caribbean Sea. Nutrient run-off—from agriculture and poor sewerage disposal systems—is having a destructive impact on coastal ecosystems, damaging sea grass beds and coral reefs and finding its way into the sea life that lives on the resources.

Exploitation of offshore gas and crude oil reserves, particularly off the Venezuelan coast, is increasing the potential for oil spills, as well as producing heavy-metal pollutants that accumulate within the sea's food chain. Around 50 percent of the world's tourist cruise-ship industry takes place in the Caribbean Sea. These ships, along with substantial numbers of local commercial trading and fishing vessels, are placing ever-increasing stress on the Caribbean environment.

Gulf of Mexico

With a surface area of around 600,000 square miles (1,550,000 km²), the Gulf of Mexico is the ninth largest body of water on Earth. It is bounded to the north by the southern coast of the United States, with Mexico lying to the west. To the east, the gulf is joined to the Atlantic Ocean through the narrow Straits of Florida. To the south, the Yucatan Channel divides the west coast of Cuba and Mexico's Yucatan Peninsula.

ABOVE The great resource of oil is found throughout the Gulf of Mexico, with oil rigs such as this punctuating the waters and detracting from their beauty.

BELOW Feeding the great Gulf of Mexico is the Mississippi delta, the mouth of the second-longest river in the United States. The 5,000-year deltaic process has increased the coast-line of Louisiana into the gulf.

DEPTH AND CURRENTS

Waters within the gulf are generally quite deep, with depths in the Mexican Basin at the center of the gulf reaching 17,070 ft (5,203 m). Closer to shore, depths decrease markedly with an extensive continental shelf running almost continuously around the northern, western, and southern edges of the gulf. This shelf is widest around the west coast of Florida and the northern coast of the Yucatan Peninsula.

No large islands lie within the gulf. The islands of the Florida Keys, off the tip of the Florida Peninsula, and a few other small islands hug the coast along the northern shore. Currents within the gulf are highly variable, but tend to move in a clockwise direction. The principal current enters from the Caribbean Sea through the Yucatan Channel, then exits through the Straits of Florida into the Atlantic Ocean.

SALINITY

A number of very large rivers flow into the gulf, including the mighty Mississippi River that flows through a vast catchment area. Others include the Alabama and Apalachicola rivers, which originate in the Appalachian Mountains. These rivers supply such significant volumes of fresh water that the waters in the center of the gulf contain significantly higher levels of salinity than the coastal waters.

ENVIRONMENT

The Gulf of Mexico is an extremely highly productive environment. Extensive barrier systems are found along the western edge of the gulf, beginning in Galveston, Texas, and running several hundred miles southward to northern Mexico. The gulf also features significant tidal flats and mangrove forests. Deep-sea coral reef systems at depths between 165 and 650 ft (50 and 200 m) support a wide diversity of aquatic life.

Scotia Sea

Lying between South America and the Antarctic Peninsula, the Scotia Sea is one of the roughest and most frigid bodies of water on Earth. It takes its name from the Scottish National Antarctic Expedition ship, *Scotia*, that explored its waters between 1902 and 1904.

RIDGES AND TRENCHES

The Scotia Sea covers an area of about 350,000 square miles (900,000 km²). The western edge of the sea is marked by the Drake Passage, where the Atlantic and Pacific Oceans meet off Cape Horn. The northern, eastern, and southern boundaries of the sea are formed by the Scotia Ridge, an extensive submarine ridge with a length of around 2,700 miles (4,350 km).

The sea lies in a highly tectonically active region. Volcanic activity has created extensive ridge systems as well as the South Sandwich Trench, where depths plunge to almost 26,900 ft (8,200 m). Depths across the rest of the sea are highly variable, with numerous ridges and seamounts dotting the sea floor. Depths tend to decrease toward the western edge of the sea near Drake Passage.

CURRENTS

Currents in the Scotia Sea are influenced by the vast Antarctic Circumpolar Current that encircles the entire Antarctic continent. The Weddell Sea Deep Water Current makes its way out of the Weddell Sea toward the Atlantic, and passes through the Scotia Sea. Water enters the sea through narrow passages in the southern part of the Scotia Ridge. It then flows north toward the Argentine Basin.

ENVIRONMENT

A number of important islands are found within the sea. South Georgia is the most northerly of the islands and the most significant. The South Sandwich Islands are found on the eastern edge of the sea, marking the sea's boundary with the Atlantic Ocean. This chain of six islands—Southern Thule, Bristol, Montagu, Saunders, Candlemas, and Traversay—is the result of relatively recent volcanic activity. Along with South Georgia they lie atop the Scotia Ridge. The South Orkney Islands and South Shetland Islands lie close to the Antarctic coastline in the south.

All of these islands contain highly fragile tundra environments and are covered with ice for most of the year. Few land animals inhabit the islands, but they are important habitats for seabirds, penguins, and seals. Large populations of each are found on all the islands, while cold-water corals and a number of other rare species inhabit the numerous seamounts that dot the Scotia Sea floor.

ABOVE The hostile waters that surround Antarctica have become something of a tourist mecca. Here a ship carrying eco-tourists plows through ice in the south Scotia Sea.

TOP LEFT This satellite image shows the Drake Passage in the Scotia Sea. Drake Passage runs between Cape Horn at the tip of South America and the South Shetland Islands in Antarctica. It is named after Sir Francis Drake.

Greenland Sea

The Greenland Sea is an extension or arm of the Arctic Ocean. It is bounded by Greenland to the west, Svalbard (Spitsbergen) to the east, the Arctic Ocean to the north, and Iceland and the Norwegian Sea to the south.

ABOVE The Greenland Sea contains large fish and mammals, making fishing a very lucrative but dangerous business.

ABOVE RIGHT The volcanic landscape of Jan Mayen Island receives an average of five days of sunshine per year.

CHANGING CRUST

The Greenland Sea covers an area of approximately 465,000 square miles (1,205,000 km²), which is one third of one percent of the world's ocean area. Its average depth is around 4,750 ft (1,540 m). Its deepest point, located west of Svalbard, is around 16,000 ft (4,800 m).

Consisting of two large basins, the sea is separated on the west by the Jan Mayen Rise, part of the Mid-Atlantic Ridge at the juncture of the western end of the Eurasian tectonic plate, and the eastern margin of the North American tectonic plate. The Mid-Atlantic Ridge is an ever-growing center of volcanic activity, where new oceanic crust is being created by the growth process of accretion.

Jan Mayen Island, situated northeast of Iceland, is a surface expression of the ridge, and marks the location of a mantle plume, where more volcanic magma reaches the surface. The northern extension of the ridge system is known as Mohns Ridge.

CLIMATE

The Greenland Sea is the main outlet of the Arctic Ocean to the Atlantic, and is largely ice-bound in winter due to the sub-Arctic climate. The northern winter sea ice boundary passes through the Greenland Sea, with the northwest region ice-covered and the southeast margin ice-free. Drifting Arctic Ocean icebergs mean that the northern region of the sea is rarely open to navigation. However, global warming effects have recently led to a proposal for an Arctic Sea shipping route, to run between Churchill in Manitoba, Canada, and Murmansk in Russia, skirting the southern Greenland Sea.

The East Greenland Current, a cold surface flow, traverses the sea. The frigid southwest-flowing water from the Arctic Circle splits northeast of Iceland, and helps to produce vortices where waters of different temperatures and nutrient components mingle. These whirlpools support a rich aquatic food chain that sustains fishing, especially in north Icelandic ports.

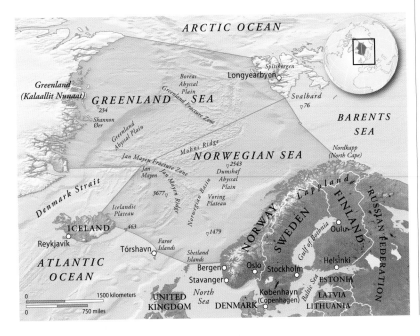

Norwegian Sea

The Norwegian Sea is part of the North Atlantic Ocean. It lies northwest of Norway, between the North Sea and the Greenland Sea. It adjoins the Iceland Sea on the west and the Barents Sea on the northeast.

ENVIRONMENT

The Norwegian Sea covers around 533,000 square miles (1,380,000 km²). Its mean depth is approximately 5,300 ft (1,600 m), with a maximum depth of around 13,202 ft (3,970 m).

In its southwestern quadrant, the Norwegian Sea is separated from the Atlantic Ocean by a submarine ridge running between Iceland and the Faroe Islands. To the north, the Jan Mayen Ridge separates it from the Arctic Ocean.

Simply Breathtaking!

Norway's famed fjorded coast frames the eastern margin of the Norwegian Sea. Valley glaciers, born in the Scandinavian highlands during the Pleistocene era, gouged out steep river valleys, leaving fjords behind when the last Ice Age ended and the sea level rose, drowning the coastal reaches of the ice-carved terrain. Breathtaking scenery may be observed from the many ferryboats and ocean liners that cruise past the majestic, rugged, coastal panoramas, especially during the summer tourist season.

The Norwegian Sea, the Greenland Sea, and the Icelandic Sea are known as the Nordic Seas. The warm Norwegian Current keeps the western and northern coasts of Norway completely ice-free, even though the Arctic Circle bisects the sea. The current is a branch of the northeast-flowing Gulf Stream, which originates in the tropical Gulf of Mexico and continues as the North Atlantic Drift. These warm coastal conditions may be compared with Baltic Sea locations at the same latitude that completely freeze over in winter.

GLOBAL WARMING

The Norwegian Sea's hydrological situation contrasts its warm-water surface current with a very cold deep current running along the west coast of Norway. The result is a blend of different waters, containing a mix of nutrients that support a rich aquatic food chain, including cod, herrings, sardines, and anchovies. Recent changes in the currents are thought to result from global warming and are being closely monitored.

In 1993, large-scale extraction of crude oil and natural gas—mainly by the UK and Norway—began on the continental shelf under the Norwegian Sea.

ABOVE Sweeping concrete creates beauty in this bridge at Lofoten on the east coast of the Norwegian Sea.

BELOW Geirangerfjorden, on the southeast of the Norwegian Sea, is considered to be the most beautiful fjord in Norway.

Irish Sea

Covering an area of around 40,000 square miles (100,000 km²), the Irish Sea is bounded by England to the east, Ireland to the west, and Wales to the south. The North Channel, located in the north of the sea, and the St George's Channel in the south, connect the Irish Sea to the Atlantic Ocean.

ABOVE Conwy Castle (bottom center), finished in 1289, over-looks the Irish Sea.

ABOVE RIGHT Waves of the Irish Sea sweep over the pier at Blackpool, UK.

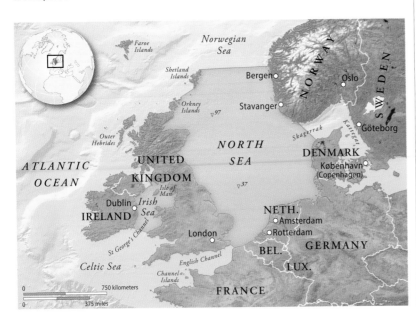

GEOGRAPHY

The Irish Sea is mostly shallow with a mean depth of 295 ft (90 m), the deepest point measuring 576 ft (175 m). A series of deeper basins runs in a north-south direction on the western side of the sea, the deepest points being located in the North Channel. The Isle of Man is located in the mid-northern area of the sea. The Isle of Anglesey is separated from northern Wales by a narrow channel, the Menai Strait.

Extensive sandbanks lie off the northern Irish and western English coasts, creating a significant hazard to shipping in the sea. Extensive estuarine systems line both the eastern and western shores of the sea. The Dee, Mersey, and Ribble estuaries, the Firth of Clyde, and the Belfast Lough are among the most significant. These estuaries provide substantial and valuable habitats to a wide variety of species. Salt marshes and extensive dune systems also line the shores and are valuable habitats.

FEEDING GROUND

The Irish Sea is an important habitat of many large marine species. Ten species of shark are found in the sea, including the basking shark that frequents its waters in the warmer months from April to July. Second only to the whale shark in size, the basking shark is attracted by the abundance of plankton in the sea at this time of year. Baleen whales, such as hump-backs and blue whales, feed on the plankton, while toothed whales, including killer whales, are attracted by the large number of seals in the area. The grey seal and the common harbor seal are the most numerous, feeding on the mackerel and pollock that are found in significant numbers throughout the sea.

North Sea

The North Sea, located adjacent to the North Atlantic Ocean, covers an area of approximately 220,000 square miles (570,000 km^2). The sea is bound by the UK to the west, continental Europe to the east and southeast, and Norway to the north. The Orkney and Shetland Island groups, off the north coast of Scotland, mark its northwest boundary and are its only significant islands.

CURRENTS

Generally the North Sea is quite shallow, with an average depth of around 250 ft (75 m). Depths increase toward Norway in the northeast, with maximum depths reaching around 2,500 ft (750 m).

Currents in the North Sea tend to flow from the north, drawing in water from the Atlantic Ocean and moving in a counterclockwise direction. Another current flows in through the English Channel along the coastlines of Belgium and the Netherlands. Tidal currents within the sea are highly variable, and the coastline features some of the highest and strongest tides in the world.

The North Sea is comparatively cold, with annual surface temperatures ranging between 32°F and 68°F (0°C and 20°C). The north is colder with less seasonal temperature variation. The North Sea is known for its strong winds and gales, bringing on rough seas, particularly through the winter months.

ENVIRONMENT

Environments within and around the North Sea are very diverse. Mountainous rocky regions lie to the north, with deep fjords found along the Norwegian coastline. Extensive estuarine systems and vast mud flats lie along the UK coastline. Sand-dune systems have developed along the coastline of the Netherlands and Denmark, while large, shallow barrier systems are found in the sheltered waters off Denmark. Massive kelp forests grow in the sheltered coastal waters and support large communities of fish and marine mammals, including grey and harbor seals. The sea also supports significant colonies of 31 species of seabirds.

Surrounded by densely populated nations, the North Sea is subject to a variety of human influences. It supports a vast commercial fishing industry that harvests over two million tons of seafood annually. It is dotted with numerous oil wells, and is crossed by some of the world's busiest shipping lanes.

ABOVE Small trams carry tourists down to the beach at Saltburn-by-the-Sea, where donkey rides are available along the sand.

BELOW Scheveningen on the Netherlands coastline is a popular North Sea resort town, where windsurfing is a favored sport.

Baltic Sea

The Baltic Sea is an eastern arm of the North Atlantic Ocean. It lies between latitudes 53°N to 66°N, and longitudes 20°E to 26°E. It is bounded by the Scandinavian Peninsula to the west, the mainland of Europe to the east and south, and the Danish islands to the southwest.

ENVIRONMENT

BELOW Mons Klint, the steep chalk cliffs along the eastern coast of the Danish island of Mon in the Baltic Sea, are a popular tourist attraction.

The Baltic Sea contains four subdivisions—the Gulfs of Bothnia, Finland, Riga, and Gdansk are located on its northern, eastern, and southern peripheries. The sea drains through Kattegat Bay, then into Skagerrak Strait and the North Sea. Covering 145,560 square miles (377,000 km²), an area slightly smaller than California, the sea occupies a basin formed by glacial erosion. It adjoins around 4,968 miles (8,000 km) of coastline. The sea is around 1,000 miles (1,600 km) long and an average 120 miles (193 km) wide. Its mean depth is around 180 ft (55 m), with a maximum depth of 1,506 ft (459 m) on its western—Swedish—side.

Seasonal sea ice covers around 45 percent of the sea's area. Many islands dot the sea, whose tides have lower ranges than those of its western neighbor, the North Sea. Salinity in the Baltic Sea is reduced by the many rivers that flow into it.

MULTINATIONAL SHORES

Baltic Sea coasts have been settled since prehistoric times, and the waters have been navigated by countless mariners. Swedish Vikings sailed over the sea on their travels eastward to what would become Russia, and places further south. During the period of the Hanseatic League, from the thirteenth to seventeenth centuries, commerce flowed between numerous Baltic ports and locations on the North Sea.

At the Baltic Sea's southwest corner, the Kiel Canal—Kaiser-Wilhelm Kanal—was completed in 1895. It is a shortcut to the North Sea, and was a major target for Allied bombers during World War II. Today it is the most heavily used artificial seaway in the world, with 43,000 ships passing through it in 2007.

Nine European countries share sections of the Baltic shoreline. They are Finland in the north, then, proceeding clockwise, the Russian Federation, the Baltic states of Estonia, Latvia, and Lithuania, followed by Kaliningrad—an exclave of the Russian Federation—Poland, Germany, Denmark, and Sweden.

ABOVE Kiel Canal in Germany is a 61-mile (98-km) man-made waterway that links the North Sea with the Baltic Sea. The shortcut saves around 320 miles (520 km).

Barents Sea

The Barents Sea is a shallow section of the Arctic Ocean situated northeast of Norway, and bracketed by the Russian mainland, the Kola Peninsula, the huge Arctic islands of Novaya Zemlya, and the archipelago of Franz Josef Land. The Norwegian island group of Svalbard is located to the west.

WARM CURRENTS

Named for Dutch explorer Willem Barentsz, the Barents Sea is some 800 miles (1,300 km) long and 650 miles (1,050 km) wide. It covers an area of about 542,000 square miles (1,405,000 km²), and has an average depth of around 750 ft (230 m). Its deepest point is around 2,000 ft (600 m) in the Bear Island Trench. Its waters are warmed by the North Atlantic Drift current, which keeps its principal ports of Vardö in Norway, and Murmansk in Russia, ice-free all year.

MILITARY USES

The Barents Sea played a major role during the Cold War, largely because the Soviet surface ships and the submarines of the Northern Fleet were based on the Murmansk Fjord, and near the Kola Peninsula. Both the American and Soviet navies carried out numerous submarine patrols in the Barents Sea as well as the adjacent Arctic Ocean.

Unfortunately the Barents Sea, along with the Kara Sea to the east, has become a dumping zone for retired Soviet naval ships and submarines. These vessels, many of them nuclear-powered, were scuttled because the Russian government declined to pay for their ongoing maintenance or "safe" disposal, if such a thing is possible. The result is ever-increasing radioactive contamination of the Barents Sea and its aquatic life.

The sea gained infamy in August 2000 when the Russian navy's submarine *Kursk* sank after an internal explosion, breaking in two with the loss of 118 crewmembers. The *Kursk* was raised the following year.

During World War II, a very important shipping route, the Murmansk Run, crossed the Barents Sea.

Allied war machinery, mostly manufactured in the United States, was delivered to the Soviet Union to assist its monumental battle against Nazi Germany on the Eastern Front. Crews on 78 convoys delivered vital supplies to the Soviets, navigating the Barents Sea at the end of the voyage. Their contribution played a great part in the eventual German defeat.

ABOVE The heavily industrialized port of Murmansk in the Russian Federation sits beside Kola Bay on the Barents Sea. It is the largest city north of the Arctic Circle.

ABOVE An inlet of the Barents Sea, the Varanger Fjord is at the extreme northeast of Norway. Unlike most fjords, it has not been carved by glaciers.

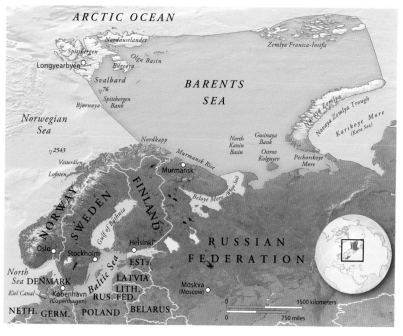

Mediterranean Sea

The Mediterranean Sea is a large sea at the junction of Asia, Europe, and Africa. It covers an area of around 970,000 square miles (2,510,000 km²), and is connected to the Atlantic Ocean in the west by Strait of Gibraltar. This is the only natural vent for the sea, but the Suez Canal, opened in 1869, creates an easterly connection to the Red Sea, and ultimately the Indian Ocean. To the east lies the Black Sea, joined to the Mediterranean by the Sea of Marmara, the Dardanelles, and the Bosporus Strait.

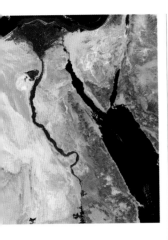

ABOVE The Nile delta is seen clearly in dark green as it spills into the Mediterranean Sea. The Red Sea is on the right.

BELOW The Mediterranean coastal town of Lloret de Mar in Catalonia attracts thousands to its safe beach and warm waters. It is considered one of the cleanest beaches on Spain's Costa Brava.

EUROPE'S SEA

Around the Mediterranean lie the smaller Adriatic, Aegean, Tyrrhenian, and Ionian Seas. Numerous countries abut the Mediterranean, making the area one of the world's most densely populated coastal regions. The coastline is more than 28,600 miles (46,000 km) long. To the north lie Spain, France, Italy, Albania, Greece, and Turkey; to the east Syria, Lebanon, and Israel. Egypt, Libya, Tunisia, Algeria, and Morocco are found along the southern coast. The island nations of Malta and Cyprus lie within the sea.

There are thousands of islands within the Mediterranean, the largest situated on the northern, European side. The most significant include Sicily, the Italian possession of Sardinia, and Corsica, a French possession to the west of Italy. Crete, a Greek possession, and Cyprus lie to the east.

DEEP DIVIDE

Depths within the Mediterranean average 4,900 ft (1,500 m), but vary greatly. The sea is divided in two by an extensive submarine ridge that runs between the large island of Sicily and the Italian mainland, then south toward Tunisia. In this area, known as the Sicilian Straits, depths do not exceed 1,500 ft (460 m). The eastern basin is deeper, with the sea floor plunging to around 16,000 ft (4,900 m) in the Ionian Basin.

HOT AND COLD

Despite the large number of rivers that flow into the Mediterranean, including Egypt's mighty Nile, much more water is lost through evaporation than flows in from rivers. This causes large amounts of water to flow into the sea from the Atlantic Ocean. This significant flow—the Algerian Current—moves in an easterly direction along Africa's northern coastline, where it joins the Libyo-Egyptian Current that carries the waters further east, then northward toward the Turkish coast. The northern current moves west along the northern coastline of the Mediterranean toward the Strait of Gibraltar. This current is highly erratic, with eddies and counter currents swirling around thousands of small islands, bays, inlets, and rock reefs. A much smaller surface current flows in from the Black Sea through the Dardanelles.

Temperatures within most of the sea are relatively warm, although there can be significant variation. The warmest waters are found off the coast of Libya, where summer temperatures average 88°F (31°C). The coolest waters lie to the north, where the Mediterranean meets the Adriatic off the coast of Albania. Here the winter temperatures drop to around 41°F (5°C), occasionally forming thin ice sheets.

BIODIVERSITY

Although featuring relatively low productivity, there is nonetheless a high degree of biodiversity within the Mediterranean. Mammals include the fin, sperm, pilot, and Cuvier's beaked whale, and several dolphin species including the bottlenose, common, striped, and Risso's. Small numbers of minke, killer, and false killer whales prey on the 750 endemic fish species. Five species of turtle are found, along with several species of shark and ray. The only native seal is the critically endangered monk seal, and sightings are increasingly rare, apart from a small colony in the Aegean Sea. The Mediterranean is the primary spawning ground for the sizable Atlantic bluefin tuna. The sea has been also prone to invasive species since the opening of the Suez Canal.

A major threat to the ecology of the Mediterranean is industrial runoff and habitat loss caused by intense coastal development. Water pollution, overfishing, oil spills, and toxic emissions from the numerous craft that ply its busy shipping lanes also pose major dangers to the environment.

ABOVE Considered one of the most beautiful places along the Mediterranean Sea, Cinque Terre is part of the Italian Riviera. Consisting of five villages not accessible by car, the area has retained its unspoiled charm and is a World Heritage Site.

Adriatic Sea

Separating the Italian and Balkan peninsulas, the Adriatic Sea is a northern arm of the Mediterranean Sea. Covering an area of just 50,590 square miles (131,050 km²), the Adriatic's small size belies its geographical, strategic, and historical importance. Some of Europe's most important ports line its shores, including perhaps the most famous of all, Venice, which lies on its northern coastline. To the south of the Adriatic lies another small sea, the Ionian, which is separated from the Adriatic by the narrow Strait of Otranto.

HIGHS AND LOWS

The average depth of the Adriatic is around 1,457 ft (444 m). The topography of its floor is highly variable. Along the east coast of Italy, which marks the western edge of the Adriatic, depths are shallower and there are no significant islands. On the eastern shore, marked by the coastlines of Croatia and Slovenia, hundreds of islands hug the shore and depths tend to be greater. The northern shore is very shallow, often less than

BELOW Often called the "Pearl of the Adriatic," the Croatian city of Dubrovnik features an old walled city established about the tenth century containing stone houses with tile roofs.

165 ft (50 m), with extensive sand-bar and barrier systems forming around river deltas. This has allowed the development of the canals and sea walls of Venice. Depths increase markedly in the south of the sea, where an extensive basin off the southernmost tip of Croatia plunges to 4,265 ft (1,300 m).

Currents in the sea draw water through the Strait of Otranto from the eastern Mediterranean, and the Ionian Sea. This current flows northward along the Italian peninsula. Significant rivers, including the Po, flow off the Italian Alps and into the sea, reducing salinity levels in the north. Water temperature within the Adriatic is also highly variable. Temperatures fall to around 50°F (10°C) during the winter months, while in summer they exceed 75°F (24°C) in many areas.

MIDDLE FEEDERS

Like other Mediterranean waters, the Adriatic features relatively poor levels of productivity, with low nutrient levels. However, small pelagic fish such as sardines are widespread, and a variety of starfish, cuttlefish, crabs, squid, and octopus are also found in abundance. In the deeper southern regions of the sea, larger fish such as saratoga and tuna abound.

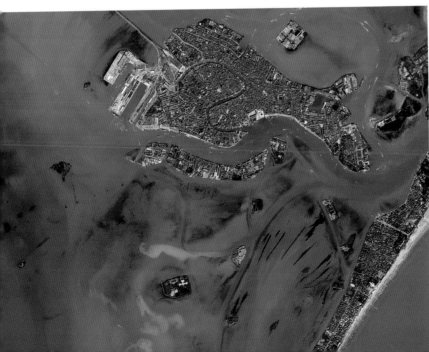

LEFT This satellite image shows the Grand Canal in Venice as it curves through the heart of the terracotta roofs of the city. The large causeway leading to the mainland is visible left to right.

Aegean Sea

Covering an area of around 83,000 square miles (214,000 km²), the Aegean Sea is a small eastern arm of the Mediterranean Sea. It was around the Aegean that the great ancient Greek civilizations developed and flourished. The western and northern coasts of the sea are bordered by Greece, while Turkey lies to the east. The Aegean is connected to Turkey's Sea of Marmara by the narrow Dardanelles strait, and in turn by the even narrower Bosporus to the Black Sea. The Aegean thus forms a boundary between Europe and Asia.

ISLAND PARADISE

Dozens of significant islands—mostly Greek—lie within the Aegean Sea. Crete and Rhodes are the largest and along with Karpathos, form the southern boundary of the sea, dividing it from the Mediterranean. Other significant islands include Lesbos and Chios near the Turkish coast.

HOT AND COLD

Depths within the Aegean Sea are generally quite shallow, with extensive continental shelves off the northern and northeastern coastlines. The sea experiences considerable tectonic activity, with numerous earthquakes and volcanic eruptions in the recent past. A series of trenches lines the sea; the deepest, situated to the east of Crete, plunges to 11,627 ft (3,543 m).

The Aegean is characterized by unpredictable and violent currents. Water eddies around the island systems and flows are further complicated by the numerous bays and inlets that line the coastlines. Cold water flows into the Aegean from the Black Sea in the northeast, while in the south, warm water flows in from the Mediterranean Sea along the Greek coast.

OVERFISHING

The seas of the Mediterranean generally experience relatively low levels of productivity, and the Aegean is one of the most lifeless water bodies on Earth. The waters flowing from the Mediterranean are nutrient-poor, while the colder water flowing from the Black Sea, although more nutrient-rich, is not sufficient in quantity to enrich the entire Aegean. However, significant numbers of fish populate the sea in the warmer months, attracting a variety of marine mammals. These include dolphins, Mediterranean monk seals, Cuvier's beaked whales, and sperm whales, all of which are threatened by unsustainable fishing practices.

ABOVE A male bittern, a member of the Heron family, selects his next meal. Bitterns are found on many Greek islands.

BELOW Aerial view of the town and castle on the Greek island of Astipalea, in the Aegean Sea.

Gulf of Guinea

A large, open arm of the Atlantic Ocean, the Gulf of Guinea is bordered by west and central Africa, extending from Côte d'Ivoire to Cape López in Gabon. The coastline is formed by the western margin of the African tectonic plate, a boundary that corresponds to the continental margin of South America—this fortunate coincidence provided confirmation of the theory of continental drift.

VOLCANIC UNDERFLOOR

Coastal indentations around the gulf include the bights of Benin and Bonny, and the Bay of Mondah. The floor of the gulf is bounded by the Mid-Atlantic Ridge to the west, and the offshore Angola Plain to the south. The gulf reaches depths of 16,722 ft (5097 m). The oceanic border of the gulf is a rhumb line that extends from Cape Palmas in Liberia to Cape López.

The volcanic Cameroon Line Islands extend approximately 450 miles (724 km) southwest from Mount Cameroon into the gulf. The islands include Bioko (Fernando Pó), Annobón (Pagalu), Elobey Grande, Elobey Chico, and Corisco—all provinces of Equatorial Guinea, and São Tomé and Príncipe.

HEAVY SWELLS

Due to the orientation of Africa's west coast, south-westerly swells generate long shore currents that flow northward toward Cameroon along the eastern margin of the Gulf of Guinea, and eastward along the northern margin of the gulf. This water circulation is reinforced offshore by the Benguela and Guinea currents. The continental shelf is relatively narrow, allowing deep ocean waves and surface currents to approach the shore unimpeded, where they influence sediment transport, coastal ecology, and human activity. Coastal upwelling, and hence a rich production of plants and animals, occurs seasonally off the Côte d'Ivoire, and the Gold and Slave coasts.

WHERE'S THE SALT?

The warm surface water of the gulf is relatively low in salinity. In August, owing to reduced solar radiation, high levels of precipitation, and the discharge of large rivers such as the Volta and Niger, surface salinity in the gulf is less than 30 parts per thousand—well below the 35 parts per thousand average for ocean water. This warm water is separated from deeper, more saline, and colder water by a shallow thermocline—a layer of water between upper and lower levels that lies less than 100 ft (30 m) below the surface.

BELOW Low-lying coastal villages such as this one are built right along the coast of Côte d'Ivoire, which borders the Gulf of Guinea.

Red Sea and Gulf of Aden

The Red Sea is bordered to the west by Egypt, Sudan, and Eritrea, and to the east by Saudi Arabia and Yemen. The Gulf of Aden is an arm of the Arabian Sea, and is connected to the Red Sea by the Strait of Bab al Mandab, which is bracketed by Yemen to the north and the Horn of Africa to the south. Both were formed by the separation of the African and Arabian tectonic plates, a process that began during the Eocene epoch—55 to 38 million years ago—and continues today.

LEFT A fleet of Chinese container vessels sails through the Gulf of Aden. They are escorted by a Chinese naval fleet to protect them from Somali pirates, who are a danger in the area.

RED SEA

The Red Sea covers an area of some 169,100 square miles (440,000 km²). The sea extends from Suez in the north to the Strait of Bab al Mandab in the south, a distance of around 1,370 miles (2,190 km). It has a breadth of 228 miles (365 km) at its widest point. Its average depth is 1,608 ft (490 m); its maximum depth is 10,029 ft (3,039 m) near Port Sudan. The Suez Canal, opened in 1869, created a passage between the Red Sea and the Mediterranean Sea.

High evaporation resulting from its tropical location within the Saharo-Arabian belt, very little inflow of fresh water from precipitation or drainage, and geothermal heat released in its medial trench combine to make the Red Sea among the world's warmest and most saline seas. Its average temperature is around 72°F (22°C) and its salinity is approximately 40 parts per thousand—significantly above the oceanic average of 35 parts per thousand.

The tidal range is modest, ranging between 2 ft (0.6 m) near the mouth of the Gulf of Suez, and 3 ft (0.9 m) in the south near the Strait of Babal Mandab.

GULF OF ADEN

The Gulf of Aden extends from Djibouti's Gulf of Tadjoura in the west to Cape Guardafui on the Horn of Africa in the east. It covers an area of approximately 205,000 square miles (533,000 km²). The gulf extends around 920 miles (1,472 km) from east to west, and

ABOVE Making its home in the Red Sea, this magnificent sea anemone floats its tentacles to attract small fish and crustaceans, which are paralyzed by contact and then moved to the mouth of the anemone.

averages around 300 miles (480 km) in width. Its maximum depth of some 17,417 ft (5,278 m) lies in the Alula-Fartak Trench, a fault branching from the Sheba Ridge that runs along its entire length.

Surface temperatures in gulf waters average around 70°F (21.1°C), but can vary greatly depending upon the season and the intensity of the monsoon rains. Salinity also varies, but averages around 36 parts per thousand, which is near the oceanic average.

The Gulf and the Gulf of Oman

The Gulf (also known as the Arabian Gulf or the Persian Gulf) and the Gulf of Oman are arms of the Indian Ocean, separated from each other by the Strait of Hormuz. Flanked by oil-rich countries, both of these gulfs are strategic shipping routes for the world's oil supplies.

BELOW Although fishing is still a lucrative industry in the Gulf of Oman, recent years have seen rapid depletion of fish stocks due to increased shipping and oil spills.

BELOW Oil reserves in the Gulf region are not confined to land. The Gulf itself is scattered with large oil and gas rigs mining some of the largest crude oil and gas fields in the world.

THE GULF

The Gulf is flanked by Iran to the east; by Iraq, Kuwait, Saudi Arabia, Bahrain, and Qatar to the west; and by the United Arab Emirates to the south. It is approximately 593 miles (954 km) long, with a maximum width of 210 miles (338 km). It has a surface area of 92,500 square miles (240,000 km^2). The Gulf is relatively shallow—although it reaches more than 330 ft (100 m) in depth near the Strait of Hormuz, its average depth is around 115 ft (35 m).

The principal sources of fresh water entering The Gulf are the Shatt al-Arab River, and many streams originating in the Zagros Mountains of Iran. Owing to high temperatures, The Gulf loses around 78 cubic miles (326 km^3) of water to evaporation annually. As a result, the level of salinity is nearly one and a half times greater than that of most oceans.

THE GULF OF OMAN

The Gulf of Oman is bounded to the north by Iran, and to the southwest by Oman and the United Arab Emirates. It is around 350 miles (560 km) long, and broadens from 35 miles (56 km) at the Strait of Hormuz, to approximately 200 miles (320 km) at Gwatar Bay on the Iran–Pakistan border. The depth

of the Gulf of Oman increases from 218 ft (66 m) at the northern end, to 10,995 ft (3,351 m) where the gulf merges with the Arabian Sea. It is a vital shipping route for the world's crude oil supplies.

CROSSROADS OF CIVILIZATION

The rich social history of the Gulf region is tied to trade. Prior to the Achaemenid (Persian) ascendancy in around 800 BCE, inhabitants of Dilmun, Sumeria, Magan, Babylon, Assyria, Elam, Bit-Iakin, Phoenicia, Medea, and others, occupied the Gulf region as settlers, traders, or conquerors. The region also played an important role in linking the diverse civilizations of the Levant, Mesopotamia, and Iran with the Indus Valley civilization and other borderlands of the Indian Ocean. The northern region was later dominated by the Seleucid and Parthian empires, and in around 300 CE, the Sassanid Empire extended Persian control over the entire region.

Since the arrival of Islam in the seventh century CE, an enormous body of literature has been produced, recording the unfolding history of the region. Following Vasco da Gama's voyages in the early sixteenth century, the Portuguese became attracted by the region's wealth; in 1521, they invaded Bahrain and seized control of the lucrative pearl industry. The Safavid ruler, Shah Abbas, expelled the Portuguese in 1602, and initiated commerce with the Portuguese, Dutch, Spanish, French, British, and others. In the eighteenth century, the British Empire expanded its influence to the region, partly because of its importance as a direct passage to its colony of India.

OIL BOTTLENECK

Asphalt, oil seeps, and gas from subterranean hydrocarbon deposits have been exploited in the region for millennia. Their presence and use are well documented

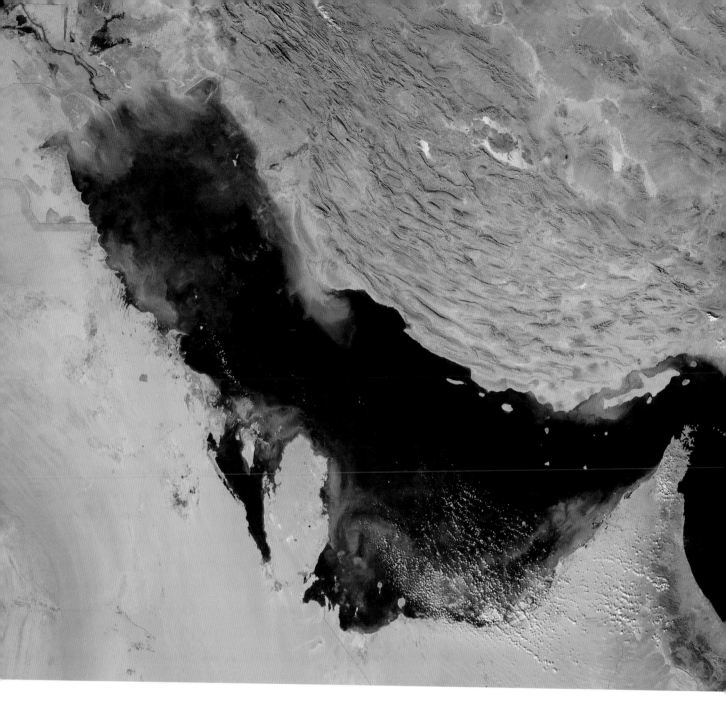

in archeological records, the Old Testament, and the so-called "eternal fires" that played an important role in Zoroastrianism and other religions. Kerosene was distilled by the Persian chemist Muhammad ibn Zakariya ar-Razi in the ninth century CE.

The commercial exploitation of oil in the region was launched following Englishman William Knox D'Arcy's major discovery at Masjed Soleymān in 1908. The region now produces around 21 million barrels of oil per day. Owing to the importance of petroleum in the industrialized world, control of the region remains highly contested. The huge tankers passing through the Strait of Hormuz transport over half of the world's seaborne oil, underscoring its strategic importance. It is estimated that around a quarter of a million barrels of oil pollute the waters of the region annually.

FRAGILE HABITAT

The region contains a variety of habitats that support a corresponding diversity of wildlife. Saltflats, mud-flats, coastal dunes, sand hummocks, artesian springs, mangroves, reefs, sea grass, and other features support more than 700 species of fish, provide nesting sites for turtles, and provide refuge for dugongs and other threatened marine animals.

Around 250 bird species have been recorded in the region—including endangered species such as the Socotra cormorant and Khor Kalba kingfisher. Despite increasing conservation initiatives, such as Bahrain's Al Areen Wildlife Reserve, the region faces continuing threats from oil spills, overgrazing, the loss of man-groves, and disturbance by fishing boats, recreational users, and the military.

ABOVE This satellite image shows The Gulf and the sedi-ment seeping into it. The Strait of Hormuz is seen on the right. This narrow strait is the division between The Gulf and the Gulf of Oman, making it one of the most geographically important areas in the world.

Arabian Sea

A large, open arm of the northwest Indian Ocean, the Arabian Sea is bordered by Iran and Pakistan to the north, Somalia, Yemen, and Oman to the west, and India to the east. The oceanic border of the sea is a line extending from Cape Guardafui in Somalia, to Cape Comorin at the southernmost tip of the Indian subcontinent.

RIGHT Goa, India's smallest state in area, has the Arabian Sea as its western border. Here fishermen pull in nets from the sea.

ABOVE A man collects plants along the seashore on the western coast of India, which borders the Arabian Sea. The plants will be used in ayurvedic medicine.

SUBCONTINENT RUNOFF

The Arabian Sea covers around 1,491,130 square miles (3,862,009 km²). Its maximum width is 1,866 miles (3,002 km), and it extends 1,086 miles (1,748 km) from north to south. The sea has an average depth of 8,970 ft (2,734 m), and a maximum depth of 15,262 ft (4,652 m).

Its bays include the Gulf of Aden, the Gulf of Oman, the Gulf of Kutch, and the Gulf of Cambay. Fresh water enters the sea from the Indus River in Pakistan; the Mahi, the Narmada, and the Tapi in India; and several smaller rivers along the Indian coast. Islands include Socotra, Masira, the Kuria Muria group, and the Lakshadweep group. During winter, dry monsoon winds blow from southwest Asia, reversing during the summer and bringing heavy rain and storms.

TRADING MECCA

The sea continues to play an important role in trade. Its major ports are Gwadar and Karachi in Pakistan;

Kandla, Porbandar, Veraval, Bharuch, Surat, Mumbai, Nhava Sheva, Ratnagiri, Panaji, Mangalore, Cochin, and Alleppey in India; and Muscat in Oman.

FEEDING MILLIONS

The Arabian Sea is notable for its diversity of marine life. Sardines, tuna, wahoo, and billfish, as well as sharks, are fished commercially. Unfortunately, the ecosystem is increasingly threatened by oil spills, sedimentation, and runoff that reduce oxygen availability. These factors are causing ever-increasing destruction to aquatic species.

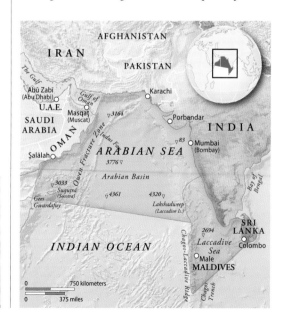

Ancient Trade

There is evidence that maritime trade on the Arabian Sea has been occurring since at least the eighth millennium BCE. In around 2500 BCE, the Harappan civilization extended along the coast from southeastern Iran to the Gulf of Cambay, and inland to Kashmir. The Harappans established trade and cultural relationships with the peoples of the Persian Gulf, Mesopotamia, and the eastern Mediterranean, plying the Arabian Sea in innovative plank-built ships, powered by a single mast supporting a sail of woven reeds or cloth.

Laccadive Sea

The Laccadive Sea is bound to the east by India's Malabar Coast, the Gulf of Mannar, and the western coastal zone of Sri Lanka. It extends westward to include the Lakshadweep and Maldive islands—low atolls formed by submarine volcanic mountains rising from the Chagos–Laccadive Plateau.

TROPICAL HEAVEN

The Laccadive Sea reaches depths of approximately 15,535 ft (4,735 m). Within the sea, India's Lakshadweep Union Territory is composed of 36 islands, 10 of which are inhabited. The Republic of Maldives includes some 1,190 islands. The Lakshadweep-Maldives-Chagos Archipelago is the world's largest coral reef and atoll system.

The archipelago is strongly affected by tropical monsoons. The northeasterly winter winds are dry, while summer southeasterlies bring heavy precipitation, ranging from 63 in (1,600 mm) in the drier islands of Lakshadweep, to more than 150 in (3,800 mm) in the Maldives.

Temperatures vary little, ranging from 75°F (24°C) to 86°F (30°C). Humidity is high. While some tropical rainforest can still be found in remote and relatively unspoiled areas, little original vegetation remains. There are few endemic plants or animals.

ANIMAL ARCHIPELAGO

Native mammals include two species of fruit bat, and the Indian flying fox. Among the important resident and breeding bird species are the Maldivian pond heron, lesser frigate, white tern, black-naped tern, brown-winged tern, and large-crested tern. Large rookeries are found throughout the archipelago.

The islands are home to several species of turtle, including the endangered green turtle, leatherback, loggerhead, hawksbill, and the Olive Ridley. Reptiles include snakes, frogs, toads, geckoes, and various other lizards. The short-beaked saddleback dolphin is endemic, while tuna, kingfish, barracuda, snapper, bonefish, wahoo, and shark are fished commercially.

HUMAN THREAT

Humans have inhabited the archipelago since at least the fifth century BCE. By 1800 CE, most of the forest had been cleared and replaced by coconut plantations and other subsistence and commercial crops, including sapote (chocolate pudding fruit), mango, guava, citrus, banana, yam, pineapple, watermelon, almond, sweet potato, taro, and millet. As crops displaced the forest, domestic animals and introduced rodents reduced the native fauna.

The fragile ecosystems of the archipelago are threatened by pollution from factories, oil spills, waste disposal, ground-water depletion, mechanized fishing, and tourism. Climate change accompanied by rising sea levels also threatens the atolls.

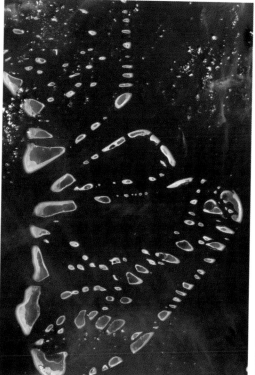

ABOVE This aerial view of one of the Maldive atolls shows the extent of the reef system. An atoll is actually a raised area of dead coral encircling a lagoon.

ABOVE A fish, immune to the poison of the anemone, hides in its tentacles waiting for prey.

LEFT Captured by satellite, the Malosmadulu Atolls, part of the Maldives, resemble a pattern of drops on a dark sea.

Bay of Bengal

The Bay of Bengal is a triangular northeast arm of the Indian Ocean. Its southern boundary is defined by a line extending from southern Sri Lanka to the northern tip of Sumatra, Indonesia. Its northern apex is the coast of Bangladesh.

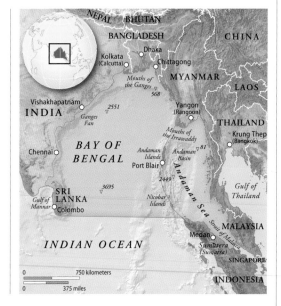

ABOVE The area around the Bay of Bengal is prone to extreme weather. This monsoon is fast approaching the coast. A monsoon brings seasonal prevailing winds and driving rain.

TOP RIGHT Shipbreaking has become big business in India and Bangladesh because of the low cost of labor. Old ships are broken up and sold for their steel content. Unfortunately, hazardous substances can be present also, and chemicals and asbestos dust are often released into the atmosphere.

End of the Shipping Line

Since 1972, Bangladesh has become the world's second-largest ship-breaking (dismantling and recycling) center. Freighters, tankers, and warships make their final voyage across the Bay of Bengal into retirement on the southeast coast. They are beached near the city of Chittagong at high tide, then methodically dismantled by some 200,000 workers.

RIVER DELTAS

The Bay of Bengal is bounded by the countries of Sri Lanka, India, Bangladesh, Myanmar (Burma), and Indonesia, as well as India's Andaman and Nicobar islands. It covers an area of 889,000 square miles (2,172,000 km^2), with a length of 1,300 miles (2,090 km) and a maximum width of 1,000 miles (1,610 km). It has a maximum depth of 15,400 ft (3,694 m) and a mean depth of 8,500 ft (2,600 m).

Numerous rivers, including the Ganges, Krishna, Padma, Brahmaputra, Meghna, Jamuna, Ayeyarwady, Godavari, Mahanadi, and Kaveri, discharge into the bay. Their sedimentary loads have formed large deltas, around which agriculture supports large populations.

NATURAL DISASTERS

From June to September the southwesterly summer monsoon brings rainfall to the bay and its surrounds. Tropical revolving storms, or cyclones, often cause great destruction as their surging waters inundate low-lying coasts, especially in Bangladesh. During the twentieth century, Bay of Bengal cyclones killed over one million people and destroyed countless crops and houses. In November 1970, Cyclone Bhola caused at least 300,000 fatalities in Bangladesh in the greatest weather-related disaster of the twentieth century. In 2008, Cyclone Nargis caused the worst natural disaster in the recorded history of Myanmar (Burma).

INDUSTRIAL RUNOFF

Global climate change is causing a rise in sea levels, which will have devastating effects on the bay's coastline communities because of their generally low elevations. The bay's waters are also being heavily polluted by rivers carrying wastes from hundreds of towns and cities, and runoff from farms and industries.

Andaman Sea

The Andaman Sea, a northeast extension of the Indian Ocean, is located southeast of the Bay of Bengal, south of Myanmar (Burma), west of Thailand, and east of the Andaman archipelago. Its southwest border is formed by the Indonesian island of Sumatra. The southeast "tail" of the sea progressively narrows to form the vital Strait of Malacca, its strategic shipping lanes separating the Malay Peninsula from Sumatra.

UNSTABLE SEA FLOOR

The Andaman Sea covers an area of approximately 308,000 square miles (797,000 km²), measuring 750 miles (1,200 km) from north to south, and 400 miles (650 km) from east to west. Its average depth is around 2,854 ft (870 m); its maximum depth 12,392 ft (3,777 m). The distributaries of the Irrawaddy River delta enter the north section of the Andaman Sea, and along with the Salween River—which flows through China, then Myanmar (Burma), and Thailand—account for the majority of runoff into the sea.

The Andaman Sea lies on the boundary between two tectonic plates, the Burma and Sunda Plates.

This active subduction zone, a trench where the Sunda Plate dives beneath the Burma Plate, produces continual earthquakes that often bring widespread devastation to the mainland and neighboring island groups. The zone also generates highly destructive tsunamis.

BELOW Thailand is home to some of the most beautiful beaches in Asia. Phra Nang is known for its rock formations and is only accessible by boat.

Tsunami

On December 26, 2004, a massive earthquake measuring 9.2 on the Richter scale struck the Andaman Sea region. Its epicenter was northwest of the Sumatran city of Banda Aceh. The sudden displacement of the ocean floor produced a tsunami that killed over 220,000 people in 12 countries, and caused billions of dollars in damage. Banda Aceh (above, day after tsunami) was the first province hit by the gigantic waves, followed by sections of the Thai Peninsula, particularly the Isthmus of Kra. The Nicobar and Andaman archipelagos were then pummeled by the lethal waves, and the tsunami's deadly progress went on to affect Sri Lanka, India, Myanmar (Burma), and other countries. Its waves traveled westward 3,400 miles (5,500 km) across the Indian Ocean at the speed of a jet aircraft, even causing fatalities and devastation on the northeast coast of Africa. Half a decade later, recovery and reconstruction efforts on the wave-battered shores continue.

Gulf of Thailand

The Gulf of Thailand, also known as the Gulf of Siam, is a shallow arm of the South China Sea, which is in turn part of the Pacific Ocean. It is bordered by Vietnam, and the kingdoms of Cambodia (Kampuchea) and Thailand. At the northern end lies the Bay of Bangkok, where the Chao Phraya River enters.

ABOVE The Gulf of Thailand is dotted with volcanic islands, spiking the landscape with heavily forested peaks that fall to serene beaches.

WARM AND SHALLOW

The Gulf of Thailand covers around 123,550 square miles (320,000 km²). It measures 500 miles (800 km) from north to south, and around 350 miles (560 km) at its widest point. The gulf is relatively shallow, with a mean depth of around 150 ft (45 m) and a maximum depth of 260 ft (80 m). The gulf's small volume and the large inflow of fresh river water means that its waters are relatively low in salinity, and laden with sediments. Its mean temperature is a very warm 84°F (29°C). It is home to many coral reefs, making it a popular recreational diving destination and somewhat of a tourist mecca, with luxury resorts throughout the region.

During the Pleistocene Epoch's Ice Age, when sea levels were much lower, the Gulf of Thailand did not exist; it was part of the Chao Phraya River valley.

RIGHT Thailand is a frequent departure point for refugees wishing to migrate to other countries. Known as "boat people," they often pay huge sums to secure passage on a dangerously overladen and inadequate vessel.

"Boat People"

During the late 1970s and 1980s, the Gulf of Thailand and South China Sea were often used as an escape route by Vietnamese "boat people"—refugees trying to escape the turmoil that engulfed the country following the end of the Vietnam War in 1975. The first boat people crossed the Gulf of Thailand in May 1975, landing on Malaysia's east coast. Malaysia supported eight refugee camps on its east coast, and also had camps on the states of Sabah and Sarawak on Borneo.

South China Sea

The South China Sea is a very large western extension of the Pacific Ocean and is framed by the Asian mainland. The People's Republic of China, the Socialist Republic of Vietnam, and the Malay Peninsula form the sea's northern and western margins, while the island of Borneo and the Philippines form the southeastern and eastern flanks of the sea. The gulfs of Tonkin and Thailand form part of the South China Sea, and are connected to the East China Sea through the Taiwan (or Formosa) Strait.

DOUBLE BASIN

The South China Sea covers around 1,390,000 square miles (3,600,000 km²). It measures around 1,430 miles (2,300 km) on a northeast to southwest axis, and is 1,120 miles (1,800 km) from east to west. The seabed consists of two distinct regions; a deep northeast basin with depths of up to 18,000 ft (5,490 m), and a very large submerged plain—the Sunda platform—in the southwest, where it is generally much shallower, with an average depth of 200 ft (60 m). The Sunda platform is part of the Asian continental shelf. Over 200 islands and reefs, most uninhabited, dot the sea.

Geographical relationships in southern Asia were very different during the glacial Pleistocene Epoch, when this area was a land bridge connecting Borneo to the Asian mainland.

The Spratly Island archipelago is claimed by five countries in the region and ownership of the Paracel Islands is also disputed. The South China Sea is one of the world's most traveled seaways, and so of great strategic importance.

FLOODS AND RAIN

Major rivers entering the South China Sea include the Min, Jiulong, Rajang, Pasig, and Pahang. The Vietnamese Red and Mekong rivers have formed substantial

fertile delta areas that support large populations. The South China Sea is prone to destructive typhoons, which are generated in the eastern central Pacific Ocean and track westward and northward. These storms affect northern Borneo, southern Japan, the Philippine islands, Vietnam, China, and Japan.

The sea was crossed by "boat people" fleeing the chaos that followed the war in Vietnam in 1975.

ABOVE A traditional two-mast Chinese junk with battern sails moves smoothly before the wind in Halong Bay in the Gulf of Tonkin. These junks are still used for fishing and transport, although the novelty of sailing in a junk is popular with tourists to the region.

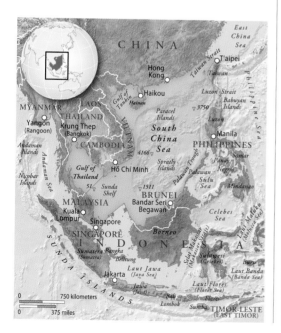

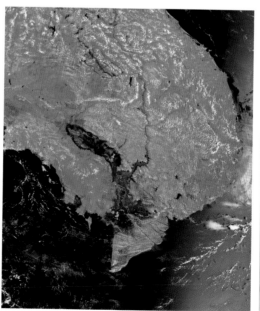

LEFT The delta of the Mekong River, on the South China Sea, is clearly seen as a false color of red in this satellite image. In dry months salt water intrudes into the delta.

Yellow Sea

The Yellow Sea—Huang Hai—is an arm of the East China Sea, which in turn is a marginal sea of the Pacific Ocean that separates the Korean peninsula from the east coast of China. The People's Republic of China, the Democratic People's Republic of Korea (North Korea), and the Republic of Korea (South Korea) form the three sides of the sea.

BELOW The silt in the Yellow Sea is so heavy that at times it seems that it's a solid body. Here two ferries approach each other across the muddy waters near Shanghai, on the western edge of the Yellow Sea.

MUDDY WATERS

The Yellow Sea is relatively shallow, with a mean depth of 144 ft (44 m) and a maximum depth of around 500 ft (152 m). The sea covers around 156,000 square miles (404,000 km²). To the east and north, Korea Bay and Liaodong Gulf are the sea's major inlets. The Huang He, Huai, Liao, and Yalu rivers drain into the sea.

The Yellow Sea is named for the color of the sediment carried by the Huang He (Yellow River), the world's largest carrier of suspended material, mainly from loess (silt) deposits eroding upstream in the Ordos Desert.

STRATEGIC TIDES

The Yellow Sea experiences high tidal ranges and strong currents. These tides played an important role during the Korean War (1950–1952), when the United Nations ground forces undertook an amphibious invasion at Inchon, Korea. The landings, meticulously planned to take advantage of the tides, were considered a strategic masterpiece on the part of US General Douglas MacArthur, heading the UN forces.

OLYMPIC CLEANUP

The shores of the Yellow Sea have become very heavily urbanized and industrialized, with the result that water pollution from many different sources is contributing to the deterioration of water quality. Prior to the 2008 Olympic Games in China, the sailing events at Qingdao were jeopardized by an algal bloom in polluted water. In response, the government organized a fleet of 400 boats, crewed by some 3,000 people, to clean up the venue. Three decades of industrial expansion have taken a severe toll on the Yellow Sea.

RIGHT Just prior to the opening of the Olympic Games in Beijing, the sailing venue at Qingdao, on the east coast of China, was found to be covered in green algae. Here hundreds of boats organized by the Olympic Committee are cleaning up the algae so the sailing events can take place.

East China Sea

The East China Sea—Eastern Sea—is an arm of the western Pacific Ocean, framed on its eastern margin by the Ryukyu Islands and Kyushu Island of Japan, on the west by the central coast of mainland China, and on the south by the island of Taiwan.

ASIAN LINKS

The East China Sea is linked to the South China Sea by the Formosa Strait, and to the Sea of Japan (East Sea) by the Korea Strait. To the northwest, it opens into the Yellow Sea. The East China and South China seas are collectively known as the China Sea.

The East China Sea covers around 480,000 square miles (1,243,200 km²). Its average depth is around 1,227 ft (374 m); its greatest depth is 9,126 ft (2,782 m) just north of the southern Ryukyu Islands. It is situated north of the Tropic of Cancer, and warm-water surface currents enter it from both the South China and Philippine seas. Much of its western seabed forms part of the Asian continental shelf. A group of submerged reefs lines its northern perimeter.

PACIFIC POLLUTER

The sea's principal ports are Shanghai, Hangzhou, Ningbo, Fuzhou, and Kirin. China's longest river, the Yangtze, discharges into the sea, depositing a large sediment load that has formed an extensive delta on its western margin.

As a result of the vast populations around the delta, and numerous factories and farms upstream, the river is the largest contributor to marine pollution in the Pacific Ocean. Ocean-going ships are able to travel hundreds of miles inland.

PASSAGE OF WAR

In the 1930s, Japanese military forces crossed the sea to invade Shanghai and other regions of China. From March to June 1945, the Battle of Okinawa was fought between the Allies and the Japanese on the western edge of the sea, culminating in World War II's largest amphibious Pacific assault.

ABOVE The stone statue of the legendary general Zhong stands watch over the East China Sea.

BELOW This satellite image shows the spill from the Yangtze River into the East China Sea.

Philippine Sea

The Philippine Sea is located in the western Pacific Ocean to the east of the Philippine archipelago, and covers approximately 380,000 square miles (1,000,000 km^2). Along with the Philippines, its limits are defined by Palau and Yap to the southeast, the Marianas and Ogasawara Islands to the east, the islands of Japan to the north, the Ryukyu Islands to the northwest, and the island of Taiwan to the west, along with the Philippine island of Luzon.

LEFT The stunning Rock Islands of Palau, at the southern end of the Philippine Sea, are formed by coral uprises pushed to the surface through tectonic activity. They are home to various kinds of non-poisonous jellyfish found only in Palau.

DEEPER THAN DEEP

The floor of the Philippine Sea is formed by the Philippine Sea Plate, whose subduction under the Eurasian Plate is the source of considerable tectonic activity and geological instability. The 820-mile (1,320-km) Philippine Trench in the west of the sea is a product of that movement. The Galathea Depth, off the island of Mindanao, is the deepest point of the Philippine Trench, plunging to 35,000 ft (10,540 m). The Marianas Trench, which marks the eastern edge of the Philippine Sea Plate, is the world's deepest point—35,796 ft (10,911 m) below sea level. An undersea ridge, the Kyushu-Palau Ridge, bisects the Philippine Sea from north to south.

EXPLOITATION

The Philippine Sea is rich in marine life, including various species of coral, shark, tuna, octopus, and eel. Japanese fishing fleets exploit the sea regularly, as do fishing vessels from the Philippines, China, and other nations. There are frequent territorial disputes between the Philippines and other countries over tuna fishing in the Philippine Sea.

BAGYO

Every year typhoons sweep across the tropical waters of the Philippine Sea, often making landfall in the Philippines, the island of Taiwan, Japan, or the mainland in China or Vietnam. Six or seven typhoons—known locally as bagyo—on average strike the Philippines annually. The peak typhoon months are August to October, but they occur all year round.

Marianas Turkey Shoot

On June 19–20, 1944, the eastern Philippine Sea was the scene of the largest aircraft-carrier battle, and one of the largest naval battles, of all time. The Battle of the Philippine Sea—also known as the "Marianas turkey shoot"—resulted in a decisive victory for the US Navy over that of Japan, which lost three aircraft carriers and some 600 aircraft. It was a major turning point in the Pacific theater of World War II.

Sea of Japan (East Sea)

The Sea of Japan, also known as the East Sea or the East Sea of Korea, is in the western Pacific Ocean. It is almost completely enclosed by the Japanese archipelago to the east, the Korean peninsula to the west, and the east coast of Russia and the Russian island of Sakhalin to the north.

STILL WATERS

Five narrow channels connect the Sea of Japan (East Sea) to Pacific waters. From north to south they are the Strait of Tartary, La Perouse Strait, Tsugaru Strait, the Kanmon Straits (also known as the Straits of Shimonoseki) and the Korea Strait, which itself is divided by the Japanese island of Tsushima into the western channel and Tsushima Strait. Because the sea is so effectively enclosed, it features virtually no tidal movements.

The surface area of the Sea of Japan (East Sea) is around 378,000 square miles (978,000 km²). The average depth is 5,750 ft (1,753 m), the deepest point being 12,277 ft (3,742 m) in the Japan Basin to the north. The other two basins, the Yamato Basin and Tsushima Basin, are shallower. The continental shelf beneath the sea is wide on the Japanese side, but narrow near the coast of Korea. The sea was land-locked before the East Asia landbridge disappeared.

ROCKY DISPUTE

The waters of the sea are rich fishing grounds. They also contain significant deposits of minerals, natural gas, and petroleum. Because of these riches, Japan and Korea have long been locked in dispute about owner-ship of a cluster of tiny rocky islands in the south-central part of the sea known as the Liancourt Rocks. The Japanese refer to the largest of these islands as Takeshima (Bamboo Island), while Koreans call it Dokdo (Solitary Island). The islands are uninhabited apart from a small detail of police guards and other officials from the Republic of Korea.

WHAT'S IN A NAME?

Japan and Korea are in a long-standing dispute about the name of the sea. The Republic of Korea considers "Sea of Japan" to be an anachronistic remnant from Japanese colonial control of Korea in the early twenti-eth century and prefers the name "East Sea." The government of North Korea favors "East Sea of Korea." In 2007, the United Nations declined to take sides and asked Japan and Korea to resolve the issue themselves.

ABOVE Terraced rice fields along the coast of Noto, on Honshu Island in Japan, match the wave patterns of the Sea of Japan (East Sea).

Seas of Indonesia

Indonesia is an archipelago of more than 17,500 islands separated by numerous seas and straits. Between Indonesia and Australia lie the Timor Sea and the Arafura Sea. To the north are the Philippine Sea and the Celebes Sea, with the sovereign territory of the Philippines situated on their far shores. Elsewhere to the north, the South China Sea, the Strait of Malacca, and the Andaman Sea separate islands of Indonesia from the shores of the Malay Peninsula and other non-Indonesian territories.

ABOVE The mantis shrimp is an aggressive crustacean found in waters around Indonesia. It can crush a human finger.

BETWEEN THE ISLANDS

The major seas between islands and clusters of islands within Indonesia itself are the Java Sea in the center of the archipelago nation, the much smaller Bali Sea to the east, the Flores Sea, and the Banda Sea. The Savu Sea lies between Timor and Flores and other southern Indonesian islands. To the north, in the vicinity of the Moluccan Islands—the Spice Islands—are the Molucca Sea, the Ceram Sea, and the Halmahera Sea.

The Makassar Strait separates the two Indonesian islands of Borneo and Sulawesi, and is a major shipping route connecting the Java Sea with the Celebes Sea. The Karimata Strait, off the western coast of Borneo, is a busy international shipping lane between the South China Sea and the Java Sea. The Wallace Line, which marks the zoogeographical boundary between Asian and Australian flora and fauna, runs right through the Celebes Sea and the Makassar Strait, then into the Indian Ocean via the deep waters of the narrow Lombok Strait between the Indonesian islands of Bali and Lombok.

SLIDING RIDGES

The seas of Indonesia lie above a broad zone of tectonic instability, where the continental Eurasian and Australian plates and the oceanic Indian and Pacific plates come together. The region features frequent earthquakes, tidal waves, and volcanic eruptions. Many of the seas are punctuated by volcanic islands, some of which—most notably Krakatoa and Tambora at the southern margin of the Java Sea—have experienced spectacular and devastating eruptions of colossal magnitude. There are also numerous undersea volcanic zones. Under the western region of the Banda Sea lie two active volcanoes, the Emperor of China and Nieuwerkerk, which form a ridge along the seabed. The Celebes Sea, the deepest of the Indonesian seas plunging to 20,300 ft (6,200 m), was once part of a wider oceanic basin.

FOOD AND TRANSPORT

The seas of Indonesia are important in terms of the fishing industry and the marine life they support. All are important routes for regional transportation, and many of the islands in this complex and diverse nation feature their own unique local identity. Because it is much easier to travel over the water than across the rough topography and dense vegetation of Indonesia's islands, the seas have served to unify the various parts of the archipelago from historic times to the present. They have been linked to the rise and demise of various empires and sultanates, and the spread of religious and other cultural influences. They facilitate the trade in spices, timber, food products, and other resources from far-flung islands, which are exchanged for consumer durables and other products that are made in, or imported into, the Java heartland. Not surprisingly, piracy has thrived in Indonesian waters for centuries, and continues to pose a threat to small fishing vessels and large container ships alike, in the Celebes Sea, the Strait of Malacca, and elsewhere.

Java Sea

The Java Sea (*Luat Jawa* in Indonesian) covers an area of approximately 123,000 square miles (320,000 km²). Until the sixteenth century, it was the focus of extensive maritime empires. In more recent times, it has been subject to colonial exploitation, and has been a major crossroads of the spice trade. It continues to be an important shipping route within Indonesia, Southeast Asia generally, and between Southeast Asia and other parts of the world. The greatest economic activity is along the shores of the island of Java to the south, particularly near the large port cities of Jakarta and Semarang. Offshore oil facilities dot the Java Sea. Fishing and tourism are also important.

A group of 69 small islands known as Karimunjawa—"a stone's throw from Java"—is located in the south-central area of the Java Sea. Twenty-two of the islands, which feature coral reefs and other protected marine life, are set aside as a marine national park. In February and March 1942, the Java Sea was the scene of a major World War II battle, in which Australian, USA, and other Allied navy forces were soundly defeated by the Japanese.

ABOVE The famous eruption of Krakatoa in 1883, which was heard as far away as Perth, Australia, destroyed two-thirds of the island. Since that time, continuous activity has caused the formation of a new island named Anak Krakatau—Child of Krakatoa—seen here in the foreground. Surfacing in 1930, the island continues to rise at an average height of 5 in (13 cm) per week.

Timor Sea

Separating Australia from the island of Timor, the Timor Sea covers approximately 235,000 square miles (610,000 km²). The majority of the sea is less than 650 ft (200 m) in depth, but in the cavernous Timor Trough on the northwestern edge of the sea, depths exceed 10,800 ft (3,300 m).

RIGHT Darwin, the capital of the Northern Territory, sits on the Timor Sea. Its geography enables a view of the sunset to the west over parts of the sea.

BELOW At the conclusion of the Mardayin ceremony across the Top End of Australia, Aboriginal people dance in the waters of the Timor Sea to wash off the ocher and clay that has been used in the ritual painting of their bodies.

UNINTERRUPTED WATERS

Located between latitudes 10°S and 15°S, the Timor Sea is well within the tropics. Its warm waters and the influence of the southwest trade winds produce many extensive tropical storms. During late spring and summer—October to March—many tropical cyclones (known elsewhere as hurricanes or typhoons) commonly form above the sea. The Timor Current runs in a southwesterly direction all year, and pushes warm water southward along Australia's west coast.

Few significant islands are located within the sea. A few reefs, such as the Holothuria group, are found on the eastern edge of the Timor Sea toward the western shore of the Australian continent. There are also a few sandy shoals, but generally the sea is uninterrupted by landmasses.

NATURAL RESOURCES

The warm tropical waters of the Timor Sea make it a highly productive biome. Extensive fish stocks attract predatory sharks and large numbers of dolphins. Commercial fishing boats harvest numerous species including crustaceans such as scampi, together with a wide variety of other fish species. However, illegal fishing for delicacies such as shark fin remains a major threat to the sea's ecosystem.

The sea also has extensive natural resources that are increasingly being exploited. Already, vast reserves of natural gas have been discovered, and recently researchers have discovered methane gas seeping out of the sea floor at depths of up to 270 ft (85 m). Ownership of these lucrative gas reserves has been subject to dispute, with both Australia and Timor-Leste (East Timor)—the newly independent former province of Indonesia—making territorial claims. In 2001, the Timor Sea Agreement established a joint exploration area, and granted the rights to more than 90 percent of the petroleum reserves in the Timor Sea to Timor-Leste.

Arafura Sea

Covering an area of 250,000 square miles (650,000 km²), the Arafura Sea lies to the north of the Australian continent and separates it from the western region of Papua New Guinea. To the west the Arafura Sea merges with the Timor Sea; to the east lies the narrow Torres Strait.

SHALLOW AND WARM

The sea lies atop the Arafura Shelf, which is part of the much larger Sahul Shelf. During the last ice age when sea levels were much lower, this shelf was an extensive flat plain that formed a land bridge between Australia and New Guinea, and aided the migration of humans between Asia and Australia.

The sea itself is quite shallow, with depths ranging between 165 to 265 ft (50 to 80 m) and increasing in depth toward its western edge. The sea floor is predominantly flat, with the only major island system being the Aru Islands located in the northwest corner of the sea.

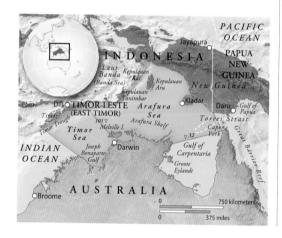

This collection of islands, part of Indonesia, is the result of localized tectonic uplift. It borders the Aru Trench, which plunges more than 12,000 ft (3,600 m) and marks the western boundary of the Arafura and Timor Seas.

The warm tropical waters of the Arafura Sea are an ideal incubator for tropical storms. Intense low-pressure systems—known as cyclones in the western Pacific and hurricanes or typhoons elsewhere—form in late spring and summer—October to March.

DIVERSITY

The Arafura Sea is one of the world's most diverse marine environments. Its warm waters are a haven for an extensive range of fish species, turtles, and large predators including a wide variety of sharks.

Along with the Coral Sea to the east of Australia, the Arafura has been relatively unspoiled by human activity. However, large-scale illegal commercial fishing is placing significant stress on the local environment. Authorities from Australia and Indonesia regularly apprehend trawlers from various Asian countries operating in their territorial waters. This unsustainable fishing has sparked fears that marine stocks will collapse, which would have a devastating impact on the local communities that depend upon fish as their major source of protein.

ABOVE An old Indonesian fishing boat lies on a beach in the Aru Islands, part of the Maluku province of Indonesia and within the Arafura Sea.

BELOW Commercial fishing in the Arafura Sea is a lucrative business. This trawler has just pulled in nets loaded with shrimp and local fish.

Solomon Sea

Bounded by the islands of New Guinea to the east, New Britain to the north, and the Solomon Islands to the west, the Solomon Sea covers an area of around 280,000 square miles (720,000 km²).

ABOVE The islands within the Solomon Sea are remote and relatively self-sustaining. This outrigger canoe is setting out from Yanaba Island to visit Egum Island in the background.

REMOTE PARADISE

The region of the Solomon Sea is extremely remote and its isolation has minimized human impact. It lies atop the Solomon Sea plate, a highly tectonically active zone with subduction zones in the north and south, and a major fault line in the east.

Three major island chains, the D'Entrecasteaux Islands, Trobriand Islands, and Louisiade Archipelago, lie in the southwest corner of the sea.

On the northern edge, the large island of New Britain, part of Papua New Guinea, is a zone of significant volcanic activity and acts as a barrier between the Solomon Sea and the Bismarck Sea to the north.

In this region the sea floor plunges approximately 30,000 ft (9,140 m) into the vast New Britain Trench, making it one of the deepest locations in the world. The trench is the result of immense tectonic forces at play in this region. The whole of the Solomon Sea is comparatively deep, with most of the sea floor lying at around 13,000 ft (4,000 m).

DEEP CURRENTS

Located between latitudes 6°S and 11°S, the Solomon Sea is well within the tropical zone and its waters are among the warmest in the world. The western edge of the sea features extensive reef systems in shallow waters adjacent to the eastern coast of Papua New Guinea. A strong ocean current moves northward along this coastline. Another surface current moves northward along the western coastline of the Solomon Islands, and past Bougainville Island on the eastern edge of the sea. Recent research has also found a southerly countercurrent flowing at greater depths along the eastern edge of the sea. These currents are thought to play a significant role in the upwellings that take place thousands of miles away, in the eastern region of the South Pacific Ocean. These upwellings in turn propel the *El Niño* and *El Niña* weather patterns that affect the climate throughout the entire Pacific region and its adjoining land areas.

BELOW The western areas of the Solomon Islands, in the west of the Solomon Sea, form waves of highly vegetated land with deep lagoons on one side and coral reefs on the other.

Bismarck Sea

Named after nineteenth-century German statesman Otto von Bismarck, the Bismarck Sea lies to the northeast of Papua New Guinea. The island of New Britain separates the Bismarck from the Solomon Sea to the south. To the east, the sea is bounded by the long, narrow island of New Ireland.

DOTTED WITH REEFS

The Bismarck Sea is relatively small, covering an area of around 15,000 square miles (40,000 km^2). Islands with extensive reef systems are dotted along its western boundary near the east coast of Papua New Guinea. The Admiralty Islands complex, dominated by Manus Island, forms the northern boundary of the sea.

Depths in the sea range from 6,600 to 8,200 ft (2,000 m to 2,500 m). The entire sea lies atop the Bismarck plate, an area of considerable tectonic activity. This has led to extensive submarine trench and ridge systems. A sizable ridge runs in a north-south direction midway across the sea, effectively dividing its floor into two distinct basins.

SWIRLING INTO THE PACIFIC

Lying in latitudes 2°S to 5°S, just south of the equator, the Bismarck Sea is a highly productive tropical biome, containing one of the world's most diverse marine environments. Along with the Solomon Sea, it forms part of the Western Pacific Warm Pool, one of the world's warmest marine areas. These waters play a significant role in affecting large ocean circulations that influence the entire Pacific Ocean.

Currents within the Bismarck Sea are dynamic. The New Guinea Coastal Current (NGCC) flows along the eastern coastline of Papua New Guinea, entering the Bismarck from the Solomon Sea in the south through the Vitiaz Strait. Another current enters the Bismark Sea through the Ysabel Channel in the northeast region of the sea, and flows in a counter-clockwise direction against the NGCC.

Battle of the Bismarck Sea

Due to its isolation, the Bismarck Sea has been relatively unspoiled by human activity. But in March 1943 at the height of World War II, a fierce naval battle erupted between Allied (Australian and USA) and Japanese forces. The Japanese lost eight transport ships, four destroyers, and 20 aircraft, while the Allies lost just five aircraft.

ABOVE This aerial view shows sedimentary deposits entering the Bismarck Sea from a fresh-water river on the northern coast of Papua New Guinea.

Gulf of Carpentaria

The Gulf of Carpentaria is a large, shallow sea that is effectively an extension of the Arafura Sea that lies to its north. The gulf is bounded on the east by the vast Cape York Peninsula, the most northerly point of continental Australia. To the west lies Arnhem Land, a region of Australia's Northern Territory that is under the control of the indigenous Aboriginal people. Prior to the end of the last ice age, the area was a flat, dry plain.

BELOW This satellite image shows the Gulf of Carpentaria as the slightly square-bottomed dark area on the right. Gulf country is very isolated and is prone to cyclones and a very wet season in late summer—from December to March—with heavy daily rain, often causing flooding.

BEWARE OF CROCODILES!

The surface area of the gulf is around 116,000 square miles (300,000 km²). Two major islands lie within the gulf—Mornington Island in the southwest, and Groote Eylandt in the east. A number of smaller islands hug the coastline of Australia.

Several significant river systems empty into the gulf, including the Mitchell, Flinders, and Roper rivers. Extensive estuarine systems are found along much of the coastline, inhabited by significant numbers of huge and fearsome saltwater crocodiles. Researchers have recently discovered extensive coral-reef systems in the southern region of the gulf. These patch reefs have been found in relatively deep water of around 75 ft (28 m). The gulf's warm, tropical waters are highly productive and support a great diversity of marine life forms.

GULF COUNTRY

Located between latitudes 12°S and 17°S, the Gulf of Carpentaria lies well within the tropics. The climate is hot, and only two distinct seasons exist. The cooler dry season from around April to November is characterized by winds from the southeast and east, which draw dry air from the arid inland areas of the state of Queensland. Between December and March, winds shift and bring moisture-laden warm air from the northwest; most of the region's annual rainfall occurs within intense tropical storms during this period.

The waters of the Gulf of Carpentaria and the land surrounding it, known as "gulf country," are among the most isolated regions in Australia, and indeed the world. There are no large human settlements along the coastline, and thus the environment of the gulf is relatively unspoiled.

ABOVE Saltwater crocodiles are prevalent in northern Australia and the Gulf of Carpentaria. They are the largest of all living crocodiles, with males growing to around 16 ft (5 m) in length.

Coral Sea

The Coral Sea is the southwestern arm of the South Pacific Ocean, situated between the countries of Australia to the west, Papua New Guinea to the north, and Vanuatu to the east. Australia's Great Barrier Reef, the largest coral reef in the world, frames the western perimeter of the sea. To the south the Coral Sea adjoins the Tasman Sea at latitude 30°S. Alignment of the sea is roughly northwest to southeast.

WARM CURRENTS AND REVOLVING STORMS

The Coral Sea covers an area of 1,615,262 square miles (4,183,510 km²). Its mean depth is around 7,857 ft (2,394 m); its greatest depth of 30,079 ft (9,165 m) is in the South Solomon Trench near the Santa Cruz Islands. To the northwest, the Gulf of Papua opens into the Torres Strait and the Arafura Sea to the west. A surface current, the South Equatorial, brings warm water from the Pacific. Only a few minor island groups lie near the center of the sea, but along its western and eastern margins, numerous archipelagos are found.

The South Pacific Ocean, just to the east of the Coral Sea, is the birthplace for around 12 percent of the world's tropical revolving storms, known locally as cyclones. These track westward, then curve to the south, often causing great destruction.

Today many tourist resorts are found along the Coral Sea coastline. Patrons take advantage of the wide variety of recreational activities available in its diverse, relatively unspoiled tropical environment.

RIGHT Bordering the Coral Sea, the Great Barrier Reef is the largest structure on Earth made by living organisms. The reef protects the northeastern coast of the Australian mainland.

BELOW The crew abandons the *USS Lexington* after torpedo hits.

Not a Ship in Sight

From May 4 to 8, 1942, the crucial World War II Battle of the Coral Sea was fought between Japan and the Allies—the United States and Australia. It was unusual in that it was fought completely in the air, as carrier-borne aircraft attacked each other. It was the first engagement in history in which neither side's ships saw or fired upon each other, and although it was roughly even in terms of casualties and loss of aircraft, it halted the Japanese advance south from New Guinea. Australians call it "the battle that saved Australia."

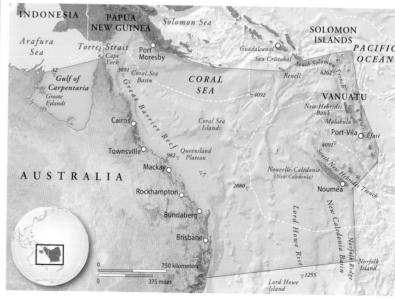

115

Tasman Sea

An arm of the southwest South Pacific Ocean, the Tasman Sea lies between Australia and New Zealand. The sea bears the name of Dutch explorer Abel Janszoon Tasman, the first recorded European to visit the region (1642–1644). In 1770, English explorer Captain James Cook sailed over much of the sea during his first voyage of exploration.

ABOVE Ball's Pyramid, an island in the Lord Howe Island group, is around 1,800 ft (550 m) high. The Lord Howe Island group is part of New South Wales, an eastern state of Australia.

EAST TO WEST

The Tasman Sea covers around 900,000 square miles (2,300,000 km²). Its maximum depth is 17,000 ft (5,090 m) about half way between Tasmania and New Zealand's South Island. The northern boundary of the sea is latitude 30°S. The east-west distance across the sea is 1,400 miles (2,250 km.) To the east it connects to the South Pacific Ocean through the Cook Strait, which separates the North Island and South Island of New Zealand. To the west it meets the Indian Ocean through Bass Strait. The southern boundary of the sea is a line connecting the southern point of Auckland Island, New Zealand, to Tasmania's South East Cape.

BUMPY BOTTOM

Several small island groups dot the northern region of the Tasman Sea, including Norfolk Island, Lord Howe Island, and Ball's Pyramid. The sea overlies several guyots in its southwestern quarter, including Taupo and Gascoyne. The Tasman Sea's submarine topography displays several rises, ridges, and plateaus, along with basins and the Tasman abyssal plain to the southwest. A warm-water surface current—the East Australian—flows southward off the Australian coast and helps to moderate climatic conditions.

COLONIZATION

Over the centuries, the Tasman Sea has been crossed countless times, by almost every imaginable type of marine vessel. The Maori people migrated to New Zealand from Polynesia to the north around 1,000 years ago. The first European settlers arrived in Australia in 1788. Sydney, New South Wales, Australia's major urban center with a population of around 4.4 million, is the largest metropolis located on the coast of the Tasman Sea.

The Great Australian Bight

The Great Australian Bight stretches more than 750 miles (1,200 km) along the southern edge of the Australian continent. The eastern boundary of the bight is marked by Cape Catastrophe on the Eyre Peninsula in South Australia, and the western boundary by Cape Pasley in Western Australia. It was first charted in 1802 by English captain Matthew Flinders during his circumnavigation of Australia.

LEFT Gouged out by the giant waves of the great Southern Ocean that sweep into the bight, the southern coast of Western Australia is rugged and steep, forming cliffs up to 200 ft (60 m) high.

ABOVE The great white shark, or white pointer, haunts the cold waters of the Great Australian Bight. It is a predatory creature, attacking one or two swimmers in Australia every year.

GIANT STEP

The Great Australian Bight is characterized by a very wide, shallow continental shelf, in parts more than 100 nautical miles (190 km) in breadth. The mass of water that forms the bight is contrasted by the very deep waters beyond the shelf, which quickly plunge to a depth of more than 13,000 ft (4,000 m). Although the bight is generally shallow, the seabed undulates in places, with several seamounts dotted across its floor.

A large step in the continental shelf, known as the Ceduna Trench, is located on the eastern edge of the bight. It consists of an extensive system of channels where depths in some places exceed 2,500 ft (1,000 m).

MIGHTY CLIFFS

The Great Australian Bight lies off the Nullarbor Plain, a vast arid area of southern Australia that supplies minimal surface rainwater runoff into the bight. Hot, dry northerly winds from the desert that cause considerable evaporation are also common. These factors combine to create unusually high salinity in the bight.

Currents within the bight are affected by both the Indian and Southern oceans. Close to the coastline the current flows west to east, and is near the surface. This current brings in warm waters from the Timor Sea, drawn by the Leeuwin current that flows down the western coastline of Australia. Further offshore, the Flinders Current flows from east to west and brings colder, nutrient-rich waters into the bight.

Large schools of southern bluefin tuna gather in the bight, particularly in the summer months of December to March. Australian sea lions are also attracted by the abundance of fish. The sea lions in turn attract great white sharks, which can reach over 19 ft (6 m) in length, and are among the largest predators in the ocean.

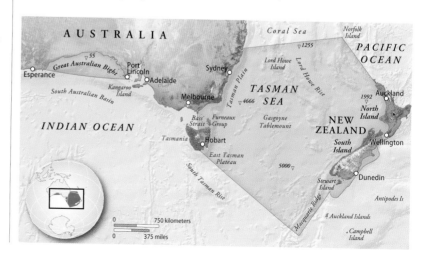

Seas of Antarctica

The seas of Antarctica are the most isolated waters on Earth, and the least charted. They are also among the most treacherous, with enormous icebergs, thick and ever-shifting pack ice, and submerged rocks and banks all posing threats to shipping. Recent accidents involving cruise ships in the seas of Antarctica bear testament to their dangers.

RIGHT The Antarctic cruise ship *Polar Circle* cuts through the pack ice in the Weddell Sea as tourists watch from the bow.

BELOW Great killer whales *(Orcinus orca)* travel through a passage in the ice at McMurdo Sound, to prey on Antarctic cod and seals. The name "orca" was given to these huge mammals by the ancient Romans.

WEDDELL SEA

Covering an area of around 1,081,000 square miles (2,800,000 km^2) the Weddell Sea is the largest of the Antarctic seas. Its western shoreline is formed by the Antarctic Peninsula that stretches northward toward South America. To the east lies the Antarctic region of Coats Land. The Southern Ocean lies to the north.

For most of the year, the Weddell is covered with thick ice. The cold waters of the Weddell have a strong effect on global ocean currents. Much of the deep cold water that flows around the world's oceans originates in the Weddell Sea.

RIGHT The warmer waters of summer in Antarctica—November to March—cause splits in the ice shelves. These passages form the routes for whales to reach their feeding grounds.

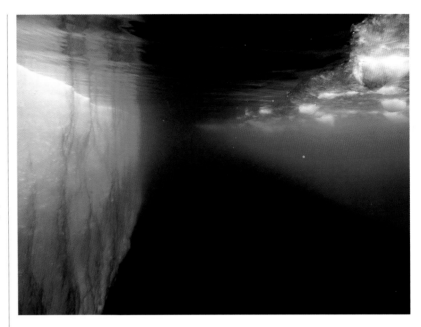

BELLINGSHAUSEN SEA

Lying on the western side of the Antarctic Peninsula is the small Bellingshausen Sea. Its southern shoreline is formed by Ellsworth Land. An extensive continental shelf lies off the coast, with an average depth of less than 330 ft (100 m). Several significant islands lie within the sea, including the large Thurston Island that forms the western boundary of the Bellingshausen, dividing it from the Amundsen Sea. The vast Alexander Island, which stretches along the western shore of the Antarctic Peninsula, is divided from the mainland by the narrow and extremely shallow George VI Sound.

AMUNDSEN SEA

To the west of the Bellingshausen lies the Amundsen Sea, its southern shoreline formed by Marie Byrd Land. The Amundsen and Bellingshausen seas have much in common, being subject to the Circumpolar Deep Water current. This current carries water with an average temperature of just 34°F (1°C), still a degree warmer than the other Antarctic seas.

ROSS SEA

Lying off the vast Ross Ice Shelf that forms its southern boundary, the Ross Sea covers around 370,000 square miles (960,000 km²). The sea is a large bay formed by the Edward VII Peninsula to the east, the northern shoreline of Victoria Land, and with Cape Adare marking its western edge. The mountains of the Prince Albert and Admiralty ranges tower over the western coast, along with numerous volcanoes and huge piles of volcanic rock. Water depths within the Ross Sea are generally shallow, the western region of the sea averaging less than 1,000 ft (300 m). The Ross Sea is the best charted of the Antarctic Seas and its coastline has been extensively explored. McMurdo Sound on the western edge of the Ross Ice Shelf hosts research bases for the United States and New Zealand.

DAVIS SEA

The Davis Sea lies off the coast of Queen Mary Land, and meets the Indian Ocean at its northern boundary. The vast Shackleton Ice Shelf forms the eastern border, and the West Ice Shelf forms the western border of this small sea. Russia and Australia maintain permanent bases along its coastline.

COSMONAUT, HAAKON VII, AND LAZAREV SEAS

To the east of the Weddell Sea lie a number of small seas—the Cosmonaut, Haakon VII, and Lazarev seas. Extensive ridge systems lie within these seas, and a vast ice shelf lines this region of the Antarctic coast.

Frigid Feast

Despite the popular image of Antarctica as a frozen desolate wasteland, its seas are very productive. Large fish stocks support huge numbers of seals, penguins, and sea birds such as petrels. Several species of whale, including large humpbacks, frequent the Antarctic seas in the summer, attracted by the huge amounts of krill that well up from the deep. Isolation has not made the seas impervious to the impact of human activities. Climate change poses a grave threat, with increasing temperatures changing the hydrology of the seas. Dissolved carbon dioxide is acidifying the seas, reducing the ability of numerous species to form shells.

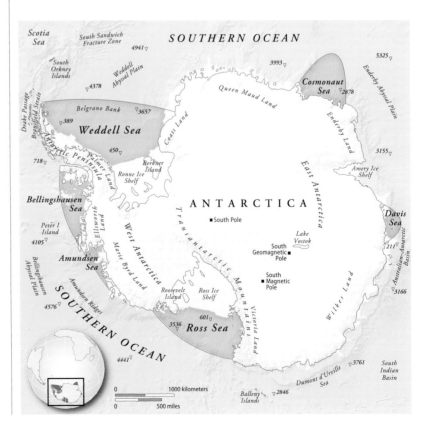

Inland Seas

Inland seas are large bodies of water that are almost completely surrounded by land. They differ from large lakes, such as the Great Lakes of North America and Africa's Lake Victoria, in that they contain salty—rather than fresh—water.

RIGHT Abandoned oil rigs are located only feet from the popular beach of Shikhov in the southern suburb of Baku, Azerbaijan, on the Caspian Sea. Bathers seemingly ignore the rusting hulks and residual pollution of the oily graveyard.

BLACK SEA

Covering an area of around 163,000 square miles (422,000 km^2), the Black Sea is connected to the Aegean Sea by the Sea of Marmara, through the extremely narrow Bosporus Strait. The northern shoreline is formed by the coast of Ukraine; the coasts of Moldova, Romania, and Bulgaria lie to the west. Turkey stretches along its southern shore, while the coastlines of Georgia and the Russian Federation form its eastern border.

The Black Sea is a vast basin, formed amid mountain ranges gradually created by tectonic activity. Over the last few million years, it has at times been a vast landlocked freshwater lake, at other times a saltwater sea connected to the Mediterranean Sea. Around 6,000 to 8,000 years ago the Bosporus formed, creating the link that now joins the Black Sea to the Mediterranean Sea.

The coastlines of the Black Sea are remarkably smooth and even, featuring few significant bays, inlets, or islands. An extensive lake and barrier system lines its eastern coastline. In the northeast corner lies the world's shallowest sea, the Sea of Azov.

The Black Sea is shallowest in the north, due to an extensive continental shelf. Depths gradually increase toward the south, reaching approximately 7,250 ft (2,210 m).

CASPIAN SEA

The Caspian Sea is the world's largest fully enclosed body of water, covering an area of 149,200 square miles (386,400 km^2).

Iran's northern coastline forms its southern shore, while the coasts of Turkmenistan and Kazakhstan lie to the east. To the north lies Russia and to the west lies Azerbaijan.

Water from some of eastern Europe's largest rivers, including the Volga and Ural, flow into the Caspian. Until around 5.5 million years ago the Caspian was linked to the Black Sea, but tectonic movements have since closed that passage.

The mouth of the Volga, which enters the Caspian Sea in its northwest corner, has formed a vast delta. Most of the remaining coastline is low-lying, formed by sediments washed down from the highlands by river systems. Along the mid-eastern coastline is the Garabogazköl Bay, formerly a large inlet of the Caspian, but now a lake separated from the sea by a massive artificial barrier.

Overall the Caspian is a shallow sea, especially in the north where depths range between 13 ft (4 m) and 26 ft (8 m). A submarine ridge divides the northern Caspian from the mid-Caspian, where depths reach around 460 ft (140 m). Another ridgeline, the Abseron Bank, lies along the southern boundary. The Abseron Bank features a wide continental shelf, shallow depths, and a series of submerged ridges and small islands. Pollution is a threat to the Caspian Sea.

ABOVE Ice fishing is a popular pastime on the Aral Sea. Fishermen ride out to the center of the frozen sea and drill holes through the ice where they fish with line and hook or spear.

Disappearing Sea

Uncontrolled irrigation saw water volumes in the Aral Sea drop by more than 50 percent by the late 1980s. Salinity levels rose substantially; this in turn affected the ecosystem, and virtually destroyed the sea's thriving fishing industry. By 1989, sea levels had fallen to such an extent that the Aral split into two separate lakes, the "greater sea" in the south and the "lesser sea" in the north. By 2007, it had shrunk to a mere 10 percent of its original volume, and formed three lakes, two of which are too salty to support any marine life. The Aral has also been heavily polluted by pesticides, fertilizers, heavy industry, and weapons testing.

ARAL SEA

Once one of the world's largest inland bodies of water, the Aral Sea is known today as an unmitigated environmental disaster. It once covered an area of 26,300 square miles (68,000 km²), but unsustainable water harvesting for irrigation has caused volumes to decline steadily.

The Aral Sea is surrounded by Kazakhstan and Uzbekistan, their border running through its center in an east-west direction. The region is characterized by dry desert climates with annual rainfall averaging less than 4 in (100 mm). Most of the sea's inflow comes from the large Syr Darya and Amu Darya rivers, which feed in around 24 cubic miles (100 km³) of water annually. The Aral Sea depression was formed by a subsidence of the earth's crust around 1.6 million years ago. The depression began to fill with water about 140,000 years ago, and reached its peak approximately 10,000 years ago.

RIGHT The man-made channel on the left was built to assist irrigation of cotton fields. Instead it drained the Aral Sea, which is now almost dry. The Amu Darya River delta can be seen on the right.

Straits and Channels

Straits and channels are narrow passages of water that connect two larger water bodies. As with all Earth's physical features, the names we use today are generally those assigned by the original mapmakers, and often reflect cultural traditions, native languages, and colonial history.

ABOVE This aerial view shows a ferry traveling between Ocracoke Island and Cape Hatteras, at Outer Banks, North Carolina, USA. Outer Banks is actually a series of barrier islands that form a passage separating North Carolina from the Atlantic Ocean.

BY ANY OTHER NAME

These passages are often given other names. "Pass," for example, is used for most of the waterways that join the Bering Sea and Pacific Ocean between the Aleutian Islands, while "passage" and "channel" are often used in the Caribbean region. Sea links between North Carolina's Outer Banks and the Atlantic Ocean and various sounds are called "inlets." To add further confusion, narrow waterways are often identified in local languages, particularly in Asia.

ANCIENT ROUTES

Throughout most of human history, water has been a major barrier to travel. During the fourth glacial advance of the last Ice Age, the sea level was several hundred feet lower than today. This left much of the shallow continental shelf, and many of today's straits and channels, exposed as dry land. Flora, fauna, and people could move freely across terrain that later became a barrier to migration as sea levels rose.

Perhaps the best-known example is Beringia, the land bridge that joined northeast Asia to present-day Alaska, across what is now the Bering Strait. It allowed numerous plant and animal species to migrate between the New and Old Worlds. Many archeologists believe that ancient Asian peoples crossed Beringia on their way to becoming the first American settlers.

Similarly, the British Isles were once connected to mainland Europe across what are now the English Channel and North Sea; much of southeast Asia was also high and dry. To the west of the deep Lombok Strait that separates the Indonesian islands of Bali and Lombok, many of today's islands were connected to the Asian mainland. Here, the Wallace Line—named for the nineteenth century English naturalist Alfred Wallace—presented a barrier that prevented faunal migration. To the east are found the marsupials of Australia and Oceania; to the west, the vastly different Oriental faunal realm includes tigers, rhinoceroses, and apes. Archeological evidence suggests that Lombok Strait was the first major strait navigated by humans. When Australia was first settled around 50,000 years ago, the

strait's 50-mile (80 km) barrier had to be crossed before humans could reach the hitherto uninhabited island continent in the south.

HISTORICAL IMPORTANCE

Early historical records recognized the importance of various straits, when writing first appeared around 5,000 years ago. Egyptians traveled across the narrow Strait of Bab el Mandeb—Gate of Tears—between the Red Sea and Gulf of Aden. Present-day Istanbul, is located on the narrow Bosporus, a strait that, along with the Sea of Marmara and Dardanelles, links the Mediterranean and Black Seas. Trade was conducted

Pillars of Hercules

In European history, few straits have played a more prominent role than the Strait of Gibraltar—the western Mediterranean outlet into the Atlantic. Early seafarers named the promontories each side of this 8.84-mile (14.24 km) channel the "Pillars of Hercules." They rightly feared the treacherous and uncharted waters of the Atlantic that lay beyond. Only the intrepid Phoenicians are known to have passed through the Strait of Gibraltar regularly before the dawn of the Christian era, but as time passed, it became one of the world's most important marine thoroughfares.

ABOVE The powerful waves and currents that run through the Strait of Gibraltar brought this ship to its knees. Broken in two, the Liberian ship, *Fedra*, ran aground in bad weather in 2008. The crew of 31 was rescued by Gibraltar's Marine Rescue Service.

ABOVE The Strait of Malacca, dividing the Malay Peninsula from the Indonesian island of Sumatra, is one of the most strategic shipping lanes in the world. However, it still provides good fishing for those living on its coast.

between Mesopotamia in Asia Minor and other regions of The Gulf including Pakistan's Indus Valley. Ships also passed through the Strait of Hormuz, the narrow passage between The Gulf and Gulf of Oman.

AGE OF DISCOVERY

Outside of the Mediterranean region, Europe's most adventurous early explorers were the Vikings. The Skagerrak and Kattegat straits between the North and Baltic seas were their doorway to the Atlantic. They also sailed westward through the Denmark Strait between Iceland and Greenland. By 1000 CE, the intrepid Norsemen had crossed the rough Davis Strait between Greenland and Baffin Island, and the narrow Labrador Strait—Strait of Belle Isle—which led them to the mainland of North America.

Choke Points

Perhaps more than any other country, the British have taken advantage of the geopolitical importance of straits and other strategic locations. At the peak of their colonial power, they held sway over most of the world's major strategic navigational "choke points," apart from the US-controlled Panama Canal. This dominance allowed the British navy to rule the seas and create a vast empire upon which "the sun never set."

Russia and then the Soviet Union has long sought to gain control of warm water routes to allow year-round access to the world's oceans. During the Cold War, the West developed a strategy of containment against the USSR. Ships traveling between the Baltic Sea and North Sea had to pass through the western-controlled Kattegat and Skagerrak straits. Turkey controlled access to and from the Black Sea via the narrow Bosporus and Dardanelles straits, and the Sea of Marmara. In the Middle East, the West successfully thwarted Soviet attempts to gain control of the Strait of Hormuz through which much of the world's oil supply is shipped.

From the fifteenth century, sailors during the European Age of Exploration used straits to great advantage. Over two centuries, hundreds of passages were mapped, named, and often claimed by European powers. Christopher Columbus and those who followed him gave names to numerous straits, channels, and passages in the Caribbean Sea—although most of them today bear English names.

On their pioneering round-the-world voyage in 1519–1521, Spanish explorer Ferdinand Magellan and his crew were the first Europeans to sail through the narrow, frigid, and stormy strait off the southern tip of continental South America that still bears his name.

As early as 1300 CE, Arabs were involved in the lucrative spice trade centered in Indonesia's Malacca Islands. Magellan arrived in the Philippines in 1521, and in 1565 Spain claimed the islands as the Spanish East Indies. By the 1620s, the Portuguese had also established themselves in the Malaccas. Within a short time, other Europeans were exploring the maze of straits that separate the islands of Southeast Asia. Of the region's many straits, none was more important than the Strait of Malacca, the narrow passage that separates Malaysia and Singapore from the Indonesian island of Sumatra.

Columbus made a huge geographical error upon reaching America, believing at first that he had reached the East Indies—hence the name "Indians" for indigenous Americans. His mistake was soon realized, thus sparking a search for a sea route to the east through, or around, the huge continental barrier. The quest to find an Arctic Northwest Passage faced three significant barriers—a hostile climate, frozen seas, and the Canadian Archipelago.

Despite numerous attempts, it was not until 1906 that Roald Amundsen, in his vessel *Gjoa*, successfully navigated the treacherous Northwest Passage. Today the passage is rarely used, being of little economic value, but global warming could transform it into a major shipping route between Atlantic and Pacific ports as ice masses melt.

MAN MADE

Over the passage of time, the world's straits have increased greatly in importance and where natural water links did not exist, several were created. The Suez Canal opened in 1869, creating a passage between the Mediterranean and Red seas. It reduced the sailing distance between European ports and the Indian Ocean by more than 6,000 miles (9,700 km). The Panama Canal, opened in 1914, created an artificial strait between North and South America that joined the Atlantic and Pacific Oceans. Traveling through the 48-mile (77 km) passage saves around 8,000 miles (13,000 km) compared with the route around the Strait of Magellan. Today, many vessels, particularly oil tankers, are too large to pass through either canal. The Panama Canal is currently being widened.

ABOVE The Moon rises over Saddle Island along the Labrador Strait, often called the Strait of Belle Isle. The strait separates the Labrador Peninsula from the island of Newfoundland in Canada.

LEFT The busy Bosporus, or Istanbul Strait, divides Turkey, and is one of the world's narrowest straits, providing a vital link as it connects the Black Sea with the Sea of Marmara and beyond.

Coastal Zones

The most distinctive feature on Earth is arguably the shoreline, the border that separates land from sea. It is also a most desirable environment for human occupation and utilization. Very conspicuous when viewed from space, coasts span virtually all latitudes, except for a zone near the North Pole and a narrow belt around Antarctica.

LEADING EDGES

The basic form of the world's coasts is the result of continental drift that has tended to create rugged, mountainous, earthquake- and volcano-prone strips along the leading edges of migrating tectonic plates, and low-lying plains along their trailing edges.

Although plate movement is very slow, the forms it creates are distinctive. Plate movement is also largely responsible for the creation of drainage basins, where rivers flow across the coastline and dump their loads into the sea, often creating deltas.

Calculations of the length of Earth's shoreline, depending on the generalization by cartographers, range from about 250,000 miles (400,000 km) to over 620,000 miles (1,000,000 km). Today's coastline is longer than it was in the past, because continents have separated throughout geological history.

WIND AND WAVES

Coastal zones are characterized by interfaces between water and land, water and air, and land and air. It is within these interfaces that coastal processes operate. Waves are the most important factor affecting the coast at the water/land interface. They are caused by several different types of forces—astronomical forces, which produce tides; impulsive forces, such as those from volcanic eruptions, earthquakes, or landslides, which can produce destructive waves including the deadly tsunami; and the more predictable forces like hurricanes and typhoons that cause storm waves and storm surges.

Geologically, waves serve as erosional, depositional, and transportational agents in the modification of the shoreline. They can be strong, especially along mid-latitude coasts, or gentle, like the swell-waves that are common in low latitudes. Although wind is primarily important because of the waves it generates, it can also modify the coast through erosion, transportation, and deposition. Where wind is sufficiently strong and persistent, sand dunes are likely to develop.

There are some coastal environments where chemical and biological processes are more important than wave action. Seawater is a fluid that is only about 97 percent pure water; the rest consists of chemical elements and compounds in solution such as sodium chloride, calcium carbonate, silicon dioxide, and iron, as well as gases like carbon dioxide and nitrogen. Shorelines dominated by chemically- and biologically-created forms include coral reefs, mangrove swamps, and salt marshes.

UPS AND DOWNS

The specific landforms that occur along the coast, stemming from a geological base as modified by a variety of processes, include cliffs, beaches, lagoons, estuaries, deltas, and dunes. Cliffy coasts consist of soft rock, hard rock, or ice, as found in Antarctica.

Beaches make up approximately 20 percent of the world's shoreline. It is estimated that some 70 percent of the world's beaches are being eroded.

Deltas, although present only along about 1.5 percent of the world's coast, have become one of the most intensely utilized of coastal landforms. They are complex features in their own right, possessing numerous distributaries, levees, lakes, marshes, and mudflats. They, along with other coastal wetlands, serve as major nursery grounds for life in the sea.

Estuaries, a common form along the coasts of all occupied continents, are continually being modified, especially by the continual sediment brought into them by streams and rivers. Lagoons, many of which are created by the development of long offshore bars, are usually shallow, have highly variable salinities, and are biologically rich.

AT THE BEACH

At which point along the trail of evolution hominids gathered along the coast is unknown. Whenever it may have been, those first coastal scavengers, gatherers, and hunters, found a variety of resources not available inland. By the time the sea level reached its present height, agriculture and animal husbandry, although not necessarily originating there, were being practiced in floodplains and deltas. They were accompanied by the construction of permanent settlements, the development of social and political organizations, and maritime commerce.

ABOVE Ecola State Park, in Oregon, USA, features a craggy shoreline that attracts a variety of interesting marine life in the many rockpools that form along the shores. The coast is known for its gray whale sightings during migration in winter and spring.

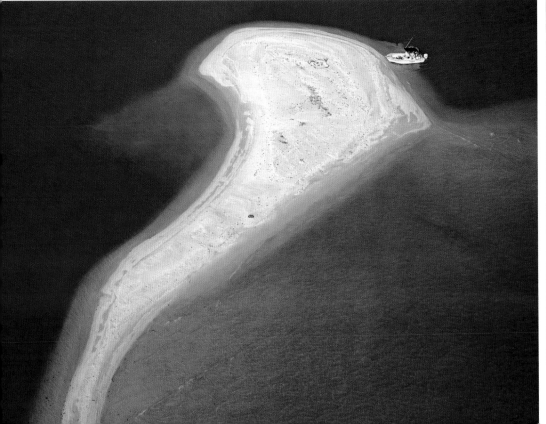

ABOVE This aerial view shows the spectacular Aval Cliffs in Etretat, France. Over millions of years, the cliffs have been eroded to their current outline.

LEFT Although home to the alligator, the Florida Everglades are a wonder of nature and, with precaution, are the perfect place to pull ashore or fish. This motorboat has pulled onto a sandbar in Ten Thousand Islands National Wildlife Refuge, in Florida, USA.

OPPOSITE Daytona Beach in Florida, USA, has hard-packed sand that enables vehicle access. The result is a motorsport mecca with hundreds of motor vehicles moving up and down the beach, with very little regard for the coastal environment.

ABOVE Located on the edge of the Arabian Sea along the Gulf of Oman, Muscat has rocky mountains dominating the landscape and forming a rocky coast.

BELOW Older civilizations, such as along Cefalu Harbor, Sicily, have built right to the water's edge, leaving little foreshore.

Naturally protected bays and river mouths were chosen as harbors, and protection was afforded to them with the construction of breakwaters. Such early engineering projects were very localized and modest in comparison to the widespread and massive modifications that are found along the world's coastlines today.

The "humanization" of coasts accelerated during the periods of the great maritime explorations and the Industrial Revolution. Whereas the former expanded the possibilities for colonization around the world with every new discovery, the latter gave impetus to increased development and exploitation of resources.

During pre-Industrial Revolution days, only about 20 percent of the world's largest cities were coastal. By 1800, the number was nearly 50 percent, and by the early twentieth century it had reached at least 70 percent. It is estimated that today more than 40 percent of the world's population lives on, or nearby, the coast.

CHANGING RESOURCES

A multitude of resources are found in the coastal zone—animal and plant life, minerals, and the more nebulous attributes of space, climate, and beauty. Almost everything humans do in the coastal zone alters it as a resource base. Many modifications are very conspicuous and border upon the shoreline itself. Sea walls, groynes, jetties, breakwaters, and dikes now extend along thousands of miles of coast. In some nations, such protective structures occupy long

stretches. For example, 80 percent of the Belgian coastline is bordered by artificial structures, as is more than half of Japan's coastline, and nearly 40 percent of the coastline of the UK.

Resources vary greatly in type, quality, quantity, and degree of exploitation. Estuaries, long noted for their fisheries, have suffered not only from overfishing but also land or swamp reclamation, pollution, mining of oil and gas, the damming of rivers upstream, and industrial, commercial, and residential development.

Coastal wetlands such as marshes, swamps, and mangroves are also highly productive ecosystems, and many are suffering a similar fate. Reclamation has greatly reduced the wetlands around the world, a reduction that has been exacerbated by pollution from both land and sea.

Coral reefs have served as a resource base for millennia. However, they were not generally under stress until the introduction of modern technology and tourism. The rise in sea levels, which appears to be accelerating, may well be more important in the long run than local human activities in determining the fate of precious coral reefs.

NATURAL DISASTERS

Disasters such as earthquakes, volcanic eruptions, and landslides along coastlines have an almost instantaneous impact on coastal dwellers and their infrastructures. Most of them, however, tend to be localized in importance unless they generate a tsunami. Such was the case in the Chilean earthquake in 1960 that caused destruction in Japan, and the tsunami generated by the 2004 Indonesian earthquake that crossed the Indian Ocean. Most disasters along coastlines are atmospheric in origin. Tropical cyclones—also known as hurricanes or typhoons—can be particularly destructive to coastal areas between about 5° and 30° latitude. Although their impact may be felt beyond the coastal zone, they are most dangerous in low-lying areas such as in Bangladesh, where as many as half a million people have been killed by a single cyclone; southern China; and the Mexican Gulf coast of the United States. Other hazards and disasters affecting coasts include subsidence, biological changes—such as "red tides" caused by toxic algal blooms; and war—for example, the torching of oil wells during the Gulf War.

CONSERVATION

The coastal zone—despite its unpredictable terrestrial, atmospheric, and oceanographic processes—has long been favored by humans for commerce, industry, residence, recreation, and resources. In the process of occupation and development, many coastal zones have been drastically changed from their original state. But today governments and public groups are spending time and money to determine ways we can effectively manage, repair, and conserve one of the world's most important environments—the coastal zone.

Estuaries

Estuaries, although occupying only a small proportion of the world's coastal zone, have been among the most intensely utilized of Earth's landscapes for much of human history. Their attractiveness is the result of the hydrological, climatological, and biological characteristics that are present at the interface between land and sea. It is not surprising that many of the world's major cities are estuarine, and that much of the world's commerce uses estuarine waters.

ABOVE The great estuary of the Severn River forms part of the divide between England and Wales. The estuary has a tidal range of around 50 ft (15 m)—one of the highest in the world.

DROWNED VALLEYS

An estuary is an enclosed body of water that has an open connection with the sea, along with a supply of fresh water. Estuaries come in all sizes and shapes, and occupy a variety of natural settings. They may have the shape of a funnel, or be linear along the shoreline. Much of their variability stems from their geological heritage, but they are all drowned valleys, many having formed during the last major post-glacial rise in sea level. During glacial times, when the sea level was more than 330 ft (100 m) lower than at present, deep trenches were carved across the continental shelf.

While the sea level was rising, and subsequent to its stabilization about 6,000 years ago, entrenched valleys and other naturally occurring coastal valleys received sediment that was transported into them by the rivers and streams that flow into the sea. The degree of filling has varied greatly, ranging from those barely affected such as the Thames estuary in England, to those that have been overfilled, such as the Mississippi River

whose mouth is now occupied by the large Mississippi delta. Thus the formerly drowned valley estuary has been converted into a lengthy riverine estuary, where the river carries in its own sedimentary deposits.

OFFSHORE BARRIERS

Some estuaries are valleys blocked off from the sea by bay-mouth and offshore barrier bars; others such as San Francisco Bay are the result of tectonic activity; others were formed by glaciers and are known as fjords, as found along the coast of Norway and the South Island of New Zealand.

Offshore barriers usually form on gently sloping coasts where waves transfer sediment from the shore and create a barrier. Some of these bars form very far seaward of the mainland shore, resulting in long, wide, estuarine lagoons.

When tectonic activity causes portions of the landscape to drop below sea level, estuaries—many of which are quite short—often form along the irregular

shoreline. Fjords are typically steep-sided, narrow, and U-shaped, and often very deep. They are essentially ice-scoured river valleys and usually have substantial amounts of fresh water flowing into them.

TIDAL INLETS

Most estuaries are dominated by a single stream, but there are many situations where numerous streams enter a coastal body of water—such as a lagoon or sound—creating a series of sub-estuaries. Such complexes are connected to the sea by tidal inlets.

Whereas the settings of estuaries are varied, all have cross-sectional—transverse—and longitudinal profiles. They are affected by tidal and salinity variations, with tidal conditions defining the cross-section profile, and salinity the longitudinal character of the estuary.

The cross-section belts consist of supratidal—above tide level; intertidal—with alternating flooding and draining during tidal cycles; and subtidal—below tide level. These are caused by variations in tides, which range from virtually zero in the Mediterranean Sea, to around 55 ft (17 m) in the Bay of Fundy on the eastern border between Canada and the United States.

Longitudinally, estuaries reflect the relative proportions of fresh and salt water. In the upper, or fluvial, portion, freshwater dominates; in the middle zone, the primary mixing of fresh and salt water occurs; and in the lower, or oceanic, portion, salt water prevails. Longitudinal characteristics are often highly seasonal.

HIGH STREAM FLOWS

During periods of high stream flow, the fluvial, or freshwater, portion may extend into the sea, whereas during low flows, salt water may extend far up the river, often as a saltwater "wedge" flowing along the bottom of the river channel. In the case of the Mississippi River, this high stream flow can reach upstream as far as 95 miles (150 km). In desert estuaries, where freshwater inputs are usually intermittent, the entire estuary is likely to become ocean-dominated for parts of the year.

ABOVE Morbihan, in the region of Brittany, France, is named after the almost landlocked Morbihan Gulf on the south coast. The ancient town of Vanne is located on estuaries opening onto the gulf.

ABOVE Flamingos feed along the shallows of the saline estuary at Walvis Bay, in Namibia.

WATER MIX

Estuaries are characterized by the interaction between ocean and river, which involves freshwater and salt-water mixing, river flow, and wave and tidal action. All of these processes greatly affect the depositional characteristics of an estuary.

The sediments reaching an estuary consist of a large range of materials, including those from stream erosion, tidal drift, wind erosion, plant and animal remains, near-shore ocean bed erosion, and, in ever-increasing amounts, humans' domestic and industrial debris. The relative amounts of these many deposits vary with estuarine dynamics and geographical location relative to source regions.

In Chesapeake Bay, a large compound estuary in the eastern United States, there is a great variation in the amount of inorganic and organic material longitudinally along its extent because of the large variations in river inputs and human endeavors.

NATURAL TRAPS

Positioned in the transition zone between land and sea, estuaries provide some of the best features of both. Being natural traps for nutrients, they are among the earth's most productive ecosystems, so it is not surprising that humans have gravitated to them from time immemorial. Their richness in food sources invites exploitation. Indeed, in the United States it has been calculated that approximately 75 percent of commercial fish—both fin and shellfish—come from estuarine waters. Accompanying these "harvests," some of which have been calamitous for stock numbers, has been the colonization of many of the world's estuarine environments. Their semi-enclosed nature has been instrumental to the development of harbors, and their juxtaposition between sea and river makes them natural transportation centers. More than two-thirds of the world's 32 largest cities are located on estuaries—for example, London, New York, and Shanghai.

HUMAN INTERFERENCE

With such intense human pressure, it is not surprising that the "health" of many estuaries is suffering greatly. Although some smaller estuaries—for example, on the coast of Australia—are still in an almost-pristine condition, those where humans have concentrated have been heavily modified. The process of constructing shoreline settlements usually affects estuarine aquatic life forms. Foundations, sea walls, piers, jetties, and dredging not only impact upon estuaries directly, but also affect their circulation patterns, chemistry, and biology. Not all human-generated modifications to estuaries are of immediate local origin. Because the estuary freshwater comes from inland, whatever happens upstream will affect it—for example, mining, dam construction, deforestation, and farming.

Estuaries are geologically youthful features and, since their formation, they have always been in a state of flux. Humans, with their penchant for exploitation, have added an increasingly dominant ingredient to the natural mix. In addition to the alteration, and in many cases destruction, of estuarine ecosystems, millions of acres of estuarine wetland have been lost in the name of land reclamation.

The rise in sea level that is now occurring carries its own special challenges. Estuaries, the presence of most of which owes their existence to past sea-level rise, will be markedly affected. Although the nature of physical and biological responses in estuaries to a sea-level rise is unknown, it is quite certain that a substantial rise will have a major impact on the large proportion of the world's population that dwells in estuarine settings, and will demand creative management decisions.

LEFT Low tide leaves boats stuck on the mud flats on the estuary of the River Esk, at Whitby, in Yorkshire, UK. The ruins of Whitby Abbey can be seen in looking down on the port.

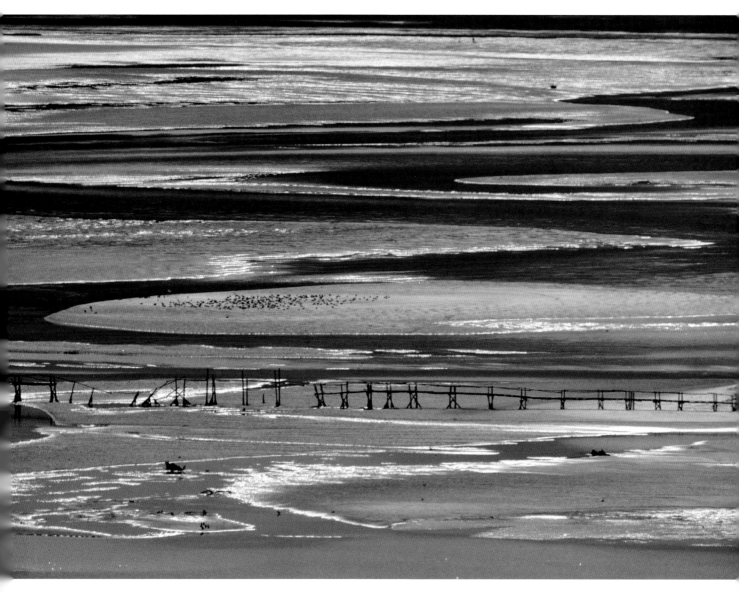

Muddy Waters

The actual deposition of sediments in the estuary depends on the carrying capacity of both fresh and salt water, and the dynamics of the mixing of the two. This is especially true for estuaries with large inputs of clay. The electrochemical action of salt water produces flocculation—aggregation into clumps, or "flocs"—of clay. The increased density of the flocs causes them to be deposited when the current's velocity decreases as fresh water merges with salt water. Although flocculation is a common phenomenon in all estuaries, the extent to which it occurs depends on the amount of clay, and the unique mixing characteristics of the water column. Generally, the higher the tidal range the greater the mixing.

Mudflats and salt marshes are important sub-environments in many estuarine systems. They are both formed on relatively flat, intertidal surfaces that are subjected to complex and often frequent erosional and depositional action. The sequence is usually from the water of the estuary through the mudflat to the salt marsh. Mudflat surfaces are frequently disturbed by wave action and thus have a dynamic surface. Salt marshes, mostly because of the protection provided by the grasses and their roots, are much less subject to the vagaries of wave action. In addition, salt marshes are excellent sediment traps.

ABOVE Low tide on the Bitou River estuary at Plettenberg Bay, Eastern Cape, South Africa, reveals boundary fences and mud flats.

LEFT The Loire estuary in France is the source of rich salt fields. Until the early 1900s, salt merchants would visit the villages and towns and sell salt in exchange for grain.

Tidal Flats

Tidal flats are important coastal features usually found along estuaries. They are often referred to as boundary environments because they are neither exclusively marine nor terrestrial, but exhibit features of both. As their name suggests, they are extensive plains subject to tidal movements. Twice a day tides inundate the flats, then recede and leave them exposed to the sun.

ABOVE Tidal flats are favorite feeding grounds for snipes. They wade through the soft mud searching for food using long, slender bills.

RIGHT The coastline south of Bridgend, Wales, in the United Kingdom is subject to extreme tides that leave tessellated mud-flats at low tide.

RICH MUD

Tidal flats are most often found along temperate and tropical coasts. Typically they form on the seaward side of other low-lying coastal environments, such as swampy mangrove forests and salt marshes. The flats are composed of nutrient-rich mud that is constantly waterlogged. The saturation of these sediments means that there is virtually no oxygen within the soil. This state of affairs is further exacerbated by the presence of large numbers of oxygen-eating bacteria, which reduce oxygen levels even further. Such an environment is referred to as anaerobic, or airless.

INFAUNA

The lack of oxygen, the periodic inundation of salt water and then exposure to direct sunlight, coupled with exposure to often strong onshore winds, would seem to combine to make tidal flats one of the harshest and least hospitable environments on Earth. But they are, in fact, highly productive regions that support a large variety of life forms.

Large numbers of burrowing animals make their home in the soft sediments, seeking shelter from the sun and the tides. Such animals are collectively referred to as "infauna." They mainly comprise small invertebrates, including mollusks and crustaceans that feed on the detritus brought in on the incoming tide.

Worms are usually the most prolific species within a tidal flat ecosystem. Some species, such as the lugworm, live a sedentary life filtering sediment for bacteria. Others, such as the king ragworm, are large predators measuring up to 3 ft (1 m) in length. King ragworms feature powerful jaws that they use to devour other worms.

Shellfish are also found in large numbers on tidal flats. The most widespread are bivalves, a mollusk with two shells. Oysters, mussels, scallops, and cockles are examples of bivalve mollusks. The two shells protect a stomach, respiratory system, and series of muscles. Some bivalves have a foot that they employ to creep along the surface and burrow into the sediments when the tidal flats are exposed at low tide. Others, such as oysters, have lost this feature and evolved to become

LEFT Folly Beach is located on Folly Island, a barrier island in South Carolina, USA, on the Atlantic Ocean. As the tide recedes twice a day, long stretches of muddy sand are revealed.

sedentary, fixing themselves to the edge of rocks, plants, and other immobile items. In turn, these animals provide food for a range of more complex species, particularly wading birds and, when the tide is in, fish and other marine creatures.

Characteristics of tidal-flat birds include large feet that provide stability in the sodden mud, and long bills that are used for burrowing. Typical examples include the many species of oystercatcher that are widespread throughout the world, except in the polar regions.

BACTERIA EATERS

The apparently desolate nature of tidal flats has led some to conclude that they hold little ecological or economic value. However, they play a crucial role in converting decaying materials into energy that is transferred up the food web for the benefit of more complex species.

The millions of bacteria and infauna that populate the tidal flats consume vast amounts of material that would otherwise rot into the sediments. In turn these tiny animals provide a food source for larger animals such as birds and crustaceans.

Tidal flats also play a crucial role in providing an important habitat for migratory birds that often fly many thousands of miles over the course of a year. They provide food and shelter, and interconnected networks of tidal flats along migratory routes are used annually by numerous bird species. For example, British tidal flats lie on the migration route for species of ducks, geese, and wading birds that migrate annually between the Arctic Circle and the Mediterranean Sea.

FOOD CHAIN

Tidal flats are threatened globally by a range of human activities. Inland rivers carry vast amounts of runoff toward the coast. When this runoff is generated in urban and agricultural areas, it often contains pollutants and excess nutrients that wreak havoc on coastal environments. These poisons build up in the sediments of tidal flats in a process known as bioaccumulation. The toxins in the sediments are then consumed by the infauna and eventually make their way up the food chain. Dangerous carcinogens such as DDT and dioxin are found in many tidal flats throughout the world. Land reclamation projects also pose a great threat.

ABOVE Spring brings the return of surfbirds to the mud-flats of Alaska's Copper River. Snow-covered mountains can be seen in the background. These birds travel as far south as the Strait of Magellan during winter.

Mangroves and Salt Marshes

Mangroves are highly specialized trees that dominate many intertidal wetland systems along coastal zones, while salt marshes form along intertidal zones in middle and high latitudes. Mangroves and salt marshes are highly vulnerable ecosystems, sensitive to the impact of human activities.

OPPOSITE The shoots of some species of mangroves begin below the surface of the water and resemble smooth, rounded stumps. They provide a home for many marine organisms.

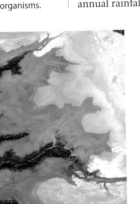

ABOVE This aerial view of the coast of Western Australia shows surreal patterns of mudflats and estuaries lined with mangroves.

BELOW The salt marshes of Guérande, France, produce some of the finest sea salt in the world.

MANGROVES

There are 69 separate species of mangrove, growing mostly in tropical and subtropical regions. The most significant mangrove communities are found in areas where water temperatures exceed 75°F (24°C), and annual rainfall exceeds 490 in (1,245 mm). Mangroves are prevalent along the coastlines of Central America, southeastern Africa, northern Australia, The Gulf (Persian Gulf), western India, and Southeast Asia.

GASPING FOR AIR

Mangrove forests grow on mudflats in the sheltered waters of coastal estuaries. Susceptible to storm action, they tend to grow in the quiet waters that form behind sand spits, and in bays and inlets. They are among the few plants to successfully adapt to this difficult environment, which features very high levels of salinity, waterlogged soils, and very little oxygen.

Most trees obtain oxygen from the tiny air spaces between soil particles, absorbing it through their root systems. But the soils in which mangroves grow contain no air spaces. Some species, such as the gray mangrove growing along Australia's east coast, send up pneumatophores—small breathing tubes that grow above the soil line. Others species, such as the spider mangrove, grow aerial roots, and stilt- and prop-root systems that grow above the water line. Not only do these roots allow mangroves to gain access to oxygen, they also trap

sediments that increase the extent of tidal flats, thus rendering the environment more hospitable. Glands on the leaves of mangroves excrete salts that accumulate within them. The cells of root systems of mangroves are designed to allow water to enter, while excluding salt particles.

MUDDY NUTRIENTS

Mangrove forests are among the most productive ecosystems on Earth. Research conducted in northeastern Australia revealed that a single spoonful of mangrove sediment contains more than 10 billion bacteria. Huge amounts of decaying matter are produced by mangroves as they shed leaves, bark, and flowers, thus providing a steady stream of nutrients into the food chain. This in turn supports a wide variety of fauna. Crustaceans find shelter in the soft mud and complex tangle of roots. Further inland, more solid mud supports larger animals, including huge saltwater crocodiles that nest among the trees. At high tide, numerous fish flood into mangrove forests to feed on small crabs and shrimps. Mangroves also provide excellent habitats for a wide variety of birds.

SALT MARSHES

Extensive salt-marsh systems are found along the US east coast, the Alaskan Gulf, the Gulf of Mexico, parts of Siberia, the southern coasts of the UK and Ireland, the northern coasts of France, Germany, and Spain, and the southern coast of New Zealand's South Island.

Most salt marshes are fully inundated by seawater only when tides are at their highest. They can only form in areas well protected from storm damage. They commonly form on sheltered landward sides of sand spits and inlets. Salt marshes often form behind the protection of mangrove forests, particularly in higher latitudes. Salt marshes are relatively unproductive. Sedge grasses are found in areas that are often flooded, as are oysters, small prawns, and other crustaceans. Further inland the diversity increases, as sedges give way to other salt-tolerant grasses, larger animals, and a variety of birds.

HUMAN IMPACT

The flat lands that salt marshes inhabit are ideal for land reclamation, so large areas have been destroyed to make way for factories, housing estates, tourist resorts, and other developments. This is a particularly serious problem in Southeast Asia and Europe.

On the Ocean Floor

For centuries, common wisdom held that the ocean floor was a relatively featureless plain, broken here and there by islands. Actually, nothing could be further from the truth! From its depths rise the world's highest (from base to peak) mountains and longest mountain range. Beneath its average depth of 16,000 ft (5,000 m) plunge canyons that dwarf those on dry land. In many respects, its terrain is as varied as that of Earth's land surface.

MAPPING THE OCEAN BASIN

Traditionally, a weighted line was used to measure water depth. This method of sounding was limited to

ABOVE Satellite topographical imaging shows the features of the ocean floor, increasing our knowledge of this terrain.

making spot measurements in relatively shallow water. Knowledge of ocean floor terrain was enhanced by technological developments introduced during World War II. By the 1940s, sounding with sonar became a more reliable and widely used technique. Today, echo sounding uses sound impulses to determine water depth. Dozens of individual beams, attached to a fast-moving vessel, make the depth measurement of wide swathes of ocean floor possible. During recent decades, satellites using radar have greatly boosted our knowledge of ocean basin terrain. In addition, satellite-based Global Positioning System (GPS) technology makes it possible to locate and map features precisely.

Hazards From the Ocean Floor

Some environmental hazards also originate on the ocean floor. A tremor can produce a deadly tsunami. The 2004 earthquake in the Indian Ocean off the coast of Sumatra caused a devastating tidal wave that resulted in an estimated 250,000 deaths, and billions of dollars worth of property damage (left). A tsunami also can be caused by the underwater collapse or violent eruption of a volcano, or a large earth flow. Uncharted seamounts and near-shore shoals can create numerous navigational hazards.

The ocean floor offers a varied and fascinating environment. In terms of our knowledge of its unique features and landscapes, it remains a frontier containing many secrets yet to be revealed.

Today, bathymetric maps are nearly as precise as those of Earth's land surfaces. Nevertheless, a number of oceanic depths continue to be debated. The exact depth of the Challenger Deep in the Mariana Trench is undetermined. During the twentieth century, it was variously measured to be between 26,850 ft (8,184 m) and 35,838 ft (10,924 m) deep. A measurement of 35,797 ft (10,911 m), taken in 1995 by a Japanese deep-sea probe, is believed to be the most accurate to date. As is true of other global data, advances in technology greatly expand our knowledge.

OCEAN FLOOR TERRAIN

The topography of each ocean floor is different, though they have many features in common. The terrain of the Pacific Basin, for example, features many more island groups. It also has eight of the nine deepest oceanic trenches. The Pacific also contains an estimated 50,000 guyots—flat-topped seamounts not found elsewhere.

Most ocean floor terrain was formed by the same tectonic agents that created terrestrial landforms. The movement of tectonic plates and other forces result in folding, faulting, and warping of the sea floor just as on land. In many places—such as Hawaii, Indonesia, and Japan—volcanic activity has been a major agent in creating ocean floor terrain and islands.

In the absence of rain, ice, and wind, underwater agents of weathering and erosion, such as currents, are

ABOVE Lava from the erupting Kilauea on the island of Hawai'i meets the sea. This volcano has been continuously erupting since January 1983.

BELOW Divers explore a fissure in the Mid-Atlantic Ridge in Iceland. The Mid-Atlantic Ridge is essentially a long underwater mountain chain that runs for 10,000 miles (16,000 km) from north to south.

quite different from those responsible for the formation of Earth's terrestrial geomorphic landscapes.

Although most of the features of the ocean floor (other than islands) are not visible from the surface, many are extremely important. The shallow water of continental shelves, such as Newfoundland's Grand Banks, can contribute to excellent fishing grounds that have long attracted fishermen. Ocean floor topography can influence the formation of huge waves that erode unprotected coastal areas.

Whereas topographic features of the ocean floor are of interest to some scientists, it is those that rise above the surface that are of greatest importance to most of us. The global sea is dotted with tens of thousands of islands. Some of these stand alone, whereas others form archipelagos—groups of islands such as Indonesia, Japan, and Hawaii. Some are very densely populated: Indonesia, a nation composed of several thousand islands, is the world's fourth most populated country. The majority of islands, however, are uninhabited by humans. Coral reefs, built on the limestone skeletons of polyps and rising from the sea floor, are one of Earth's most unique, diverse, and fragile ecosystems. Coral also forms atolls—low-lying, semi-circular islands that surround a lagoon. Remote islands, such as those of the Galapagos, offer biologists, botanists, ecologists, geographers, and other scientists a rich laboratory for the study of unique ecosystems.

Features of the Ocean Floor

Early mariners believed that the ocean was a bottomless abyss. They attempted to measure ocean depths by casting ropes or cables overboard, but these were usually far too short to reach the sea floor. They also believed that the ocean floor was a featureless plain, but nothing could be further from the truth.

OPPOSITE One of the planet's most active volcanoes, Kilauea on the island of Hawai'i, erupts, sending forth masses of lava. Volcanic eruptions caused the Hawaiian Islands to be created.

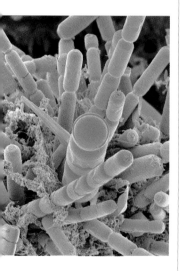

ABOVE Diatoms are microscopic unicellular organisms. Their remains become part of the sediment on the ocean floor.

RIGHT Smoke billows from a new volcanic vent in the North Atlantic off Iceland's coast in 1965. The lava formed a new island atop volcanic ash. The island of Surtsey, which was formed by a similar volcanic eruption in 1953, can be seen at the rear right.

Technological advances such as sonar sounding and the satellite altimeter revealed that the ocean floor has as many different topographical features as the continents, including troughs, abyssal plains, oceanic basins, submarine ridges that form long mountain chains, hydrothermal vents, trenches, island arcs, and canyons that plunge to spectacular depths.

The submarine mountain chains encircle Earth as the mid-ocean ridges that form the divergent margins of two tectonic plates. Convection currents within the mantle force lava into the rift, thus generating new oceanic crust and causing the phenomenon known as sea floor spreading. As measuring instruments became more sophisticated and our knowledge increased, it became possible to explain the mechanisms that drive "continental drift," a phenomenon first proposed by German scientist Alfred Wegener in 1915. As the sea floor spreads, continents move apart, and measurements indicate that the oldest oceanic crust is found where it meets continental crust, and the youngest is found at mid-ocean ridges.

The dense but comparatively thin oceanic crust, with an average thickness of approximately 4 to 6 miles (6 to 10 km), meets the less dense continental crust, with an average thickness of around 22 miles (35 km), at the continental margins, which account for more than a quarter of the oceanic area. Continental margins, which consist of three regions—the continental shelf, slope, and rise—surround continents and stretch outward from the shoreline to the abyssal plains.

Continental shelves are covered by relatively shallow water, marked by deep canyons where large rivers enter. Sediments from land erosion are washed onto the shelf, and down the steeply angled continental slope, where they form a deep-sea fan similar to the alluvial fans found at the base of continental mountain ranges.

Earthquakes and Volcanoes

Seismic and volcanic activity is common along diverging tectonic plates. Earthquakes occur along faults developed in fracture zones associated with rifting. Upwelling of lava along the rift is accompanied by the release of geothermally heated water through vents and fissures. The temperature of this mineral-rich water can reach 750°F (400°C), and as it escapes into the cool surrounding water, minerals precipitate to form "chimneys" around the vents. Shelves and slopes surround the continents, stretching outward to abyssal plains, the flattest, smoothest, and least explored regions of the planet.

The continental rise at the base of the slope is the meeting place of oceanic crust and continental crust. Abyssal plains are constantly fed by sediments, comprising skeletons of plankton, coral and other organisms, and fine particles of dust and other material, swept from the land by wind and currents.

The discovery of the Mid-Atlantic Ridge in 1872 was a complete revelation. It was found to be part of a system of mid-ocean ridges that form the world's longest mountain range, stretching about 10,000 miles (16,000 km) from north to south, and is part of a continuous submarine mountain range that stretches some 25,000 miles (40,000 km) along the floors of all the oceans. It features cliffs over 3,300 ft (1,000 m) high, a ridge around 8,200 ft (2,500 m) below sea level, and edges that plunge to around 16,400 ft (5,000 m).

SEAMOUNTS AND ISLAND CHAINS

The release of magma is not restricted to submarine ridges. Convection currents within the earth's mantle form hot spots under the spreading ocean floor. Molten magma punches through the crust, flows out as lava over the ocean floor, then cools down quickly to form a submarine volcano. Flat-topped seamounts are known as guyots; pointed seamounts are sea peaks.

The chain of seamounts that forms the Hawaiian Islands is the result of hot spot activity under the Pacific Plate. The entire chain of over 80 volcanoes is mostly submarine. The islands are a small part of the chain; only the most recently active protrude above sea level. The seamounts, which are supported on the relatively thin ocean crust by convection currents, eventually sink below sea level as continental drift causes the tectonic plate to move away from the rising magma over the hot spot. The Hawaiian Islands are gradually "migrating" northward, and will eventually reach Alaska.

Ocean Troughs and Shallows—Western Hemisphere

Ocean Troughs and Shallows—Eastern Hemisphere

Ocean Floor Dynamics

Continents and oceans form a natural topographic division of the earth's surface. Continental crust lies mainly above sea level and is composed of very different rock to oceanic crust, which lies below sea level. Oceanic basins cover around 70 percent of the total ocean area, and about half of the earth's total surface area.

OPPOSITE Enormous plumes of steam, smoke, and ash were ejected after an underwater volcano erupted off the coast of Tonga's capital, Nuku'alofa, in March 2009.

OCEANIC BASINS

Oceanic basins are the areas of the abyssal plain that are bounded by ridges, trenches, or continents. The oceanic crust underlying oceanic basins is composed of dense igneous rock, rich in iron and magnesian minerals such as basalt and gabbro. The crust, with a thickness of approximately 4 to 6 miles (6 to 10 km), floats isostatically on the underlying mantle. Because the less dense continents rise above the oceans, they supply eroded materials to the ocean basins. In this manner, continents can be considered the complement of oceanic basins. Oceans also receive various other sediments such as skeletons of planktonic organisms (diatoms, radiolarians, and foraminifera), and eroded material from coral reefs.

The basins of the earth's five main oceans (Atlantic, Pacific, Indian, Southern, and Arctic) differ from each other in many respects. Some are actively changing, while others are inactive, depending on the geological processes involved. Nevertheless, they contain certain features in common, including oceanic ridges, trenches, abyssal plains, seamounts, and guyots. Speaking in geological terms, continental shelves, deep ocean trenches, and mid-ocean ridges are not considered to be part of oceanic basins.

Actively growing oceanic basins feature a divergent plate boundary with new oceanic crust being generated at the mid-ocean ridge, and sea floor spreading that pushes the tectonic plates apart. There will usually be a convergent plate margin with a subduction zone forming a trench where the oceanic crust sinks, or is subducted, beneath a continent.

The Atlantic and Arctic Oceans both feature active basins, with a mid-ocean ridge at the spreading center. The Mediterranean Sea is an actively shrinking basin, while the Pacific Ocean, also shrinking, has both a spreading ridge and oceanic trenches.

The oldest basins are only around 200 million years old—which is very young, considering that Earth was formed approximately 4.6 billion years ago. This means that continental crust, which is too low in density to be subducted, is generally much older than oceanic crust. Parts of some continents are known to be between three to four billion years old.

RIGHT The fault line of the Mid-Atlantic Ridge in Thingvellir National Park in Iceland, which is possibly the best place in the world to see the actual rift of a rift valley. Scientists have been studying the geology of Iceland to gain a better understanding of how the oceans formed.

RIGHT Submersible vehicles are helping scientists to discover more about what goes on in the depths of the ocean. The *Pisces V* was developed to study the Loihi seamount off Hawai'i.

BELOW The cycle of opening and closing ocean basins is known as the Wilson Cycle. This NASA image of the Sinai Peninsula shows the Red Sea, which is thought to be at an early stage in the Wilson Cycle.

SUBDUCTION AND TRENCHES

Why does the earth not expand as the sea floor spreads out from the mid-ocean ridges and the continents move apart? Sea-floor expansion is compensated for by the subduction of oceanic crust into the mantle, where it melts, is recycled, then eventually returns as oceanic crust at the mid-ocean ridges.

Along many convergent plate margins, thinner and denser oceanic plates sink under less dense continental plates, and form trenches in the sea floor known as subduction zones. A trench is a narrow, elongated depression of the sea floor parallel to the convergent margin. Trenches are the deepest feature of oceans. The deepest spot on earth, the Marianas Trench, plunges to almost 36,000 ft (11,000 km) where the fast-moving Pacific Plate converges with the Philippine Plate.

Subterranean and subaquatic earthquakes and volcanic activity are associated with subduction. The cold plate melts, and merges with mantle material at a depth of approximately 75 miles (120 km). It then forms magma that rises through the overlying plate to produce a line of volcanoes that are parallel to the convergent margin. Where the volcanoes emerge from

the sea floor, they form an island arc parallel to the trench and about 120 miles (200 km) from it.

The area on the trench side of the volcanic front is known as the fore arc, the area behind the front is the back arc; both are sites of sediment deposition. The back arcs are fed by eroded materials from continents and volcanoes, and lie undisturbed. However, fore arc sediments spill over into the trenches in the form of violent underwater avalanches known as turbidity currents. If the subduction zone is active, the sediments do not last long. Some are scraped off as the oceanic plate or slab is subducted into the mantle, others sink toward the mantle and are metamorphosed.

In less active (and inactive) subduction zones, the trenches may fill with sediment, eventually forming troughs that are wider and shallower than trenches. They are regions of complex currents and upwellings that bring nutrient-rich waters closer to the surface, and that support vast concentrations of marine life. Deep underwater ridges and seamounts can also influence these upwellings.

UNDERWATER FLAT-TOPPED TABLES

Oceanic plateaus, or guyots, are broad, flat-topped elevations of the sea floor. They are usually formed by high-energy mantle plumes that rise beneath mid-ocean ridges. Some, such as Iceland, push above sea level, but most remain submerged.

Another type of oceanic plateau is composed of submerged continental crust that was once part of a much larger continent. An example is the Lord Howe Rise that extends from southwest of New Caledonia to the Challenger Plateau west of New Zealand. This section of crust rifted away from eastern Australia during ocean ridge activity that occurred around 80 to 60 million years ago. The Lord Howe Rise is now 500 miles (800 km) from mainland Australia.

SMOKERS

Upwelling of lava along the rift of the mid-ocean ridge is accompanied by the release of geothermally heated water through vents and fissures. The temperature of

The Wilson Cycle

The Wilson Cycle describes the gradual, periodic opening and closing of ocean basins. Tectonic plates either pull apart along divergent or spreading margins, move together along convergent or collisional margins, or slide past each other along transform boundaries. Divergence, and the creation of new oceanic mantle and crust, can take tens or hundreds of millions of years. But eventually divergence stops, and the two continents begin to move back toward each other, converging to form a new plate boundary. This occurs when oceanic crust breaks and begins to descend into the mantle along a subduction zone.

this mineral-rich water can reach 750°F (400°C), and as it escapes into the cool surrounding seawater, the minerals precipitate to form "chimneys" around the vents. They are called "smokers" because the mineral-rich fluids swirl like smoke as they meet the cold ocean water. Chimneys can grow rapidly; the highest smoker recorded grew to the equivalent of a 15-story building before collapsing and toppling to the sea floor.

Chimneys are now believed to play an important role in the ocean's temperature, chemistry, and circulation patterns. Submersible vehicles are able to collect samples from the chimneys and vents, mostly metal sulfides. These vehicles have discovered that a rich ecosystem surrounds these vents, including bacteria, crustaceans, giant tubeworms, and fish that live in total darkness. Without light for photosynthesis to support algae plants, the food web depends on the chemosynthesis of bacteria.

COLD VENTS OR SEEPS AND COLD-WATER REEFS

Cold vents occur where brine, which is rich in hydrogen sulfide and hydrocarbons including methane, seeps out onto the ocean floor and forms pools. Cold vents also support a very diverse biota, which is similarly dependent on the chemosynthesis of bacteria and other primitive organisms.

Associated with these seeps is the formation of ice-like crystalline solids known as gas hydrates. They are formed from a mixture of water and natural gas, usually methane, and for stability they require suitable physical conditions of pressure, temperature, and gas saturation. Gas hydrates act as a cementing agent in the pore spaces between sediment particles, and they show strong potential as a future supply of gas. Over time, cold seeps develop a variety of sea-floor features such as reefs and carbonate rock formations, which are found in the fossil record as mounds of coarse, shell-rich crystals.

Cold-water coral reefs are a relatively recent discovery, extending some hundreds of feet above the ocean floor, at depths of anywhere between 130–6,600 ft (40–2,000 m). The largest cold-water coral reef lies off Norway's coast. These animals depend on the products of chemosynthetic bacteria rather than those of symbiotic algae that tropical corals depend on.

ABOVE Lord Howe Island is a volcanic feature associated with the Lord Howe Rise, a submerged plateau of continental crust, that rifted away from eastern Australia, now some 500 miles (800 km) away.

Islands and Archipelagos

The internationally accepted definition of an island is "a naturally formed area of land, surrounded by water, which is above water at high tide." An archipelago is a clustered group of islands, or an elongate island chain. Indonesia and islands of the Canadian Arctic are examples of the former; the Lesser Antilles in the Caribbean and the Hawaiian Islands illustrate the latter.

BELOW Prisoners are moved from Devil's Island, French Guiana, following the closure of the penal colony there in the mid-1940s.

Tens of thousands of islands and hundreds of archipelagos exist within the global sea. Some are remote pieces of earthen material that rise above sea level. Tiny Easter Island is one of Earth's most isolated inhabited places. It is separated from its closest inhabited neighbor, Pitcairn Island (with a population of less than 50), by a distance of 1,290 miles (2,075 km). On the other hand, the Indonesian archipelago includes over 17,000 islands, about 6,000 of which are inhabited. It is the planet's fourth most populated country. In area, the world's islands range from minute specks of land, to Greenland's 840,000 square miles (2,175,590 km²).

Devil's Island—Île du Diable

Perhaps no island is more infamous than Devil's Island and its association with France's notorious French Guiana penal colony. The island with the demonic name is the smallest (35 acres/12 ha) of the three Îles du Salut (Islands of Salvation), located about 7 miles (11 km) off French Guiana's coast. Between 1852 and the prison's closing in 1946, an estimated 80,000 French prisoners were exiled to the remote tropical outpost in northeastern South America. Few survived the prison's harsh environment and conditions.

Surprisingly, Devil's Island itself played but a minor role in the prison colony. During the colony's 94-year span, fewer than 50 prisoners were assigned to the island that is synonymous with the entire system. Even the island's name predates the prison colony by nearly a century. In 1763, a group of French citizens attempted to colonize the Guiana Coast. Within a year, searing heat and humidity, floods, deadly malaria, and various other tropical hazards had taken the lives of most settlers. The remaining 2,000 sought refuge (their salvation, hence the island group's name) on the small islands lying just off the coast. The smallest of the three islands, however, had steep flanks and its shore was swept by rapid currents that made landing difficult, conditions attributed to the work of the Devil. Thus, it was named "Devil's Island."

ISLAND FORMATION

Five geologic processes explain the formation of nearly all islands. The first process is diastrophism—the action of forces that cause Earth's crust to move. As a result of faulting or folding, islands were formed. Many large islands, especially those adjacent to continents, owe their origin to diastrophic forces. They include Britain, Madagascar, Borneo, Tasmania, and the Greater Antilles.

Many islands were formed by a second agent—volcanic action. The Azores, Iceland, and a number of other islands associated with the Mid-Atlantic Ridge are volcanic in origin. Volcanic archipelagos in the Pacific Basin include Japan, the Philippines, the Hawaiian chain, and New Zealand. Nearly all of Indonesia is volcanic in origin, and the archipelago has experienced some of the planet's most devastating eruptions.

Various low-lying tropical and subtropical islands were formed by a third agent, coral polyps. Many Pacific islands are atolls, formed by coral growing on the submerged flanks of volcanoes. As the volcano subsides, the coral continues to grow, eventually forming an atoll. Coral atolls are particularly common in Micronesia and Polynesia.

Sandy islands represent a fourth process. They are especially common along coasts that have substantial accumulations of sand, together with the wave and current action necessary to move and deposit fine particulate material. Such near-shore barrier islands include the Outer Banks of North Carolina and numerous long, narrow, low-lying islands that hug much of the Gulf Coast of both the USA and Mexico. Canada's Sable Island, lying in the Atlantic off the coast of Nova Scotia, is one of the most treacherous sand-formed islands. An estimated 350 ships have been wrecked on or near the island, giving it the nickname "Graveyard of the Atlantic," a name and distinction that it shares with North Carolina's Outer Banks. Many North Sea islands immediately off the coast of mainland Europe, such as the Frisians, also are sandy barrier islands.

ABOVE In June 1991, the strato-volcano Mt Pinatau erupted on the Philippines island of Luzon. The Philippines was formed by such dramatic volcanic action.

LEFT The San Juan Islands lie off the coast of Washington State, USA, close to Vancouver Island. They were formed by a number of geological processes, the most significant of which was glaciation.

151

ABOVE Coral was the main agent in the formation of the Great Bahama Bank. The blue color in this image from NASA's Moderate Resolution Imaging Spectroradiometer indicates the presence of the coral reefs.

RIGHT The island of Java in Indonesia has many volcanoes, so it is not surprising to learn that its origin is entirely volcanic. A number of Java's volcanoes are still active.

Coastal areas that have experienced yet another geological process—glaciation—exhibit a fifth island category. As glaciers flow to the sea, they scour fjords. Eventually, a web of glacially scoured troughs can isolate a parcel of land from the continental mass, creating an island. In the Southern Hemisphere, islands of this type are common off southern Chile and New Zealand's South Island. In the Northern Hemisphere, they appear off the coasts of Alaska and British Columbia, Greenland, and Norway.

As a general rule, islands that are of tectonic origin (that is, formed by either diastrophism or volcanism) are better suited to human habitation than are low-lying coral atolls or those that were formed by sand accumulation. These islands are less vulnerable to tropical storms, tsunamis, or a rise in sea level. Mountainous islands generally offer better protection (unless they are active volcanoes) and a much better fresh-water supply. Their more varied ecosystems provide greater options to inhabitants.

MAJOR ISLANDS AND ARCHIPELAGOS

The Pacific Ocean Basin contains the greatest number and variety of islands and archipelagos. Large islands include New Guinea, Borneo, Taiwan, Sakhalin, and the North and South islands of New Zealand. The Philippines, Japan, Indonesia, Alaska's Aleutian chain, and the Hawaiian Islands rank among the principal archipelagos. Smaller islands, by the thousands, include those of Melanesia, located northeast of Australia, Micronesia in the west-central Pacific, and Polynesia, which stretches within a triangle from New Zealand to Hawaii, and Easter Island.

The Atlantic Ocean also has its fair share of islands. Greenland, Newfoundland, Britain, Hispaniola, Cuba, Ireland, and Iceland are the largest. The Greater and Lesser Antilles are the main archipelagos. Scattered about the Atlantic Basin are many hundreds of smaller islands and island groups. In the western margin of the basin, the Bahamas, Bermuda, and Canada's Prince Edward Island and Cape Breton are small islands of economic importance. In the eastern basin, the various small island groups surrounding the British Isles, the Azores, Madeira, Canary Islands, and Cape Verde are the most notable.

Madagascar, Sri Lanka, and Sumatra are the largest islands within the Indian Ocean Basin. Major archipelagos include the Seychelles, the Maldives, and the Andaman Islands. The Southern Ocean also has many islands, but they are of little economic importance and support little population. The same can be said for the many islands scattered about the Arctic Ocean Basin. They include the Canadian Archipelago, Norway's Svalbard, and Russia's Novaya Zemlya.

ISLANDS IN HISTORY

Islands have played a very significant historical role ever since humans first ventured out to sea in times

The "Dinkum Sands" Debate

In 1978, a heated legal dispute began, involving the State of Alaska and the US government over rightful ownership of numerous shoals located in the Beaufort Sea near Alaska's Prudhoe Bay oil fields (above). One of the contested features was Dinkum Sands, formed from sand, gravel, and ice, and which lies in Arctic waters about 12 miles (19 km) off the Alaskan coast. As is true of many barrier islands, Dinkum Sands is sometimes an island and at other times it is a submerged shoal. These changes result from daily tidal shifts, as well as seasonal changes in sea level, and ice conditions that affect the feature's height.

At stake were several billion dollars of oil-lease money held in escrow and, of course, billions more in revenue should oil and natural gas reserves in the Arctic be further exploited. The federal government claimed that Alaska's 12-mile (19-km) limit began at its continental coastline. Alaska insisted that its territory extended 12 miles (19 km) beyond the archipelago of shoals. Had the US Supreme Court ruled in Alaska's favor, the state-controlled area of Arctic continental shelf would have more than doubled. In 1996, after 18 years of deliberation, the US Supreme Court ruled that Dinkum Sands and Alaska's other "now you see them, now you don't" features were shoals, not islands. The decision was a devastating economic blow to the state and its people.

long past. Many islands and archipelagos that lie close to continental land masses were first settled some tens of thousands of years ago. Britain, the islands of Indonesia and Melanesia, the Japanese Archipelago, and various islands in the Mediterranean Basin are among those that have left an indelible mark on the chronicles of time.

Both the East and West Indies played very prominent roles in global economic history. During the era of sailing and steam vessels, many islands served as important strategic points militarily and as places to take on fresh water and other supplies. Senegal's Gorée was one of many islands lying close to the African coast that served as a departure point for the Atlantic slave trade, while French Guiana's Devil's Island ranks as one of history's most notorious places.

Many islands have etched their way into contemporary popular culture. Who has not heard of the "island paradises" of Tahiti, Bali, or the Seychelles?

ABOVE An eighteenth-century engraving of a slave merchant on the island of Gorée, Senegal. The island was a departure point for the slave trade.

Magnificent Marine Life

No wonder today's oceans teem with life. It was in the sea, more than 3.5 billion years ago, that life began, in the form of simple unicellular organisms. From this humble beginning, marine life evolved into the vast diversity seen today, from the tiny phytoplankton at the bottom of the food chain to the blue whale, the largest animal ever to live on Earth.

The earliest cells, prokaryotes, were structurally similar to today's bacteria and photosynthetic cyanobacteria. Over one billion years passed before more complex cells, the eukaryotes, began to evolve into the bodies of today's higher organisms.

The cells of most living creatures contain around 70 percent water, the essential ingredient for all biological processes. The chemical composition of this water is very similar to that of seawater—a reminder of the marine origin of all cells.

THE PRIMARY PRODUCERS

Eukaryotic cells that contain plastids use photosynthesis powered by radiant energy from the Sun, along with carbon dioxide and water, to produce organic molecules. These primary producers—the various groups of unicellular and multicellular algae—form the basis of the oceans' food chains.

Microscopic unicellular algae, phytoplankton, float in the water. Other types of algae are attached to the seafloor, ranging from a slippery covering on rocks to giant kelp measuring up to 260 ft (80 m) in length.

ABOVE Glaucous gulls (*Larus hyperboreus*) spend the breeding season in Arctic regions, and fly south during the winter.

ABOVE RIGHT Anemone crabs (*Neopetrolisthes* sp.) make their home amid the tentacles of sea anemones in tropical waters of the Pacific and Indian oceans.

BELOW The flukes of these whales appear to be striking a balletic pose as these giants of the deep dive for food. Flukes are the wing-shaped fins at the end of a whale's tail.

Symbiosis is the intimate association between some dinoflagellate algae (or zoozanthellae) and their various invertebrate hosts, such as coral polyps. It is this association that has converted the nutrient-poor waters of tropical oceans into some of the world's greatest areas of biodiversity, and that gave birth to the world's largest living organisms—coral reefs.

Some land plants have adapted to the marine environment, including the seagrasses that form "meadows" in shallow, sheltered coastal waters. Ecologically, these are very important because they provide nursery grounds, habitats, and food for large numbers of marine organisms.

ANIMAL LIFE

Fossil evidence reveals that there was an explosion of life during the Cambrian period 545 to 495 million years ago. During this time, most of the major animal

and plant groups (phyla) appeared. They were exclusively marine, but all are represented in today's oceans. One exception is the phylum Onychophora, a small group of terrestrial animals known as peripatus (velvet worms), whose origin can, nevertheless, be traced back to the Cambrian period.

In fact, 17 of the world's 36 animal phyla are still exclusively marine. Some other phyla are predominantly marine but contain a few freshwater species, including Porifera (sponges) and Cnidaria (jellyfish, sea anemones, corals). As the second-largest animal phylum, marine mollusks are overwhelmingly more diverse than those in freshwater or on land. Although a few freshwater and terrestrial gastropods exist, squid, cuttlefish, and octopus are exclusively marine.

Two significant phyla of animals—arthropods and vertebrates—are less diverse in oceans than in freshwater or on land. Among arthropods, only crustaceans have maintained a strong association with the sea, while insects, spiders, centipedes, and millipedes have all adapted to life on land.

Fish comprise over half of all vertebrate species; about one-third of these occur in freshwater. This is a consequence of the evolution and radiation in freshwater of the largest group of fish—teleosts—which adapted to the oceans relatively recently. Many primarily terrestrial vertebrates have adapted to life in the sea, including turtles, penguins, seals, dolphins, and whales.

LIFE IN THE DEEP

The extreme physical conditions of the deepest sea were once believed to be too harsh to sustain life. But

ABOVE The mermaid's wine glass (*Acetabularia crenulata*) is a small alga found in shallow waters.

TOP Tropical coral reef environments contain a huge diversity of colorful marine life.

recent explorations using submersible craft have revealed a spectacular diversity of life around thermal vents of mid-ocean ridges and other deep seafloor structures, such as the Galapagos Rift in the Pacific Ocean off the coast of South America. Here, in total darkness, bacteria use chemical (rather than light) energy to convert carbon dioxide into organic molecules that support a complex ecosystem, including fish and a variety of invertebrates. Among the most unusual of these organisms are tube-like worms, which can grow to more than 3 ft (90 cm) in length. These remarkable worms have no digestive system, but instead, symbiotically cultivate "gardens" of bacteria in their bodies that they are later able to consume for their own nutritional requirements.

Limestone Cities—Coral Reefs

Coral reefs are the largest living communal structures on Earth. Some, such as Australia's Great Barrier Reef, are so gigantic they can be seen from space. Reef-building corals are confined to the shallow, clear, warm waters of the tropics between latitudes 30°N and 30°S of the Equator.

BELOW Coral reefs mostly occur in warm tropical waters. Home to a wide and colorful variety of marine life, their existence is under threat from pollution, climate change, and unsustainable fishing practices.

REEF BUILDERS

Reef-building corals rely on the abundance of light in clear tropical waters to produce much of their food and their calcareous skeleton. The reef builders are mostly the scleractinian or stony corals; others include the hydrozoan fire corals (genus Millepora) and an octocoral, the blue coral *(Heliopora coerulea)*. These corals form hard calcareous (aragonitic) skeletons and become cemented together with the shells and skeletons of other marine organisms to encrust coralline algae and form gigantic limestone reefs. In some places these reefs stretch for hundreds of miles.

Coral reefs can be seen as the "rainforests" of the ocean, in that they both thrive in relatively nutrient-poor environments and yet support the world's greatest diversity of life. Coral reefs sustain a remarkable diversity of sponges, anemones, corals, marine worms, crustaceans, mollusks, echinoderms, fish, reptiles, and algae, to name but a few. This high biodiversity serves as a rich storage bank of genetic resources.

STRUCTURE OF A REEF

In general, the structure of a coral reef consists of a fore reef or reef slope facing the ocean, a reef crest,

and a reef flat that is the broadest section of the reef extending toward the shore. Coral growth is richest along the fore reef and crest because of nutrients that are brought in by waves. The decrease in light intensity as water depth increases means that coral growth diminishes down the slope. The reef crest is a buffer against wave action so that the back reef is a zone of lower energy and a region where sediments from the land are deposited in shallow water. Coral growth is patchy in the back reef zone because of the lack of nutrients, the cover of sediments, and its exposure to the air at times of extreme low tides.

The two most important factors controlling reef structure are changes in sea level together with the nature of the underlying substrate. Sea level fluctuates with the amount of ice at the poles. A buildup of polar ice during periods of glaciation ties up vast volumes of seawater resulting in a fall in sea level.

During interglacial periods, the sea level rises as the ice melts. Sea level also changes relative to land when the continental crust floating on the mantle either rises or falls as an isostatic adjustment to loading or off-loading of materials such as sediments, ice, and volcanic flows. Isostatic adjustment can be compared to loading and off-loading cargo ships.

Coral also grows on substrates, such as limestone formed from old reef frameworks and various rocks of the seafloor.

FRINGING REEFS, BARRIER REEFS, AND ATOLLS

There are three major types of reef. Fringing reefs border the shoreline with a narrow stretch of shallow water separating them from the shore. The reef begins to grow vertically from beneath the surface of the water. If sea level is rising, it will continue to grow upward. Only when the sea level remains fairly constant does the reef spread horizontally toward the sea. At a length of around 160 miles (260 km), Ningaloo Reef, off the coast of Western Australia, is the world's largest fringing reef.

Barrier reefs usually develop along the edges of continental shelves and are separated from the mainland by open water. They do not necessarily form as a continuous strip; instead spurs, channels, and canyons may break them into composites of smaller reefs. The reef usually grows on older reefs that were left stranded by a lowering of sea level and then re-submerged with an increase in sea level. The largest is the Great Barrier Reef on the east coast of Australia. It stretches some 1,200 miles (2,000 km).

Atolls are circular reefs that grow at or near the surface of the sea. These typically donut-shaped reefs with a central lagoon start as a fringing reef around a seamount or volcano and continue to grow as the seamount subsides below the surface or sea level rises. They can be deep-sea atolls in the case of seamount subsidence or atolls on the continental shelf.

ABOVE A diver explores plate coral (*Turbinaria* sp.) in Fijian waters. The free-living polyps of plate coral are among the largest of all the corals.

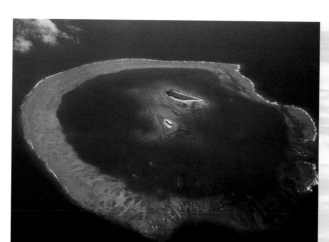

Darwin's Explanation of Atoll Formation

Volcanic islands that form from hotspot activity gradually sink back into the oceanic crust. Those that form in the tropics develop fringing reefs, and provided the island sinks at the same rate as coral growth, the fringing reef continues to grow upward until eventually the island sinks below sea level, leaving the reef to form an atoll with a central lagoon. Darwin formed this hypothesis through careful observations during his five-year voyage on the *HMS Beagle* as it passed through the South Pacific in 1842.

At left is an aerial view of part of the Lau Group of islands that lie on the far east of Fiji. There are around 60 islands in the group, most of which are atolls. The atolls in the northern part of the group are volcanic in origin.

The Great Barrier Reef

The Great Barrier Reef World Heritage Area is one of the most spectacular natural wonders on our planet. It is by far the world's largest World Heritage Area, stretching for 1,200 miles (2,000 km) along the coast of Queensland and covering 134,286 square miles (347,800 km²), an area larger than that of the United Kingdom, the Netherlands, and Switzerland combined.

RIGHT The sandy cays of the Great Barrier Reef are important nesting grounds for the green turtle (Chelonia mydas). Significant turtle populations can be found off Queensland's coast.

OPPOSITE An aerial view of the Great Barrier Reef, the most protected coral reef system in the world. The Great Barrier Reef Marine Park Authority was set up in the 1970s to protect this unique natural heritage site.

ABOVE Tube feet on the underside of the sea stars' arms allow the echinoderms to move about the sea floor looking for food.

CHAIN OF JEWELS

The Great Barrier Reef is the largest coral reef system that has ever existed. The timing of major reef growth remains uncertain for many reefs, including the Great Barrier Reef, although recent geological research suggests that it began to form about 600,000 years ago. It is not one long, unbroken reef, but an interlocking chain of approximately 3,400 individual reefs, ranging in area from 2.4 acres (1 ha) to more than 38 square miles (100 km²), with some 600 continental islands (rocky outcrops from the continental shelf) and 350 coral cays (sandy islands formed from sediments deposited on the surface of coral reefs).

The complex of species that inhabits this reef is amazingly similar to reefs throughout the Indo–Pacific, although many of these are subjected to intense human disturbance. By comparison, the Great Barrier Reef is relatively pristine, making it vitally important as a refuge for all endangered species of the Indo–Pacific reefs. It was declared a World Heritage Area in 1981.

BREATHTAKING DIVERSITY

Like most ecosystems, the food cycle of the Great Barrier Reef starts with the activities of a number of photosynthetic organisms. These range in size from microscopic plankton to 500 species of algae to various sea grasses. The islands around the reef also support terrestrial plants such as grasses, vines, and shrubs together with relatively large trees, such as the coastal she-oak (Casuarina equisetifolia) and pisonias (Pisonia species) found on Heron Island. Mangroves occur in a few of the northern sections of the reef.

The Great Barrier Reef's tropical waters are teeming with marine life. There are some 400 species of corals, 4,000 species of mollusks, as well as many other invertebrate groups including sponges, anemones,

various types of marine worms, crustaceans (prawns, crabs, and lobsters), and echinoderms (sea urchins and sea stars). Of the vertebrates, there are approximately 1,500 species of fish, including sharks and rays, 242 species of birds, and reptiles such as turtles and sea snakes. Many species of whales and dolphins are regular visitors to the reef.

The reef includes major feeding grounds for the endangered dugong (Dugong dugon) and nesting grounds of world significance for two endangered species of marine turtle—the green turtle (Chelonia mydas) and the loggerhead turtle (Caretta caretta)—as well as the habitat for four other species of marine turtle. Given the severe pressures being placed on these species elsewhere, the Great Barrier Reef may be the turtles' last refuge.

BATTLE FOR THE REEF

The Great Barrier Reef faces a number of significant threats, including pollution and coral damage from reef walking and boat mooring. Runoff from agricultural practices on the mainland has dramatic effects—fertilizers, effluent, and sediment from land clearing cause massive pollution. Apart from the direct human impact, there are also the threats from climate change. With global warming comes a rise in seawater temperatures, and with this may come mass coral-bleaching events, where the living coral polyps are destroyed and only the calcareous skeleton remains. During 2002, more than 60 percent of the reef suffered bleaching. Cyclic outbreaks of the crown-of-thorns starfish, with its insatiable appetite for coral polyps, sees massive amounts of coral reef destroyed. This, in turn, has a significant effect on all reef life.

On the Fringe

Ningaloo Reef is one of the world's largest fringing reefs, stretching 174 miles (280 km) along the coastline of Western Australia, north of Perth. Its length, together with widths extending up to 4½ miles (7.5 km) off shore, make it the most extensive fringing reef on the western side of a continent. At its narrowest point Ningaloo is only 323 ft (100 m) from the beach, making it easily accessible to divers and snorkelers. However, as a result of the isolation and aridity of this area of Western Australia, the reef remains relatively pristine and there is minimal development.

An upwelling of plankton-rich water on Ningaloo Reef has given rise to a unique overlap of tropical and temperate marine and terrestrial life. The reef is famous for whale sharks, manta rays, humpback whales, dugongs, and turtles. It boasts 250 species of corals and over 450 fish species.

Pacific Ocean Atolls and Coral Reefs

A small-scale map of the world shows the Pacific as little more than a vast expanse of open ocean, but it actually contains most of the world's islands and atolls, many with reef islets that rise less than 10 ft (3 m) above sea level. Most coral reefs are found in the tropics.

OPPOSITE Kayangel Atoll in the north of Palau, Micronesia. A superb diving location, the atoll is home to a range of coral, dolphins, turtles, and large fish such as barracuda. The Republic of Palau consists of an archipelago of six groups of islands.

RIGHT Illegal fishing and aquaculture structures are removed in Manila Bay, the Philippines, in 2009, as part of a government campaign to preserve the sensitive marine environment.

ABOVE An array of armaments from a World War II Japanese naval vessel sits on the sea floor near Koror in Palau. It has been colonized by marine plants and provides a home for many fish.

There are around 30,000 islands in the Pacific Ocean. The islands are grouped in various ways depending on geographic division, size, and political units, but these demarcations have very little bearing when it comes to atolls and coral reefs.

A much more useful distinction can be made between islands that occur along plate boundaries and those that occur within a plate—the intraplate islands. The Pacific is almost entirely surrounded by active plate margins, which are characterized by volcanism with island formation. Some of the larger continental islands along convergent plate margins, such as Papua New Guinea and the archipelagos of the Philippines and Japan in the tropical western Pacific, are characterized by fringing and barrier reefs.

Intraplate islands are usually found in clusters or linear chains, created by hotspot activity that spews out magma from the mantle to form volcanoes or seamounts on the sea floor. Examples of intraplate islands include island chains such as Hawaii, the Marquesas, and the Tuamotus.

Low islands are usually isolated reefs and atolls that have been formed from the fringing reefs that exist around submerged seamounts and coral platforms. Atolls with their small, sandy islands often enclose substantial, circular lagoons.

There are more than 175 atolls and isolated coral islets found in the tropical Pacific, many concentrated in the Caroline Islands, Marshall Islands, Kiribati, Tuvalu, Phoenix Islands, Tokelau, Northern Cook Islands, Line Islands, and Gambier Islands. Together, these spread across 5,600 miles (9,000 km), but the total land area of the atolls and islands is only around 700 square miles (1,800 km²), which is far less than the combined areas of their central lagoons.

THREATS TO ATOLLS AND REEFS

Although many of the world's coral reefs and atolls are under grave threat from human disturbance, those of

the Pacific are relatively safe, with some 60 percent considered to be only at low risk. However, one of the most endangered reef areas in the world is around the Philippines, which, with more than 7,100 islands, is the world's second-largest archipelago nation after Indonesia. The main threats come from destructive fishing methods using explosives and poison, overfishing, and pollution runoff from logging, agriculture, and urban development. The reefs of Southeast Asia are the most species-rich on Earth and, because of high human population density, are also the most threatened.

UNIQUE ATOLLS AND REEFS

The Johnston Atoll, around 870 miles (1,400 km) west of Hawaii, is one of the Pacific Ocean's smallest and most isolated. It hosts about 300 species of fish—many endemic—and many breeding and migratory seabirds. It is also visited by the endangered green turtle.

At latitude 31° 33'S, Lord Howe Island is the world's southernmost reef. A warm current carries tropical species, and provides ideal conditions for the development of a fringing reef that contains approximately 80 coral species. Along the southern coast of Honshu, Japan, at a latitude of around 34°N, and with water temperatures as low as 52°F (11°C), is the world's northernmost coral reef.

Another unique Pacific atoll is Chuuk (Truk) Lagoon in the Central Caroline Islands. Its massive barrier reef encloses a lagoon with 26 volcanic islands and 22 low coral islets. It is very well known for its exceptional diversity of fish, marine invertebrates, and around 300 species of coral. During World War II, American forces sank some 70 Japanese naval vessels there, and those wrecks have since been colonized by numerous species. The lagoon has become one of the world's most prized diving destinations, offering luxuriant reef growth as well as historical significance.

The Reality of an Atoll

Atolls and isolated coral islands are the stuff of romance. Many a yarn has been written about life on a desert island, but very few actually support human habitation. Atoll formation in the tropical Pacific is relatively modern, with growth beginning during the Holocene period around 10,000 years ago. At this time sea levels began to rise and, by the mid-Holocene period, stable atoll islets were forming. Only during the last 2,000 years have islets been stable enough to support human occupation, and their future viability is threatened by rising sea levels. As a result, it is likely that they will remain suitable for human habitation for only a few more decades.

Other Atolls and Reefs

Reef tourism is a major global industry, but most of the world's coral reefs are in serious trouble. Humans are threatening the survival of reefs and atolls through overfishing, pollution, and mechanical destruction caused by boating and trampling. So although reef-based tourism provides significant economic benefits, these will dry up unless healthy reef ecosystems are maintained. Urgent steps must be taken to ensure their conservation.

BELOW South Male atoll in the Maldives. The economy of the Maldives is based mostly on fishing, which has been the main occupation for locals for hundreds of years, although in recent times, tourism has become increasingly important.

In the Pacific Ocean, most reefs (with the exception of those in the Philippines and Southeast Asia) are not yet endangered, but many reef systems in the world's other oceans are under grave threat. The Coral Triangle (Indonesia, Philippines, Papua New Guinea), Tanzania, the Comoros archipelago off East Africa, and the Lesser Antilles of the Caribbean are particularly at risk.

THE INDIAN OCEAN

Indonesia is the world's largest archipelago—it has approximately 17,000 islands, which include many uncharted and periodically submerged atolls and reefs. Indonesia is geographically divided into the Sundaland and Wallacea hotspots. Sundaland, which comprises Malaysia and the western half of the Indonesian archipelago (Bali, Java, Sumatra, and Borneo), encompasses some 618,000 square miles (1.6 million km²).

Wallacea covers almost 135,000 square miles (350,000 km²) and is separated from Sundaland by the Wallace Line—the boundary between Asian and Oceanic species, which evolved separately as a result of the natural barrier formed by deep straits between eastern Indonesia and Papua New Guinea. Wallacea includes the islands and atolls of Lombok, Sumbawa, Komodo, Flores, Sumba, Savu, Roti, Timor, the Moluccas, and Sulawesi.

A tectonic hotspot in the northern Indian Ocean has produced Sri Lanka, the Maldives, the Chagos Islands, and some other, smaller archipelagos. Global warming, coral mining, overfishing, and ornamental fish collection threaten this region.

The Maldives is a long, narrow country formed by 22 natural atolls and a number of islands and reefs. It includes Huvadu, one of the world's largest atolls with

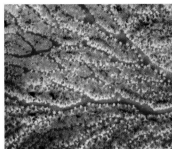

many habitable islands around its rim. It covers around 1,120 square miles (2,900 km²). The many beautiful diving grounds found in the Maldives make it a prime destination for recreational divers.

The Seychelles is an archipelago nation of 115 islands that lie northeast of the island of Madagascar. It contains Aldabra, the world's second-largest atoll with a land area of around 60 square miles (155 km²). The Seychelles has been designated a World Heritage site because of its rare and distinctive fauna, including the world's largest population of Aldabra giant tortoises. Aldabra, relatively untouched by humans, is not yet considered to be at risk.

The Red Sea and Gulf of Aden, arms of the northwestern Indian Ocean, have become very popular tourist destinations. Although the Red Sea hosts fewer species of corals, it nonetheless hosts more endemic species than the eastern Indian Ocean. It is part of a hotspot region that includes the Gulfs of Aqaba and Suez, and is threatened by tourism, coastal industrial developments, and oil spills from tankers.

In the southern Indian Ocean, an area of around 390 square miles (1,000 km²) of reefs surrounding the Southern Mascarene Islands is also under threat from rapidly growing human populations, pollution, agricultural development, and overfishing.

ATLANTIC OCEAN

Coral growth in the Atlantic Ocean is restricted by the vast amount of sediments carried in by some of the world's largest rivers—the Amazon, Orinoco, Mississippi, Niger, and Congo. The Caribbean Sea sits on a tectonic plate bounded by island arcs to the east and north, and contains over 7,000 islands, islets, reefs, and cays, including Cuba and the Bahamas. The countries in this region are collectively known as the West Indies. Minor reefs can be found off the coast of Brazil, the Gulf of Mexico, Florida, and around Bermuda in the

northwest Atlantic. Although only around eight percent of the world's reefs are found here, the corals are unique, sharing only seven genera with the reefs of the Indo–Pacific. The region is threatened by coastal development as well as global warming.

In the eastern Atlantic, reefs in the Gulf of Guinea off the West African coast are threatened by pollution and river runoff. The Cape Verde Islands in the mid-Atlantic Ocean are also threatened by coastal development and other human activities.

ABOVE Vein-like red branches of a coral (Subergorgia sp.) color the temperate waters off Sipadan Island, Borneo.

BELOW Scuba divers are able to enjoy a close-up view of colorful marine life and sponges when they explore the waters around atolls and reefs.

Ocean Nomads (Global Roamers)

It seems remarkable that the blue whale, the world's largest animal, feeds on swarms of krill, one of the ocean's most minuscule inhabitants. These tiny shrimp-like crustaceans are so abundant that a blue whale eats about 6.5 tons (6 tonnes) each day. Krill are part of the vast plankton community that thrives in the exceptionally nutrient-rich waters of the colder oceans.

RIGHT An image of the Black Sea taken from NASA's Aqua Satellite. The blue and green colors come from masses of phytoplankton swirling about close to the surface. The green color indicates the presence of chlorophyll in the cells of these microorganisms.

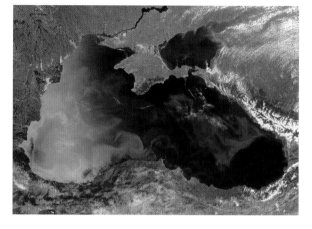

CHANCE CURRENTS

The term plankton describes those organisms that drift in the surface layers of the ocean. They do not have the power to move against ocean currents. The plankton community consists of microscopic to small algae and animals (phytoplankton and zooplankton, respectively) together with massive numbers of bacteria, some of which are photosynthetic. Photosynthesis is the process by which phytoplankton use radiant energy from the sun to convert carbon dioxide and water into organic food molecules. This process is essential to the ocean ecosystem and is the basis of the food chain upon which all marine animal life ultimately depends.

COCOONED BY THE COLD

The abundance and composition of plankton varies enormously from place to place. One of the primary factors influencing abundance is the availability of nutrients. In general, nutrient levels are highest in cold to temperate waters, especially in areas where there is upwelling of nutrient-rich water from the ocean depths. Warmer, tropical oceans are generally nutrient-poor and so lack the abundance of plankton.

Although plankton is restricted in its horizontal movement, most planktonic organisms are capable of daily vertical migrations. Zooplankton sinks deeper

BELOW The magnificent blue whale *(Balaenoptera musculus)*, the largest animal in the world, eats mainly krill, tiny crustaceans classified as zooplankton. To gain sufficient sustenance, a blue whale must consume well over 6 tons of krill every day.

into the water column during the day and ascends to the surface at night. Phytoplankton remains closer to the surface during the sunlight hours so that photosynthesis can take place. They tend to move down the water column at night to take advantage of the higher nutrient levels present in the deeper water.

FLORA AND FAUNA

There is an enormous diversity of phytoplankton, ranging from the simple cells of the photosynthetic bacteria called cyanobacteria, to the more complex single-celled algae, such as diatoms and dinoflagellates. Together, the photosynthetic activity of phytoplankton is more productive than that of all the plants, forests, and grasslands on land.

Zooplankton graze on either phytoplankton or are predators on each other. Some zooplankton remain in the plankton community throughout their entire life cycle, while others are the eggs and larval stages of marine animals that eventually develop into adults. Those that are totally planktonic include jellyfish, comb jellies, polychaetes, gastropods, ascidians, arrow worms, and particularly crustaceans, such as krill.

Those marine animals that spend only a portion of their life cycle as zooplankton have larvae that feed on phytoplankton before they ultimately metamorphose into the adult form. They include the larval stages of sponges, corals, worms, mollusks, crustaceans, echinoderms, and even fish.

PLANKTON PREDATORS

Marine animals use a number of feeding strategies to take advantage of the rich supply of nutrients provided by plankton. Many sedentary animals, such as sea

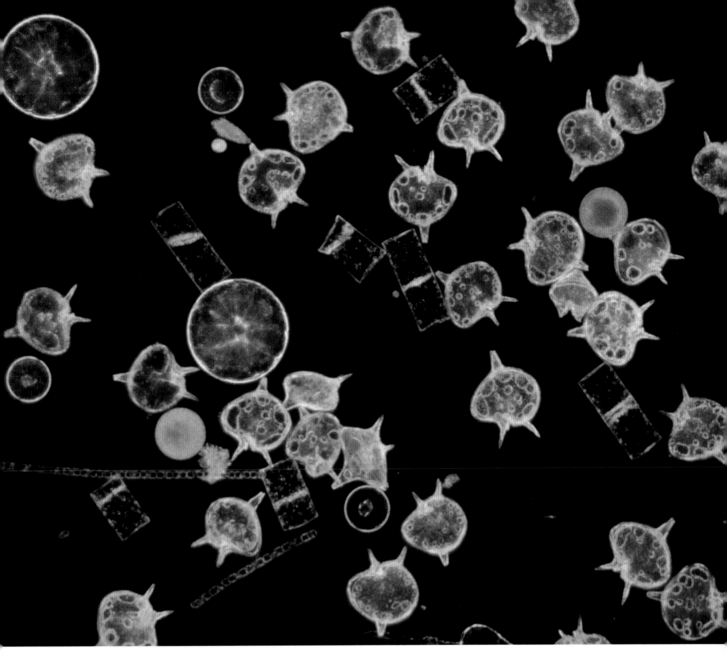

anemones, corals, and barnacles, feed on plankton by trapping them as they drift by. Others, such as sponges, bivalves, and sea squirts, filter their food from currents they create and direct toward their mouths. Active animals swim to locate and feed on zooplankton. Fish, squid, penguins, and other seabirds specifically target larger zooplankton. Large active animals such as baleen whales, manta rays, basking sharks, and whale sharks filter out plankton, particularly krill, while they are swimming or breaching.

THE BLUE LAYER

The large community of organisms that float right at the interface of the ocean and the atmosphere is known collectively as the blue layer, mainly because its color camouflages it from both above and below. Along with plankton, the creatures of the blue layer rely on ocean currents to drive them across the seas, but are further propelled by prevailing winds, which sometimes leave

them stranded along the seashore. The Portuguese man-o-war or bluebottle (*Physalia physalia*) is actually a colony of individuals supported by a gas-filled float. It has stinging tentacles trailing beneath it to capture plankton and small fish. The by-the-wind sailor (*Velella velella*) has a raised "sail" on a disk-shaped float. This sail takes advantage of the wind in order to move the colony across the surface as it collects plankton with its short stinging tentacles.

ABOVE Marine plankton are a critical part of the ocean's food chain. These colorful and variously-shaped microscopic organisms include diatoms, ctenophores, and copepods.

Weight of the World

Clouds of krill are sometimes so large that they can be seen from space. The total biomass of some species has been estimated as some 500 million metric tons, and it is thought that the total weight of all species is more than the total weight of all humans on Earth. Krill are an essential link in the food chain that supports the marine ecosystems. Without them Antarctic life would disappear. They migrate vertically in the water column, descending to 328 ft (100 m) during the day to avoid predators and return to feed on phytoplankton at night.

The Reef Builders

From little things, big things grow—and from a tiny coral polyp blooms the majestic monument that is a coral reef. Present-day coral reefs are the largest structures built by a living organism, and while these underwater dominions can measure more than 1,000 kilometers in length, the polyp responsible for their construction is no more than a few millimeters in diameter.

BELOW There are more than 6,000 different species of corals and a variety of colony shapes, varying from jagged branching staghorns to flattened plates and rounded domes. A reef is made up of millions of colonies cemented together with other calcareous marine organisms.

JEWEL IN A CUP

Corals belong to the large group of animals called Cnidaria (pronounced nide-area). This name is derived from the Greek word for nettle, describing the characteristic stinging barbs (cnidae) found in the surface body cells and especially on the tentacles surrounding the mouth of the polyp.

The simple body plan of the cup-shaped polyp includes a single opening to the gut through which both food and waste products pass ("mouth"). The body wall is composed of two layers of tissue only: the epidermis, which protects the body from the outside; and the absorptive endodermis that lines the gut. Between the two tissues is a layer of jelly-like material called the mesoglea (pronounced me-so-GLEE-ar), which gives cnidarians their characteristic texture and support. The lower part of the epidermis secretes calcium carbonate (aragonite) that forms the layers of skeleton. These skeletons form the basis of reef development.

AN INTERNAL VEGETABLE PATCH

Corals could not produce their stony skeletons if it were not for golden-brown, single-celled algae called zooxanthellae. In this symbiotic relationship, zooxanthellae are cultivated within the "garden" of the polyp's endodermis. Metabolic waste from the polyp, including phosphates, nitrates, and carbon dioxide, provides the algae with "fertilizer." The algae in turn uses radiant energy from the sun to produce carbohydrates by the process of photosynthesis. The polyp then uses some of the carbohydrates and oxygen produced for its own nutrition. Skeleton formation is also a product of photosynthetic activity and this can only occur where radiant energy is abundant: in shallow, clear water during daylight. Polyps do not rely solely on zooxanthellae for food; they also require protein. They capture drifting plankton using the cnidae on their tentacles.

FUTURE GENERATIONS

Coral polyps reproduce both asexually and sexually. Each polyp can divide asexually into two polyps by a process known as budding. In this way, corals form colonies consisting of many thousands of individual polyps joined together, all supported by their calcareous skeleton. These polyps are clones: that is, they are genetically identical. The actual living part of the colony is a very thin veneer of polyps spread over the surface of the skeleton.

Sexual reproduction, however, produces non-identical offspring. Polyps release huge numbers of sperm and eggs just after the full moon of November in the southern hemisphere and August in the northern hemisphere. Fertilized eggs hatch into larvae, which spend some time in the plankton before settling as polyps that form a new colony.

SOFT AND FALSE CORALS

Corals belong to a group of cnidarians called Anthozoa, which also includes sea anemones and a variety of soft and false corals. The true corals, the skeleton builders, are the Scleractinia and these are by far the main reef builders. In contrast to the process that forms the external skeletons of true corals, the internal calcareous skeleton of the soft and false corals forms within the mesoglea of the body.

Soft corals have a leathery texture brought about by the presence of needles of calcium carbonate embedded in the jelly of the mesoglea. They can form massive colonies, a meter or more in diameter, and can be a variety of shapes such as tabletops or upright finger-like projections.

Gorgonians are a group of false corals commonly called sea fans because of their fan-shaped colonies. Unlike true corals, the supporting skeleton is colored (for example red, orange, or yellow) and the color is retained even after death. Some species, particularly those with a hard skeleton, are prized for jewelry as "precious" coral.

LEFT The vividly colored tips of a stalk of *Acropora echinata*— a type of staghorn coral—are seen here in close-up.

LEFT Thousands of white filaments outline the fiery red branches of the Gorgonian sea fan, found in the Indian Ocean waters off Myanmar.

BELOW Connected to fleshy stalks, the filament-like polyps of soft coral are seen here in close-up. A colony of some 25,000 individual polyps can take only three years to form.

Coral bleaching

The colors of living corals are actually quite subdued, despite the garish hues of coral souvenirs. Although many corals have their own pigments, much of the color comes from the zooxanthellae (algae) in the tissues of the polyps. Over the past few decades there has been an alarming increase in the incidence of coral bleaching, where the reef becomes icicle-white. It is thought that the polyps expel the zooxanthellae in response to environmental stress. These stresses include increases in water temperature, pollutants, and sediment deposition.

Marine Plants

It may come as a surprise to learn that the seaweeds flourishing in coastal waters worldwide are not the main food producers of the ocean. The most prolific producers by far are the phytoplankton, the microscopic single-celled plants and other simple algae that float in the upper layer of the ocean.

SEA GARDENS

The term "alga" (plural algae) refers to a diversity of marine plants that produce organic compounds from carbon dioxide by photosynthesis, releasing oxygen as a byproduct. Algae are the Earth's primary producers, forming the foundation of the food chain upon which all other marine life depends. Because photosynthesis depends on solar radiant energy, algae are restricted to the photic zone of the ocean. This is the depth to which sunlight is able to penetrate, ranging from 33 to 330 ft

BELOW *Halimeda opuntia* is a green alga often found in intertidal zones. Here a brightly colored sea slug *(Nembrotha cristata)* forages among its lush foliage.

RIGHT Intertidal kelp are clearly visible at low tides. These green algae have adapted to the ebb and flow of the tides and the changing levels of light to which they are exposed.

(10 to 100 m), depending on the clarity of the water. The availability of varous mineral nutrients also plays a critical role. Regions of high productivity occur where deep, nutrient-laden waters are brought to the surface by upwelling currents. It is no coincidence that these regions support the most productive fishing grounds of the world's oceans.

Apart from phytoplankton, other algae flourish on the sea floor, from the intertidal shoreline to the adjacent shallow water of the continental shelf. These algae include unicellular forms that grow among the sediments, as well as multicellular macroalgae that are collectively referred to as seaweeds.

Seaweeds range from slippery, turf-like filaments to dense underwater forests of tough, leathery fronds of kelp that can grow up to 260 ft (80 m) in length at an astonishing 1½ ft (0.5 m) per day. Macroalgae provide food for grazing and browsing herbivores, such as some mollusks, echinoderms, and fishes. They are usually firmly attached to the substrate by a holdfast, but can be dislodged during storms.

ALGAL DIVERSITY

Although all algae photosynthesize, they belong to many different and often unrelated groups. Their body form, chlorophyll type, and the presence of ancillary light-harvesting pigments help to identify the various types. The bodies of macroalgae do not have leaves, stems, or roots like most land plants. Instead, the body, called a thallus, is responsible for absorbing water, carbon dioxide, and minerals over its general surface.

Green algae (Division Chlorophyta) encompass unicellular and macroalgae that are adapted to well-illuminated habitats, such as the intertidal and shallow subtidal zones of the shoreline. They display a wide variety of shapes, ranging from short filaments to more elaborate forms composed of flat sheets (genus Ulva), finger-like filaments (genus Codium) or bunches of grape-like spheres (genus Caulerpa).

Brown algae (Division Phaeophyta) include a broad range of conspicuous seaweeds. Those with bodies composed of tough, flat straps are often referred to as kelp, with the giant kelps (genus Macrocystis) being the most spectacular. Sargassum is a distinctive brown macroalga that has air-filled sacs to maintain buoyancy. Its name is derived from the Sargasso Sea, where many species of free-floating sargassum occur. The brown color results from the blending of light-harvesting yellowish pigments and the green of the chlorophyll, a mix that allows photosynthesis at lower light intensities.

Red algae (Division Rhodophyta) take their color from red light-harvesting pigments that allow them to photosynthesize at very low light intensities. They occur in waters down to and even beyond the photic zone. While many macroalgae contain calcium carbonate for structural support, some red algae are called coralline algae because their bodies are so hard they resemble coral. Species of *Lithothamnion* are responsible for the important function of binding coral skeletons into rigid reef frameworks.

GRASSES OF THE SEA

Algae are not the only plants living in the oceans. Sea grasses are flowering plants that live below the tide level on soft sediments in protected areas. They form the equivalent of grassy meadows, providing feeding grounds for a variety of animals, including the endangered dugong or sea cow *(Dugong dugon)*.

Sea grasses have roots for absorption of minerals from the sediments and grow vegetatively by producing runners, which are called stolons. They have rather inconspicuous flowers, and pollen is transported from one flower to another by currents.

There are a number of flowering plants that have become salt tolerant but do not live fully submerged. These plants flourish along the shoreline of estuaries, with the most conspicuous being mangroves. They occur mostly in tropical and subtropical latitudes,

growing in fine silt in estuaries and coastal regions that are protected from wave action. There are approximately 50 species of mangroves belonging to a number of families of flowering plants. The mangroves have adapted to cope with water loss, salt uptake, and low oxygen levels in the silt.

ABOVE Giant kelp off the Californian coast. These plants thrive in nutrient-rich waters and can grow well over 12 in (30 cm) each day.

LEFT An anglerfish finds both food and cover among the fronds of a sea grass. Sea grasses occur in the photic zone, and are home to a huge variety of life, including fish, worms, and some marine mammals.

Marine Worms

The thought of a worm's soft, slimy body makes many people's skin crawl, but this large and disparate invertebrate group showcases a breathtaking diversity of color and size—fan worms are some of the ocean's most beautiful creatures. Worms are found in a range of environments, from clear tropical waters to the cold, dark ocean floor.

THE LONG AND THE SHORT

Worms vary in size from microscopic to many tens of feet in length. They live on land, in fresh water, and many are parasitic. It is the ocean, however, that claims the greatest diversity of worms. Here there are flatworms, ribbon worms, peanut worms, spoon worms, and bristle worms, to name but a few.

GRACEFUL GLIDERS—FLATWORMS

Although most marine flatworms (Platyhelminthes) are inconspicuous because of their size and transparency, some members of the polyclad group can be very colorful and beautifully patterned.

BELOW The aptly named zebra flatworm *(Pseudoceros sp.)* are bilaterally symmetrical, meaning that both left and right sides of the animal are mirror images of one another.

Most flatworms live a cryptic lifestyle, inhabiting crevices and living under boulders. They move by the synchronized beating of tiny hair-like structures, which gives them a characteristic elegant gliding motion. Some can swim by causing undulations to pass down the sides of the body. They feed by capturing other slow-moving animals in their sticky, flat body. The food is then ingested through a muscular gullet on their underside that can be protruded over the prey.

AT A STRETCH— RIBBON WORMS

Ribbon or proboscis worms (Nemertea) resemble flatworms but their body is more rounded, considerably more muscular, and usually much longer. They range in size from a fraction of an inch to nearly 100 ft (30 m), which makes them among the longest animals in the world. They are not quite as colorful as flatworms, but they have a distinctive and characteristic proboscis at the front end of the body that can be turned inside out (everted). The proboscis is shot out some distance to capture prey on its sticky surface and is then retracted to deliver the prey to the mouth. Just like flatworms, ribbon worms generally have a mysterious life style.

PEANUTS AND SPOONS

Peanut and spoon worms are sedentary (slow-moving) worms. Similar to the ribbon or proboscis worms, they can evert the front part of the body to feed on prey. In the contracted state, peanut worms (Sipuncula) resemble an unshelled peanut but the front end of the animal can be slowly turned inside out to make the body long and thin, with the mouth positioned at the tip. Small tentacles shovel nutrient-containing sediment into the mouth.

Spoon worms (Echiura) are similar, except that the protruded front end of the body is spoon-shaped and lined with movable hairs that drive food particles toward the mouth. In some species the structure is more like a gutter and is forked at the tip to increase the surface area for food capture. The body usually lies concealed within the sediment.

RINGS AND BRISTLES—POLYCHAETES

Bristle worms (Polychaeta), along with the earthworms and their relatives (Oligochaeta), and leeches (Hirudinea), are members of the large phylum Annelida. Members of this group have a body divided into a large number of sections or rings. A segmented body makes possible an entire array of controlled and efficient movements that are not possible for other

LEFT Tube worms come in
a wide variety of forms, but all
have a segmented body. They
belong to the large phylum of
marine worms called Annelida—
there are over 17,000 species
in the phylum.

BELOW Fan worms are among
the most beautiful of all the
creatures found in the oceans.
The feather-like extensions,
which filter tiny particles of
food from the water, give
these animals their alternative
name—feather duster worms.

varieties of worms. The body movements are coordinated by a "brain" and a nerve cord, with different parts of the body creating waves or undulations that allow swimming or crawling. Many bristle worms also have a pair of paddles on each body segment to help increase the force of movement. Waves of contraction and elongation (called peristalsis)—helped along by traction provided by tiny needle-like bristles that extend from the body (chaetae)—result in an extremely efficient burrowing action.

Bristle worms are almost exclusively marine dwellers and are by far the most diverse of the segmented worms. Some burrow through the sediments but come to the surface to move around and feed. For others, feeding and burrowing are one and the same activity. Some of the most exquisitely beautiful worms build permanent tubes to live in. They collect food using a variety of methods. The feather duster or fan worm (Sabellidae) has a crown of feather-like extensions on its head that it exposes from the opening of the tube. These extensions have grooves and beating hairs that collect particles of food from the water and direct them toward the mouth.

Shell Life

Many of the most treasured items found by beachcombers as they stroll along the seashore are colorful and intricately patterned shells. These sculptural art forms created by nature were once the hard parts of living mollusks. With approximately 100,000 described species, mollusks are second only to the arthropods (insects, spiders, and crustaceans) in number of species.

ABOVE The purple-ringed top snail (*Calliostoma annulatum*) lives in shallow waters usually among blades of kelp. The animal inside the colorful shell is bright orange.

PEARLS OF THE SEA

Mollusks are surely the most diverse of all the major animal groups when it comes to body form and way of life. Cuttlefish, octopus, squid, snails, abalone, mussels, clams, scallops, and oysters all belong to this group. Many are delicious and nourishing food for humans and other animals. Some mollusks, such as those whose shells are lined with mother-of-pearl, are prized for jewelry and buttons. An aberration in shell secretion by some oysters produces what many consider to be the most elegant of human adornments—the pearl.

MEET THE MOLLUSKS

Mollusks include immobile oysters and mussels (bivalves); the slow-moving limpets, slugs, and snails (gastropods); chitons (polyplacophorans); and the most active and coordinated of all the invertebrates, the cephalopods. This group includes octopus, cuttlefish, and squid.

A mollusk's body is divided into three regions. The head contains the mouth and sensory organs, such as eyes and tentacles. The second region is the muscular foot used for locomotion, and the third, on top of the foot, is the visceral mass containing most of the body's vital organs. The skin of the visceral mass, called the mantle, secretes the hard protective shell of calcium carbonate that shields this exposed and delicate part of the body. A fold in the mantle forms the very important mantle cavity that is in direct contact with the outside environment. Water is continually flushing this cavity, delivering oxygen to the gills and removing waste products from the kidneys and rectum.

The diversity of body forms in the various groups of mollusks is a result of the loss or modification of one or more of these basic features. Many groups lack the protective shell. The mantle cavity of cephalopods has been modified to produce effective jet propulsion for rapid movement, and the muscular foot has been modified to form a ring of tentacles that are utilized to capture prey.

SHELL ADVANTAGE—GASTROPODS

With approximately 70,000 described species, gastropods are by far the largest group of mollusks and their success can be attributed to their mostly spiraled, protective shell. Gastropods include the only terrestrial mollusks, the familiar land snails and slugs, but by far, most gastropods live in the sea.

While other mollusks have the mantle cavity at the back of the body, the visceral mass of gastropods has been rotated through 180 degrees to bring the mantle cavity to the front above the head. The mantle cavity now forms a space into which the head and foot can be withdrawn so that the shell encloses the entire body. A trapdoor (operculum) provides further protection by sealing the opening to the shell and thus preventing desiccation during low tide. It also provides an effective defense against predators.

Snail shells come in a bewildering array of shapes, sizes, colors, and textures. There are turbans (periwinkles), cones (cone shells, volutes, strombs), clubs (whelks), trumpets (tritons), and eggs (cowries). Many groups of gastropods have tent-shaped shells and are collectively called limpets. This shape provides little resistance to wave action and a limpet's strong muscular foot acts like a suction pad on the rock surface.

Gastropods feed by using a rasp-like structure—the radula—which has numerous rows of teeth. As the radula pitches back and forth, the rasping action removes plant tissue or flesh from prey. Cone shells have a modified radular tooth shaped like a small

Pearl Formation

Pearls are formed when an irritant, such as a grain of sand, lodges between the shell and the body (mantle) of some bivalve mollusks. In response, the animal secretes layer after layer of the innermost pearly or nacreous material of the shell around the irritant to encapsulate it. The natural production of a perfect pearl is accidental and rare. However, introducing an artificial irritant into oysters maintained under farmed conditions can now produce cultured pearls.

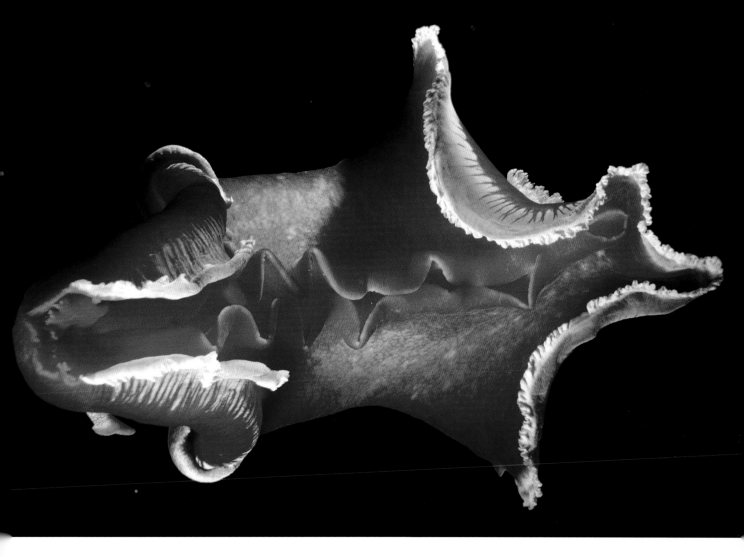

harpoon. The harpoon injects a neurotoxin to immobilize prey before it is consumed. A few of the larger species have a toxin so potent it can kill a human.

Gastropods have varied reproductive strategies. Males and females are separate individuals in some species, while in other species both male and female sexual organs are present (hermaphroditic). Some of the marine species release eggs and sperm into the sea where fertilization occurs, but most species fertilize eggs following copulation. The fertilized eggs are then laid in a protective jelly coating or egg capsule. The eggs eventually hatch as tiny larvae that spend some time in the plankton before they settle and metamorphose into an adult form.

Shell loss in sea slugs allows them to shelter in crevices. Some, such as the sea hare, retain a mantle cavity containing the gills, but one group of sea slugs, the nudibranchs, have replaced the mantle cavity with naked gills that appear like feathery projections on their backs. Some nudibranchs feed on coral polyps, extracting the algae from the coral tissues. The algae are not digested but instead accumulate in the skin where they continue to photosynthesize and so contribute to the nudibranch's nutrition.

Camouflage plays an important protective role for these soft-bodied and vulnerable creatures by helping

them to merge into the background. By contrast, the bright colors and patterns of some flamboyant species act as a warning to potential predators to stay clear.

TWO-SIDED—BIVALVES

Bivalves are the most sedentary of all mollusks. Indeed many, such as oysters and mussels, are permanently attached to rocks or other solid substrates. Two shells, known as valves, extend down the sides of the laterally compressed bodies of bivalves. These valves are hinged at the apex, which is held together by a ligament. The valves open to form a gape at their base.

Some bivalves gain protection from predators by burrowing into soft sediment. Burrowing bivalves use their foot like a spade to dig into the sediment. Some bivalves bore into hard substrates, such as clay, sandstone, coral, and wood. The infamous shipworm is a bivalve that destroys wharves and wooden boats. Boring is accomplished by serrations on the shell that act like a rasp.

The vast majority of bivalves are filter feeders. They extract their food from water that is passed through the mantle cavity, where enormously enlarged gills trap microscopic food particles. Once collected, these particles are then delivered to the mouth. Burrowing and boring bivalves maintain a connection with the

ABOVE One of the most ostentatious of gastropods is the Spanish dancer (*Hexabranchus sanguineus*), with its colorful body that is reminiscent of the swirling skirts of a flamenco dancer.

175

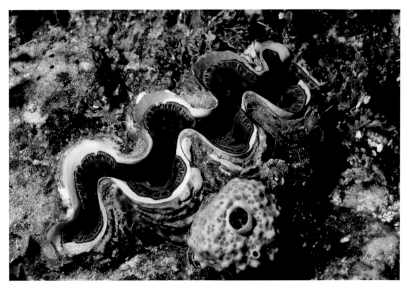

ABOVE The giant clam (*Tridacna sp.*) is a most impressive mollusk. These amazing creatures inhabit the warm shallow waters of the Pacific and Indian oceans.

TOP With its bright red mantle and dramatic tentacles, the flame scallop (*Lima scabra*) is a striking mollusk. Found in nests of rocks or coral, it feeds exclusively on phytoplankton.

water by extending the body to form a siphon that circulates water to and from the mantle cavity.

Bivalves have two powerful muscles connecting the valves to hold them tightly shut. When the muscles relax, the valves are opened slightly by the elastic hinge ligament. Scallops employ this mechanism to great effect for jet propulsion by making the valves open and close rapidly like castanets. As a consequence, the muscles linking the valves are exceptionally well developed. It is these muscles that make scallops a sought-after delicacy.

SHELL DIVISIONS—CHITONS

The most distinctive feature of a chiton is the division of its shell into eight overlapping plates that are embedded in a leathery girdle. This provides the body with flexibility when moving over uneven surfaces. The head is indistinct, making it hard to tell one end from the other. They are similar to limpets in that their large foot holds on tightly to rock as they scrape the surface film of algae using their extremely tough radula.

SMART MOVERS—CEPHALOPODS

The diversity of cephalopods today is minor when compared with those that are found in the fossil record. Millions of years ago there were giant ammonites with shells the size of tractor tires. Several species of nautilus are the only survivors of these ancient shelled cephalopods. The shell of a nautilus (genus Nautilus) coils on itself rather than forming the helical spiral of a

gastropod shell. Furthermore, a cutaway section of the shell reveals that it is divided into a number of chambers. The animal lives only in the most recently formed chamber, and uses the remaining chambers to provide buoyancy control. The animal's tentacles encircle the head and extend from the shell opening.

In all cephalopods, water is drawn through the mantle cavity and expelled with such force that it produces jet propulsion. This accounts for the agility of cephalopods when compared with other mollusks. In general, cephalopod shells have been either lost or

reduced and internalized, for example the familiar cuttlebone that provides support and buoyancy to the cuttlefish. In squid, the very reduced internal structure is a thin and leaf-shaped pen. This provides support for the animal's torpedo-shaped body. Octopuses have lost the shell altogether.

Squid are by far the most active predator, while cuttlefish hover with neutral buoyancy, only lunging forward to capture passing prey. Most octopuses are bottom dwellers, living in crevices from which they emerge to hunt for prey, such as crabs.

ABOVE A cuttlefish glides through coral. These mollusks have an internal shell and are masters of disguise—the skin's pigmented cells reflect light in different colors, providing this graceful animal with camouflage for any occasion.

Crustacea

There are approximately 50,000 described species of crustaceans, making them the third largest group of arthropods after insects and arachnids. Yet they are the most diverse, ranging in size from tiny planktonic copepods through barnacles and hermit crabs to the giant spider crabs of Japan with a span of almost 10 ft (3 m) from claw to claw.

Crustaceans are the most aquatic of the arthropods with the vast majority living in the sea—they form a considerable proportion of plankton. Others live on the sea floor among the seaweeds and in crevices, or burrowing into soft sediments. Some have paddle-like appendages that make them efficient swimmers. The most unusual crustaceans are the barnacles, because their body is completely enclosed inside a shell that is permanently attached to the substrate.

Many types of crustaceans are prized as gourmet delicacies. Most are the decapods, the "ten-legged" group—prawns, shrimps, scampi, crayfish, lobsters, and crabs. The reason decapods make such good food is because in proportion to their body size, they have large muscles, making them a great source of protein.

ABOVE A prawn crawls over rocks in search of food. Prawns differ from shrimp in a number of ways, one being the structure of their gills. Prawn gills tend to be branching, while those of shrimp are more layered.

WHAT DISTINGUISHES A CRUSTACEAN?

With so much diversity it is hard to find characteristics shared by all crustaceans. Of their paired appendages or limbs, the first two pairs at the front of the head are feelers or antennae. Most crustacean appendages are made up of two branches, while those of other arthropods have only one. But these characteristics do not hold for all crustaceans. Barnacles have dispensed with antennae, and the walking limbs of crabs and lobsters have become single-branched.

Crustaceans reproduce sexually by producing eggs and sperm. In some species, the fertilized eggs are released into the sea where they hatch into tiny larvae, which become part of the plankton before they metamorphose into adults. However, most crustaceans brood their eggs on some part of the body until they hatch at an advanced stage, therefore increasing their chances of survival.

TEN "LEGS" MAKE A DECAPOD

Of the crustaceans, the familiar Decapoda has the most species; some of these have the largest body size of all the arthropods. Decapods are an ideal model for the crustacean body form. In keeping with all arthropods, the body is enclosed in a protective exoskeleton. The joints allow flexibility, particularly in the appendages. Muscles attached to the inside of the exoskeleton allow movement around these joints.

Like all arthropods, crustaceans shed their exoskeleton, by a process called molting, in order to grow. Just after molting, when the exoskeleton is soft and expandable, there is a growth spurt. After a few days, the exoskeleton hardens once again. At this stage, crabs are commercially harvested to satisfy those who enjoy eating "soft-shelled crabs."

Like most crustaceans, the decapod body is divided into three regions. The first is the head, with two pairs of antennae and six pairs of appendages that surround the mouth on the underside of the head. These grind, sieve, and manipulate food.

Barnacles and Boats

The hard calcareous exoskeletons of barnacles resemble the shells of mollusks. But a barnacle is a crustacean lying on its back feeding with its six pairs of feathery limbs extended from the shell to grab plankton as it drifts past. There are basically two types of barnacles—acorn barnacles, which look like mini-volcanoes cemented to the rocky shore, wharf piles, and boat hulls; and goose barnacles (pictured) with their leathery attachment stalks often seen washed up on beaches attached to floating logs.

The second region is the thorax with five pairs of appendages—the ten walking legs. In many species, one or more of the thoracic limbs bears claws that are capable of gripping tightly onto both food and potential predators. In some decapods the claws are massive, making formidable weapons for defense, quite apart from their ability to shred food.

The head and thorax are covered in a saddle-shaped shell, the carapace that makes a single rigid unit. By contrast, the crustacean abdomen is made up of six flexible segments. Five of these segments bear paddle-like swimming limbs, and the last forms a tail fan. This can be used for backward escape by rapidly flexing the abdomen under the thorax. This, of course, requires a large muscle, which fills the entire abdominal cavity and forms the main source of flesh.

In comparison to the abdomen of lobsters and prawns, the abdomen of crabs is not used for loco-motion. Rather, it is flattened and folded neatly under the thorax, giving crabs the ability to move around in all directions on their legs.

HERMIT CRABS, NATURE'S SQUATTERS
Hermit crabs use empty gastropod shells to protect their soft abdomen. Only the head and anterior part of the thorax protrude from the shell as the hermit crab moves about. Even this can be withdrawn completely into the shell when the crab is threatened.

ABOVE The large eyes of the mantis shrimp, such as this one (*Odontodactylus scyllarus*), are used to detect prey. Similar to those of preying mantids, the first pair of the mantis shrimp's walking limbs is an effective weapon for both defense and food capture. The legs have vicious spines to hold the prey in a tight grip.

LEFT As hermit crabs grow they have to find bigger shells to occupy, so they can only live in an environment that has many empty shells.

Stars, Spines, Tunics—Echinoderms and Tunicates

Depictions of the ocean's beauty invariably include a sea star, an iconic image of marine life. Sea stars, sea lilies, feather stars, brittle stars, sea urchins, and sea cucumbers are members of the invertebrate phylum Echinodermata, the spiny-skinned animals. Their less conspicuous ocean relatives—the tunicates—are chordates, a group that also includes the vertebrates.

OPPOSITE An elegant opalescent blue tunicate, *Rhopalaea crassa,* emerges through branches of purple soft coral in the waters of the Philippines. Tunicates are filter feeders.

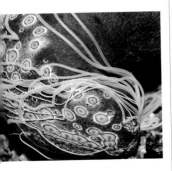

TOP A sea cucumber (*Bohadschia argus*) ejects sticky threads when it is disturbed or feels threatened. There are over 1,200 species of these sausage-shaped echinoderms.

ABOVE A bat starfish (*Asterina miniata*) feeds on a jellyfish. Bat stars often inhabit tide pools, and because they are bright red or orange in color, they are quite easy to see during low tide.

FLOWERS OF THE SEA

Echinoderms live in the sea where they inhabit rocky surfaces or sediments. Although they are not usually free-swimming, their life cycles include larval stages that are planktonic. It is difficult to distinguish a head or tail, because as adults most have arms that radiate from a central body like the points of a star. The flower-like radial symmetry of the echinoderms is generally based on multiples of five. Echinoderms and tunicates are distantly related. They are both deuterostomes, which means the mouth forms after the anus during embryonic development; in most invertebrates the mouth forms first.

HYDRAULIC PUMPS

Echinoderms depend on a water vascular or hydraulic system to move and to gather food. Within their bodies there is a ring canal from which radiating canals extend into each arm. Seawater enters the system through a small pore and then flows along each radial canal into tentacle-like extensions called tube feet or podia. The system operates like a hydraulic pump so that fluid pressure extends the podia, which then retract when the pressure is released.

The thin walls of echinoderm podia also function as gills, with the exchange of gas taking place from the surrounding seawater.

REPRODUCTION

Asexual reproduction is common in echinoderms. A small fragment, for example an arm of a sea star, can regenerate into a new individual. For sexual reproduction, the sperm and eggs are usually released into the sea where fertilization occurs. Free-living larvae hatch from the fertilized eggs and live among the plankton before settling and metamorphosing into the mature adult form.

ECHINODERM DIVERSITY

Sea lilies and feather stars belong to the group called crinoids, which were once far more abundant than they are today. Modern crinoids are either mobile or sessile. Feather stars lack a stem and hang on to the rocky substrate using a series of appendages with hooks, called cirri. The sessile sea lilies are limited to bending movements of the stalk.

Crinoids have a cup-shaped body with the mouth and anus pointing upward. Elongated arms with side branches encircle the animal's mouth. Tiny podia lining the grooves in the arms help to channel minute food particles to the centrally located mouth.

Sea stars (Asteroidea) are virtually upside-down crinoids. The mouth and podia in the grooves along the arms point downward against the substrate. The podia with suckers at their tips are used for locomotion rather than for channeling food particles. Sea stars feed by everting or pushing out their stomach from the mouth to envelop and digest their prey.

Brittle stars (Ophiuroidea) differ from sea stars in having longer flexible arms that are distinctly separated from their oval-shaped body. Snake-like actions of the arms allow them to move about on seafloor sediments, which makes brittle stars the most mobile of all the echinoderms. The podia are used to direct surface detritus to the mouth.

The spiniest echinoderms are the sea urchins (Echinoidea). Spine sizes range from a thin fur-like covering to long needle-sharp spines that are capable of puncturing human skin. These spines are not only protective, but are also used for locomotion. While some sea urchins graze on the thin film of algae of the rock surface, others collect food particles with their podia as they burrow through sediments.

With their soft, elongate, and worm-like bodies, sea cucumbers (Holothuroidea) are the most unusual of all echinoderms. The mouth is at one end and the anus at the other. A ring of tentacle-like podia constantly stuff sediments into the mouth. Many human societies harvest holothurians for food, when they are variously known as trepang, bêche-de-mer, or sea slug.

TUNICATES

Tunicates (Urochordata), for instance sea squirts and salps, are the most primitive members of the Chordata. Apart from being deuterostomes, their larval stage has a notochord (a strengthening rod down the back), a feature shared with vertebrates during their embryonic development. Other shared features include a dorsal nerve cord above the notochord and openings to the pharynx (area behind the mouth) that form gill slits.

Adult tunicates are mostly sessile animals that are covered by a leathery vest or "tunic," with two openings to their bottle-shaped body. Water is taken through one opening where small particles of food are filtered through the gill slits. Excess water is expelled through the second opening. Salps are free-floating, barrel-shaped tunicates. They use the intake and expulsion of water for limited propulsion.

FISHES

With more than 28,000 species, fishes inhabit almost every imaginable habitat across the underwater realm. Their diversity is breathtaking, with the variety of colors, forms, sizes, and behaviors seemingly endless. Streamlined shapes, precision fins, and gills for underwater breathing make fishes the ultimate "swimming machines."

FINS AND GILLS, HIGHS AND LOWS

Fishes make up more than half of all vertebrate species on our planet. They differ from other vertebrates—amphibians, reptiles, birds, and mammals—in being superbly adapted for aquatic life, using their fins for swimming, maneuverability, and balance, and their gills to obtain oxygen from water for breathing.

Fishes live almost anywhere there is water. Some inhabit alpine pools as high as 3 miles (5 km) above sea level, and others live in ocean trenches as deep as 7 miles (11 km) under the sea. Some live in Antarctic waters at temperatures below freezing, whereas others are denizens of hot springs warmer than 104°F (40°C). Subterranean species have even been pumped up from deep wells. But it is the world's oceans that are home to approximately 59 percent of all known fish species.

Fishes display an impressive variety of sizes, shapes, and colors, from the diminutive coral-reef goby that is less than ¾ in (10 mm) long to the whale shark that reaches almost 40 ft (12 m) in length. Coral reef species rival the spectacular patterns and hues of birds and butterflies, while others mimic seaweed fronds or rocks as clever camouflage. Fishes also vary greatly in lifespan—some live less than a year, whereas others live for two hundred.

In terms of scientific classification, there are five major groups. The most primitive group is the jawless fishes, or hagfishes, which are mostly scavengers found on the sea floor. Although they are often included with the vertebrates, they do not have true vertebrate elements. The lampreys, the second group of jawless fishes, are parasitic feeders. These fishes do have vertebrate elements and belong with the other vertebrates. The cartilaginous fishes include the sharks, skates, and rays. Members of this group have jaws but the skeleton is made of cartilage rather than bone. By far the largest group of jawed fishes is the bony fishes. As the name implies, the skeleton is made of bone. The last jawed group with a bony skeleton is the lobe-finned fishes. This group includes the lungfishes and coelacanths and has characteristics more related to the tetrapods (amphibians, reptiles, birds, and mammals) than to other fishes.

RITE TO REPLICATE

The methods of reproduction used by fishes vary greatly. Most species lay eggs that are then fertilized outside the body, but some have internal fertilization. Those that lay eggs either release the fertilized eggs into the water column where they float and then hatch into larvae that disperse in the currents, or they deposit them on the bottom, where often they are guarded by one or more parent. The vast majority of eggs laid on the bottom also hatch into larvae that disperse in the water column. Those with internal fertilization may then lay the eggs; hold the developing eggs inside for a time and then release the larvae; or hold the developing eggs inside until live young are released.

Sex change is another fascinating reproductive mechanism found in fishes. Most remain male or female throughout their lives, but some change from male to female and still others from female to male. A few species are able to alternate between sexes. There also are some fishes that have both functional male and female reproductive organs.

COMMON SENSE

Fishes have a wide variety of sensory mechanisms. In addition to eyes for vision, fishes have a lateral-line system, including organs on the surface of the body that detect disturbances in the surrounding water. Fishes also have the ability to hear, often increasing this ability by having connections between the ear and the swim bladder that vibrate in response to sound. The sense of smell and taste is highly developed, with some sharks able to detect fish scent at levels of one part per 25 million parts seawater. Many fishes also have organs that detect or even create electrical currents, which they then use to locate food.

Considering the great diversity of fishes, it is not surprising that a wide variety of plants and animals serve as food. Some feed only on plant material, others on both plants and animals, and many only on specific animal groups. The mechanisms and behaviors for finding food vary widely, as do the techniques for avoiding being eaten.

LEFT A school of bluestriped gruntfish *(Haemulon sciurus)* swim among the coral. These colorful fish grow to a length of around 18 in (45 cm).

TOP Snappers live and travel in schools. Carnivorous fishes, their diet consists mainly of smaller fish and crustaceans.

CENTER A male cardinalfish with a mouthful of eggs. Cardinalfish belong to the family Apogonidae, and inhabit shallow waters in coral reefs. Many males carry the eggs in their mouths until they are ready to hatch.

BELOW RIGHT A lemon shark *(Negaprion brevirostris)* surrounded by remora fish. Most sharks have five gill slits, although some species have six or seven. The gills themselves are made of cartilage.

BELOW LEFT Its iridiscent blue color makes the neon goby *(Elacatinus oceanops)* an easily recognizable fish. Native to the western Atlantic, these fishes reach a mature length of about 2½ in (6 cm).

Tooth and Jaw

Hagfishes and lampreys are jawless fishes. Lampreys have an oval disk-like mouth; hagfishes have a slit-like mouth. Although they lack many of the characteristic fish features, they nonetheless make up two of the four classes considered to be "fishes." Sharks, skates, and rays have a skeleton made of cartilage and tough skin covered in unique, protective, streamlining scales called dermal denticles.

OPPOSITE Manta rays *(Manta birostris)* can reach a width of 20 ft (6 m) across the pectoral fins and weigh almost 3,000 lbs (1,360 kg). They are able to make tremendous leaps out of the water.

RIGHT Dermal denticles of a great white shark magnified 2,200 times. Denticles are small tooth-like structures that cover the shark's skin.

BELOW The disk-like mouth of a lamprey, in this case *Petromyzon marinus*, showing the fish's horny teeth, which are arranged in concentric circles.

SLIMY KNOTS AND SLIM BLOODSUCKERS

The hagfishes are the most primitive of the organisms that we call fishes, with fossil hagfishes appearing at least 40 million years before any other fishes. They lack jaws, bones, scales, paired fins, and well-developed eyes. They have fleshy filaments called barbels surrounding an oval mouth and teeth only on the tongue. Hagfishes produce liberal amounts of slime, which is used as an effective defense mechanism. There are approximately 70 species, all of which are restricted to marine environments. Hagfishes are the only fishes with body fluids that are the same salinity as seawater, which is similar to invertebrates. Their method of reproduction does not involve a larval stage—instead the eggs hatch into miniature adults.

Hagfishes are scavengers, mostly boring into the bodies of dying or dead fishes and feeding on the insides. They tear pieces of flesh from their prey by tying themselves into a distinctive knot to gain leverage. They also eat invertebrates living on the sea floor.

The 38 species of lampreys make up the other group of jawless fishes. Lampreys also lack bones, scales, and paired fins, but have well-developed eyes (as adults) and a disk-like mouth lined with horny teeth. Marine lampreys are parasitic predators that attach to other fishes. They use their teeth to bore into the prey's flesh and drain the blood and fluids, assisted by an anti-coagulating substance in the saliva.

KEEP IT FLEXIBLE

The jawed cartilaginous fishes—those whose skeleton is made from cartilage—include approximately 970 species of sharks, skates, and rays. These fishes have distinctive placoid (tooth-like) scales or denticles, paired fins, five to seven separate gill openings, and teeth that are constantly replaced throughout their life. The dorsal fins are rigid and cannot be raised up and down as in other jawed fishes. All have internal fertilization, with the sperm being transferred to the female by the male's modified pelvic fins. Some species then lay the eggs, whereas in some, the young develop inside the female. In some shark species, the young are even known to eat each other while still inside the female.

A shark's separate gill openings are on the sides of the body, whereas in skates and rays they are on the underside. In addition, the front edges of a shark's pectoral fins are not attached to the side of the head—in skates and rays they are attached to form a disk or "wings." Most shark species have separate teeth, but skates and rays have teeth that are fused into plates and are used for crushing food.

SIZING UP SHARKS

Sharks vary greatly in size, from the 40-ft (12 m) whale shark *(Rhincodon typus)* to the 8-in (20 cm) dwarf lantern shark *(Etmopterus perryi)*. Although it is the largest shark (and the largest fish), the whale shark feeds exclusively on plankton. The great white shark

(Carcharodon carcharias) is one of the largest predatory fish in the ocean and can reach at least 20 ft (6 m) in length. The tiger shark *(Galeocerdo cuvier)* can reach at least 24.3 ft (7.4 m). Both feed on large prey, including birds, turtles, dolphins, whales, and seals. They have also been known to attack humans.

MOVEABLE FEAST

Sharks live in a variety of habitats and feed on a wide range of organisms. Besides organs for sight and smell, many sharks have electro-receptors to detect electric currents created by swimming prey or those buried beneath sand. Most skates and rays live near the bottom, where they feed on organisms that are buried under the sand, often using their pectoral fins to sweep the sand away. They are capable of crushing large clams between their teeth. The largest ray species is the manta ray *(Manta birostris)*. It swims in the water column where it filters plankton through specialized gill slits. Stingrays have a defensive venomous spine on their whip-like tails. Electric rays have electric organs in their pectoral fins that are used for defense and capturing food.

RIGHT A fearsome great white shark *(Carcharodon carcharias)* breaks the surface, baring its rows of incredibly sharp teeth. Sharks constantly grow, shed, and regrow their teeth.

Fins, Bones, and Gills

The bony or ray-finned fishes are the second major group of jawed fishes. Just over half of the 27,000 species in this large and very diverse group are ocean dwellers, while the remaining species live in fresh water. They exploit every kind of aquatic habitat, from the ocean floor to the surface shallows—some even live on or inside other species.

AQUATIC ASSORTMENT

Bony fishes (class Actinopterygii) are divided into 46 different orders and 457 families. The majority of ocean species inhabit shallow warm waters; the next greatest concentration is in the deep sea, with fewer numbers in shallow cold waters and open ocean surface habitats.

These fishes have a skeleton of true bone; teeth that are fused to the jaw bones; soft, segmented rays in the fins so that they can be raised or lowered; and gill clefts that have one common opening instead of separate ones, as is the case in sharks. The body may be covered with overlapping scales, but these are different from those found in sharks. Some bony fishes, thought to be more primitive, do not have spines in their fins, including sardines, anchovies, and salmon. More advanced species tend to have spines in their fins and are represented by fishes such as snapper and tuna.

STAYING AFLOAT

Unlike sharks, which are heavier than water and must keep swimming or sink to the bottom, most bony fishes maintain neutral buoyancy when swimming. This weightlessness in the water affords them greater maneuverability—they can swim quickly or hover delicately while expending much less energy. Neutral buoyancy is achieved by an internal gas-filled bladder (swim bladder), along with special organs that allow gas to enter or leave as a fish moves up or down in the water. Some deep-sea fishes maintain neutral buoyancy by having very light bones as well as lipids and wax esters that are less dense than seawater. Having neutral buoyancy is a handicap for bottom-dwelling fishes, so most lack a swim bladder.

BELOW The knife-like appendage at the tail of an eye-stripe surgeonfish (Acanthurus dussumieri) resembles a surgical scalpel and is equally as sharp. These fish are found in the warm shallow waters of the tropics.

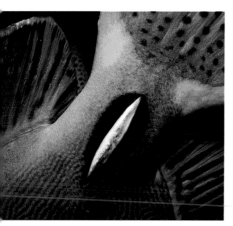

IN THE SWIM

Swimming is accomplished in many different ways. Fishes such as eels swim by undulating their entire body, whereas the fast-swimming fishes, including tuna, swim only with their tail while keeping the body straight. Wrasses and similar species paddle with their pectoral fins, whereas seahorses use only their dorsal fins. Triggerfishes and flatfishes swim by moving their dorsal and anal fins. Damselfishes move up and down, and forward and backward, using their pectoral fins (combined with other fins) for both locomotion and balance. Because swimming movements require large muscles, up to 70 percent of a fish's total weight can be attributed to swimming muscles.

VITAL BREATH

Fishes breathe through gills that can remove oxygen from the water. Bony fishes pump water into their mouths and then force it back over the gills and out of the common gill opening. A number of the fast-swimming fishes, such as tuna, simply open their mouths and water is forced over the gills.

The efficiency of fish gills is the highest of all the organisms that breathe in water—up to 95 percent of oxygen that is present in the water is extracted as the water passes over the gills. Some fishes have also evolved specific mechanisms that allow them to obtain

oxygen by alternative methods, and these fish are capable of surviving for some time out of water.

KEEPING THE HEAT

The body temperature of most fishes is the same as the water temperature, largely because the blood passing through their gills is exposed to the water. Bony fishes, such as the tuna and some large sharks, have body temperatures that are higher than the surrounding water. This is because heat builds up in their muscles during fast swimming, and some of that heat crosses over into the blood, flowing into the body's core through a counter-current exchange system.

FOSSIL FIND

The lobe-finned fishes (class Sarcopterygii) make up the second group of jawed bony fishes. Of this group only the coelacanths (*Latimeria* species) occur in the ocean; lungfishes live in fresh water. There are two species of coelacanths—one off southern Africa and the other from Indonesian waters.

For many years, coelacanths were known only from fossils. The first live specimen was captured off the South African coast in 1938. Because of this relatively recent discovery, these remarkable fishes are now referred to as "living" fossils.

Coelacanths inhabit deep water, at more than 492 ft (150 m), mostly along steeply sloping rocky areas. They give birth to as many as 26 live young.

Their lobe-like pectoral and pelvic fins, which resemble the limbs of tetrapods (amphibians, reptiles, birds, and mammals), as well as various other internal anatomical features, suggests quite a close relationship to many of the terrestrial vertebrates.

ABOVE Reaching lengths of up to 6 ½ ft (2 m), the southern bluefin tuna (*Thunnus maccoyii*) is one of the fastest of the bony fishes. Southern bluefin tuna have a lifespan of about 40 years.

Fishes of the Coral Reef

The world's coral reefs are a riot of color and movement, due in most part to the rich array of exquisite fish species. Coral-reef fishes live within a specific temperature zone in the ocean. Coral grows best where the mean annual water temperature is at least 74°F (23.5°C); when water temperatures fall below 68°F (20°C) little reef formation occurs.

OPPOSITE Anemonefishes, such as the false clown anemonefish *(Amphiprion ocellaris)*, find a safe haven in the stinging tentacles of the sea anemone. In return, the feces of the clownfish nourish the sea anemone.

ZONING OUT

The broad Tropical Zone in the world oceans—which is bordered north and south by average annual temperatures of 68°F (20°C)—has been divided into four primary zones, each with its own assemblage of coral-reef fishes. These zones are the Indo–Pacific, the West African, the West Indian, and the Pacific American. The Indo–Pacific region, which includes the Indian and Pacific oceans, boasts the greatest diversity by far, with around 4,000 species, or 18 percent of all living fishes. In Micronesia, 103 different fish families have been observed, but some of these are more completely associated with the coral-reef environment than others, for example the wrasses, parrotfishes, surgeonfishes, butterflyfishes, angelfishes, and damselfishes.

PARROTFISHES

The parrotfishes (family Scaridae) are so named because their teeth are fused into a distinctive beak-like structure. Many, especially the males, are also brightly colored. Parrotfishes are one of the major plant-eating families on the coral reef. They graze on thread-like algae and sea grass and also nibble coral to obtain the plant material that grows inside. They have specialized tooth plates at the back of their mouths that can crush and grind coral. This grinding activity produces large quantities of the soft sediment found around reefs.

Along with other plant-eating fishes and some invertebrates, parrotfishes are responsible for the clear sand area that usually surrounds a coral reef, a result of them eating the vegetation as far out as they can go

BELOW The dental structure of the parrotfish gives this amazing fish its name. The teeth, which resemble a parrot's beak, are used to bite algae from coral. Parrotfish are usually brightly colored, mostly in shades of blue, green, and yellow.

without being eaten themselves. Coloration is often markedly different in male, female, and young parrotfishes, and in the past each may have been described as a separate species. These cases of "mistaken identity" have been realized only since the advent of scuba diving, when biologists were able to observe these "different species" spawning together. Parrotfishes are unique in making a defensive mucus cocoon around their bodies at night.

WRASSES

Wrasses (family Labridae) are related to parrotfishes, and the sexes and young are also differently colored. Unlike parrotfishes, wrasses feed on animals and not plant material. Along with parrotfishes, wrasses are one of the groups that have the ability to change sex. Individuals that are initially females may turn into males, and take on male coloration. In some species this change has been related to social behavior. These usually are species in which a single male controls a territory that includes a number of females with whom he spawns. If something happens to the male, the most dominant female can turn into a male and then spawn with the group of females.

SURGEONFISHES

Surgeonfishes (family Acanthuridae) are another family of plant-eating fishes. Unlike parrotfishes, they do not bite coral, but they do graze on algae and sea grass. The name "surgeonfish" comes from a sharp, knife-like spine just before the caudal fin. Often, large schools of these fishes are seen moving over the reef, grazing on algae, typically with their heads down and their tails up. It has been suggested that this relates to the evolution of the protective spines near the tail.

BUTTERFLIES, ANGELS, AND DAMSELS

Butterflyfishes (family Chaetodontidae) are some of the most conspicuous and colorful fishes on the reef. They feed during the day, but rest in coral crevices at night. They have long, brush-like teeth that are used for feeding on coral and the tentacles of marine worms, as well as on small invertebrates and fish eggs. Some species have long snouts for feeding deep inside crevices. A few species feed primarily on zooplankton (animal plankton), and form large groups that hang in mid-water. Butterflyfishes typically form pairs that stay together for a number of years, patrolling a home range that they defend from others.

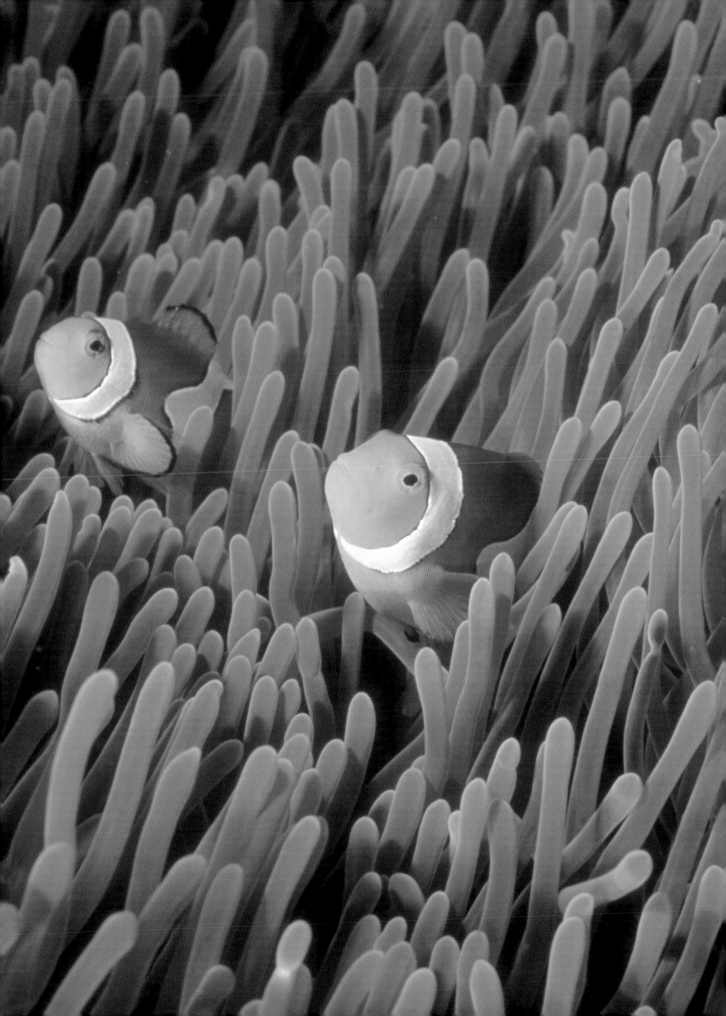

ABOVE Copperband butterflyfish (*Chelmon rostratus*) are among the most colorful fish in a coral reef. Adults reach a length of around 8 in (20 cm).

ABOVE RIGHT The well-named queen angelfish (*Holacanthus ciliaris*) is a brilliant blue and yellow color. These shy fishes feed by day, hiding among rocks and coral at night.

BELOW Yellowtail surgeonfish (*Prionurus punctatus*) graze on sea grass. The plant-eating fishes are gray with small black spots and a bright yellow tail.

Angelfishes (family Pomacanthidae) are closely related to the butterflyfishes, but they typically feed on sponges, soft-bodied invertebrates, algae, and fish eggs. These fishes also change sex, beginning life as females and then changing to males. As with some of the wrasses, often a single male defends a territory that includes a number of females.

Damselfishes (family Pomacentridae) form another major component of the coral-reef fish fauna. The family is large in both the number of species as well as individuals on a particular reef. Feeding habits vary widely in this group, with some feeding on plankton in the water above the reef, some on various invertebrates, and yet others on algae that they grow in "gardens" in territories they defend.

MARINE METROPOLIS

One of the first questions that comes to mind when observing a coral reef is: "How can so many fishes coexist on such a small reef?" A number of different considerations go toward answering this question. A coral reef is brimming with diversity and activity, but in addition to those species that are easily seen, there are many more that eke out an existence hidden from view among the coral cracks and crevices. Also, many fishes are not full-time residents but rather visitors or transients, passing through for a few hours or a few days. Some of these are predators, such as fast-moving jacks and mackerels.

FORCE OF HABIT

For the many species that do live on the reef, there are a number of ways to divide the habitat. For example, species from many different families are specialized plankton feeders, foraging in the water column above the reef. They play an important role in transferring energy from the open ocean to the coral-reef community. These fishes eat a large percentage of plankton when it is swept across the reef from open water by currents; they are sometimes referred to as a "wall of mouths." Many of these fishes then serve as food for the larger fishes on the reef. Most of the energy they transfer to the reef, however, is in the form of their feces, which fall down on the reef, providing food for invertebrates and some other fishes. These invertebrates and fishes, in turn, are then food for other larger fishes on the reef.

OPEN NIGHT AND DAY

Feeding structures are another way to understand the complexities of reef organization. One major method of sharing space and food on a reef is for some species to feed only during the day and others only at night. Many species that feed at night only obtain their food away from the reef. So, although there may be large groups of grunts, snappers, or red squirrelfishes on the reef during the day, at night they move away from their daytime shelter to feed on invertebrates and small fishes in adjacent sand and sea grass habitats. Some other red fishes, including cardinalfishes, bigeyes, and some squirrelfishes, also feed at night, but they feed above the reef on plankton that is present only at night. Some eels also move over the reef at night, feeding on fishes hiding in the reef.

As daylight breaks, the night species retreat back into the reef for cover and the daytime fishes move out from their nighttime hiding places. The first to appear

are small sea basses, butterflyfishes, and damselfishes. Many daytime fishes tend to live on different parts of the reef and feed on different kinds of foods. As dusk approaches, the daytime fishes slowly sink into the reef before the nighttime fishes come out, and the reef is unusually quiet. This is a very dangerous time for some species because many predators such as jacks, mackerels, barracudas, and sharks swim over the reef to feed, and the light becomes too low for daytime schooling species to maintain schools that provide protection.

AVOIDING DANGER

Fishes have many unique ways of minimizing danger from predators. Schooling behavior is one—the milling morass of many fishes tends to be disorienting to a predator, making it difficult to isolate a specific target. Many species evade predators by hiding, sheltering in crevices among the coral when danger threatens. Other fishes have cryptic coloration that helps them to blend in with the surroundings, making it very difficult for a predator to see them. Anemonefishes live among the stinging tentacles of sea anemones—they are protected from the stings, but other fishes dare not venture too close. Surgeonfishes have sharp spines near their tail, and other fishes, such as the angelfishes, have formidable spines on the head.

Some fishes use chemical defenses. Pufferfishes taste bad and are toxic; predators who try to eat them have been observed to spit them out. A number of fishes, such as those in the scorpionfish family, like the turkeyfish, have venomous spines. Often, venomous fishes have a warning coloration, such as a bright patch on a fin that can be flashed at a predator. Predators soon learn to avoid them. This phenomenon has led to some interesting cases of mimicry in which non-venomous or non-toxic species have evolved coloration that mimics a protected venomous species. For example, the filefish (*Paraluteres prionurus*) mimics the toby (*Canthigaster valentine*), a toxic species. These similar-looking fishes belong to entirely different families.

ABOVE Safety in numbers—to ward off larger predators, a variety of fish form a school together, including French grunts *(Haemulon flavolineatum)*, bluestriped grunts *(Haemulon sciurus)*, and porkfish *(Anisotremus virginicus)*.

Open Ocean Dwellers

The open ocean stretches across more than 70 percent of the world's surface. This sweeping expanse of blue water is home to some of the fastest predators on the planet, as well as to the ocean's ramblers, constantly searching for food, a mate, or even hitching a ride on a companion.

BENEATH THE WAVES

The open ocean is divided, according to depth, into a number of zones, with the upper 656 ft (200 m) called the epipelagic zone. It is also known as the photic zone because it is the area where light penetrates. This is an important zone because it is here that phytoplankton (plant plankton) undergo photosynthesis, and capture the energy of the Sun. The zooplankton (the animal plankton) in this zone feed on the abundant phytoplankton. Where nutrient-rich water wells up from below, productivity can be very high indeed. Many of the world's major fisheries exploit fishes, for example tuna, in this zone. Organisms that live in the waters below depend on the feces and dead bodies of the organisms in this zone sinking to the bottom to provide a valuable food source.

WIDE BLUE OCEAN

Surface-zone species are known as pelagic fishes. Pelagic fishes are found not only in the open ocean but also in coastal waters. There is a broad range of species in this ocean habitat, including sharks and many types of bony fishes. Pelagic fishes are drawn from many unrelated fish families, but they share many similar adaptations to surface-zone life. Most of them have very silvery undersurfaces and dark upper surfaces, a pattern that is referred to as countershading, and which makes them difficult to see from both above and below against the surface of the water. They also usually have very streamlined bodies and small fins, suited for fast and continuous swimming.

OPEN WIDE

The base of the fish food chain in this zone starts with herrings, sardines, anchovies, and their relatives. These are generally smaller fishes, usually under 10 in (25 cm) long, which typically school as they swim through the water with their mouths wide open, filtering out phytoplankton and zooplankton with their fine gill rakers. The energy produced by the phytoplankton is ultimately passed from these fishes to those higher up the food chain. Many of these fishes also migrate during their lives, swimming from their feeding area up the major currents to a spawning ground. There, eggs and sperm are shed, and the developing eggs and larvae then drift downcurrent to where they will feed as adults.

BELOW A large school of sardines swims through the water eating plankton, which they filter from the water through their gills. Sardines are important prey for larger fishes.

TAKING FLIGHT

One group of open-water fishes often seen by boaters is the flyingfishes (family Exocoetidae). When disturbed, they swim along the surface propelled by a caudal fin that vibrates up to 50 beats a second, with fins at their sides. After gaining enough speed they then take flight by spreading their wing-like pectoral and often pelvic fins. The average flight speed is approximately 35 mph (56 km/h), and flights usually last around 10 seconds; one flight was clocked at 42 seconds. The evolution of this unique body form and behavior allows escape from the larger predators.

NEED FOR SPEED

One group of predators in this zone is the tuna (family Scombridae). These high-speed fishes are capable of swimming at speeds of 65 mph (100 km/h). As well as a torpedo-shaped body that reduces drag, tuna have several other significant adaptations for speed, including fins that fold down against their body, often into grooves, lessening drag when they swim. A stiffened caudal fin reduces drag further by allowing the tail to vibrate rapidly without great lateral movement of the body. This is possible because the vertebrae in front of that fin are modified and interlocking to make the tail region rigid. The caudal-fin rays also stiffen the vertebral column by overlapping it. Bluefin tuna (*Thunnus* species*)* can reach a length of about 13 ft (4 m) and a weight of 1,102 lbs (500 kg). But tuna also serve as food for a range of other fishes in this habitat. Swordfishes (family Xiphiidae), and many of the

billfishes, such sailfishes and marlins (family Istiophoridae), feed on tuna as well as on other fishes.

HITCHING A RIDE

Large pelagic fishes often have hitchhikers called remoras or sharksuckers. Remoras (family Echeneidae) are fishes with a dorsal fin that has modified into a sucking disc located far forward on the head. They attach to sharks and other large bony fishes as they swim, moving over the surface of the host's body and gills removing ectoparasites. Remoras also release from the host when it is feeding and eat the scraps that may be floating in the water.

LEFT A flyingfish (*Exocoetus sp.)* in full flight. The large pectoral fins of these remarkable fishes allow them to make short flights above the surface of the water when they are threatened.

BELOW A large manta ray plays host to a group of remoras, which are also known as suckerfish. These fish feed on the bigger fish's leftovers, as well as microscopic organisms on the host's body. A sucker-like disk allows them to attach themselves to large pelagic fish such as rays and sharks.

Deep-sea Denizens

In the dimness of the deep ocean, where the last remnants of sunlight barely penetrate, a variety of fishes—some quite bizarre in form—search for food in the gloom. Pressures on survival are high here, including the intense pressure of tons of water weighing down on its inhabitants.

LIFE IN THE DARKNESS

Under the surface epipelagic zone—deeper than 656 ft (200 m)—there is not enough light for plant growth. This deep-sea habitat is divided into the mesopelagic zone, 656 to 3,280 ft (200 to 1,000 m), and the bathypelagic zone, which is below 3,280 ft (1,000 m). Some light penetrates the mesopelagic zone (mostly blue–green wavelengths), which fishes can perceive, but the bathypelagic zone is completely dark. Life in this lightless habitat has resulted in a fascinating array of adaptations. These fishes not only have to feed in darkness, they must also be able to find mates, reproduce, and avoid being eaten. In addition, they must

RIGHT Flabby whalefishes (*Cetomimus* sp.) are among the most deep-living fish known, with some species recorded at depths of over 2 miles (3.5 km).

BELOW Hatchetfish (family Sternoptychidae) are found in the bathypelagic zone. They have large eyes, which help them find prey in the dark depths of the ocean.

deal with very cold water and the enormous pressure experienced at these depths. Given these restraints, it is perhaps surprising that more than 2,000 species are found in these very deep waters.

LET THERE BE LIGHT

Although there are many unrelated families of deep-sea fishes, all of them have a number of common adaptations to help them survive in this unique habitat. Many have light-producing organs called photophores. Some create light through chemical reactions, whereas others have light-producing bacteria living inside their photophores. Many fishes in the mesopelagic zone have photophores on their bellies and lower sides. This helps to break up their silhouettes against the light coming from above. The light produced by the photophores is in the blue–green spectrum, which is the same as in the surrounding water.

Photophores also play an important role in prey capture. The dragonfishes (family Stomiidae), deep-sea anglers (family Ceratiidae), and many other fishes have a light organ at the end of a barbel or modified fin, which often contains luminous bacteria. When smaller fishes or invertebrates are attracted to the light and mistake it for a food item, the fish quickly snaps them up. Some hatchetfishes (*Argyropelecus* species) have photophores inside their mouth, again luring prey to their demise. Many of these fishes have huge fangs that help capture the prey once it is close.

Photophores may also be important in mate recognition. The photophore patterns on lanternfishes (family Myctophidae), for example, are species-specific, and may help males and females of the same species find each other in the dark.

Most fishes living in these twilight habitats have specialized eyes to capture the paucity of light. Mesopelagic fishes have large eyes and pupils that often are elongated, as well as pure-rod retinas that increase their sensitivity to light. Fishes living in the deepest, darkest regions, however, have very small eyes. They instead become very sensitive to the tiniest vibrations in the water to locate prey.

DINING IN THE DARK

Most species living in the deeper mesopelagic zone move up into the euphotic zone at night to feed because there is a greater availability of food. This movement is called vertical migration and can involve some very small fishes—lanternfishes, for example—moving up more than 650 ft (200 m). In the morning

LEFT The loosejaw dragonfish *(Photostomias guernei)* is found in the bathypelagic zone. The bottom of the fish's mouth is absent, so that the mouth can open wider and take in larger food items.

they sink back down to darker water where there are fewer predators. In addition to the open-water species, there are bottom-dwelling (benthic) fishes and those living just above the bottom (benthopelagic). Grenadiers (family Macrouridae), the tripodfish *(Bathypterois grallator)*, and cusk-eels (family Ophidiidae) live in these regions. Cusk-eels have been found living on the bottom as deep as 26,250 ft (8,000 m). Deep-sea feeders, such as the swallowers *(Pseudoscopelus* species*)* and the gulper eel *(Eurypharynx pelecanoides)*, have mouths, throats, and guts that are greatly expandable, enabling them to eat fishes almost as large as themselves. This adaptation is an advantage for fishes that only encounter prey occasionally.

Deep-sea Love Bites

The deep-ocean habitat is vast, making it extremely difficult for fishes living there to find mates. The deep-sea anglerfishes (right) have solved this problem in a unique way.

Male anglerfishes are dwarfs, about ten times smaller than females. They have very large nostrils and beak-like denticles at the front of their jaws. When they detect the scent of a female in the water they follow it, perhaps also searching for her glow. Upon finding her, they immediately bite onto her flesh. The body tissue around the male's mouth then fuses with the body of the female and they become one, with the male then obtaining all his nutritional needs from the female. Indeed, the male becomes completely parasitic on the female and provides a ready source of sperm at spawning time.

Time and Tide—the Rocky Shores

The rocky shores of tropical regions are home to many fishes, but those in more temperate areas also contain a broad diversity of species, especially in the area between the highest and lowest tides, the rocky intertidal zone. Tide pools are important habitats for fishes, especially juvenile ones, because predation is less here than in deeper water.

RIGHT The snailfish (family Liparidae) is capable of clinging to kelp using its suction-cup ventral fins, a necessary skill in the intertidal zone.

FAR RIGHT When currents change, members of the sculpin family, such as this Irish lord fish (*Hemilepidotus hemilepidotus*), wedge their pectoral fins against rock surfaces to help them keep still, thus avoiding being swept away by strong tides.

BELOW A leopard-spotted goby (*Thorogobius ephippiatus*) usually grows to a length of about 5 in (13 cm). These fish from the family Gobiidae enjoy a diet of crustaceans, gastropods, and algae. They occur in the eastern Atlantic off Europe.

COASTAL SURVIVAL

A number of fishes that live in deeper water come to the intertidal area to lay eggs and defend their nests against predators; others come to the area during high tide to feed. Besides these temporary visitors seeking refuge in tide pools, there are many fishes that are permanent residents in this most demanding of ocean habitats. The ebb and flow of the tides presents constant and cyclic change to coastal habitats. Resident species must adapt to the extremes of temperature, desiccation, and wave force, as well as the ongoing demands for oxygen and food.

Tide-pool fishes are exposed to large temperature changes during the day—at high tide they are covered by cold water, but at low tide they are trapped in areas that are heated by the Sun. In far northern or southern areas they may be exposed to freezing temperatures. These fish also face the problem of obtaining enough oxygen, because low tide leaves them either under or between rocks with little water, or in shallow pools with solar-heated water that has been depleted of most of its oxygen. Some of these fishes have evolved mechanisms that allow them to obtain oxygen from the air—some absorb it through their skin, some through specialized tissue in the mouth, and still others through gills that are modified to work when out of the water. Desiccation is a problem for species stranded under rocks or algae. Feeding is also restricted to high-tide periods.

BODIES EXPOSED

Wave force is a major challenge in this habitat, and intertidal fishes share a number of similarities in body form, physiology, and behavior to help them survive the harsh and unrelenting environment. Most of the permanent residents are small and can fit into spaces under or between rocks. They also have very tough skin and either lack scales or have scales that are very small and firmly attached. Some species may produce mucus to aid in skin lubrication and to help prevent desiccation. Many of them also lack a swim bladder so that they can stay on the bottom during periods of high turbulence.

Pricklebacks (family Stichaeidae), found primarily in the North Pacific and Atlantic oceans, are a good example of fishes well adapted to this habitat. They have eel-like bodies that can readily squeeze between or under rocks when the tide goes out. They also press their bodies next to rocks or algae to reduce the area of skin exposed to desiccation, and then fold their body forward to the snout, covering the exposed side.

Clingfishes (family Gobiesocidae), snailfishes (family Liparidae), and gobies (family Gobiidae) have pelvic fins modified into a sucking disc that allows them to hold on when waves crash onto the rocks.

Many other fishes, such as sculpins (family Cottidae), have large pectoral fins that can be wedged against the rocks to help maintain position.

Larger predatory fishes do move in from the deeper subtidal areas to feed, and so intertidal species have evolved cryptic color patterns (crypsis) that make it easier to evade predators or go unnoticed by potential prey. A number, such as gunnels (family Pholidae), can match the red or green color of the algae they happen to be in, and the mottled color of many sculpins makes them blend in with the background. This protective coloration also helps them evade the many seabirds that feed in this area at low tide.

HOME IS WHERE THE FOOD IS

Life in the intertidal zone is greatly affected by the availability of food. This zone has an abundance of both algae and invertebrates that provides a bounty for its many inhabitants. The intertidal zone has more herbivorous (plant-eating) fishes than other temperate habitats, but not as many as the tropical seas. Studies of several different kinds of intertidal fishes have shown

that they tend to have a home tide pool. At high tide the fishes move out of their home pool to feed in a wide area, but as the tide begins to drop they move back home. Individuals that moved to a new tide pool as far away as 886 ft (270 m) travel back to their home pool when the tide changes.

ABOVE Inhabiting the eastern Pacific Ocean, bay gobies (*Lepidogobius lepidus*) can be found in the intertidal zone and down to depths of around 650 ft (200 m).

Beyond the Tides

The deeper coastal waters beyond the wave-swept intertidal zone—called the subtidal zone—extend over the continental shelf. Although some pelagic fishes are found in the open water above the shelf, most species here live in close association with the bottom, which may be rock, sand, or mud. Many species are commercially valuable as food.

FLAT OUT SWIMMING

Flatfishes (soles, flounders, and halibut) stand out as being highly adapted for life on the subtidal rocky or sandy sea floor. Flatfishes are unusual in that they have both eyes on the same side of the body. When they first hatch they differ little from other fishes, but as they grow, one eye slowly migrates to the other side. The front of the skull also twists to change the position of the jaws. Flatfishes lie on their sides with the eyes up; they also stay on their sides when swimming. They partially camouflage themselves with a dusting of sand while lying on the bottom, and can also change their coloration to match the substrate they are resting on, making it difficult for both predators and potential prey to see them. Most flatfishes feed on sand-dwelling invertebrates, often nipping off the necks of clams. Some species feed on other fishes.

BELOW Found mainly in subtidal zones in the north Atlantic, Ocean, Atlantic cod *(Gadus morhua)* feed mainly on crabs, squid, and fish. Commercially valuable, they are vulnerable to overfishing.

ROCKFISHES

Another commercially important group of fishes found in the subtidal zone is the rockfishes (family Scorpaenidae), which are often sold as ocean perch, snapper, redfish, or Pacific red snapper. Rockfishes live in the cool waters of the Northern and Southern hemispheres, with the greatest concentration in the north Pacific. There are many species, with at least 65 species off the Pacific coast of North America. Rockfishes range in depth from the intertidal zone down to 656 ft (200 m), and are found over rocky or soft substrate, often in association with kelp beds. Unlike most fishes, rockfishes have internal fertilization and the eggs develop within the female; when the larval fishes are born they spend time developing in the plankton before moving out. Advanced scientific techniques for determining the age of rockfishes showed that one species lives to at

least 205 years, another to 156 years, and yet another to 118 years. Long-lived species usually mature later, and some rockfishes do not mature until they are 22 years or older. These species are very vulnerable to fishing pressures, because many are harvested before they have had a chance to reproduce.

COD FISHING

The Atlantic cod (*Gadus morhua*) lives in the subtidal zones of the North Atlantic, along the coasts of both North America and Europe, ranging from the surface down to a depth of 1,476 ft (450 m). Most commercially caught cod are about 11 lbs (5 kg) in weight, but one weighing 210 lbs (95 kg) and reaching 70 in (178 cm) in length has been taken. Cod are usually found within 6½ ft (2 m) of the bottom over rock, gravel, sand, or clay, and feed mostly on fishes, crabs, and squid. Cod make up one of the world's most important food fishes, however overfishing has greatly reduced catches in recent years.

OUT IN THE COLD

Fishes are also found in subtidal areas in polar regions, both north and south. The Antarctic is home to some of the most interesting species, including the icefishes (suborder Notothenioidei), which have the ability to survive in water as cold as 29°F (−1.67°C), the freezing point of seawater. At these temperatures, blood and tissue are super-cooled by almost one degree Celsius, a condition that is unstable. If these species swim up from the bottom toward the surface ice, ice crystals rapidly develop in their bodies. So many species stay deep in the ocean so that this crystallization does not occur. Some shallow-water species, however, are able to swim near the ice because they have antifreeze agents (a group of serum glycopeptides) in their blood. These molecules attach to the developing ice crystals and prevent them from growing and spreading throughout the body. Some, known as crocodile icefishes, have evolved a different way of living in these icy waters. They lack hemoglobin (the oxygen-carrying pigment that colors blood red) in their blood cells, making this almost colorless fish translucent. Icefishes are able to survive without hemoglobin because they live in very cold, well-oxygenated water, and have a large volume of blood that is pumped rapidly by a large heart. They are also capable of taking oxygen in through the skin.

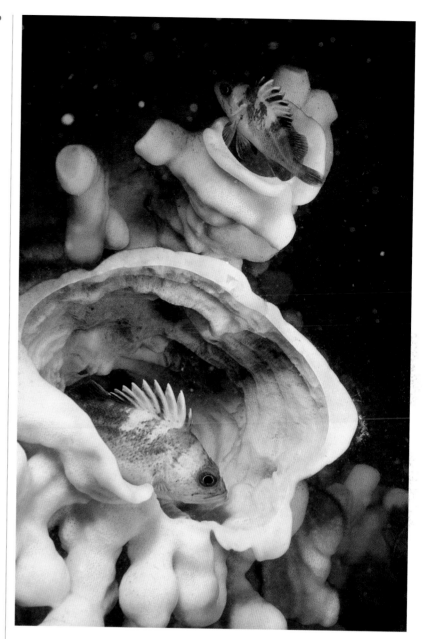

ABOVE RIGHT A quillback rockfish (*Sebastes maliger*) finds a good hiding place in a large cloud sponge in ocean reefs near Lund, British Columbia, Canada.

RIGHT Both eyes of the peacock flounder (*Bothus lunatus*) are on the fish's left side. Flatfishes such as the flounder are suited to life on the sandy ocean floor. They can be found at depths of up to 330 ft (100 m), although are more commonly seen at depths of around 65 ft (20 m).

Fishes in Estuaries and Mangroves

Estuaries are found at the mouths of rivers or streams as they flow into the ocean in areas where the land is low, such that the fresh water does not drop steeply into the ocean. Estuaries are usually semi-enclosed so the mixture of salt and freshwater is protected from the full force of waves and winds. Estuaries also are sometimes referred to as bays, lagoons, sounds, fjords, inlets, or harbors.

ABOVE Mudskippers *(Peri-opthalmus sp.)* perch on a man-grove prop root. Mudskippers can survive out of water for several hours because of the high level of air humidity in mangrove forest.

RIGHT An aerial view of the Carlton River, Tasmania, winding its way through the protected Carlton Estuary, and mixing with saltwater before flowing into the ocean.

Because of the inflow of nutrient-rich water from the land, estuaries are among the most productive aquatic habitats on Earth. As a result, estuaries are important nursery grounds for many different species of coastal marine fishes. They also have an abundance of plants and invertebrates that provide food for adult fishes. Very large estuaries, such as Chesapeake Bay on the eastern coast of North America, also support major commercial fishing operations.

PHYSICAL CHANGES

The physical characteristics of the water in estuaries change daily as the tide changes. For example, salinity increases when more seawater moves into the estuary, and decreases at low tide, when more of the water is from the rivers or streams. There is usually a gradient in salinity in an estuary, with water decreasing in salinity farther upstream. The fishes found in different parts of an estuary reflect this gradient, with those at the river mouths being mostly freshwater species, and those near the ocean mostly marine fishes. Fishes that live in this habitat must be able to deal with sudden changes in salinity, pH, and temperature.

ESTUARY RESIDENTS

There often are five different groups of fishes found in an estuary. First, fully marine species such as some of the sharks and rays move in with the seawater to feed at certain times of the year. Then there are marine migrants that either enter the estuary to reproduce, or whose larvae and juveniles grow in the area. A third group of species move through the estuary to reach a spawning area; these can be either marine species that spawn in freshwater—such as the salmon—or fresh-water fishes such as the eels that spawn in the ocean. Then there are freshwater species that live closest to the streams. There are also permanent residents who remain in the estuary throughout their lives. Some of the common groups of fishes that are permanent residents are the gobies, killifishes, pipefishes, and smelts. It is this latter group that is most interesting because they must deal with many daily fluctuations in their environment.

One of those environmental issues is salinity. The blood of freshwater fishes is saltier (has more ions) than the surrounding freshwater, so water continually flows into them by osmosis. To get rid of excess water,

they produce large amounts of urine; to retain ions while excreting water they also take up salt through the gills and mouth membranes. Saltwater fishes have just the opposite problem because the water around them is saltier than their blood, and so water continually flows out of them. So they drink large amounts of seawater, then eliminate the excess salt through the gut and gills. But some fishes—called euryhaline—have evolved ways to live in water of varying salinity. These fishes, such as the European flounder, can alter the content of ions in their blood depending on whether they are in fresh or saltwater; they also change the amounts of water that they drink and urine they produce when in different salinities. Some fishes, such as the salmon that move from salt to freshwater to spawn, and whose young move back to saltwater to grow, make these changes on a more permanent basis.

In subtropical and tropical regions, estuaries are often lined by mangrove trees that root in the soft sediment. Mangroves have many "prop roots" that arch down from the trunk to the water, providing an extensive habitat for many fishes and invertebrates. Blennies and gobies are abundant in this habitat, as are

the juveniles of many reef fishes. One goby—the mudskipper—perches on the prop roots at low tide, completely out of the water, feeding on small insects and other invertebrates. They are able to spend so much time out of the water because their gills are situated in a cavity that holds both air and water. They can also skip across the mud from tree to tree using their fins and flipping their bodies. At high tide they retreat to underwater burrows to avoid predation by larger fishes moving into the area.

ABOVE After moving downstream, young salmon (smolts) feed and grow in an estuary before they finally move out into the ocean.

RIGHT A school of banded archerfish, *Toxotes jaculatrix*, swims among mangrove prop roots, where the fish find food and shelter. Archerfish are commonly found in the mangroves of tropical Asia.

MARINE MAMMALS

From a diverse range of lineages, marine mammals have evolved into some of the most beautiful and intelligent creatures living in our oceans. Together they parade an amazing range of sizes and lifestyles that have captured our imagination for centuries.

CLASSIFICATION

The varied group of creatures that we refer to as marine mammals evolved from mammalian ancestors that lived on land. Today they represent three different orders of mammals—Carnivora, Cetacea, and Sirenia. Interestingly, while they are united by their adaptations for life at sea, they arose independently from very different ancestors.

The carnivorous marine mammals—polar bears, otters, seals, sea lions and walruses—came from ursid (bear) and mustelid (weasel) ancestors; the cetaceans—whales, dolphins, and porpoises—evolved from hoofed animals such as cows and pigs; and sirenians—manatees and dugongs—are related to elephants.

Despite this diversity, marine mammals are united by the fact, that like us, they breathe air and give birth to live young, either at sea or onshore.

SEALS, WALRUSES, AND POLAR BEARS

The five families of carnivorous mammals are grouped under the suborder Pinnipedia. The first four families are: Otariidae—sea lions and fur seals; Phocidae—true seals; Odobenidae—walruses; and Mustelidae—otters, weasels, minks, etc. The fifth family—Ursidae (bears)—is represented by a single marine species, the polar bear, which while not aquatic, is considered a marine mammal because it spends most of its time in a marine environment, albeit a frozen one.

Unlike other marine mammals, the Pinnipeds have not completely severed their links with land. Although they spend most of their lives in the water, they must return to land or ice to give birth and molt. They are found in all of the oceans of the world except the Indian Ocean, and their greatest concentrations are in the Polar seas, perhaps because these waters are so rich in plankton and fish.

WHALES, PORPOISES, AND DOLPHINS

The Cetacea order, named for the Latin *cetus*, meaning "large seal animal," lives, breeds, rests, and carries out all of its life functions in the water. They consist of about 90 known species, which are further divided into two suborders—the toothed whales or Odontoceti, which includes dolphins, and porpoises; and the baleen whales, or Mysticeti. Together they inhabit all of the world's oceans, as well as some fresh-water lakes and rivers in South America, North America, and Asia.

DUGONGS AND MANATEES

The Sirenians are believed to be the basis for the mermaid myth. They include the dugong and manatees—the only marine mammals classified as herbivores. These slow-moving creatures, which are sometimes referred to as sea cows, inhabit shallow waterways, mainly in the tropics, where they feed on seagrasses and other aquatic vegetation.

KEEPING THEIR COOL

Water, particularly very cold water, is in some ways a hostile environment for mammals to live in, since they maintain a core temperature higher than their environment. Large animals tend to have lower surface area-to-volume ratios and most marine mammals are comparatively large creatures. The largest whales—the blue whales—are enormous, growing to about 100 ft (30 m) long and weighing more than 330 lbs (150 kg). Blue whales are, by far, the largest animal that has ever lived on Earth.

Marine mammals combine their size with excellent insulation in the form of fur, or blubber—a thick layer of skin tissue that contains fat, collagen, and elastin. The Cetaceans and Sirenians are almost completely hairless, and therefore rely on blubber to insulate them. Newborn harbor porpoises pack the most punch—43 percent of their total body mass is blubber. Sea otters and polar bears rely more on fur than blubber to insulate them from the cold.

A Fine Head of Hair

Sea otters have the densest hair of the animal kingdom—up to 150 thousand strands of hair per 0.15 square inch (1 cm²) of skin. Their coats consist of two layers—a short dense underfur, and long waterproof guard hairs on top that stop the water from reaching the underfur so it stays dry, and therefore insulates most efficiently. The sea otter's hair is so dense that it traps a layer of air just above the skin, even when they are swimming. It does require regular grooming however, since the ability of the guard hairs to repel water depends on utmost cleanliness. The otter's elaborate grooming routines take advantage of its loose skin and unusually supple skeleton, which give it the ability to reach and groom fur on any part of its body.

LEFT Sea otters *(Enhydra lutris)* lie on their backs to feed and groom. These three are enjoying a feed of kelp in Monterey Bay, California, USA.

ABOVE A herd of walruses *(Odobenus rosmarus)* gather on pack ice between the Beaufort and Chukchi seas, off the coast of Alaska.

LEFT A humpback whale *(Megaptera novaeangliae)* and her calf cruise the warm waters off Hawaii.

RIGHT Dolphins delight in antics. Here two dolphins display their flukes in the Tasman Sea off the coast of eastern Australia.

Whales, Dolphins, and Porpoises

Whales, dolphins, and porpoises, like other members of the Cetacea order of marine mammals, have evolved underwater, where buoyancy compensates for gravity, and some species can reach truly epic proportions—the blue whale is the largest creature on Earth.

GIANTS OF THE DEEP

The general term "whale" usually refers to the great whales such as the sperm whale of Moby Dick fame and the gentle giant of the deep—the blue whale.

The fundamental difference between these two great whales is presence or absence of teeth. Cetaceans are divided into two suborders—Mysticeti or baleen whales; and Odontoceti or toothed whales.

Baleen whales, such as the blue whale, have baleen plates—giant comb-like structures—which they use to sift their food—usually massive numbers of krill and plankton—from the water, a bit like straining pasta through teeth.

Toothed whales hunt and feed on individual prey items. The largest of the toothed whales—the sperm whale—feeds on large prey such as squid or fish, diving as deep as 1.8 miles (3 km) in order to grab a special meal, in turn making it the deepest diving mammal in the world. Famously, the sperm whale's diet also includes the giant and colossal squid. While

BELOW Blue whales are seldom sighted as they live quiet serene lives in the depth of the oceans or way out to sea. The massive tail of this blue whale exemplifies the enormous proportions of the largest creature on Earth.

battles between these two enormous creatures—the largest colossal squid ever caught weighed in at more than 990 lbs (450 kg)—have never been observed, white scars on the bodies of sperm whales are believed to be caused by the hooks on colossal squid tentacles.

Although some whales are long and slender, while others are short and stocky, all whales share a rather streamlined torpedo-shaped body design. Because of their complete adaptation to life and locomotion in water, they have assumed a shape that looks very much like the fishes, even though they are not close relatives. The most obvious way of discerning whales from fish is by the shape and movement of the tail. The tail of a fish is vertical and moves side to side when it swims. The tail of a whale—called a fluke—is horizontal and moves up and down. A cetacean's spine bends in the similar way to a human spine.

MIGRATION MATTERS

Many of the larger whales undergo long journeys throughout the world's oceans. Their annual migrations, many of which follow regular paths over huge distances, demonstrate their astounding ability to navigate accurately through any sea.

Our understanding of the distribution and migration of whales comes from historic whaling era records, individual identification of whales photographed in different locations, visual and acoustic surveys, and recent advances in radio and satellite tracking. DNA analysis techniques are also being developed to determine the extent of integration between populations of migrating humpback whales.

Baleen whales generally migrate—in both the Northern and Southern Hemispheres—spending summer in the polar regions and migrating to the Equator in their respective winters to breed and calve. Oceanic circulation causes areas of "upwelling" where cold, nutrient-rich waters are forced up from the deep ocean to the surface, giving rise to enormous blooms of plankton and krill. These areas occur in a belt that surrounds Antarctica, and in areas of the North Atlantic and North Pacific.

Gray whales endure the longest migration, swimming from their winter breeding grounds in Baja California, Mexico, to summer breeding grounds in the rich waters of the Bering Sea, between Alaska and Siberia, and back again. The epic journey amounts to a total annual distance of 11,100 miles (18,000 km). In a gray whale's lifetime of 80 years or more, this is equivalent to two return trips to the Moon.

Biggest of the Big

The blue whale is the largest and heaviest of all whales, and also the largest animal on Earth. As with all baleen whales, the females are larger than the males. On average they grow to 82–85 ft (25–26 m) long, but they have been measured up to 104 ft (31.6 m) in length and 419,000 lbs (190 tonnes). Their heart is about the size of a small car and a human could crawl through their aorta.

Newborn blue whale calves weigh in at around 4,410–6,610 lbs (2–3 tonnes) and can be as long as 26 ft (8 m). Every day, they drink about 53 gallons (200 liters) of their mother's milk and gain as much as 200 lbs (90 kg) in weight—roughly equivalent to the weight of an adult human!

The blues whale's epic tale does not end there—they are also the loudest animals on Earth. Their low frequency pulses, or whale song, have been measured at up to 188 decibels. Human shouting is 70 decibels; sounds over 120 decibels are painful to human ears.

ABOVE There is probably no greater exhilaration than witnessing the breaching of a humpback whale. Barnacles can be seen along the top of the whale's head.

LEFT This rare sighting shows a pod of whales all opening their mouths as they reach the surface.

ABOVE Masses of seabirds congregate around this whale hoping to feed off any krill left after the whale eats. Baleen whales such as this one, strain krill and small sea creatures into their mouths.

SEA SONGS

For animals that range across such vast areas, being able to communicate over large distances is essential in order to find other whales for mating. Whales rely on sound as a tool for long distance communication because sound can travel many miles underwater. Sight, in contrast, only works over a very short distance. The vocalizations of blue whales—which are below the range of human hearing—have been detected from a distance of 1,800 miles (3,000 km) away.

This has lead to a number of different species of whales developing a variety of unusual sounds to communicate, including the well-known song of the humpback whale. Only male humpbacks create whale song, and it is thought to be used to attract females. It's thought that other whale songs, such as those of fin and blue whales, have a similar reproductive purpose.

When the eerie underwater rumblings of male humpback whales were first heard in the 1970s people were captivated by their complex and melodic groans and whistles. They are perhaps the only animals in the world that can boast a top-selling record in the pop charts. Their songs change slightly from year to year; but amazingly, at any one time, they all sing basically the same wonderful song.

WHALING

It is ironic that the blubber that is crucial to the whales' survival has also lead to their exploitation. Ancient cave paintings tell us that whale hunting dates back thousands of years. At first, coastal fishing communities caught an occasional whale, and prized its red meat. But as these nations developed safer boats and stronger weapons, they began to hunt more efficiently, travel further from home, and for longer. The Basque people from the Mediterranean were the first to take to the high seas, hunting for whales in the sixteenth century. Like most early whalers, the Basques threw harpoons by hand. It was not long before the whalers discovered that blubber, once cut from the dead whale and melted down into oil, could be used to fuel lamps, as lubricants, candles, and as a base for perfumes and soaps.

By the late nineteenth century, whaling had gone global. The development of harpoon guns, explosive harpoon heads, and steam-driven whaling boats made large-scale commercial whaling so efficient that many whale species came close to extinction. Each factory ship could process hundreds of whales per season.

By 1935, southern right whales were no longer hunted—there were so few left that they became too hard to find. So the whalers went after the blue whale, wiping out 98 percent of their population in the Southern Hemisphere. This pattern continued for species after species.

Fortunately, the arrival of petroleum as an alternative fuel source signaled a reprieve for the world's remaining whale populations. By the 1970s, most whaling stations had closed due to fewer whales, public concern, and political pressure—many of the world's most influential conservation organizations were born in the battle to "Save the Whale." Concerns in several Western nations about the morality of whaling led the International Whaling Commission (IWC) to declare

a moratorium on commercial whaling in 1986. Since then, many whale populations have begun to recover.

However, despite the IWC moratorium on commercial whaling, some whaling still does occur. Subsistence whaling by aboriginal peoples is not subject to the moratorium, and in 1982 Norway had legally claimed an exemption, which is the right of any country under the terms of the 1946 convention.

Perhaps most controversially, the IWC also allows countries to grant special permits to catch whales for scientific purposes. "Scientific whaling" is not under the control of the IWC—permits and quotas are at the total discretion of each nation. More than 12,300 fin, sperm, sei, Bryde's, and minke whales have been killed using scientific permits since the moratorium on commercial whaling came into effect in 1986.

ABOVE This young humpback whale calf wallows along on the surface, keeping an eye on the photographer, and, no doubt, its mother.

TOP Commercial whaling managed to wipe out the majority of the world's whale populations. This very early twentieth-century painting depicts whaling with a hand spear off the Cape of Good Hope, South Africa.

DOLPHINS

Dolphins are members of the Delphinidae family of cetaceans, which sits under the suborder Odontoceti—derived from the Greek term for sea animals having teeth. The Delphinidae are by far the most diverse of the cetacean families, with numerous variations between species. Somewhat confusingly, many of the larger species in the Delphinidae family, such as the orca and the pilot, are commonly called whales, rather than dolphins. They are also sometimes collectively known as "blackfish." They vary in size from 4 ft (1.2 m) and 88 lbs (40 kg)—Maui's Dolphin; up to 30 ft (9.5 m) and 22,000 lbs (10 tonnes)—the orca or killer whale.

Dolphins are found in all oceans and some rivers around the world, and live in coastal to pelagic ocean habitats. While all dolphins are carnivores, their feeding habits have become highly specialized; some feed exclusively on either fish or cephalopods—squid, octopus, and cuttlefish—while others, such as the killer whale, prey on other cetaceans and pinnipeds, as well as on birds and large fish.

Dolphins tend to form long-lasting groups that range in size from a few animals called pods, to larger groups of up to several hundred members, known as schools or herds. There are well-known accounts of dolphins forming super schools of thousands of members, to herd large swarms of fish into a ball, or fish being forced ahead of dolphins swimming in a crescent formation, where they are attacked from all directions. Groups of dolphins will even beach themselves to access the fish they chase onto sandbanks.

Dolphins communicate with one another through a variety of tactile, visual, and auditory abilities. Touch, including rubbing, flipper-to-flipper, and flipper-to-flank contact has been observed in both captive and wild dolphins. Some areas of the dolphin's body appear

Dolphins and Porpoises—What's the Difference?

In the past, the terms "porpoise" and "dolphin" have been used interchangeably, with one or the other favored in different parts of the world. However, strictly speaking, porpoises refer to a group of six species within the Phocoenidae family. Dolphins belong to the Delphinidae family, and there are distinct physical and behavioral differences between the two.

Porpoises tend to be smaller and stouter in their appearance. The vaquita porpoise is the smallest of the species, and among the smallest of all cetaceans. The average length of an adult individual is 4 ft (1.2 m). They have rounded heads with no discernible beak—except for a faint hint in the Dall's porpoise—and flattened teeth, shaped like little spades, which are useful for catching small fish such as sardines and mackerel. Dolphins, in contrast, have conical and pointed teeth for seizing and holding larger fish. In addition, the porpoise's dorsal fin is generally triangular, rather than curved like that of many dolphins and large whales. Porpoises live in coastal areas in more northern latitudes, such as around the perimeters of North America, Canada, Europe, and Japan. They are generally shy and elusive, and therefore less likely to interact with humans, preferring not to surface around boats, as dolphins do.

to have special communication significance. Visual communication, such as tail slapping, where dolphins slap their tails against the surface of the water up to dozens of times, creates loud sounds both above and below the water, usually conveys threat or frustration.

Sound, however, is considered the primary form of dolphin communication, with vocalizations ranging from whistles, to squeaks and snorts produced in their nasal passages. Dolphins famously use a technique called "echolocation," where they send a stream of high frequency clicks into their surroundings, which then bounce back to the animal according to the presence of nearby solid objects. This helps them to build up a three dimensional "sound picture" of their underwater environment and any prey that might be in it.

OCEAN ACROBATS

Many cetaceans are known for their spectacular aerial displays, and dolphins are no exception. The bottlenose and dusky dolphins are the most outstanding acrobats of the dolphin family. They have been known to breach or leap as high as 22 ft (7 m) into the air and turn somersaults before re-entering the water.

Scientists are not certain about the purpose of breaching; they could be communicating to other dolphins, attempting to dislodge parasites, or perhaps simply do it for fun!

Dusky dolphins are known for three breach types, which they exhibit at three different stages of cooperative feeding—head-first re-entry leaps, noisy leaps, and acrobatic leaps. Noisy leaps may act as a sound barrier to disorient prey and keep them tightly schooled.

The most impressive is the long-snouted spinner dolphin which hurls itself into the air, then spins on its longitudinal axis as many as seven times in a single leap.

ABOVE Dolphins seem to be the sea creatures that enjoy play more than any others. This bottlenose dolphin leaps into the air, using its fluke to propel itself upward.

Seals, Sea Lions, and Walruses

Seals, sea lions, and walruses all belong to the group of mammals whose four "legs" have developed into flippers. Called pinnipeds, they have adapted to their amphibious environment with highly specialized bodies, allowing them to swim fast and maneuver freely under water.

SEALS

True seals, or earless seals, are one of the three main groups of mammals within the suborder, Pinnipedia. All true seals are members of the family Phocidae.

The Phocids can be recognized by their lack of external ears—hence "earless seal"—and their inability to rotate their pelvis to position the hind limbs under the body, which means that they are unable to "walk" on land like the Otariids. Instead they move about in a lunging caterpillar-like motion. For these reasons, they are also sometimes called crawling seals to distinguish them from the fur seals and sea lions of the family Otariidae.

NORTH AND SOUTH

Seals live in the oceans of both hemispheres, though they are mostly confined to polar, subpolar, and temperate climates, with the exception of the more tropical monk seals. Most of the northern species breed on ice, except for the harbor seal, which breeds as far south as Baja California, Mexico. The four Antarctic seal species breed on ice, generally south of the Antarctic Convergence at 50–60°S. Remarkably, Weddell seals spend the whole year in Antarctic waters, even when the surface of the ocean freezes solid. To survive, they must maintain breathing holes in the ice, using their canine-like teeth to scour away the ice as it refreezes.

BELOW A baby harp seal (*Pagophilus groenlandicus*) is left alone to fend for itself after 12 days of nursing. It is during this period that it is vulnerable to polar bears and seal hunters.

RIGHT King penguins (*Aptenodytes patagonicus*) walk among harems of Southern elephant seals (*Mirounga leonina*) during breeding season at St Andrews Bay, on South Georgia Island. Elephant seals have a large proboscis that resembles an elephant's trunk.

Antarctic seals have no native terrestrial predators, therefore they behave very differently from the Northern Hemisphere seals. They show little fear of humans, and it was for this reason that seal populations were easily decimated by early human hunters from the mid-1700s onward.

KEEPING WARM

Seals are well adapted to cold polar environments with thick blubber layers, often several inches thick, that act both as a food reserve during lactation, and as insulation. For many years, seals were killed for their blubber, which was boiled down to make oil.

Most of the true seals also have a layer of fur, giving additional insulation on land. In cold conditions, loss of heat through the flippers, which do not have an insulating covering, is minimized by reducing the flow of blood to them, with only enough circulation being maintained to prevent freezing.

The most obvious differences between the seal species are the size and relative size of the sexes. At

Hold Your Breath!

What they lack in agility on land, seals make up for in the water. Respiration and circulation in true seals are finely adapted for spending long periods of time underwater. After submerging, their lungs collapse under the pressure of the water and any residual air is pushed into the bronchial tubes, to exit through the mouth or nose. By the time the animal reaches a depth of around 200 ft (60 m), it has no free gas in its body, protecting it from "the bends," which is caused by free gas bubbles appearing in the blood as a diver ascends.

Weddell seals can dive as deep as 2,300 ft (700 m) for as long as an hour. However, the current depth record of 1 mile (1.7 km) belongs to Southern elephant seals.

the small end of the scale, some ringed seals reach weights of about 198 lbs (90 kg), whereas a fully-grown male Southern elephant seal, can weigh more than 8,800 lbs (4 tonnes).

However, the female leopard seal is substantially larger than the male. In other species, the males are much larger than females.

ANTARCTICA'S MARINE OPPORTUNIST

Leopard seals eat almost anything, and they're the only pinniped that consumes warm-blooded vertebrates as part of their diet. With its massive head, long snout, and gaping jaws—which give the animal an overall reptilian appearance—this solitary predator looks very different from other seal species found off Antarctica. Along with the killer whale, they are considered the top predator of the seas and islands around Antarctica.

Analysis of leopard seal faeces has revealed that Adélie penguins are a favorite food, but other seal species, fish, squid, and krill are also consumed. Lacking the necessary teeth to slice their food, instead they flay their prey. Leopard seals have also been known to scavenge the carrion of whales.

BELOW Despite appearing to be in danger, this penguin is quite safe among most seals. Only leopard seals are known to include penguins in their diet.

ABOVE Taking in the breeze, this Antarctic fur seal is covered in moulted penguin feathers.

LURKING FOR PREY

Leopard seals look clumsy and ungraceful on land, but in the water they are formidable hunters and excellent swimmers. Their feeding behavior is most easily seen when their prey is a penguin. During the summer months, they lurk around the edges of the ice shelf, catching incoming or outgoing penguins. They have also been known to rise swiftly toward thin ice, breaking it, and knocking penguins into the water. When they catch them, they throw them into the air to rip the skin and feathers from their bodies.

UNSAVORY REPUTATION

When threatened, many pinnipeds will bite or chase intruders, but the leopard seal is the only seal species with a reputation for apparently unprovoked attacks on people. Early Antarctic explorers describe harrowing encounters with leopard seals. Although some attacks have been well documented, including seals suddenly lunging through cracks in the ice to snap at people's feet, most scientists believe it would be a case of mistaken identity. From underwater, the dark vertical shape of a human is similar to the shape of an emperor penguin.

SEA LIONS AND FUR SEALS

Sea lions and fur seals belong to the Otariid family of eared seals. The name Otariid comes from the Greek *otarion*, meaning "little ear," referring to the small but very visible external ear flaps, which can be used to distinguish them from the Phocids. Apart from their external ears, the Otariids can be distinguished from the true seals by their use fore flippers as the principal means of propulsion through water.

Sea lions are generally larger than most fur seals, and have blunter snouts. While all Otariids have fur, the difference between the two is that in sea lions, relatively coarse hairs predominate, while in the fur seals, a dense underfur is also present.

VARIED DIET

Otariids are carnivorous, feeding on fish, squid, and krill. Sea lions tend to feed closer to shore in "upwelling zones," where rising currents carry nutrients to the surface, feeding on a variety of fish such as herring, while the smaller fur seals tend to take longer, offshore foraging trips, and can subsist on large numbers of smaller prey items. Many also take their food, such as rock lobsters and octopus, from the bottom of the sea.

Australian fur seals have been caught in traps and trawling nets at depths of more than 300 ft (100 m), but eared seals are generally shallow feeders.

A BALANCING ACT

The hind flippers of eared seals are less adapted for swimming that those of true seals, remaining closer in form to the rear limbs of the terrestrial mammals from which Pinnipeds evolved. They also differ from true seals in that these flippers can be rotated under the animal while it is on land, partially supporting the body and helping in locomotion and maneuvering.

The iconic ball-balancing circus seal that we know from the movies and television is generally a species of sea lion. A bull fur seal can gallop across a rocky beach in pursuit of a rival, and on broken terrain they can run faster than a human in defense of their harem, or in pursuit of food.

Krill Not Crab

Crabeater seals *(Lobodon carcinophaga)* are by far the most abundant large marine mammals in the world, with an estimated population of about 15 million. Despite their name, these seals don't eat crabs; its primary food is krill. Their name originates from the German word, krebs, which describes other crustacea as well as crabs.

Crabeater seals inhabit one of the most dynamic and dramatic habitats in the world—Antarctic pack ice—where they exploit this resource in ways not open to other marine mammals, such as whales, which feed in the open water. The seals rest on the pack ice both as a means of escaping predation, and perhaps also to save energy. They can travel large distances using this method, due to the drifting of ice floes moving southward in spring, and northward in autumn. Ice, seals, and krill all drift together, which means that crabeaters have constant access to food simply by slipping between the floes into the deep abundant waters beneath. Crabeaters have been observed to cross almost half of Antarctica's circumference this way in just a few months.

Killer whales and leopard seals are the main predator of crabeater seals, particularly young pups. Most adult crabeater seals bear the scars of unsuccessful attacks from leopard seals during their youth. The large population increase of crabeater seals has been associated with the near-extinction of the large baleen whales in the early twentieth century. This is because the whales, like the crabeater seal, eat krill, so it's possible that the seal owes its current success to the decline of the baleen whale population.

ABOVE A curious herd of Australian sea lions weave in and out of the seaweed in the water around Hopkins Island, off South Australia.

LEFT Floating booms, used to contain any accidental oil spills, are a favorite resting place for sea lions, near San Francisco, California, USA.

Pinnipeds and People

Pinnipeds and humans have had a close relationship since primitive humans spread to the coastal regions where seals were abundant. Seals are ideal food supplies for hunter-gatherers; they're just large enough that a single killing provides ample reward, yet not so big that there are major risks involved in hunting them across the ice.

Pinnipeds have long played an important role in the lives of Arctic peoples. The first seal harpooning is an important rite of passage for an Inuit boy. No part of the seal is wasted—the hides may be sewn together to form a thick coat, while walrus tusks can be carved into works of art.

In the Southern Hemisphere, fur sealing was combined with the hunting of elephant seals for their oil. It is estimated that 200,000 Australian fur seals were killed for their fur in the eighteenth and nineteenth centuries, wiping many breeding populations out. There is currently no commercial sealing and most fur seal species have regained their former abundance.

Today, Pinnipeds face threats from habitat loss, overfishing, oil spills, and entanglement in marine debris such as polypropylene packaging bands, nylon string, and fishing nets.

SETTING UP HOUSE

Eared seals are found on North Pacific coasts from Japan to Mexico; on the Galapagos Islands and the western coast of South America, from northern Peru and round Cape Horn to southern Brazil; on the south-west coasts of southern Africa; on the southern coast of Australia and South Island, New Zealand; and on sub-Antarctic islands.

Eared seals tend to be highly social, forming large herds during the breeding season. Within these herds, individual males maintain harems. The males are much larger than the females, at least three times heavier in the South American fur seal and Californian sea lion, and as much as five times in the Northern fur seal. This disparity in size among marine mammals is rivaled only by the elephant seals, a true seal species, which can be up to five times heavier than the female.

Males arrive at breeding grounds before females and set up territories, which they defend aggressively. Successful males later segregate the females into harems of 3–40 individuals, depending on their size and strength. This group strategy is known as polygynous

breeding, as opposed to monogamous breeding, in which a male mates with only one mate. Competition for space on the icy breeding grounds is often so intense that males cannot leave their patch even to hunt for food. Instead they go hungry, sometimes fasting for as long as 60 days.

WALRUSES

With their wrinkled skin, bloodshot eyes, and two protruding front teeth, there's no mistaking the walrus. These somewhat strange marine mammals are most often found near the Arctic Circle, lying on the ice with hundreds of companions. They are extremely sociable creatures, forming noisy herds of hundreds and, sometimes, more than 2,000 individuals.

THE BIGGER THE TEETH...

The walrus's most conspicuous feature is their fanglike, extended upper canines, which grow continuously throughout their life, exceeding 3 ft (1 m) in some males. These "tusks" have many functions, including acting as a defensive weapon, icepick, and occasionally they are even employed as a fifth limb—walrus emerging from the water onto an ice floe occasionally use

BELOW Eared seals seem to be very affectionate. Here, a seal pup and its mother in Namibia, Africa, enjoy a few moments caressing each other.

LEFT Male fur seals maintain a harem of females and disputes about territory often arise among the different groups.

BELOW A walrus's tusks continue to grow throughout its life. The length of the tusks usually determines the status of the bull. Coarse whiskers which sense food, are the primary feeding tool.

their tusks to bite into the ice to help them heave their body forward. However, their primary role lies in signifying the bearer's status in walrus society. Generally, the walrus with the largest tusks tends to be the dominant one. Simply by posturing to display the size of its tusks, a dominant animal can move unchallenged into the most comfortable or advantageous position in the colony. However, if a dominant male encounters another walrus with tusks of comparable size, a confrontation may escalate to a stabbing duel.

AND THOSE WHISKERS

Accompanying the tusks are about 450 coarse whiskers, called vibrissae, which can grow to 12 in (30 cm) long. Their vibrissae are highly sensitive and play an important part in feeding—they can discriminate objects about the size of pencil erasers. On the dark ocean floor, walruses use them to "feel out" food—animals that live on the seabed such as mussels and crabs.

BUILT-IN BUOYANCY

Another lesser-known physical characteristic of the walrus is their pharyngeal pouches. Located in the throat region, when filled, these two expandable

pockets—which can hold up to 1.8 cubic ft (50 liters) of air—allow them to bob up and down in a vertical position. This also allows walruses to be able to sleep and rest in an upright position. Another role of the pharyngeal pouches is that of amplifiers and resonance chambers for the bell-like sounds that males produce during the mating season.

Gentle Ocean Grazers

Manatees and dugongs are sometimes known as sea cows because they graze on the extensive sea-grass beds that flourish in warm, shallow tropical waters. These large, docile marine mammals spend their entire life in the water, although surprisingly their closest living relative is the elephant.

OPPOSITE A West Indian manatee grazes on the sea floor. One difference between manatees and dugongs is their teeth. Dugongs have tusk-like incisors, while manatees have molars and premolars that move forward in the jaw over time and are continually replaced.

TAIL TO TELL

Manatees and dugongs are very closely related, both belonging to the Order Sirenia. The most obvious difference between the two is the shape of the tail. Manatees have a rounded, wedge-shaped tail, while dugongs have a more dolphin-like tail, rising to a point at each end. This powerful tail is used for propulsion, while the smaller front limbs are used for steering. Manatees and dugongs can grow up to 13 ft (4 m) and weigh up to 1,000 lbs (400 kg). Like other marine mammals, they must rise to the surface to breathe before diving again, typically holding their breath for around 20 minutes. Their grayish, seal-like body is sparsely covered with short hairs.

WARM-WATER DWELLERS

Dugongs (*Dugong dugon*) are found in tropical waters of the Indian and Pacific oceans. Now considered endangered, most of the world's population is found in the waters of northern Australia (around 85,000 individuals), particularly in the sheltered waters behind the Great Barrier Reef, which stretches some 1,200 miles (2,000 km) down the northeastern coast of the island continent. Smaller yet significant populations can also be found off Australia's northwestern coast. Isolated populations are found in areas of the Indian Ocean around India and Sri Lanka, the Red Sea and Arabian Gulf, and the seas of Indonesia and the Philippines.

The four species of manatee are also found in tropical and subtropical waters. The West Indian manatee (*Trichechus manatus*) is found mainly in the Caribbean Sea and the western Atlantic. A significant population of West Indian manatees is also found in Florida. This population, which is often referred to as the Florida manatee, lives mostly in the coastal waters off the Florida peninsula, but they do migrate as far north as Rhode Island. Along with the Antillean manatee (*T. bernhardi*), found in the waters of Central and South America, it is endangered. The West African manatee (*T. senegalensis*) is found along the western coast of Africa. The Amazonian manatee (*T. inunguis*) is the only member of the sirenian order to live in fresh water. They inhabit the rivers of the Amazon Basin, mostly in Brazil. They are all but extinct in Colombia, Peru, and Ecuador, where they were once relatively common.

SLOW BREEDERS

Generally living to around 70 years of age, dugongs and manatees have relatively low reproductive rates. Females become sexually mature at around 5 years and males around 9 years. Sirenians give birth to live offspring. The gestation period is around 13 months, and females give birth to a single calf on average every two and a half to five years. Once born, the calf will remain dependent on its mother for up to two years. This low reproductive rate is one of the factors contributing to the limited success in conserving the species.

GIANTS IN DECLINE

Manatee and dugong numbers are in decline in all the major regions where they are to be found. The backs of many of these slow-moving animals are dotted with scars, which have been inflicted during collisions with boats, in particular boat propellers. These collisions can be fatal, especially for young animals. This is a particular problem where populations are living close to large human populations.

Another significant threat for sirenians is the loss of sea-grass beds, thus reducing critical food resources. Dugongs and manatees feed on the entire sea-grass plant—they uproot it from the sandy sea floor using lobed, flexible lips covered with sensory bristles; one sign of dugong and manatee activity is a distinctive trough cleared in the sea-grass beds. The algal blooms that are associated with excessive nutrients in the water, for example the fertilizer runoff from agriculture and domestic sewerage outfalls, reduce sunlight penetration and oxygen levels. This, in turn, causes a reduction in sea-grass productivity and ultimately a decline in food resources for manatees and dugongs. Industrial pollutants are another problem adding to sea-grass decline. Increased turbidity associated with shipping also affects sea-grass beds because it reduces available sunlight for photosynthesis. Illegal hunting for meat is yet another threat in some parts of the animals' range.

BELOW A manatee swims with her calf. A newborn calf weighs around 65–70 lbs (about 30 kg) and is about 3–4 ft (0.9–1.2 m) long. It will stay with its mother for up to two years. Calves begin eating vegetation when they are a few weeks old.

SEABIRDS

Many birds feed and nest around the waters of lakes, rivers, streams, and the oceans, but not all are seabirds. Seabirds are different from other birds that live around water because they have become highly adapted to spending most of their lives feeding in the open sea or ocean, often far from land.

FEW OF MANY

Seabirds include a wide diversity of relatively few groups of birds. One group includes the penguins; the second includes albatrosses, shearwaters, and petrels; the third includes pelicans, frigate birds, tropic birds, gannets, boobies, and cormorants; and the fourth includes skuas, gulls, terns, auks, guillemots, and puffins.

DIET AND FEEDING

It is no surprise that seabirds feed on the most abundant marine prey—fishes, squid, and plankton, particularly krill. To do this, seabirds employ three major strategies to catch their prey—surface feeding, plunge diving, and pursuit diving.

Surface feeders skim or hover just above the surface dipping their beaks below the water to catch krill, fish, and squid. They are amongst the most acrobatic of birds. Their beaks may also be modified to suit their lifestyle. Skimmers, as their name implies, fly close to the water surface with only their lower elongate mandible submerged. This automatically snaps shut when it comes in contact with prey. Other seabirds swim on the water surface, where they snatch prey that comes within head-dipping distance.

Plunge diving is perhaps the most spectacular feeding strategy, especially during the feeding frenzy when a flock of gannets locates a shoal of fish. The energy obtained during the high dive overcomes buoyancy and propels them at great speed toward their prey. As a consequence, minimal energy is expended.

Pursuit divers are either propelled by specially adapted wings, such as the flipper-like wings of penguins, or webbed feet such as those of cormorants, or both. The former have either lost their power of flight, or like the auks, flight is very limited. Webbed feet usually make seabirds clumsy when walking on land.

There are some seabirds such as gulls, terns, skuas, and the aptly named frigate bird that add to their diets by forcing others to give up their catch. Gulls and skuas will opportunistically take unguarded eggs and nestlings, and scavenge on dead bodies.

BREEDING

Seabirds generally live longer that other birds—some as much as 60 years—and they reach maturity later than other birds—up to 10 years. They have fewer offspring than most birds. Some might have just one clutch of eggs, or even just one egg per year. There are those that produce eggs only every two years. Extended parenting compensates for the low rate of breeding.

Seabirds tend to breed in colonies on cliffs or isolated islands, where a pair will either bond for the breeding season or for life. There is also considerable nesting site fidelity among some species, with pairs returning to the same nest site each year.

MIGRATION

Highly mobile seabirds are capable of flying vast distances to feed, but the term migration is restricted to regular seasonal journeys. A common pattern amongst seabirds is to migrate to tropical regions after summer breeding in polar regions. The advantage of this is the increased time for foraging during the long daylight hours of the high latitudes. However, some seabirds travel much further than this, crossing the equator in their migrations.

Arctic terns fly from their summer breeding grounds in the Arctic to their summer non-breeding grounds in the Antarctic, a distance of some 12,000 miles (19,000 km) each way. A similar pattern, but in the opposite direction, is made by the sooty shearwater. These birds breed in New Zealand, Tasmania, Tierra del Fuego, and the Falkland Islands. They travel northward up the western side of the Pacific and Atlantic Oceans to reach the Arctic. The reverse migration then takes them down the eastern side of these oceans. A massive 46,000 miles (74,000 km) has been recorded for a bird traveling from New Zealand and back, via Japan, Alaska, and California. As a consequence of this pattern of migration, Arctic terns and sooty shearwaters perform the most extensive migrations, and experience more hours of sunlight than any other creature on Earth.

Direct Impact!

While there might be benefits provided by humans discarding food scraps, the vast majority of seabirds have been negatively impacted by human activities, particularly through pollution. Direct impacts come from the harvesting of birds for food, oil, and feathers, and birds caught up as the bycatch of fishing practices. Seabirds are also vulnerable introduced animals against which they have no defenses in their isolated habitats. These effects include direct predation on birds, chicks, and eggs by cats, foxes, and rats, as well as the destruction of habitat by rabbits and goats.

LEFT Blue-footed boobies in a feeding frenzy as they plunge head-first into the water to catch fish near the Galapagos Islands. The high dive creates enough propulsion to reach the fish.

RIGHT Male frigate birds inflate red gular sacs along their necks to attract females during the mating season.

RIGHT Skuas are renowned scavengers. Here a skua scoops down in an attempt to steal a penguin egg. The male on the right is screeching to frighten off the predatory bird.

LEFT A flock of Arctic terns keep watch on a polar bear in the Arctic, hoping to feed on the scraps of his prey.

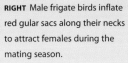

Ocean Gliders

Albatrosses, gannets, and gulls are among the ocean's top airborne predators. As well as being agile fliers with excellent eyesight, they are particularly sensitive to variations in ocean currents and water temperatures. This helps to guide them to their main food source—the small fish, squid, and krill of the ocean's surface waters.

LONG-RANGE FLIERS

Albatrosses are the largest of all seabirds. Population concentrations closely correspond to major ocean upwellings—locations where oceanic currents bring nutrient-rich cold waters into the ocean's upper layers and create rich feeding grounds. Although they are commonly found feeding on the refuse thrown over-board by trawlers and other ships, albatrosses usually eat squid, as well as schooling surface fish.

The majority of the 22 albatross species are found in the southern Pacific, southern Indian, and Southern oceans. Several species are also found in the northern Pacific toward the Arctic. The sub-Antarctic islands, especially those in the Scotia Sea, such as South Georgia and the Sandwich Islands, are critically important breeding grounds for more than half of the world's species.

Diomedea exulans, the wandering albatross, is the largest species, and has a wingspan of more than 11½ ft (3.5 m). It is found throughout the waters of the Southern Hemisphere. Like other albatrosses, it migrates vast distances—one study tracked a single bird traveling 3,730 miles (6,000 km) in just 12 days.

Albatrosses have significant life spans, with some individuals living for more than 60 years. Although living a mostly solitary existence, they mate for life. Their reproductive rates are very low, with females laying a single egg and most species breeding only once every two years. The chicks remain in the nest for up to nine months, with both parents caring for them.

Albatross numbers are in decline throughout the world, with 21 species considered endangered. Like many marine species, they are victims of modern commercial fishing practices. The enormous drift nets towed by fishing trawlers often trap diving albatrosses, as do hooks on long lines used in commercial bluefin tuna fishing. It is estimated that more than 100,000 albatrosses die each year as a result of long-liners.

AVIAN TORPEDOES

Gannets are large black and white seabirds with a wingspan of approximately 6½ ft (2 m). The northern gannet *(Morus bassanus)* is found in the North Atlantic Ocean, the Australasian gannet *(M. serrator)* is found in the temperate waters of southern Australia and New Zealand, and the Cape gannet *(M. capensis)* inhabits the mid to southern coastlines of Africa.

Gannets hunt for fish by plunging from great heights—up to 100 ft (30 m)—into the sea, reaching speeds of around 60 miles per hour (100 kph) as they descend. They can also swim under water for up to 10 seconds in pursuit of their prey. Gannets also have a number of special adaptations, including powerful eyesight that allows them to scan for food, and a layer of air sacs below their skin to help absorb the impact of crashing through the water when they dive. As well, they have no external nostrils—this allows them to stay under water for longer.

Gannets reach breeding age at about six or seven years of age and breed in large colonies, most commonly on islands. Chicks hatch around two months after the eggs are laid and will remain in the nest for around three months or so.

Gannet populations suffer from commercial fishing practices, such as drift netting, and the loss of breeding grounds also has a detrimental effect on numbers.

LIFE ON THE COAST

Gulls are perhaps the best known of all seabirds. There are 45 species found throughout the world's oceans, from the polar regions to the equator. However, most gulls prefer colder and temperate waters. The silver gull *(Chroicocephalus novaehollandiae)* of northern Australia is the only species that permanently inhabits tropical waters. Some gulls live well inland, on the shores of inland lakes and rivers.

Most gulls are coastal-dwelling birds. Only one—the kittiwake (genus Rissa)—ventures out into the open ocean. Kittiwakes have exceptional maneuverability in flight, allowing them to twist and turn sharply and even hover to seize their food. Gulls are well known for being opportunistic feeders, scavenging food scraps and diving to steal food off the plates of unsuspecting diners. Their normal diet, however, includes small surface fish. They rarely dive in pursuit of their prey.

Typically, gulls lay two or three eggs each year, with both the parents incubating the eggs for three or four weeks in large colonies based on clifftops, offshore stacks, and small rocky islands, although there are some species that create single nests. At around five weeks the chicks become independent.

ABOVE A pair of Cape gannets *(Morus capensis)* stretch their necks upward in a gesture of greeting. Found mainly in southern Africa, these birds remain with the same breeding partner for a number of seasons.

LEFT A gannet plunges into Nova Scotia's chilly waters in search of prey. Because they dive from great heights, gannets are able to go deeper into the water than other seabirds, thus increasing their chances of finding food.

BELOW A courting ritual between two gray-headed albatrosses *(Thalassarche chrysostoma)*. There are large colonies of these seabirds on South Georgia in the southern Atlantic Ocean.

Penguins

Even though they frequent some of the most remote and inhospitable regions on Earth, penguins are arguably one of the most recognizable and enigmatic ocean-dwelling creatures. Though they are considered birds—they lay eggs and have feathers—penguins cannot fly and spend most of their lives at sea.

RIGHT Penguins are very social creatures and here a flock is enjoying a swim in the clear crisp southern waters. Although native to the Southern Hemisphere, penguins can be found as far north as the Equator.

BELOW The macaroni penguin (*Eudyptes chrysolophus*) boasts a yellow crest above its eyes with a black crown on its head. The crest takes about four years to fully develop.

RIGHT An aptly-named chinstrap penguin (*Pygoscelis antarcticus*) flaps its stunted wings. Chinstrap penguins build nests from stones and usually lay two eggs at a time.

SOUTHERN SURVIVORS

Contrary to some of the most pervasive images of penguins in popular culture, only two of the 18 known species—the emperor and the Adélie—breed on the Antarctic continent. The greatest concentrations and largest number of species occur further north between the latitudes of 45° and 60°. These populations include the gentoos, chinstraps, macaroni, and royal penguins, which breed on the sub-Antarctic islands as well as on the Antarctic Peninsula.

Penguins also live in warmer zones of the Southern Hemisphere. Located on the Equator, the Galapagos penguin represents the most northerly penguin species. They can be found only on the small clump of desert islands off the coast of Ecuador known as the Galapagos Islands. Others, such as the Humboldt penguin breed on the Pacific coast of South America and offshore islands of Chile and Peru. Penguins that live in these zones stay cool by going to sea during the day or hiding in deep burrows, protected from the heat.

WHO'S EATING WHO?

Penguins have an inbuilt water filter located in the skull above their eyes—a gland that allows them to drink sea water and eat salty foods such as the crustaceans, squid, and fish that form the main part of their diet. Their tongues are also barbed to help them hold onto any slippery prey.

Penguins, in turn, are preyed upon by variety of land and sea creatures. Although they mostly inhabit regions free of terrestrial predators, at sea they must contend with formidable marine mammals such as leopard seals and killer whales, and in warmer areas, sharks. While ashore in some areas, very skilled aerial predators such as skuas can often be found lurking on the edges of penguin colonies on the look-out for a potential meal. Both male and female penguins take turns to guard their penguin chicks and eggs from these marauding birds.

On sub-Antarctic islands, introduced species such as dogs, cats, and rabbits threaten the survival of breeding penguins.

OCEAN FLIGHT

Penguins belong to the bird family called Spheniscidae. All the members of this group are flightless, but if you observe them in the water you'll see that they do fly, just not through the air. Whatever evolutionary event resulted in penguins being unable to fly, the transition to swimming has been incredibly successful—today they are among the most specialized and well-adapted of the ocean dwellers.

With wings that have evolved into flattened, paddle-like flippers, penguins are strong swift swimmers, spending as much as 80 percent of their lives in water, coming ashore for extended periods only to

breed and molt. Their streamlined body shape differs from that of flying birds, and is more similar to other long-distance swimmers such as whales and dolphins. They intersperse swimming with a practice known as "porpoising," where they leap out of the water, soaring in a graceful arc before plunging into the water again. Traveling like this penguins can reach speeds of up to 6–7 mph (10–12 km/h). Porpoising may also help penguins escape large predators such as killer whales and leopard seals.

Penguins are also extremely accomplished divers. Their unusually dense bones and short powerful flippers give them the ability to dive and hunt where no other bird can go. Although the smaller species generally only dive for a few minutes at a time, larger species such as the great emperors can dive much deeper. They regularly dive between 330–660 ft (100–200 m) deep and can last around six minutes before they need to surface. They have been recorded

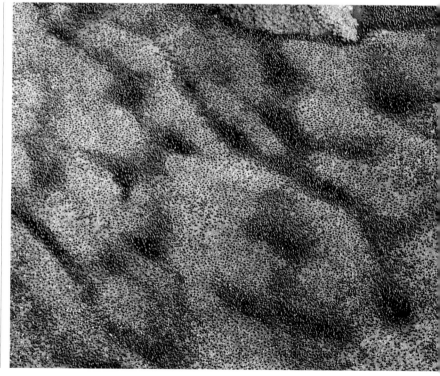

RIGHT Seen from the air, this massive colony of king penguins (*Aptenodytes patagonicus*) is on South Georgia Island. The reddish brown color are the young chicks in the colony.

RIGHT The march of the emperor penguins takes place across the ice of Antarctica. Emperor penguins *(Aptenodytes forsteri)* are the largest and most social of the species.

staying underwater for more than 20 minutes and diving as deep as 1,850 ft (565 m). Even much smaller species, such as the gentoo, can dive to depths exceeding 500 ft (150 m). During a dive, the heart rate of the Adélie penguin drops from 100 to 20 beats per minute. This reduces oxygen consumption and so prolongs the dive. It is not fully understood how these deep-diving penguins avoid the "bends"—the dangerous condition that causes the formation of bubbles in the blood of human divers who decompress too rapidly.

Penguins are counter-shaded for camouflage in the water. They have a white underside and a dark (mostly black) upperside. A predator such as a leopard seal looking up from below has difficulty distinguishing between a white penguin belly and the reflective water surface. The dark plumage on their backs blends them into the dark water above.

AS FAR AS THE EYE CAN SEE

Most penguins breed in large colonies—some Adélie rookeries have been estimated at more than a million birds. Adélies don't march inland like their "movie star" emperor penguin relatives. Instead they build their nests on land close to the coast, using pebbles they collect from the rocky slopes around them, or "steal" from other nests. The shrieking and squawking from these busy locales can be heard tens of miles away.

The majority of penguins nest in the area in which they themselves were hatched, and depending on the species, will raise one or two chicks in a breeding season. Penguin couples generally remain together from season to season, although occasionally some birds do change mates.

One thing that doesn't change between species is the red color of their egg yolks and guano caused by their diet of crustaceans. Some emperor colonies are so large that the stains cased by this red color can be seen from space.

BELOW Dozens of Adélie penguins *(Pygoscelis adeliae)* scurry along the ice shelf and dive head first into the icy Antarctic waters. It is estimated that there are more than 5 million Adélie penguins on the frozen continent.

AN EPIC TALE

Unlike other penguins, emperor penguins don't build nests near the coast. Instead they haul, walk, and slide their 3 ft (1 m) tall, 77-pound (35 kg) bodies incredible distances—up to 55 miles (90 km)—to their breeding sites inland. Their destination—their birthplace—is far from coastal predators such as seals, but there's no food, and the temperature can drop as low as −40°F (−40°C). Amazingly these impressive birds incubate their eggs through the darkest, most deadly, and most violent winters on Earth.

The emperor's breeding cycle, an ancient and complicated affair, is usually linked to the annual setting and breaking up of the ice, beginning around late March and ending in December. Courting and mating begin as the darkness starts to settle on the Antarctic continent and by June, the female will have laid a single green-shelled egg. Her energy levels are now very low, so she carefully transfers the egg to the male using her feet and a shuffle, and returns to the ocean to feed. If the egg touches the icy ground during this delicate maneuver the embryo inside will quickly freeze and die. The female won't see her partner again until the egg hatches.

The male penguin then spends the next 60–70 days balancing the egg on his feet underneath a thick layer of feathery skin called a brood pouch, which insulates the fragile egg from the freezing temperatures. During the incubation period, he can't leave the egg to go and feed; he relies entirely on the fat reserves he built up over the summer. Along with this test of wills, he has to cope with blizzards of up to 125 mph (200 km/h) and temperatures as low as −112°F (−80°C). To survive, the fathers form densely packed groups called "huddles," formations that can reduce heat loss by as much as 50 percent. On the coldest days, up to 10 penguins pack into every square yard of a huddle, which takes on the appearance of a single seething mass of life. The fathers shuffle around and change places continuously so that no member of the huddle spends too much time on the bitterly cold outer edge, where the full effects of the Antarctic winds are felt.

By mid-July, the pack ice starts to melt and break up with the warmer temperatures, and the chicks begin to hatch. The female finally returns to the colony to take over feeding duties from the male who may have lost nearly half his body weight. She finds her mate among the thousands of other penguins by hearing his particular call. Just as they did with the egg, the couple dance their delicate dance once again and the newborn chick is passed to its mother. With the increased sun, the chicks grow stronger every day and the parents now alternate caring for their chicks, taking turns to guard from giant petrels, feed the chick, or return to the ocean to gather food. The fledglings remain dependent on their parents for the next six months. The young emperors who survive and grow into adulthood will be ready to breed in four to eight years.

Exploring the World's Oceans

Humans have been going "down to the sea in ships" much longer than many people realize. In the context of oceanic "exploration," however, a distinction must be made between early sea travel and deliberate expeditions of exploration and discovery. That said, can we know the mind of the first brave soul who guided his craft toward some distant, featureless, and unknown horizon?

EARLY OCEANIC TRAVEL

Many early voyages are documented through archeological and other evidence. Australia, for example, has been inhabited for an estimated 50,000 years. To reach the island continent that long ago would have required a water crossing of nearly 50 miles (80 km). Projectile points found in North America that look similar to those used in the European Solutrean culture 20,000 years ago hints at early Atlantic crossings. Ancient skeletal remains of Negroid Africans have appeared in various Atlantic coastal sites in the Americas.

Evidence of early navigation is widespread in the Pacific Basin. Earliest voyages no doubt began at least

ABOVE Prince Henry of Portugal "The Navigator" (1394–1460) inspired many ocean explorers.

BELOW Dutch explorer Cornelis de Houtman (1565–1599) found a new sea route to the East Indies (present-day Indonesia).

25,000 years ago—island hopping in the area of today's Melanesia. Some archeologists see a link between early pottery discovered in Ecuador, and Japan's Jomon culture, suggesting a chance contact between the two locations as early as 3000 BCE. The sweet potato—a native of South America—and its alternative name (cumer/kumar) was widely distributed throughout much of the Pacific region, including the insular Southeast Asia, long before Europeans arrived. The early Spanish explorers in South America found Asian poultry widespread throughout the continent. As chickens are unable to withstand cold, it is reasoned, they could not have arrived via a high latitude route. Almost two millennia before Magellan's epic voyage, Polynesian navigators had discovered most of the Pacific islands and settled those deemed livable.

Several thousand years before the dawn of the Christian era, Egyptians were traveling by water to the Land of Punt, the specific location of which is unknown. Punt may have referred to any destination in which trade was involved. Some evidence suggests that they traveled as far south as the Zambezi River on Africa's southeast coast. By 1900 BCE, Egyptians had built a canal linking the Nile River and Red Sea.

In the Mediterranean Basin, many cultures practiced navigation. None was more skilled or daring than the Phoenicians. The extent of their seafaring is unknown, because they left little record of their journeys. Some evidence hinting at early Phoenician contact has been found in locations as widespread as coastal Europe, many locations in Africa, and the Atlantic coast of Middle and Northern America.

FIFTEENTH-CENTURY EUROPEAN VOYAGES OF DISCOVERY

That the Vikings crossed the Atlantic Ocean half a millennium before Columbus's very well-documented voyage is no longer contested. However, less certain are some of the other suggested European pre-Columbian New World contacts, ranging from Portuguese fishermen to Irish monks. In most histories, serious oceanic exploration only commences with the fifteenth-century European voyages of discovery. When one considers that the Atlantic, Indian, and Pacific oceans had all been crossed—many times and by many different peoples several thousand years earlier—the bravery and daring of the "famous" European explorers becomes somewhat tarnished.

For centuries, the Pillars of Hercules (the Strait of Gibraltar) posed a huge psychological barrier beyond which few—other than the Phoenicians—dared pass. According to legend, immense fields of seaweed from which no ship could free itself (the Sargasso Sea?), huge mudflats, eerie darkness (possibly a reference to latitudes north of the Arctic Circle?), and horrible sea monsters awaited the seafarer who ventured west out of the Mediterranean Sea.

Oceanic navigation and exploration received a much-needed boost during the second decade of the fifteenth century. Prince Henry of Portugal, "The Navigator," is often given credit for the onset of the European Age of Exploration. Many myths, however, surround Prince Henry and his role. Henry himself was not a navigator; he never traveled farther than the African side of the Strait of Gibraltar. He did not develop a famous "school" of navigation; rather, he financially supported early voyages. When his Portuguese sailors reached Africa's Guinea coastal region,

ABOVE An Aboriginal rock painting from Arnhem Land, northern Australia, depicting boats from other lands.

ABOVE RIGHT A late sixteenth-century Dutch map of western Africa. The main language used on the map is Latin. Oceanus Aethiopicus is an historic name for the Atlantic Ocean.

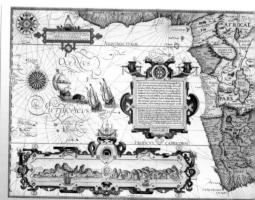

the search for a water passage to the East Indies was all but forgotten for nearly half a century, until the 1480s. Rather, Portugal instituted what became a lucrative slave trade.

By the dawn of the sixteenth century, European vessels had crossed the Indian and Atlantic oceans. The stage was now set for the "Golden Age of Geography," a period during which Europeans, sailing under many different flags, would literally unfold the world map to its present-day configuration within a period of a few centuries.

Development of Vessels

Human beings and floating vessels have developed side by side, from the simple raft to the complex super-freighter of today. We have invented many different types of vessels for trade, warfare, passenger transport, fishing, and leisure. We also find craft designed for rescue, research, and a wide variety of water sports.

OPPOSITE A Roman ship on the Copenhagen Sarcophagus, which dates from the late third century CE, showing a spritsail. This marble carving is one of the earliest representations of sprit-sails in navigation history.

BELOW Fishermen in early Ireland used animal hides stretched over a wicker frame to make a curragh, or coracle. These lightweight waterproof vessels are still in use in parts of western Ireland.

BEGINNINGS

In the beginning, inventive humans used whatever materials were at hand. If there was little wood, as in Mesopotamia, inflated skins or even clay pots were used, lashed together to make a raft. Animal skins were stretched out over a framework of bamboo, wicker, or even bone. The early Irish called such vessels curraghs, while people in the Arctic constructed hide-covered boats for fishing, whaling, and transport. To conserve scarce wood, the ancient Egyptians bundled reeds together to make rafts.

Wherever wood was plentiful, people tied logs together. They made large rafts, added masts and sails, and often traveled great distances, as the Polynesians did in their Pacific migrations. The earliest archeological evidence of a boat (from around 6300 BCE) is a wooden invention—the dugout canoe. More sophisticated canoes were carved out of tree trunks and shaped with sharp tools; others were simply hollow trunks, their ends sealed with clay.

The next step was to use a ribbed frame curving out from a keel, just as animal ribs extend from the backbone. Now it became possible to build a vessel in two ways. The Egyptians (after importing wood), Greeks, and Romans built the shell first, then added the frame for strength. The second method began with the frame, then planks were attached that were shaped to the frame. These planks were overlapped in the "clinker" style, or attached edge-to-edge, a method known as "carvel" construction. The gaps in the planks

were filled with a sealant, and the vessel was ready to sail. This basic design remained the same for large boats and ships until the nineteenth century, when people realized that metal could be used for ship hulls.

Once the wooden-framed vessel had been invented, the major issues were stability, method of propulsion, and the distance they could travel. We will begin in 3000 BCE with the Egyptians, who used the Nile as their highway. Because the wind blew from the north and the current came from the south, they used a mix of muscle and wind. To travel upstream they used a large square sail; downstream they dropped the sail and relied on the current and the oarsmen. To ensure that they did not run aground, larger oars were used for steering. The Khufu ship discovered in the Great Pyramid at Giza, which dates from about 2500 BCE, is 143 ft (44 m) long and 20 ft (6 m) wide. This was an exceptionally large vessel for the time (no wonder it was buried with a pharaoh). Slowly ships became stronger, sails larger, and boats increased in size. By the first millennium BCE they often measured up to 90 ft (27 m) long and could carry a substantial load. By this time, ships were sturdy enough to sail into the Mediterranean. Egyptian craft often visited the Phoenicians on the coast of modern-day Lebanon.

Like the Greeks who followed them, the Phoenicians used both ships driven by sail, and those that were powered by slaves with oars. Warships—or triremes—relied on oarsmen alone; the Greeks added a battering ram to punch holes in enemy ships. However, Greek cargo ships used sail only. Cargo ships were about the same size as Egyptian ships, but used a much greater area of sail—a middle mast with a square sail, and a smaller, triangular sail that supported the main sail. These ships carried up to 200 tons (180 tonnes) of cargo. The Romans used similar designs to build even stronger and larger cargo ships—up to around 180 ft (55 m) long and 45 ft (14 m) wide, with a capacity of about 1,000 tons (900 tonnes).

OVER TO CHINA

While the Egyptians, Phoenicians, Greeks, and Romans were paddling and sailing around the Mediterranean, the Chinese were already building superior ships. Indeed, the story of sailing vessels is one of Chinese excellence, and the struggle of the West to catch up with them. The model was the Chinese junk, which was adopted by many. The Chinese had already invented the segmented hull, which allowed separate

watertight compartments for safety and much larger construction. By 400 BCE, Chinese ships featured up to five sails fore and aft, large stones hung on the outside for stability, leeboards, and centerboards. They were comfortable, fast, and roomy.

Propulsion was very advanced. The sails had battens running across them, which strengthened them and improved their ability to catch the wind. One could also drop or raise the sails by means of a single rope, much like a window blind. The ships had flat bottoms for shallow waters, and also a rudder that served both to steer and to act as a keel for improved stability. The rudder could be raised in the shallows and lowered in deep water when the wind was up. The Chinese were able to complete long sea journeys to Malacca, across to India, and even to Europe.

OTHER VESSELS

In the Indian Ocean, the Arab dhow was widely used. The dhow was small, with a distinctive lateen (triangular) sail designed to make the most of monsoon winds. In Europe the major advances still relied on the basic design of the keeled and ribbed hull, with planks affixed to it. All the designs that followed until the nineteenth century were variations on this model.

Viking ships also dominated the waves. Scandinavians invented the segregated hull independently of the Chinese, and the keel. Their war (longboat) and merchant ("knarr") ships were powered by both muscle and sail. An excellent example of a knarr from the tenth century CE was found in Roskilde, Denmark. It is 54 ft (16 m) long and 15 ft (4.5 m) wide. The

European cog (from 1000 CE) was an enlarged Viking ship with a deeper hull and a large sail in the middle, but it had no oars. By 1300 the stern rudder had been added, copied from the southern Mediterranean design. It allowed sailing into the wind. The basic design had a pointed bow, square stern, and castles at both ends for shelter, cargo, and, during combat, arrows, stones, and other weapons. From here there were two variations on the cog, which took place through a mingling of northern European and Mediterranean styles. The rounded carrack added lateen sails to the single square

ABOVE The *Sancta Trinitas*, a sixteenth-century galleon. Powered by sail, galleons were large, square-masted vessels with two or more decks. They were used as warships and trade ships between the fifteenth and seventeenth centuries.

OPPOSITE Caravels plying the Indies route, from a sixteenth-century Portuguese manuscript. Caravels were capable of crossing vast expanses of ocean, and were used by explorers such as Christopher Columbus and Vasco da Gama.

RIGHT Paddle steamers in Venice in the early nineteenth century. These vessels are steam-driven; the large paddle wheels help to propel the boat forward. Paddle steamers were used in many parts of the world and are still popular pleasure craft.

BELOW The *Great Eastern* in dock on the River Thames in London in the 1850s. Made of iron, it had a double hull and was powered by four steam engines. It was used to take passengers from England to Australia and India.

sail of the cog, then the caravel with its slender hull was developed by the Portuguese in the fifteenth century. Caravels carried up to six lateen sails and were used throughout the age of discovery—Columbus used caravels to cross the Atlantic in 1492.

The invention of the gun stimulated further modifications to ship design. Cannon went below deck, castles disappeared, and covered holes (freeing ports) appeared in the sides. Ships were reinforced, enlarged, straightened (to allow more guns), and carried many more square sails. The greatest ship of this kind was the galleon. The Indiaman, first championed by the Dutch,

featured a large, rounded hull, and cannon to defend precious cargo. In the last days of sail, comfortable specialist ships carried passengers around the globe. These included small, swift coastal packets, and larger clippers, which traveled along at a good "clip."

STEEL AND STEAM

By the time of the clipper era, the steam engine had already appeared. Along with the metal hull, steam was the first major innovation in ship design for several centuries. Now propulsion came from an engine within the ship itself and sail was no longer necessary. Once the screw replaced the original paddles of river steamers, and the efficiency of engines improved in speed and fuel consumption, these ships began to ply the oceans. Other engines replaced steam, such as the internal combustion engine and later nuclear power, but the principle of self-propulsion remained the same.

Riveted metal hulls also fundamentally changed the design of ships. First used in times of war to protect wooden sailing ships from ever-increasing firepower, metal hulls quite soon came to be used on their own. Coupled with the swivel gun instead of fixed guns on the side, warships evolved into various larger and smaller types. Metal also revolutionized cargo transport, since it enabled ships to be built to unprecedented sizes, and the hull became a container in its own right. Metal ships also boasted the distinct advantage of being more robust in rough weather.

corueyra

Ro sayro

espadarte

Jacome de mello

g. biscainho

S. cruz

Ayres nunz barreto

Algarauia

Dom diogo dalmeyda

Lopo de sousa

Misse bernaldo

barü leyra

esg pera

Fr.co Lopez de sousa

Dom Jorge de meneses 6

Arribou a Lisboa

Diogo lopez de sousa

Development of Navigational and Sailing Skills

The word "navigate" comes from the Latin *navigare*, meaning "to sail." Today navigators make use of sophisticated equipment such as radar, computers, and Global Positioning Systems (GPS), but navigation remains a complex art.

ABOVE The sailor in the crow's nest, which was located high in the main mast, played a critical role in navigation. His job was to watch for land, as well as ships, reefs, sandbars, floating debris, and other shipping hazards.

CAPPING AND KENNING

In the earliest days, sailors avoided open water. Even so, navigators needed to guide ships from cape to cape, a process called "capping" or "kenning." They relied on sightings from the lookout or "crow's nest," someone who would know ("ken") when the next cape was in view, and warn the captain of reefs or sandbars.

Away from land, navigation became a very different skill. Navigators had to work with a set of variables—direction, latitude (the distance from the equator), longitude (the horizontal distance from a fixed point or prime meridian), and the ship's speed, aspect, and direction.

METHODS

For direction, the compass was (and remains) indispensable. Magnetic compasses first appeared in China in the eleventh century, and have evolved into the gyroscope or gyrocompass, a spinning device that measures true North, and is not subject to outside interferences.

Calculating latitude has always been relatively easy, especially via the heavenly bodies. One focused on the North Star (Polaris), Southern Cross, or the Sun, figured out their angles in relation to the horizon, and then used the result to determine distance north or south of the equator. Longitude was a much more difficult problem. The key was to measure how much time had passed from the last known landmark. But this needed an accurate timepiece and until 1761 none was available. Navigators used a complex process of measuring distances between the moon and other stars and then comparing their readings with charts. One major problem was that there were no charts for regions yet unencountered.

FROM FINGERS TO SEXTANTS

All sorts of devices have been used to measure latitude, including fingers, cross-staff, quadrant, astrolabe, and sextant. The basic principle behind each was to provide an accurate measurement of the angle between the Sun or key star and the horizon, from which latitude could be calculated. Many early navigators utilized hand measurements: A finger above the horizon gave you two degrees, a wrist eight degrees, a hand 18 degrees. Better still was a cross-staff, which was simply a piece of wood with a movable cross-piece. The navigator lined up one tip of the cross-piece with the Sun and

the other with the horizon and took the angle of the lines where they met at the end of the main piece. Quadrants, astrolabes, and sextants all had sights on them, a series of numbers, and a pointer or string with a weight that would indicate the correct measurement. The sextant enabled very accurate readings of latitude based on the position of the Sun at noon. It was made of a telescope, two mirrors, an arm with a pointer, and a series of measurements.

TIMEPIECES AND DEAD RECKONING

The best way to measure longitude is by determining the distance traveled from a known point. Sailors have tried various approaches, such as guesswork, watching weed or flotsam floating past, turning an hour-glass at regular intervals, throwing a piece of wood over the bow then timing it as it passes the stern, and securing to a stick a rope with knots tied at regular intervals.

RIGHT A medieval astronomer takes measurements from land. Celestial navigation relied on the geometric relationships between the positions of the stars and planets and the horizon.

Navigators then measured the passage of time by the number of knots that slipped through the fingers, which is how the term "knots" arose. The trick was to estimate speed, measure it several times a day, and then estimate the distance traveled. All these approaches were variations on "dead reckoning"—observing the ship's movement and estimating its location as closely as possible. There was much room for error.

It was only following the advent of the chronometer, invented in 1761 by John Harrison, that time could be measured properly at sea. The chronometer differed from earlier clocks in having a lever to maintain equal pressure on the spring, and a balance to deal with temperature changes. Combined with accurate sextant readings, it was finally possible to measure longitude. In many respects the chronometer refined dead reckoning, which is still used today, although now with the assistance of quartz crystal clocks, computers, satellites, radar, accelerometers to measure acceleration, and gyroscopes to provide stable compass readings.

RIGHT This painting by American artist Winslow Homer (1836–1910) shows a sailor using a sextant, a navigational device used to measure the angle between the horizon and a heavenly body, and thus determine latitude and longitude.

Seafarers of Antiquity

From the early days of human civilization, people have been sailing and exploring, and civilizations grew along major river systems such as the Nile in Egypt and the twin rivers of the Tigris and Euphrates in modern-day Iraq. People traveled along the Fertile Crescent (from modern-day Iraq through to Egypt), and the rivers were critically important. This ancient territory was called Mesopotamia, a Greek word meaning "land between the rivers."

Each of the successive empires established in this fertile land between the rivers—the Sumerians, Babylonians, Assyrians, and Persians—found it more efficient to transport people and goods by water rather than by land. It was also more economical. For example, it cost the same to transport a load of grain from one end of the Mediterranean Sea to the other as it did over 75 miles (120 km) of land. The wind in a sail was free.

ABOVE One of the earliest maps of the world is the Babylonian World Map, a clay tablet found in southern Iraq, dating from around 600 BCE.

RIGHT This painting dating from between 2420–2270 BCE is from the tomb of Kaemrhon in Giza, Egypt. It shows an Egyptian boat with sails, oars, and a large crew.

EGYPT: BEYOND THE NILE DELTA

Unfortunately, due to a lack of evidence (such as a well-preserved wreck, for example), there is little surviving information about Mesopotamian ships, other than riverboats. No doubt they sailed out of the mouths of their rivers and into the Persian Gulf, for we know that they met the Egyptians. By contrast, the Egyptians left us many pictures, descriptions, and even

a complete ship dating from around 2500 BCE, which was discovered in the Great Pyramid at Giza.

For centuries the Egyptians sailed up and down the Nile River, using the wind when heading south, and oars and the current when moving north. At the mouth of the Nile is the Mediterranean, and travelers could follow the shore to Palestine and Phoenicia (present-day Lebanon and Syria). From here, the Egyptians obtained timber, particularly cedar, and built larger ships. The ancient cities of Tyre, Sidon, and Byblos were their main ports of call. In fact, these sea-going vessels were known as "Byblos" boats.

The other Egyptian shore was the Red Sea, also a waterway protected from the worst ocean weather. In the second century BCE, historian Agatharchides wrote a work called *The Erythraean Sea*, the Greek name for the Indian Ocean. Only the fifth (and last) volume of the book survives, but he describes, in both realistic and fantastical ways, the territories surrounding the Red Sea. He mentions that according to the records he was able to find, Egyptian ships during the Old Kingdom (3000–2500 BCE) sailed down the Red Sea to the "myrrh-country," possibly the Persian Gulf.

PHOENICIA: THE "SEA PEOPLES"

No major river ran through ancient Phoenicia, so when the Phoenicians, who were known as the "sea peoples," took to the water, it was into the sea. In the cities of Tyre, Sidon, and Byblos, the Phoenicians built double- and triple-level warships, powered by oarsmen, and sailing vessels for transporting people and cargo. Built of oak and cedar, their quality was famous; the Bible describes them as "ships that sing." They knew that the Polaris star indicated north, they could navigate by the stars and thus sail at night, they could calculate how far the ship had traveled, and they learned from the winds and the currents. Although they had been there since around 3000 BCE, by 1100 BCE they were the major sea

BELOW A Phoenician merchant ship, c. seventh century BCE, crosses the Red Sea. Built mainly from high quality cedar native to their homeland, Phoenician ships were famed for their superior craftsmanship.

BOTTOM This eighth century BCE relief from the Palace of Sargon at Khorsabad, capital of the Kingdom of Assyria (in present-day Iraq), shows sailors unloading timber supplies from a boat.

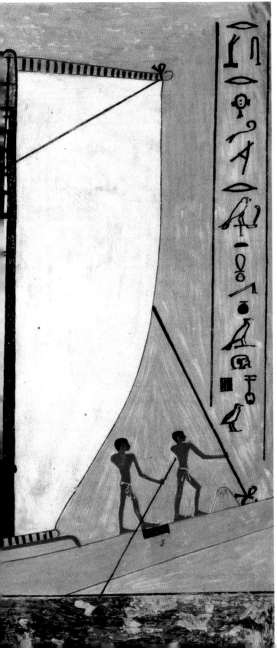

power in the Mediterranean. The Greeks directly copied from them and the Egyptians also learnt much.

Initially the Phoenicians traveled up and down the shore between their cities and Egypt. But by the eighth century BCE, they were under pressure from the growing Assyrian Empire. The result was a string of colonies right across the Mediterranean—Crete, Sicily, Malta, Sardinia, and Ibiza. At first these were established for population overflow, but the new colonies also needed supplies, so Phoenician ships soon plied the whole Mediterranean. They became known as tough colonists

and hard bargainers, so much so that Homer called them "greedy rogues." Later, the Greek writer Plutarch described them as "so strict as to dislike all humor and kindness." Their largest colony was on the north African coast—this was the famous Carthage that would challenge Rome in later centuries under Hannibal. When their homeland was over-run, Carthage became the main center of Phoenician seafaring.

At the western end of the Mediterranean is open sea. The Phoenicians sailed through what would soon be called the Pillars of Hercules, into unknown waters, in ships no larger than fishing boats. As they hugged the coast, their southern route took them as far as modern-day Gambia and Senegal, as well as the Canary Islands, which can be seen from vantage points on the mainland. Northward they passed up the coast, endured the heavy swells of the Bay of Biscay, and sailed as far as the modern-day English Channel to what the Greeks called the Cassiterides ("tin islands")—actually Cornwall and the northwest coast of Spain, from where tin and lead were brought back to the Mediterranean. Some have speculated that the Phoenicians also reached the Baltic Sea, or further down western Africa, or even across to the Americas, but there is no proof of this.

Even the oft-gentle Mediterranean can whip up a storm and sink a ship. Indeed, many wrecks have been found, some dating from between the fifth and eighth centuries BCE. The largest is around 60 ft (18 m) long, the hull rounded for cargo, and containing crockery for food preparation, an incense stand for offerings to the weather gods, and a wine decanter. The cargo was carried in large earthenware jars or "amphorae." These jars were about 3 ft (90 cm) long with pointed ends, and were arranged in a bed of sand. They carried wine, olive oil, honey, and other liquids, and the ships also carried other goods, like textiles, timber, and perfumes.

Every time we write or read we use a type of script that was first used by the Phoenicians—the phonetic script. Shipbuilding, cargo, people, and colonies require extensive book-keeping. From Egypt and Mesopotamia, scripts have been found that expressed whole concepts, words, and syllables. The Phoenicians made a major breakthrough around 1500 BCE, when they identified the individual sounds—phonemes—that make up a word. Far fewer letters are required, since phonemes are the building blocks of words. This was the model copied by the Greeks, and many other languages of Europe and the Near East.

Polynesian Voyaging

Tens of thousands of years ago, people from the Australia–New Guinea land mass began an epic migration eastward through Melanesia. Their descendants—the first Polynesians—arrived in the Marquesas around 2,300 years ago. This adventure of several thousand miles culminated with settlements in Hawaii and Easter Island from around 200 to 800 CE, and in New Zealand a few centuries later. These ancient mariners traveled in double outrigger ships—two canoes with a connecting platform, a small hut, and a wind sail or two. These craft, which were probably about 65 ft (20 m) long with a crew of several dozen, were only slightly smaller than the ocean-going vessels of later explorers such as Columbus.

Ancient Polynesian seafarers navigated by the stars using a simple fore-and-aft system. Sailors aligned their canoe along a star-defined straight line between two islands. Experienced navigators also relied on the Sun, waves, winds, birds, and cloud patterns.

Unlike ancient Mediterranean seamen who feared deep water and hugged the coast, Pacific travelers embraced open ocean travel. The voyagers' likely strategy shrewdly combined oars and sails. The crew rowed against the prevailing easterly trade winds in search of new islands. When they returned home, they rode the wind while resting their oars.

The earliest journeys to the more densely islanded western Melanesia required only a few days at sea. Farther east, the island chains became progressively more distant. These shorter trips readied the first generations of sailors, allowing them to hone their nautical and survival skills, including food storage. Later generations engaged in successively longer journeys of several weeks or months, always with the assurance that home was just a quick return trip with the winds at their backs.

GREECE: RULING THE WAVES

By the fifth century BCE, Greece, or rather Athens, had begun to rule the waves. Greek sailors adapted and improved on the Phoenician ship designs. Like the Phoenicians, the Athenians were forced by population pressures to establish new colonies. They crossed the water to Asia Minor (modern Turkey) and further afield. Colonies depended on ships to keep contact with the home city, so the Athenian fleet developed.

ABOVE A fifth century BCE Greek ship. Ancient Greece had a rich maritime tradition and by this time, had built up a sizeable and capable naval force.

BELOW A fifteenth-century representation of the navy of Julius Caesar invading England. Sailing prowess helped Rome to expand and maintain its powerful empire.

The port of Piraeus was the busiest port in the ancient world, and was populated by ship builders, tradesmen, and merchants. One of the main cargoes was human beings—the slaves who were shipped in from newly conquered regions to be sold. The Athenians also had the advantage of nearby silver mines, which enabled them to buy goods, employ the best craftsmen, buy numerous slaves, and build the strongest war fleet in the ancient world. It was this fleet that defeated the mighty Persian navy at Salamis in 480 BCE, thus ending the attempted invasion of Greece.

Intrepid Greek sailors explored the Black Sea and also ventured beyond the famed Pillars of Hercules. The most famous sailor was Pytheas, a geographer based in the Greek city of Massilia (modern-day Marseilles). In around 315 BCE, he sailed through the Pillars and turned north. We are entirely reliant on subsequent sources since his book describing the journey has not survived. It is clear that he sailed to Britain (he was one of the first to use the word), and then further north to "Thule" (perhaps Iceland or Trondheim in Norway), where he passed the Arctic Circle and encountered drift ice—quite a shock for a man from the warm Mediterranean! He also provided some of the earliest efforts to calculate longitude, and described the effect of tides in the north.

In the other direction went Eudoxus of Cyzicus, a Greek navigator who sailed to India in 118 BCE and again in 116 BCE. Until Eudoxus's daring voyages, Greek traders would meet those from India in the Arabian port of Aden, but most Greeks did not dare brave the monsoons that occurred further to the east. According to the *Geography* of Strabo (64–23 BCE), Eudoxus did this twice, returning with spices and precious stones. Within about 60 years, the Greeks had learnt to manage the monsoons, and both Greek and Roman ships regularly made the crossing to India.

FROM ROME TO INDIA

Where the Greeks left off, the Romans went further, sailing between the extremes of Britain to the north and India to the east. Roman ships in search of pepper and ginger could make the dangerous return voyage—if they survived hazards such as pirates and storms—within a year. The longer journey to east Africa (taking two years) was safer. Though the Romans made great use of European river systems, they also sailed regularly to northern parts of their empire in Gaul and Britain.

Roman voyages to east Africa were not just one-way affairs—ships also journeyed northward from Africa.

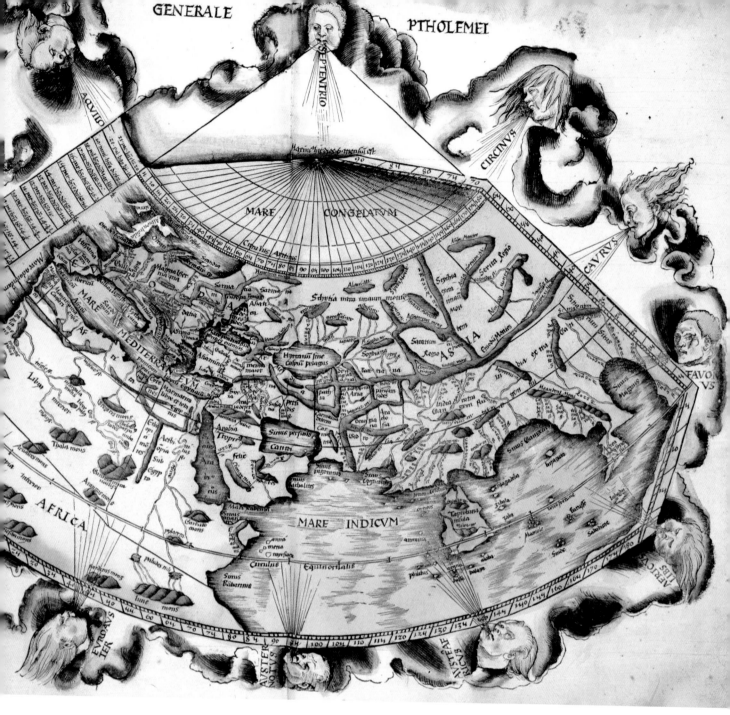

Ancient Nubia in the upper reaches of the Nile traded with India, and the Greeks traded with the powerful kingdom of Aksum (Ethiopia), and with the Somalis, whose fleets traveled up to the Arabian Peninsula to trade frankincense and other items.

When Eudoxus and the Romans who followed him arrived in India, they found a thriving seafaring civilization. India was situated at the junction between Chinese and Arab marine and overland trade. A dry dock, discovered at Lothal in Gujarat, was constructed by the Harrapan people of the Indus Valley civilization (2600–1900 BCE). Measuring 718 x 118 ft (218 x 36 m), the dock was used to refit large ships. More recent evidence comes from the treatise *Yukti Kalpa Taru*. Although published in the twelfth century CE, it

contains a great deal of information about ancient shipbuilding, and different types of ship. By the third century BCE, Indian navigators were braving Indian Ocean monsoons to make regular crossings to Arab ports. Their seafarers established colonies in Cambodia, Java, Borneo, and Socotra, and also visited Japan.

A contemporary summary of ancient seafaring knowledge is found in the famous map of Ptolemy (90–168 CE). It is most accurate in the areas where he could rely on information from seafarers, so we find a reasonably accurate picture of the Mediterranean, Black Sea, Red Sea, Persian Gulf, and northern Europe. Beyond that point the map is less accurate—southern Africa is unknown, while India and Sri Lanka are out of proportion, but China ("Sinae") does get a mention.

ABOVE In a work entitled *Geography*, Greek astronomer and scientist Ptolemy (c. 100–168 CE) wrote detailed directions for a definitive world map. Using his instructions, academics in the fifteenth century drew this map, showing what Ptolemy believed was the whole world.

The Vikings

The traditional view of the Vikings is as marauding raiders who attacked without mercy. While there is no doubt that they were fearsome warriors, they were also highly skilled shipbuilders. Their navigational skills and seamanship were without parallel. They sailed some of the roughest seas where savage storms, unseen reefs, and sea ice posed enormous risks.

RIGHT Drakkars under the command of King Olav of Norway in the late tenth century CE. Such warrior ships could have 30 oarsmen. The dragons on the ship's figureheads were intended to strike fear into the hearts of the Vikings' enemies.

BELOW Viking warriors engaged in hand-to-hand combat. Master mariners, the Vikings sailed as far as Russia, conquering and sometimes colonizing along the way. The golden age of Viking exploration was between the ninth and eleventh centuries CE.

SEAMEN AND WARRIORS

Originating in Scandinavia in what are now Norway, Denmark, and Sweden, the Vikings were excellent seamen. "Vik" is Old Norse for "fjord," and "ing" means "son"—a Viking was therefore a son of the fjord. It was in the deep sea fjords of Norway that many of the great Viking explorations began. The rugged, inhospitable terrain of northern Scandinavia turned the Vikings naturally to the sea for transport and livelihood.

The period 850–1050 CE is considered the golden era of Viking exploration. During this time the Vikings traveled across the North and Irish seas sacking, but also colonizing, parts of England, Scotland, and Ireland. They sailed up the River Seine attacking Paris, and then moved into Normandy. They also sailed south along the Iberian coast, launching assaults on Lisbon and Cadiz, even entering the Mediterranean Sea and pillaging the Italian city of Pisa.

COLONIZERS

Although renowned for their raiding, the Vikings also colonized some of their vanquished territories. To the east they used the Baltic Sea and its rivers to establish settlements in Russia—notably Novgorod and Kiev—and eventually made their way to the Black Sea. The Vikings used a settlement in Iceland, founded in 874 CE, to explore and occupy Greenland. They then used ocean currents and favorable winds to range even further afield along the east coast of North America, which they named Vinland.

VIKING SHIPS

Norse tradition buried clan chiefs with their ships, which is fortunate for marine archeologists, as entire ships have been discovered in vast burial mounds. These provide a unique insight into the naval architecture of the Vikings. Two of the most famous relics, the Tune Ship and the Gokstad Ship, were found in Norway in the late nineteenth century, and are now housed in the Viking Ship Museum in Oslo.

Another famous discovery was the three Nydam Ships found in Denmark. They are the oldest-known rowed vessels discovered in Europe.

The most famous of the Viking vessels was the drakkar, which is often referred to as the longship, or dragon ship. A warship designed to carry Viking warriors, it was usually around 100 ft (30 m) long. The drakkars were owned by Norse noblemen and generally crewed by between 20 and 30 men. Less well known, the knarr was the real workhorse of the Viking fleets. These small vessels of around 50 ft (15 m) were used to carry cargo.

Originally it was believed that all Viking vessels were constructed of oak. However, more recent finds show that ash, pine, elm, and a range of other timbers were also used. The ships had a clinker construction, with each plank overlapping another, which created a watertight hull. The planks were strapped to the frame by lengths of fiber cords coated in pitch to preserve them. Although iron was available to the Vikings, it was expensive; instead a trenail, a type of wooden pin, was often used to hold the frame together. The use of cords provided the ships with a flexibility that allowed them

ABOVE This simple yet effective construction, using a large rock wedged by a wooden post connected to a forked stake, is a Viking ship's anchor.

BELOW A dragon-prowed Viking ship from a tenth-century CE manuscript. Such ornate figureheads were found only on the ships of kings and high-ranking noblemen. Most Viking ships were more modestly decorated.

to ride out rough seas. This elasticity gave the ships great strength and assisted the Vikings in making their wide-ranging voyages. Like all ships, Viking vessels carried considerable amounts of rope. This was normally made of hemp, although ropes of horse hair were also used. A single rudder formed by a large, deep oar at the rear of the ship was steered by one man.

Images of Viking vessels usually show them adorned with ornately carved figureheads at the bow, commonly in the form of a fearsome dragon. It is very unlikely that most vessels carried such figureheads; the most significant warships no doubt did, but the majority of boats would have had a far simpler design, such as carved wooden scrolls.

The archeological finds reveal that the vessels had a bank of oars and a sail. The Viking ships were thus similar in certain respects to the galleys that plied the Mediterranean Sea during classical times. One major difference between the Viking ships and the earlier vessels was a shallow draft. This allowed them to come in close to shore but—equally significantly—to retreat rapidly. To raid effectively, escaping quickly is as important as arriving stealthily!

Cheng Ho

Long before Prince Henry the Navigator commissioned the first Portuguese seafarers to sail down the coast of Africa, and decades before the voyages of Columbus, da Gama, and Magellan made much of the world European, there were intrepid Chinese navigators who had left their own shores for distant explorations.

RIGHT An eighteenth-century Chinese map of the world, reported to be a reproduction of a map made by Cheng Ho in 1418. Although there is some doubt as to its authenticity, many believe the map shows that Cheng Ho sailed as far as Australia and North America.

THE GRAND EUNUCH

First among them was Admiral Cheng Ho (also spelled Zheng He), whose seven voyages between 1405 and 1433 traced the coastlines of Southeast Asia, the Indian subcontinent, the Arabian Peninsula, and much of the Indian Ocean coast of Africa.

Cheng Ho was born Ma Ho in 1371 in Yunnan Province in the south of China, a Muslim region that supported the weakening Mongol Dynasty. He was captured at the age of 10 by the armies of the Chinese emperor-to-be, Yongle, and, like all boys his age, was castrated and assigned to serve the court. Over time he impressed the emperor with his intelligence and leadership potential, as well as with his imposing height of nearly 7 ft (over 2 m). He became extraordinarily powerful and influential. He was assigned the Chinese name Cheng Ho and then the title "Grand Eunuch," and in 1403 was charged with the construction of a fleet of ships to explore the seas. The primary purpose of this new fleet was to display the wealth and glory of the new Ming Empire.

TREASURE VOYAGES

That first fleet of "treasure ships" numbered 317 ships and nearly 28,000 men. More than 60 of the ships were huge junks that were around 400 ft (120 m) long, then the biggest vessels ever made. Other ships carried nothing but horses. There were also various supply ships, specialized warships, ships to carry soldiers, and ships called *baochuans* that carried treasures to trade.

The first voyage was destined for Calicut (now Kozhikode) on the Malabar Coast of India, a major trading port for spices and fine silks. The expedition reached the city in late 1406 after stops in Vietnam, Java, Malacca, and Sri Lanka, and remained until favorable winds in spring 1407 enabled its return to China. The second voyage of 1407–1409 carried envoys from China to some of the same ports, although without Cheng Ho, who remained in China fulfilling another assignment. The third voyage (1409–1411) succeeded in establishing Chinese supply posts and fortifications along the coasts of Southeast and South Asia.

The fourth through seventh voyages went further, including possibly into Atlantic waters around South Africa's Cape of Good Hope. It is known for sure that on the fourth voyage (1413–1415) Cheng Ho visited Hormuz on the Persian Gulf, and the Maldives. On the return trip he defeated a rebel leader on Sumatra named Sekandar. The fifth expedition (1416–1419) concentrated on the ports of East Africa, including Mogadishu, Malindi, and Mombasa. There, the Chinese exchanged porcelains, pearls, and precious stones for zoological wonders that were taken back to China: Lions, zebras, ostriches, leopards, and a giraffe. They also sought to bring home a unicorn but without success. The sixth voyage (1421–1422) again went to Africa, although Cheng Ho himself turned back early to attend celebrations in Beijing relating to the opening of the Forbidden City. The seventh and last voyage began in 1430 and visited many of the usual ports, as well as Dhofar in Africa, and possibly Jeddah on the Red Sea, the port for the holy city of Mecca.

It is quite possible that Cheng Ho, a devout Muslim, may have made the hajj pilgrimage on that final voyage. The admiral died in 1433 on his return to China and was probably buried at sea. The detailed chronicles of his voyages highlight his diplomacy and commercial expertise, both of which helped to ensure the success of the "treasure voyages."

What Might Have Been

Emperor Yongle, who had commissioned Cheng Ho's first voyages, died in 1424. After then there was less support for such expensive ventures, and the era of exploration ended after Cheng Ho's death. Thereafter, China entered an isolationist phase. Today these voyages are a subject of great interest and pride in China. Had the new emperor not called a halt in 1435 to these travels and ordered the amassed fleets of enormous ships to be abandoned, it is probable that China, instead of Europe, would have dominated much of the globe. This is not to discount the vast achievement of Cheng Ho (left) and his fleet: China was still acknowledged as a maritime power, and continued to hold sway in the waters of East Asia.

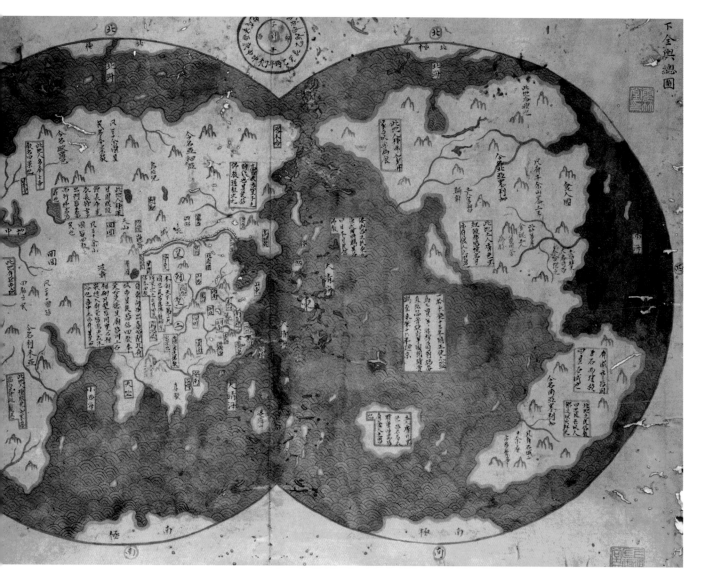

LEFT A painting of Cheng Ho at a temple shrine in Penang, Malaysia. Cheng Ho is said to have established a number of Muslim communities in parts of Southeast Asia, including in Java and on the Malay Peninsula.

Moorish and Arabic Seafarers

From the time they invaded modern Spain and Portugal in the eighth century CE, the Moors—Muslims from North Africa—provided intellectual and cultural leadership to the Mediterranean world. They named the territory they took al-Andalus and ruled for almost eight centuries (711–1492), until they were driven out by Christian forces.

BELOW The Turkish astronomer Takiuddin in his observatory in the sixteenth century. Arabic scholars were responsible for some of the most important scientific discoveries of all time.

The mathematician and astronomer Abu al-Zarqālî (1029–1087), known in the West as Arzachel, made several groundbreaking discoveries that added great precision to geographical calculation. From his base in Toledo, he invented the universal astrolabe, which illustrates and predicts the positions of heavenly bodies at any time and place on earth. He also calculated, for the first time, the exact dimensions of the Mediterranean Sea—very useful information for sailors.

BUILDING ON EARLIER DISCOVERIES

Not long afterward, Muhammad al-Idrisi (1100–1166) made use of al-Zarqālî's discoveries to produce the most accurate map of the known world. He also gathered information from Arab traders to show all the seas and countries from northern Europe through to China. Al-Idrisi is also famous for a written work, *Nuzhatul Mushtaq*, which tells of Ahmad ibn Umar who sailed into the Atlantic until he reached a "sticky and stinking sea," probably the Sargasso. This was enough to make him return home, although some still speculate that he may have reached the Americas. But in such small ships, barely larger than fishing boats, the open Atlantic was a terrifying prospect. As al-Idrisi writes, "its atmosphere is foggy, its waves are very strong, its dangers are perilous, its beasts are terrible, and its winds are full of tempests."

The greatest Moorish traveler of all was Ibn Battuta (1304–1369), who wrote, or rather dictated, a work called the *Rihla*, or "journey." He was bitten by the travel bug for 30 years, journeying more than 73,000 miles (120,000 km) from southern Europe to China, with stops in India, eastern Europe, and East Africa. The tale is a mix of material copied from other travel documents and memories of genuine experiences, and it is an extraordinary literary document. It describes local peoples and cultures, and dangers from storm, attack, and disease on land and sea. From his base in Calicut, India, he sailed to the Maldives and Sri Lanka, then boarded a Chinese junk that took him via Vietnam, the Philippines, and the Grand Canal, to Beijing.

ARAB TRADERS

The lack of timber for shipbuilding on the Arabian Peninsula meant that the Arabs took their time to become seafarers, preferring the ship of the desert, the camel, to the ship of the sea. Yet they eventually became great seafarers, sailing from the Persian Gulf to the Red Sea, then across to India and China. An early record comes from a Roman merchant around 100 BCE, who

wrote: "And the whole place is crowded with Arab ship owners and seafaring men, and is busy with the affairs of commerce; for they carry on a trade with the far-side coast and with Barygyza, sending their own ships there."

Meanwhile Greek and Roman ships traveled to the port of Aden in the Persian Gulf, to trade goods that the Arabs had brought from India. The Arabs used dhows with lateen (triangular) sails, designed to tear in a storm, since they were extremely difficult to take down. Arab traders also traversed the east African coast, establishing trading ports along the way.

The spread of Islam brought Arabs into contact with other Mediterranean peoples. Now the old trade routes with China and East Africa had another dimension—the Red Sea. Traders could sail from the Persian Gulf to the reefs of the Red Sea, then travel overland for six or seven days to the Mediterranean. There was another new impetus for seafaring—the pilgrimage, or hajj, to Mecca, which every Muslim tries to undertake at least once in their life.

While the Mediterranean was a sea of navies, the Indian Ocean was one of trade. Arab traders began

moving beyond India to China. Around 850 CE the Persian explorer and geographer ibn Khurdadhbih wrote of his seafaring exploits from Persia to China, and many other authors soon followed. They wrote of their voyages in the Indian and Pacific oceans, of their ventures into the Atlantic, to the coast of Africa, and even to the Bering Strait.

ABOVE A map of Arabia and India drawn c. 1519 by the Portuguese cartographer Pedro Reinel. As Moorish seafarers sailed to places such as Africa, India, and Asia, they developed their map-making skills.

LEFT A thirteenth-century parchment depicting Moorish sailors. One reason for the Moors to set sail was to complete the hajj, the sacred pilgrimage to Mecca. As they traveled, Moorish and Arabic seafarers spread their culture and religion to many parts of the globe.

Italian Exploration

At the start of 1400, Venice was the center of the world economy. The spices, medicines, and silks that came by way of Arab traders from India and China passed through Venice, and all European trade went back the same way. It was the intersection between west and east, between the Arab world, the Byzantine Empire, and Europe. Venice ensured its monopoly by controlling all shipping through the Mediterranean.

OPPOSITE The Genoese fleet under the command of Admiral Andrea Doria captured Coron, in the Gulf of Messina, from the Ottoman Empire in 1532. The Ottomans recaptured the city two years later.

ABOVE The maritime republics of Venice and Genoa from a fifteenth-century navigational map, called a portolan chart, which is a map based on verbal descriptions of the sites.

RIGHT The famed explorer Marco Polo sets out from Venice, accompanied by his father and his uncle, on their long journey to meet Kublai Khan in China. Marco Polo's account of his travels was enormously popular at the time and inspired a love for the exotic.

At its peak, Venice was the base for more than 3,000 ships. Many were war galleys, but most were merchant ships. They were rowed not by slaves, but by citizens whose names were drawn by lot, or by those working off debts. Life on board was tolerable, although everyone was expected to be able to manage a crossbow and javelin—either to repel attack or to discourage competitors. However, most Venetian ships were designed to sail in the calmer waters of the Mediterranean rather than on the high seas.

VENETIAN EXPLORERS

This did not stop two of the most famous Venetian explorers—Marco Polo (1254–1324) and Sebastian Cabot (1484–1557)—from traveling the known world. With his father and uncle, both of whom had previously made the trip, Marco Polo left for China in 1271. Twenty-five years later, after a long stint at the court of Kublai Khan, he returned via the sea route, stopping at India along the way. As a result of his famous book, *The Travels of Marco Polo*, he became the most famous European visitor to China, and aroused great interest in all matters Chinese. Indeed, the book inspired Christopher Columbus to set sail for eastern parts in 1492.

Although Cabot was born in Venice, he set sail from Bristol, England, in 1497 and crossed the heavy and cold seas of the North Atlantic to what he called "New Found Land"—probably modern-day Nova Scotia and Newfoundland. His great dream was to find a northwest passage to China, and so, after an expedition to the Caribbean, he set sail again in 1522 under Spanish

colors. He didn't quite make it to Cathay, being tempted by the wealth of South America. Surviving shipwreck, mutiny, and hostile Indians, he finally returned five years later to face trial and conviction for his disobedience in not pushing onward to China.

GENOA'S GOLDEN YEARS

The origins of the seaport of Genoa, on the other side of Italy from Venice, are now lost in the mists of time. This small fishing port became a republic by 1100, defeated and was defeated by Venice three centuries later, and then, when Venice entered its terminal decline, emerged as the commercial center of Europe, although this was for a brief period of just 70 years from 1557 until 1627. Hemmed in by mountains and with little space for crops, Genoese wealth came from a group of banker–financiers who directed European commerce—they organized voyages for other people, traded for other people, and banked their wealth.

How did this happen? It was actually the result of the discovery of the New World. In 1492, Christopher Columbus made his famous voyage in tiny ships to the Americas. But Columbus was from Genoa, and even though he sailed under the Spanish flag, he ensured that one-tenth of the income he generated from his discoveries was paid into the bank of San Giorgio in Genoa. Columbus made four journeys across the Atlantic; Spanish settlements followed in the new colonial rush, and wealth flowed into Genoese banks. The influx of new wealth meant that the Genoese became bankers for the Spanish crown. This connection was strengthened by the new constitution of 1528, in which Genoa came under Spanish protection. Some merchants settled in Spain, and some bankers relocated to Madrid but kept connections with home. It was, in short, Spanish wealth that made Genoa great.

Columbus was not the only Genoese seafarer, but he is the most well known. Less scrupulous perhaps was Count Enrico de Candia (from a dynastic house of Norman origin), pirate and adventurer of the early thirteenth century. By foul deed and fair, he managed to gain control of Malta and part of Cyprus, adopting the title "Count of Malta." Another seafarer was Andrea Doria, who was instrumental in establishing Genoa as a vassal of Spain. An aristocrat, he was first a mercenary, and then an admiral, of the Genoese fleet in the Mediterranean. A man of immense wealth, power, and intrigue, Doria preferred to work quietly in the background rather than take center stage.

ANDREA DORIA · PRECLARVS · TRIGINTA ACTVARIAM NAVIVM GENVENSIVM · DVX
ATQVE SEDECIM ROMÆ ET MELITÆ TOTIDEM NEAPOLIS ET TRINACRIÆ · PRÆTEREA
TRIGINTA NAVIVM GRANDIVM — CORONEM · IN MESSENIACO SINV LIBERAT ·
PROFLIGANS · DIE SEPTIMO AVGVSTI ANNO MILLESIMO QVINGENTESIMO TRICESIMO
TERTIO — LVFTIM BEI — QVI SEXAGINTA NAVES ACTVARIAS · TRIGINTA NAVES
LONGAS · CELOCESQVE QVINDECIM A MORO ALEXANDRINQ ARMATAS · DVCEBAT.

THE AGE OF DISCOVERY

Something very new began in the fifteenth century. The result was one of the most extraordinary phases of human history—the Age of Discovery. Within 200 years, European ships were able to sail any ocean.

FEARS CONQUERED

In the beginning, tiny boats set out across unknown oceans. The sailors feared sea monsters, evil spirits in pagan lands, and saw ominous signs in everything from seaweed to the flight of birds. Huge storms and massive seas awaited them; fickle winds could either tear their sails to shreds or leave them becalmed in vast oceans. Many knew they could die from sickness, thirst, starvation, or encounters with hostile people. Living conditions on their seaborne homes were cramped, smelly, noisy, and they shared them with rats, lice, bedbugs, and weevils.

Yet set out they did. The Portuguese sailed down the African coast, found its tip and the path to India opened up. After Columbus crossed the Atlantic, the Americas—for better or worse—would never be the same, as one ship after another made the crossing. While the Spanish and Portuguese colonized South and Central America, the English and French explored North America. They had set out to find a passage to the east—the fabled Northwest Passage—through North America, but they settled in the new land instead. Ferdinand Magellan rounded South America and crossed the endless Pacific in the first circumnavigation of the globe, with one ship limping home, minus Magellan. The southern lands—Australia and New Zealand—were next, and then they braved the icy oceans of both south and north.

THE NEED FOR EXPLORATION

What caused this frenetic activity? Such a seismic shift in world history had many causes. One cause was the firmly held belief that Europe was backward. They sensed that the center of the world lay eastward, for there, advanced civilizations with untold wealth could be found. All European ships set out to find the East.

The daily fare of food was another reason. Before refrigeration, the best way to preserve food, or mask the taste of food that was not fresh, was with spices. Tropical in origin, spices do not grow well in Europe, and had to be brought from the East, either via the long overland route or by sea. The value of spices may be illustrated by Magellan's voyage. From this prohibitively expensive trip, only one leaking and battered ship, *Victoria*, returned home after sailing around the world. However, the ship was loaded up with cloves and cinnamon collected while the crew was in the East Indies. That one cargo not only covered all the costs of the trip, but actually made a profit.

Food and politics were closely linked. For centuries, Europe sought the vital spices, as well as drugs and silk, through the near East. Arab traders used to link up with European traders, for many years through Venice. But when Constantinople fell in 1453, the Ottoman Empire closed the land route across Asia—or at least made it very difficult and very expensive to gain access to it. The much-desired spices and medicines were in short supply and Europe needed a solution.

Religion was yet another factor. For much of the Middle Ages, the great religious struggle was between Muslims—"Turks"—and Christians. There were periods of great tolerance and understanding, as in Moorish Spain, or in the times of Muslim rule in the near East. But there were also conflicts, hostilities, and misunderstandings. The earlier

successive crusades to drive back Muslims and recapture the "Holy Land" had failed, and Europeans found the expansion of the Ottoman Empire to the gates of Vienna unsettling. They wanted to find a way east that avoided Muslim-controlled North Africa and the near East.

There were new technologies for ships. The rudder became more advanced, and seaworthy carracks and caravels that could withstand the rigors of the open ocean were built. The leaps and bounds in navigational knowledge meant that one could sail, day and night, out of sight of land for days on end.

Linked to all these reasons were wider economic concerns. The winds of change were stirring in Europe. Merchants in towns had become increasingly influential and the old order was crumbling. Trade, people saw, generated wealth that no longer relied so heavily on land and rents. One could find a product that was desired and sell it at a profit; finance banking took off; commodities began moving at a greater rate; and a new economic order was emerging. The networks of capitalism were spreading and they generated the desire for new products, new sources, new markets, and the impulse to compete for those markets. They could only be found overseas.

LEFT The voyages of Christopher Columbus are now the stuff of legend. This reenactment of his historic landing on North American soil was in 1992.

RIGHT The 2007 "Moros y Cristianos Festival" (Moors and Christians Festival) commemorates the battles, both at sea and on land, between the two sides in times long past.

ABOVE This detail from a lacquer screen shows Portuguese ships and sailors in China. Europeans were captivated by the exotic commodities of the Orient.

LEFT Portuguese sailors in Japan direct the unloading of stocks from a ship by Indian servants, while the merchant, looking on, drinks tea on the deck.

RIGHT An illustration from the thirteenth-century Arabic manuscript *Maqamat al-Hariri*, a book of stories featuring the travelers Abu Zayd and al-Harith.

Atlantic Ocean Exploration

Sailing from the Mediterranean, through the Pillars of Hercules and into the Atlantic, there are three main directions a sailor can go—north past Europe, south along the African coast, or west into the open sea. For centuries, the last option meant sailing into the unknown, a place full of the fear of monsters, storms, evil spirits, and the edge of a perhaps flat earth. So sailors turned right or left and always kept the comforting land in sight.

ABOVE Henry the Navigator did much to foster Portuguese exploration, including crossing the vast Atlantic Ocean. He funded many of the expeditions that set out from Portugal in the fifteenth century.

RIGHT In 1497, Vasco da Gama sailed from Lisbon, with a small fleet of ships, including the *Sao Raphael* (center) and the *Sao Gabriel*. His task was to establish a sea route to India.

ON THE EDGES

Ever since the Phoenicians—700 years before Christ—had sailed up the coast of Spain and on to England, others had followed. Greeks, Romans, and northern Europeans had sailed back and forth, risking occasional storms but staying within sight of land. The turn left and the voyage down the African coast had been less popular. Again the Phoenicians had been first, and a few followed them, but they did not venture far along what seemed an endless coastline.

The western African voyage did not really become a serious route until the fifteenth century. Keen to find another way to the east, one Portuguese sailor after another pushed further south. Each sought a way around the Muslim monopoly of African trade routes through the Sahara, especially for gold and slaves. Trading posts appeared down the coast, Portuguese ships began loading up with cargo—human and otherwise—and sailing home. Prince Henry of Portugal, known as "the Navigator" (1394–1460) was the driving force behind this activity. Constantly poring over his maps, funding voyages, seeing the possibilities for the new

caravels for longer voyages, he urged his sailors onward. By 1488, Bartolomeu Diaz had found the southern tip of Africa, which he named the Cape of Storms—soon changed to the Cape of Good Hope. Ten years later, Vasco da Gama found his way to India. On his way south he had pushed out into the open ocean and sought the westerly winds that would bring him back into touch with the coast. In doing so, he sailed for three months—6,000 miles (9,660 km)—out of sight of land, an astonishing achievement.

Apart from gold and slaves, Henry was also driven by the legend of Prester John. The story of a Christian king with a fabulous realm somewhere in the east had taken hold of the European imagination for some six centuries. The story grew in the telling: Prester John was a powerful warlord; a descendant of one of the three wise men who had visited the infant Jesus; his kingdom had the fountain of youth and was close to Paradise; a letter, apparently from Prester John, was received by the emperor in Constantinople to which Pope Alexander III replied in 1177. Prester John appeared always on the verge of coming to aid the Christians against the Muslims. As did many others, Henry wanted to find this fabulous kingdom. Was it in India, or China, or Ethiopia? Prester John's realm had a knack of moving about, always out of reach.

GOING WEST TO FIND THE EAST

So far, all these voyages remained on the edges of the Atlantic. Go too far and the world might come to an abrupt end—or so sailors commonly believed. Some did venture further into open water, and the edge of the world began retreating. The Portuguese happened upon the Madeira Islands in 1420—by accident, and as a result of storms—and then the Azores seven years later. Both soon had colonies. Even though the Azores are 950 miles (1,500 km) from Lisbon, they are still on the eastern side of the Atlantic.

It was Christopher Columbus, in the pay of the newly powerful Spanish throne, who made what was then believed to be the first Atlantic crossing in 1492. Columbus's origins are shrouded in mystery. Was he Genoese, as many believe, or Spanish, or Portuguese, or, as has recently been claimed, Scottish (with the original name of Pedro Scotto)? The Portuguese had wrapped up the route south along the African coast, so there was one direction left—straight out into the

Atlantic. Columbus used some counter-intuitive thinking and dubious planning. He believed he could find the way to the East by heading west, and he argued that the world was much smaller than people believed it to be. Failing to persuade one ruler after another, he finally coaxed Queen Isabella and King Ferdinand of Spain to fund the trip. So his three tiny ships, a carrack called *Santa Maria*, and two smaller caravels named *Pinta* and *Niña*, left on August 3, 1492. A little over two months later, on October 12, they sighted land in what is now the Bahamas. Few believed Columbus would return, but return he did, in March 1493. He brought back news that excited the whole of Europe, as well as some indigenous people who caused much curiosity. His men also provided another "gift" that spread through Europe—syphilis.

Columbus made three more voyages, explored many of the islands in the Caribbean, and spent time as an autocratic governor, actively encouraging the slave trade. On the island of La Española (Hispaniola—the island that today is home to Haiti and the Dominican Republic), he endorsed many atrocities (often against the indigenous peoples), for which he narrowly escaped a prison sentence in Spain. Toward the end of his life, he became very religious, believing that his discoveries were part of God's plan for the end of the world. To his dying day he remained convinced he had discovered the western shore of Asia—hence the name he gave its inhabitants, "Indios."

FIRST STEPS ON THE AMERICAN MAINLAND

However much credit Columbus may have gained for discovering the New World, he did not touch any part of the American mainland until his third voyage in 1498. The first step on the mainland was long believed to belong to the Cabots—John and his son, Sebastian. Born in Venice, the Cabots found financial support in England from Henry VII, and sailed in one vessel, *Matthew*, across the North Atlantic. Like Columbus, they were looking for a way to the East, this time

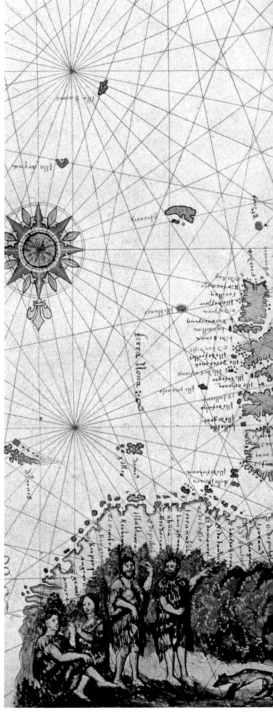

ABOVE Five hundred years before the golden age of European maritime exploration, Norse explorer Leif Ericson (c. 970–c. 1020) had sailed the Atlantic and landed on the North American continent.

through the fabled "Northwest Passage." They landed on June 24, 1497 at what they called "New Found Land," which is most likely present-day Newfoundland.

Following Columbus and the Cabots, the route westward was open; one ship after another made the Atlantic crossing. The scramble for possessions in the "New World" was on. So we find Spain (the Vespuccis, Pinson, de Bastidas, de Solis, de Leon, Cordova, and Grijalva), Portugal (Cabral), and France (Verrazzano and Cartier), all sending out expeditions to claim land. They sailed along, mapped, and explored nearly all the coasts of North and South America within four decades of Columbus's first voyage.

DIVIDING THE WORLD

France was actually a renegade in all this, for the world had not long before been divided between Portugal and Spain. This was the famous papal Treaty of Tordesillas of 1494, which divided the new discoveries by a line that ran 370 leagues (1,110 miles/1,770 km) west of the Cape Verde Islands. It fell halfway between this Portuguese possession and the new discoveries of Columbus. It also cut through a section of South America (part of today's Brazil), that Portugal would soon claim. The treaty was both an extraordinary assertion of world ownership by two European powers, and a move to appease Portugal's anger at the series of papal bulls that had granted everything westward to Spain.

INTREPID NORSEMEN

Little known to Spain, Portugal, the pope, or indeed most of Europe, was the fact that intrepid Norsemen had actually sailed across the Atlantic Ocean some five centuries earlier. They were led by the Eric the Red and his son, Leif Ericson. Originally expelled from Norway, Eric was part of a group that settled in Iceland. There too he caused trouble, was charged with murder, and banished for three years. He set sail in a sturdy knarr, the small open Norse boat that was propelled by both muscle and sail and could negotiate rough seas.

He had his sights set on a little-known land to the west, which had been sighted years before. In 982 CE, he landed in Greenland, returned to Iceland after his term was over, and encouraged others to go to Greenland to settle. Soon there was a thriving colony of up to 5,000 people. Within a few years, his son, Leif, set sail for a land even further to the west. One of their number had stumbled upon it a few years before and Leif was keen to find a resource more valuable than gold—wood, as trees do not grow in Greenland. In an extraordinary

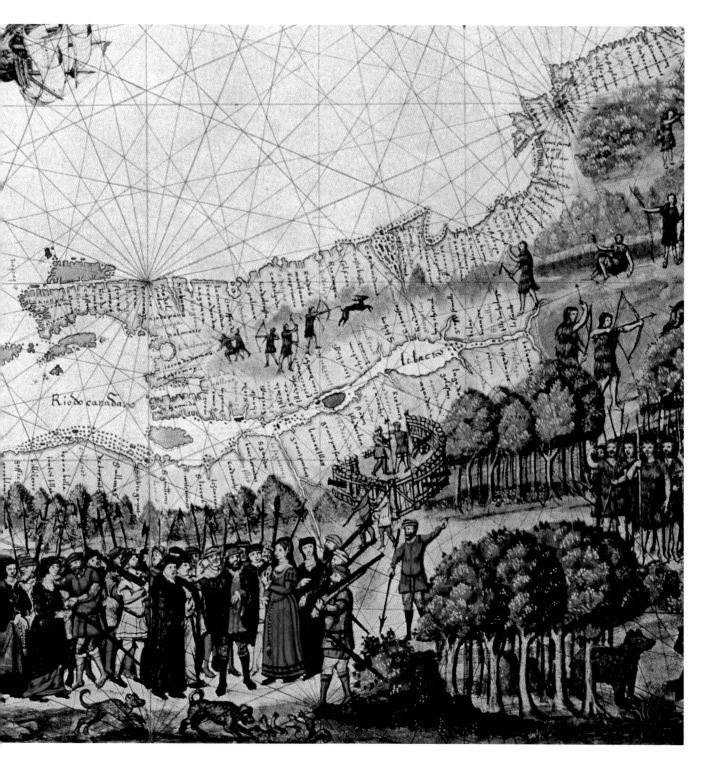

voyage he explored Baffin Island, Labrador, and New-foundland. Other journeys followed and a settlement was established at what is now L'Anse aux Meadows in Newfoundland (excavated and identified in the 1960s). Within a few years the settlement had been abandoned, partly due to the hostile indigenous Beothuks. But that did stop repeated journeys over the next centuries for the precious wood essential for the all-important ships. Between Norway, Iceland, Greenland, and North America a regular passage was in use across the Atlantic.

The Norse settlement of Greenland finally came to an end by the fifteenth century, the victim of a difficult environment, loss of contact with Norway, and the Little Ice Age, which killed the crops and cattle on which the Norsemen relied for food.

OTHER CROSSINGS?

The stories of Eric, Leif, and the Norsemen were not known until they were written down in the thirteenth and fourteenth centuries. For many hundreds of years,

ABOVE A mid-sixteenth-century map showing French explorer Jacques Cartier (1491–1557) and a group of French settlers arriving in Canada. Cartier, who claimed Canada for France, was the first person to map the Gulf of St Lawrence.

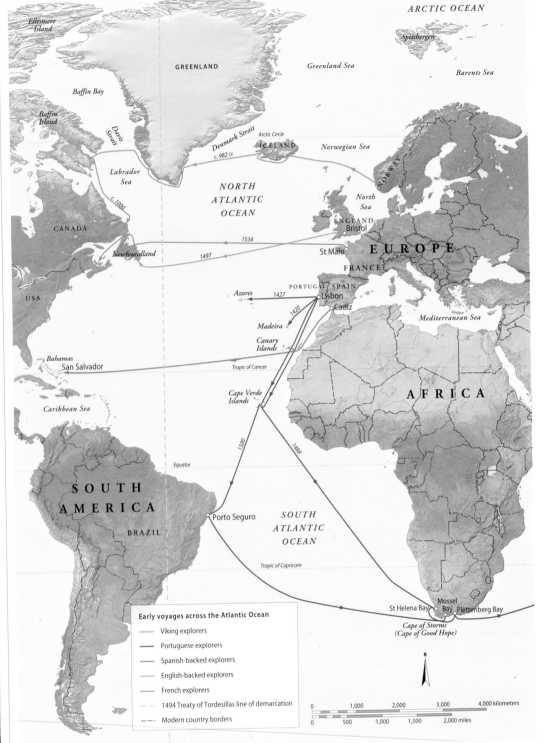

BELOW Archeological evidence discovered in 1960 proved that Norsemen settled in Newfoundland. The L'Anse Aux Meadows National Historic Site, at the Canadian province's northernmost point, displays replicas from that period, including this Viking longship.

Early voyages across the Atlantic Ocean

— Viking explorers
— Portuguese explorers
— Spanish-backed explorers
— English-backed explorers
— French explorers
--- 1494 Treaty of Tordesillas line of demarcation
-·-· Modern country borders

they were believed to be fanciful tales until the definitive discovery of settlement in Newfoundland.

But there have been many other claims that sailors crossed the Atlantic to North America before Columbus. All manner of evidence has been marshaled in support of such theories, such as ambiguous archeological finds—pots, coins, sculptures—genetics, languages, weapons, certain types of animals, plants,

or even hair styles. For some, it was the Neolithic peoples of Europe who crossed when the North Atlantic froze over during winter 15,000 years ago. For others, it was the Phoenicians back in the eighth century BCE who had made the crossing. Others argued that the Greeks also did, following in the wake of the Phoenicians.

In Columbus's own time, it was hinted that he had already made the crossing and was for that reason able to persuade the rulers of Spain to back a further expedition. Many explorers have been very keen to claim credit for what was regarded as a world-changing discovery. Perhaps it was British traders who had sailed to Iceland, but whether they sailed further is simply not known. Or perhaps it was the Irish monk, St Brendan, who set sail in a skin coracle in the sixth century in search of the Garden of Eden. Or indeed it may have been the Welsh prince, Madoc, who was supposed to have explored the Americas in 1170. And perhaps it was Portuguese fishermen caught in a current and accidentally driven to the Americas.

ARABS, AFRICANS, AND ISRAELITES

Some suggest Arab traders made the crossing, especially those from the Andalusian kingdom in Spain. It may have been Khashkhash ibn Saeed ibn Aswad in the ninth century who sailed into "an ocean of darkness and fog" and found "a strange and curious land," or ibn Farrukh in the following century, or Ahmad ibn Uhmar in the twelfth century. But all of these are mentioned only in unverifiable written works and no further evidence has been found.

Then there are the African theories. Here we find all manner of circumstantial evidence—mummies in the Americas; likenesses between pyramids in Egypt and those of the Mayas, Aztecs, and Incas that suggest ancient Egyptian contact; large sculptures from the Olmec era (1200–400 BCE), which are claimed to have African features; the presence of African plants, dark-skinned peoples, and spearheads; or the story of a large fleet sent out by Abubakari I, king of Mali, to Brazil in the fourteenth century. None of these theories has any firm proof, despite the success of Thor Heyerdahl's voyage in 1969 in *Ra II*, a boat made from the Egyptian papyrus plant following ancient guidelines.

Equally persistent are arguments that the ancient Israelites made the journey, although this evidence is again purely literary. The Book of Mormon tells of the people scattered from the Tower of Babel, and then two groups of Israelites who reached America in 600 BCE. The disappearance of ten of the tribes of Israel—apart from Judah and Benjamin—mentioned in biblical

stories has generated endless theories of where these tribes went. The British Israelites claimed that they went to Britain, and then with the expansion of the British Empire, traveled to the colonies—especially to those in North America. Once the colonists arrived, some scholars argued that the other tribes of Israel had been there before them.

In each of these speculations, we can see a desire to lay claim to the New World by those who had missed out as a result of Columbus's voyage. Huge lands, gold, and the possibilities of colonies and trade led people to argue for one or other precursor to Columbus. Others argue that peoples such as the Phoenicians, Africans, or indeed the ancient Israelites, are the source of human civilization's greatest achievements, including the Atlantic crossing. Likewise, treasure hunters and amateur explorers make their own bids for some new theories. It is entirely possible that incontestable proof will establish that someone else apart from the Norsemen first sailed across the Atlantic. We should remain open to the possibility.

ABOVE A page from a manuscript dating from around 1200, showing Irish monk St Brendan (c. 484–577) sailing from Ireland in search of a "promised land." Some accounts of his voyages say that he crossed the Atlantic.

LEFT That the Phoenicians were a significant maritime people is undisputed, and their exploits are legendary. Their sailing expertise lives on in this nineteenth-century "ex libris" book label.

Pacific Ocean Exploration

In 2008, the engine on a small Filipino fishing boat coughed, spluttered, and then died for good. So it began to drift, drawn into the large, cross-Pacific currents. Those on board knew how to live off the sea, so they waited for the current to carry them over to the Americas and back again. They did eventually make it home. Astounded family and friends were speechless, for funeral services had been held.

ANCIENT CROSSINGS

This incredible voyage showed it is possible to cross the vast Pacific in a tiny boat. Indeed, the 1970s voyages of the replica Polynesian boat, *Hokule'a*, revealed the truth of traditional migration stories in which people slowly populated the islands from Hawaii to New Zealand.

Other migrations also took place in the region. Moving from bay to bay, looking for better fishing and shelter, people slowly spread along the Pacific shores of Asia and then across to the Americas via the Bering Land Bridge which was then—more than 11,000 years ago—still above water. Along these coasts there was food aplenty. Even today, the Tlingit people in Alaska say that "when the tide is out, the table is set."

SPECULATION

Apart from these ancient Pacific peoples, there is all manner of speculation about migration. Some suggest contact between Australia and South America, based on the similarities between the Aborigines of both places. While there are one or two claims of Japanese contact, the claims of Chinese contact are legion. The Buddhist missionary, Hui Shen, is supposed to have reached the Americas in the fifth century, as is the grand fleet of Cheng Ho (Zheng He) in 1421. Even though possible, the arguments are based on purely circumstantial evidence, such as the types of chicken that are found in China and the Americas.

BELOW The first European to gaze on the waters of the Pacific Ocean was the Spaniard Vasco Núñez de Balboa (c. 1475–1519), when he crossed the Isthmus of Panama in 1513.

THE SPANISH SEA

The Treaty of Tordesillas of 1494 had—with papal approval—divided the whole world along an imaginary line that cut through center of the Atlantic from north to south. Portugal had the rights to all new seas and lands to the east, Spain to the west. For Spain that meant not only most of the Americas, but also whatever oceans lay beyond. At the time, no one had any idea that the largest ocean on the globe was waiting.

That changed with Vasco Núñez de Balboa, who made the first verified Pacific voyage by a European in the modern era. It was not long—46 miles (74 km)—but it was the first. Balboa had crossed the Isthmus of Panama in 1513 and claimed the new "South Sea" for Spain. Five years later, he built a few makeshift ships and made his short experimental voyage. Further expeditions were cut short by his beheading, for he was at the wrong end of a feud with the governor of Santa Maria (in Panama).

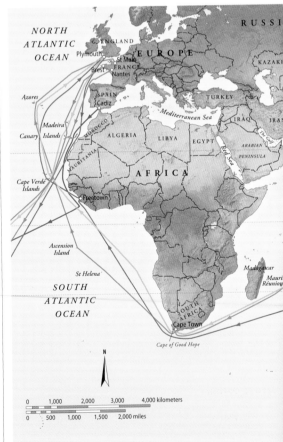

AN EXPENSIVE VOYAGE

Ferdinand Magellan—or more properly, Magalhães— took up where Balboa left off. Portuguese by birth, Magellan conceived a plan that would open up a route to the fabled Spice Islands. He would sail west, down the coast of South America, and find a way through. The king of Portugal, Manuel I, frowned at the idea, for Vasco da Gama had recently sailed around Africa and across the Indian Ocean to India. Why would he waste money on another voyage to the same place?

So Magellan went to Castile (Spain) and the court of Charles V, who gave him an attentive ear. Spanish coffers were overflowing with gold and silver from the newly conquered realms in Central and South America. With Portuguese control of the route to the east via Africa, another way had to be found to challenge Portugal for the wealth to be made from spice. Who better to undertake it than a Portuguese adventurer?

In August 1519, 232 men (from various European origins) set sail from Spain on board five ships. A little over three years later, on September 6, 1522, the ship *Victoria*, captained by Juan Sebastián Elcano, returned with 18 men. Magellan was not among them, for he had met his end in an ill-fated attack in the Philippines. Along the way the expedition faced hostile Portuguese warships, capture, mutiny, thirst, starvation, disease, the dazzling court in Brunei, found the Arabs had been to the Philippines before them, and death in battle.

But they also discovered and named the Strait of Magellan in South America, and were the first Europeans to sail across the endless Pacific Ocean (a name given to it by Magellan). They met new peoples, strange new animals, gazed at new galaxies, established the full extent of the Earth—43,400 miles (69,800 km)—and

LEFT Ferdinand Magellan (1480– 1521), the Portuguese-born explorer who gave the Strait of Magellan its name, is credited as the first person to lead a voyage across the Pacific Ocean.

ABOVE When Magellan died on his epic voyage to circle the globe, Juan Sebastián Elcano (1486–1526) took over comand of the expedition. He brought the 18 survivors back to Spain.

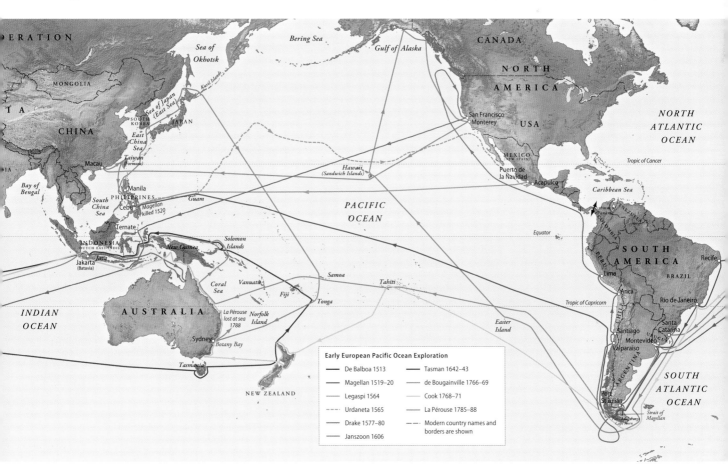

Early European Pacific Ocean Exploration

- De Balboa 1513
- Magellan 1519–20
- Legaspi 1564
- Urdaneta 1565
- Drake 1577–80
- Janszoon 1606
- Tasman 1642–43
- de Bougainville 1766–69
- Cook 1768–71
- La Pérouse 1785–88
- Modern country names and borders are shown

the fact that a day was "lost" when traveling westward around the Earth. Magellan had planned to return via the Pacific, as indeed one of the fleet attempted to do after leaving the East Indies. It was Magellan's successor, Elcano, who decided to continue sailing westward and thereby circumnavigate the globe.

Over the next 250 years or so, many others would follow in Magellan's wake, passing into the Pacific via South America. Sailors such as de Loaísa for Portugal; Mendaña and de Quiros for Spain; Le Maire, Schouten, and Roggeveen for the Netherlands; Bougainville and La Pérouse for the French; and Samuel Wallis, Philip Carteret, and Francis Drake for the English, set off to circumnavigate the world and dreamed of finding the fabled Great South Land.

URDANETA'S ROUTE

Soon the Spanish realized that expeditions that lost nearly all the ships and men were futile. So they tried a different approach—to sail from the Americas. In 1564, a small fleet under the command of Legaspi set off from New Spain (in modern-day Mexico) in order to colonize the Philippines. On board was the Augustinian monk, Andrés de Urdaneta, who was also an excellent navigator. Once in the Philippines, Legaspi decided to stay and sent Urdaneta back to New Spain for reinforcements. Urdaneta searched back and forth for favorable currents and winds, eventually finding them at 36° north. It had taken 130 days, 12,000 miles (20,000 km), and the near starvation of the crew, but they made it to Acapulco in 1565. Despite all the hardships, Urdaneta had kept meticulous notes of the journey. Known as "Urdaneta's route," it soon became the favored route from New Spain to the Philippines for the annual voyage of the Manila galleons across the "Spanish Sea."

IGNORING TORDESILLAS

The new imperial powers in northern European did not concern themselves with the Treaty of Tordesillas. The Dutch, French, and English had their own plans for colonial expansion, each hoping to crack the Portuguese and Spanish monopolies.

Through a clever mix of espionage (including the secret copying of Portuguese maps) and enterprise, the Dutch had established their own spice trade in the early

seventeenth century with what is now the Indonesian archipelago. The Dutch East India Company would reap immense rewards over the next two centuries, with trading posts stretching from Cape Town to Japan. But this new monopoly had its own opponents within the Netherlands. One of these was Isaac Le Maire. Keen to break the company's stranglehold, he financed an expedition in 1615–1616 to open the western route to the East Indies. On board were his son, Jacob Le Maire, and the captain, Willem Schouten. They rounded and named Cape Horn and made a beeline for Jakarta, coming upon the Tongan Islands en route.

The Dutch East India Company then decided to expand its trading opportunities, especially since the route to China and Japan had become very profitable. So southward they went. The first European to set foot on Australian soil was Willem Janzsoon, who made landfall in the Gulf of Carpentaria on February 26, 1606. But it was Abel Tasman who made a serious effort to explore southward. In his voyages of 1642 and 1644, Tasman found no profitable lands, but he did happen upon the northeastern coast of Australia, Van Dieman's Land (Tasmania), New Zealand (named after Zeeland in the Netherlands), and even saw Fiji.

ABOVE An early seventeenth-century painting of the fleet of the Dutch East India Company. Economic interests in the East Indies, particularly the spice trade, drove much of the exploration in the Pacific.

ABOVE Louis Antoine de Bougainville (1729–1811) was the first Frenchman to circum-navigate the globe. He claimed Tahiti for France and established a French presence in Polynesia.

THE FRENCH AND THE FIRST WOMAN

With Dutch success, the French, Danes, and English were keen to follow suit. Each formed their own East India companies and gave the Dutch some real competition. The French presence in the Pacific is due to Louis Antoine de Bougainville, who circumnavigated the globe in 1766–1769. Bougainville's voyage was a model of modern methods and concern for the crew—only seven of more than 200 men died on the journey.

Apart from claiming Tahiti for France and naming Bougainville, the largest of the Solomon Islands, his voyage achieved another significant first. On board his ship was the first European woman to sail across the Pacific Ocean and around the world. Jeanne Baré had joined the ship's crew as the valet of the botanist Philibert Commerçon, although she was soon discovered to be his mistress as well.

Almost 20 years later, the most extensive French expedition to the Pacific set out under La Pérouse. He was to perish at sea, but not before he had sailed from Cape Horn to Alaska, across to Macau and the Philippines, up to Korea, Japan, and Russia, and then on to investigate the new British colony in New South Wales, Australia. After spending time at Botany Bay observing the newly arrived First Fleet, La Pérouse sailed from Australia in March 1776 and was never seen again.

RAGAMUFFIN ON THE SEAS

The English lagged behind the European powers—when they set out they found the Spanish, Portuguese, Dutch, and French before them. One of the most famous English navigators was Francis Drake. He was variously a pirate, slave-trader, oppressor of the Irish, second-in-command of the English Fleet when

XPLORATION DU PACIFIQUE
LES ROCHERS DE VANIKORO.

it defeated the Spanish Armada in 1588, and became very wealthy as a result of his adventures. Drake was sent by Queen Elizabeth in 1577 to challenge Spanish supremacy in the Americas and the Pacific. His fleet suffered shipwreck, disease, and attacks from the Spanish, but Drake hit upon a winning plan. Wherever possible, he captured Spanish treasure galleons. They also had accurate maps, of which Drake made full use in his Pacific crossing. On the way he sailed up the west coast of the Americas, claiming for England the land north of Spain's possessions, at a place called Nova Albion in California.

OF CHRONOMETERS AND LIMES

The name most closely associated with Pacific exploration is that of the Englishman James Cook. His journeys did not take place until the eighteenth century, but he was able to make use of a range of recent discoveries that made life at sea survivable. One was the new ocean chronometer. Invented by John Harrison in 1761, it was the first instrument able to measure time accurately at sea. Another was the realization that limes were in some way able to ward off the sailor's curse, scurvy. Yet another was ship construction: Cook was able to sail a single vessel around the world (twice)—through frigid seas and the worst storms—and return intact. To all of these must be added Cook's own unique skills. He was an astonishingly good navigator and cartographer, and he had an adventurous streak that was combined with an insatiable curiosity.

Cook spent 12 of his 50 years in the Pacific, dying in Hawaii in tragic circumstances in 1779. His voyages were a mix of scientific exploration and colonial expansion. He brought with him scientists of various stripes, and he was a keen observer and recorder of all he saw. Under the auspices of the Royal Society, the first trip set out in 1768 and returned in 1771. The purpose was to record the transit of Venus across the sun in Tahiti, which he dutifully did. But then Cook sailed home westward, for the legend of the great southern continent was alive and well. He circumnavigated and mapped New Zealand's two islands (he returned to New Zealand on four more occasions),

touched the east coast of Australia and mapped it all the way to its northern tip. Naturally, he claimed these new lands for England.

The first voyage had merely whetted Cook's appetite and that of the Royal Society. Was there really a Great South Land? Within a year Cook was sent to find out, sailing in the opposite direction from the first voyage. He passed the Cape of Good Hope, and then headed neither northeast nor east in the Roaring Forties to Australia. He went further south into the mountainous seas of the Southern Ocean. Having proved to his own satisfaction that no southern land existed (he had just missed Antarctica), Cook sailed around the southern Pacific, calling in to New Zealand, Easter Island, Vanuatu, New Caledonia, Norfolk Island, and what he called the Friendly Islands.

The only part of the Pacific left to Cook was its northern reaches. This was the target of his ill-fated final voyage (1777–1779), the main purpose of which was to determine once and for all whether there was a Northwest Passage. Once in the Pacific, he sailed straight up the middle until he arrived at the Sandwich (Hawaiian) Islands. On his way north, he veered over to the Californian coast and mapped it all the way up to the Bering Strait. But he found the ice north of the strait impenetrable, despite repeated attempts. Disappointed, he returned to the Hawaiian Islands, where he was killed through a misunderstanding with the local people. The two ships of the expedition sailed home without their captain.

By now, the late 1700s, the Pacific was mapped and its lands claimed by the Europeans. Colonization rather than exploration became the next goal.

BELOW A hunting party from Captain James Cook's ships shooting walruses. During his third Pacific voyage, from 1776 to 1779, Cook mapped the western American coast to the Bering Strait. He was looking for a passage to the Atlantic.

Indian Ocean Exploration

Three factors made the Indian Ocean one of the first goals for human exploration—monsoons, trade, and civilization. If one is sailing from Africa to India, it is best to do so between June to September, for then the monsoons will blow you eastward. Then, to return home, the period from December to March is ideal, since the winds turn and blow the other way.

FROM TIME IMMEMORIAL

Some of the earliest human civilizations developed around the Indian Ocean. The ancient Egyptians sailed down the east African coast and perhaps to The Gulf, but regular trade happened only in the Roman era. Ships sailed down the Red Sea to the port of Aden; there they met Arab and Indian sailors. After Eudoxus of Cyzicus had mastered the winds and ventured to India in 118 BCE and again in 116 BCE, Roman and Greek sailors followed in his wake.

Indian navigators had also been traveling on the Indian Ocean, perhaps from the time of the Indus Valley civilization (third millennium BCE). Their

interests extended both westward and eastward. Farther east, Chinese navigators were active, sailing between Japan, Southeast Asia, the Moluccas, and India.

By the eighth century CE, Rome was on its knees, and Roman traders no longer sailed from Europe. For 700 years, the route to the Indian Ocean was controlled by Muslim Arab traders, who ventured further afield, traversing the Indian Ocean from North Africa to the East Indies. Their seagoing ships were superior to the European vessels, which were mainly used in the land-locked Mediterranean and coastal routes of Europe.

All these ships were governed by one feature—they could only sail with the wind. Going upwind required

BELOW A section from a map of the world drawn in 1457, showing Asia, India and the Ganges River, China, and the islands of Japan.

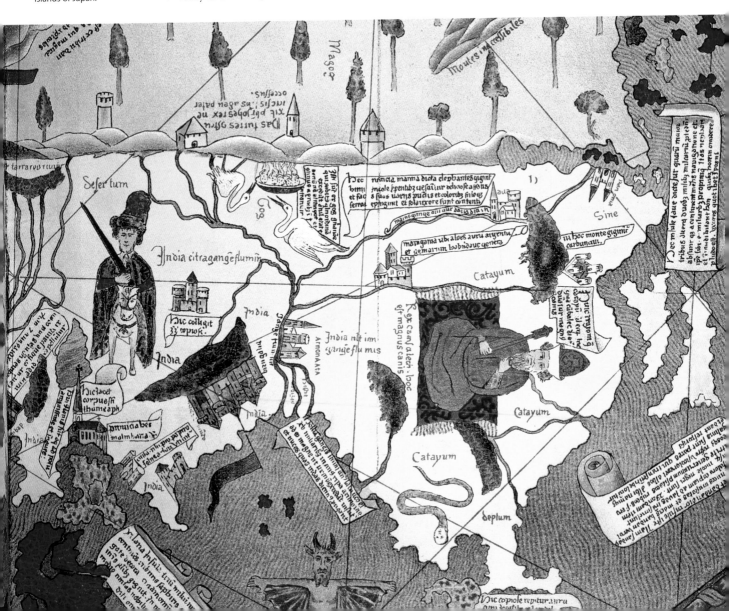

muscle power, and the Indian Ocean was far too large to row across. It was not until the discovery, by the Europeans, of tacking—sailing as closely into the wind as possible—that more venturous sailing could happen.

EUROPE CATCHES UP

Slowly, however, Europe caught up, partly through borrowing Arabic ship designs. The square-sailed cog was replaced by the carrack and caravel, which had more lateen (triangular) sails like the Arab dhows. As a result, Portugal began looking further afield. For almost a century, Portuguese ships pushed onward down the western coast of Africa, until Bartholomeu Diaz found its southern tip.

Ten years later, in 1497, Vasco da Gama took his ships all the way to India. In December that year, he passed by the southern tip of Africa, named it Cape Storm, and then his four ships pushed on into waters no European had seen before. Here, they hugged the east African coast, but now they were in Arab trade territory. Da Gama decided to impersonate an Arab at Mozambique and looted Arab ships in Mombasa. When his ruse was discovered, he found a lifesaver in Malindi, a guide who understood the monsoons and who took the Portuguese explorers to Calicut in India. The relative lack of knowledge of the Portuguese about wind patterns quickly became clear. Da Gama set out to return home in the wrong season, battered against the winds for 132 days to reach Africa (it had taken 23 on the way over), lost another ship and many men. But on his return to Lisbon, he was showered with honors and wealth. Having gained a reputation as "Mr Fix-It,"

da Gama would make two other voyages, in 1503–1504 and again in 1524, when he succumbed to malaria. He adopted what was to become the standard approach in Portuguese imperial expansion—he attacked other shipping, looted merchant ships, and forced the best trading terms possible on local inhabitants. Portuguese trade across the Indian Ocean had begun.

PORTUGAL RULES THE SEAS

The Europeans may have been newcomers, but their purpose was the same as those who had gone before— trade. Backed by the pope's decree, the Portuguese

ABOVE This Flemish tapestry dating from the early sixteenth century shows the Portuguese navigator Vasco da Gama disembarking at Calicut, southern India, in May 1489. Da Gama was the first European to reach India by sea.

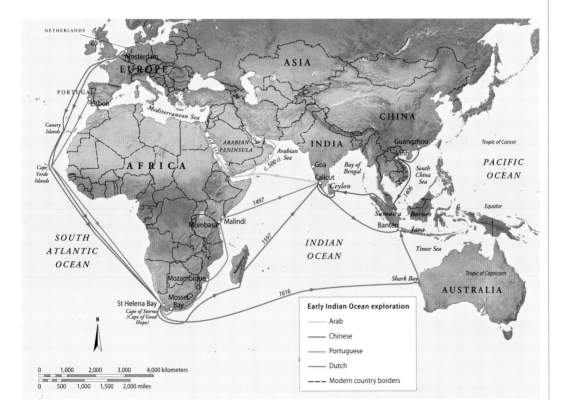

Early Indian Ocean exploration
- Arab
- Chinese
- Portuguese
- Dutch
- --- Modern country borders

established a monopoly that included the right to promote Christianity, to combat the spread of Islam, and to enslave local populations. The Portuguese followed their well-tried model, building forts and rest stops on the way. Their major settlement was at Goa in western India, which was captured in 1510 and turned into a fort, trading post, bishopric, and mission outpost (Francis Xavier used Goa as his base). Goa remained in Portuguese hands for some 450 years and was the hub of their Indian Ocean trade.

The typical route of Portuguese traders was to round the Cape of Good Hope, sail up the coast to Mozambique (which by now was a Portuguese colony), and catch the monsoon to India. Before long, their superior firepower controlled the seas. Like the Arabs before them, the Portuguese found that trade extended not just to the East Indies, but also to China and Japan. Trading posts followed and Portugal supplied Europe with its much-needed spices, silks, and medicines. They also supplied a relatively new cargo—slaves.

THE DUTCH TAKE CONTROL

Meanwhile, in Europe, the economy was changing. Conscious of Portuguese successes in the Indian Ocean, the Dutch made their own plans. Soon their economic leadership of the world would be consolidated in the East Indies. They designed a new style of ship, the "flyboat" or "flute," which could hold a massive cargo with a small crew, and the all-purpose "Indiaman," an armed cargo ship. Built with the latest methods, they were produced quickly and cheaply.

Two exploratory voyages opened up the East: Jan Huygen van Linschoten's in 1582 and Cornelis Houtman's in 1592. The latter's story resembles a modern-day spy thriller. Disguised, he boarded a Portuguese

ship, was unmasked in the Indies, and thrown into prison. Dutch merchants paid a high ransom for him, managed to get him home, and then sent him off again with four ships in 1595. Back by 1597, Houtman paved the way for Dutch expansion.

By 1602, the various merchant groups that had sent out ships were united into the Vereenigde Oost-Indische Compagnie (VOC), or the "United East India Company." The company quickly spread throughout the East Indies, established networks all the way to China and Japan, conquered Portuguese holdings in Ceylon (Sri Lanka) and India (apart from Goa), and drove off the British. Their basic trade was in mace, nutmeg, cloves, and cinnamon.

Before establishing themselves in India, the Dutch sailed the "outer" route to avoid the Portuguese. This involved setting out along Madagascar's east coast, threading through the Maldives, and then making for the East Indies. This route used trade winds and not monsoons, similar to the route used by Arab traders who were also anxious to avoid the Portuguese.

Eventually, the Dutch found an even faster way. Instead of heading north or northeast from the Cape, they sailed east, picking up the huge winds and swells of the Roaring Forties. This brought them to west Australia, where they turned north. It cut weeks off the outward journey, but it also led to a number of shipwrecks on the wild Australian shores. It remained the most daring route, most favored by the Dutch until the exploratory voyages of Captain James Cook in the eighteenth century. The Dutch left their scattered wrecks, marooned sailors, and a string of blond-haired and blue-eyed Australian Aboriginal children.

A GRIM WRECK

The most notorious shipwreck was that of the Dutch Indiaman *Batavia*. Laden with gold and silver on its maiden voyage from the Netherlands, it separated from the fleet and ran into a reef off Western Australia in June 1629. Most survived the wreck and made it to nearby islands. Francisco Palsaert, the commander of the fleet, decided to sail in an open boat to Batavia (present-day Jakarta)—an extraordinary feat. Meanwhile, one of the remaining merchants, Jeronimus Cornelisz, instituted a reign of terror among the survivors. He marooned the soldiers on another island, commandeered the food supplies and limited water, took the women he pleased for himself, and sanctioned the murder of anyone suspected of theft or dissent. Two months later, Pelsaert returned. Horrified at what he found, he executed Cornelisz and the ringleaders, rescued the soldiers, and returned to Batavia. However, Pelsaert was found guilty of negligence, relieved of his duties, and died a broken man.

OTHERS JOIN THE PARTY

The Dutch had actually formed their East India Company in response to English threats, because the

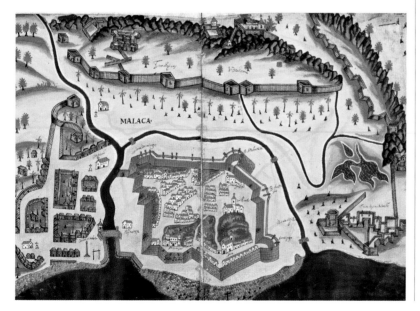

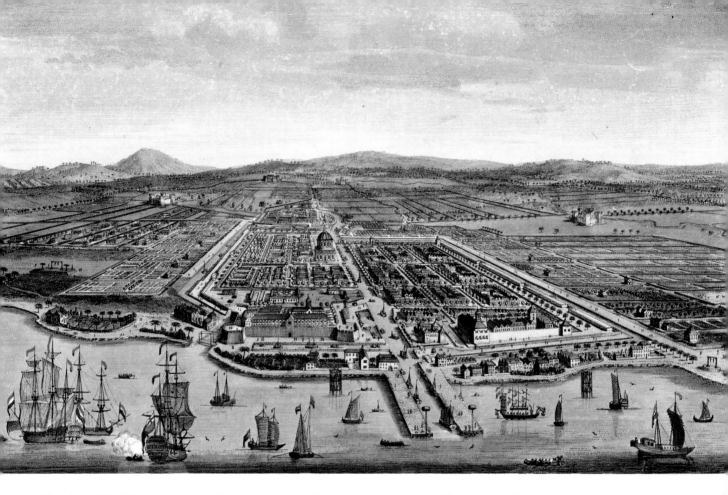

English had established their own company in 1600. Although the English had set out to trade with the East Indies, the Dutch forced them out, so they retreated to trade with China and India.

The staples were cotton, silk, indigo dye, saltpeter (for gunpowder), tea, and most infamously, opium. During these years, the Indian Ocean was a trader's highway. Ships of various nations passed each other on the main routes; they occasionally raided each other, or attacked and took a fort.

Other imperial nations soon followed, such as the French, Danish, Swedish, and even Austria. None of them was quite as successful as the Dutch or English. Each of them attempted trade monopolies, each established trading posts, and each went bankrupt by the late eighteenth century. Only the Dutch and English stayed the distance, and once the Dutch East India Company had begun to decline, the British Empire took over. By the nineteenth century, the Indian Ocean belonged to Britain.

ABOVE The town of Batavia, Java, in the eighteenth century. Batavia was the capital of the Dutch East Indies and head-quarters for the Dutch East India Company for 200 years.

LEFT Western hongs (buildings) in Canton Harbor, China, c. 1810. Hongs were used as residences, offices, and warehouses. The Danish, Spanish, American, Swedish, British, and Dutch flags indicate that these hongs were business headquarters.

Arctic Ocean Exploration

Anyone who has been north of the Arctic Circle can attest to its harsh and alluring beauty. Here is an ocean full of icebergs, drift-ice, and pack-ice. Indeed, the circumpolar people have more than 20 words for ice, and even more for snow. No wonder human beings finally crossed the frozen Arctic Ocean only in the twentieth century.

ABOVE In the mid-1850s, American oceanographer Matthew Maury (1806–1873) published *Physical Geography of the Sea and Its Meteorology*, which suggested, among other things, that there was clear water at the North Pole.

RIGHT Captain George Nares, sitting at left, rests with his crew and sled dogs during his 1875 expedition to the Greenland area of the North Pole.

MIDNIGHT SUN AND SEA ICE

Although polar peoples from Siberia to Greenland have been familiar with the Arctic for millennia, the earliest written record of the Arctic comes from the Greek sailor and geographer, Pytheas of Massilia. In describing his voyage north in approximately 315 BCE, Pytheas mentions both "the frozen ocean" and the detail that one day's sail north of "Thule [perhaps Iceland] ... the nights were very short, in some places two, in others three hours' long, so that the sun rose again a short time after it had set." Pytheas had to turn back, as his ship was not equipped to handle sea ice.

CLEAR WATER AT THE POLE?

The impossibility of sailing into the Arctic Ocean fired people's fantasies for centuries. One fantasy was that of the Open Polar Sea. This was not the belief of crackpots; it was firmly held by renowned navigators like the Dutchman Willem Barentsz (who gave his name to the Barents Sea), and the Englishman Henry Hudson in the late sixteenth and early seventeenth centuries. They reasoned that since the Sun shines for most of the day in the Arctic summer, it would generate enough heat to melt the sea ice. Furthermore, sea ice forms only around land (their experience further south), so there could not be sea ice in the middle of the Polar Sea since there is no land. Such arguments generated one futile (and often fatal) expedition after another. There were stories told that Russian sailors had seen large stretches of open water. All it needed was for someone to find it.

The first flurry of exploration in the late sixteenth and early seventeenth centuries was part of imperial competition between European powers. The Netherlands and England were keen to find a short way across to Asia, especially to counter Portuguese dominance of the route around Africa. With early failures to find the fabled Polar Sea, the theory faded.

But by the nineteenth century, the theory was revived as the discipline of oceanography took root. Arguments were drawn from knowledge of ocean currents, animal migrations, and temperature readings. Where did the warm Gulf Stream and Kuro Siwo (the Black Stream of Japan) go? Into the Polar Sea, was the

answer, where they would melt the ice. And how did whales survive their northerly migrations? There must be clear water, since whales need to surface regularly to breathe. And what about the evidence of temperature readings, which suggested that it actually became warmer once you got closer to the pole? These were arguments put forward by the "father of modern oceanography and meteorology," Matthew Maury, as well as the German cartographer, August Petermann.

FINDING FRANKLIN

Ideas are not the only catalyst for adventurers. There was also the tragedy of the John Franklin expedition to find the Northwest Passage. He set out in 1845 with one of the best equipped expeditions in history—the massive ice-breaker steamers even had steam-generated heating and fresh water, and three years' supply of food. Yet Franklin and his team were never seen again.

Franklin's complete disappearance generated many rescue efforts. In fact, so many that more people were lost in the search than in the original expedition. Among the attempts were those of Americans, Elisha Kane and

Isaac Hayes. Kane led two expeditions in 1850–1851, and 1853–1855, while Hayes led his own in 1860–1861. Both men claimed to have pushed further north than any man, and that they had seen the clear water of the Open Polar Sea. Indeed, Franklin himself had been on an expedition to find the Polar Sea with John Buchan in 1818; they had run into ice north of Spitsbergen (off Norway). But they argued that all one needed was to break through the ice to the clear sea on the other side.

Many of the expeditions were undertaken by naval men from Britain and the United States, as control of a polar crossing would be an immense military advantage. The more the explorers tried to break through, the more ice they encountered. The expeditions of George Nares, and George W. DeLong, finally proved that there was no open sea. The expedition led by the Royal Navy captain, Nares, set off in 1875, passed between Greenland and Ellesmere Island, and ran into endless ice. The American DeLong sailed in 1879 on *USS Jeanette* through the Bering Strait. Instead of a quick trip over the pole, he and his crew were caught in ice and many perished, including DeLong.

ABOVE *HMS Alert* and *HMS Discovery* on the British Arctic Expedition of 1875–1876, commanded by George Nares. Although Nares did not reach the North Pole, he and his crew made detailed explorations of Greenland and Ellesmere Island.

RIGHT An 1894 engraving of *Fram*, Nansen's ship, leaving Bergen, Norway. *Fram* was specially built to withstand the unrelenting icy conditions of the Arctic, and is reported to be the strongest wooden vessel ever built.

BELOW Members of the 1968–1969 transpolar expedition photographed in London after spending 16 months in the Arctic. The team leader, Wally Herbert (with beard), is at front left. Next to him is Kenneth Heges. In the back row are, from left, Freddie Church, Alan Gill, and Roy Koerner.

Who Really Reached the North Pole First?

It was left to Robert Peary and Wally Herbert to attempt the final goal. Peary has been described as "undoubtedly the most driven, possibly the most successful and probably the most unpleasant man in the annals of polar exploration." He made even more use than Nansen of Inuit methods, including Inuit participants, and clothing. He was also a ruthless planner and successful self-promoter, blocking attempts to verify his claim to have reached the pole on April 7, 1909. His claims were accepted for most of the twentieth century, but later debunked by the man who had actually reached the pole: Wally Herbert.

Herbert had been commissioned to write a study of Peary's expedition—*The Noose of Laurels* (which was finally published in 1989). The more Herbert researched, the more it became clear that Peary had been rather creative in his diaries. After 20 years of single-minded effort, the failure to reach the pole was too much for Peary, so he claimed to be at the pole when he was not.

These conclusions fueled much controversy, because Herbert had reached the pole himself on April 6, 1969. If Peary had failed, then Herbert may well have been the first. His achievement was part of a transpolar expedition of 1968–1969 that covered 3,800 miles (6,120 km) from Alaska to Spitsbergen. Before the successful push for the pole, he and his team wintered in one of the remotest places on earth. This is the point furthest from any land mass and yet more than 400 miles (645 km) from the pole, known to explorers as the "pole of inaccessibility." However, earlier expeditions may have reached the pole. Without today's technology, it would have been impossible to say for certain. No one can claim to have been the first person at the North Pole.

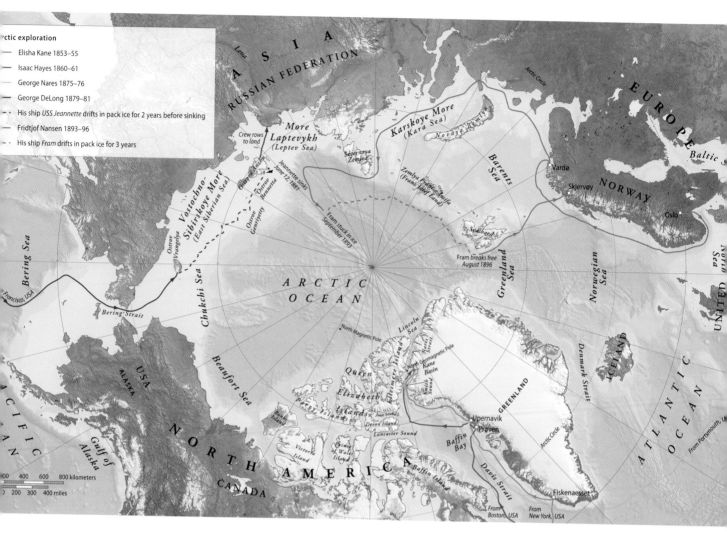

AN EXTRAORDINARY NORWEGIAN

The desire for exploration did not end, it simply went in other directions. Some continued searching for the fabled Northwest Passage; while others pursued the Northeast Passage (along the top of Russia), until the successful voyage of Finnish-born scientist and explorer Adolf Erik Nordenskiöld in 1878–1879. But a major objective became the North Pole itself.

Into this scene came an extraordinary Norwegian, Fridtjof Nansen. Born in 1861, he was a sports skier, scientist, zoologist, oceanographer, and diplomat. He was also an Arctic explorer. In planning his expedition, the scientist in Nansen came out. He was persuaded by the theory that the polar sea ice drifts slowly with the currents, especially since remains of DeLong's ship, *Jeanette*, destroyed in the ice north of the Bering Strait, had turned up on the other side of the pole.

Nansen oversaw the construction of a very special ship—*Fram*. It was the strongest wooden ship ever built. It had virtually no keel, a retractable propeller and rudder, a windmill for power, and was insulated as only the Norwegians know how to insulate. Above all, when the ice closed in, it was designed to lift and ride above the ice. Nansen also needed a crew who would

be able to stand the long cold winters. He assembled an experienced team, each of whom had superb ice skills. They also made very extensive use of the skills learned over many centuries by the people who live in the Arctic—the Inuit and Greenlanders who built appropriate shelters, and used effective clothing, sleds, dogs, and kayaks.

In 1893, *Fram* set sail for Siberia, but the ship was soon caught in the ice, and began what would turn out to be a three-year drift.

By 1894, the ship was still locked in the ice. But by this time, Nansen had conceived of another goal for the expedition—to find the North Pole. However, the ice drift was steadily taking them past the pole, rather than toward it. So Nansen and Hjalmar Johansen (who would also later accompany Roald Amundsen to the South Pole) set off with a dog team, sledges, and kayaks. They reached 86'14"°N, but became lost, and wintered in Inuit style.

Then, out of pure luck, Nansen and Johansen happened upon another expedition and made it back to Norway in time to meet *Fram*, which by now, had broken out of the ice near Spitsbergen. This was the first successful crossing of the Arctic Ocean.

ABOVE Fridtjof Nansen was a man of many talents. As well as being a superlative explorer and scientist, he also won the Nobel Peace Prize in 1922.

Southern Ocean Exploration

Early exploration into the Southern Ocean was driven by the search for land. Explorers were inspired by the long-held belief that there was a vast landmass to the south—Terra Australis Incognita, the unknown southern land.

UNKNOWN SOUTHERN LAND

The notion of the unknown southern land was one of the most persistent theories about the makeup of the world. It was first suggested by the Greek philosopher, Aristotle (384–322 BCE) and later included on the maps of Ptolemy (90–168 CE). Their arguments were impeccable for the time—the world needed a large southern mass to balance that of the Northern Hemisphere. As seas such as the Mediterranean are surrounded by land, the Indian Ocean should also be bounded by land. So great was their influence on subsequent thought that the idea of an unknown southern land persisted until the late nineteenth century.

Little by little Terra Australis shrank in size. Tierra del Fuego was not attached (as shown by Jacob Le Maire and Willem Schouten in 1615), nor was Australia (Abel Tasman in 1642–1643). Captain James Cook set out on his first two voyages to discover this mysterious southern landmass. His first journey in *HMS Endeavour* revealed that New Zealand was not attached, so on his second voyage (1772–1775) he set sail to see once and for all where Terra Australis lay. His sponsor, the Royal Society, still held that it was out there.

JAMES COOK THROUGH THE SHRIEKING SIXTIES

In 1772 Cook set out with two ships. He commanded *HMS Resolution*, while Tobias Furneaux was in charge of *HMS Adventure*. The most modern ships of their time, they were fitted with ice anchors, water-distilling

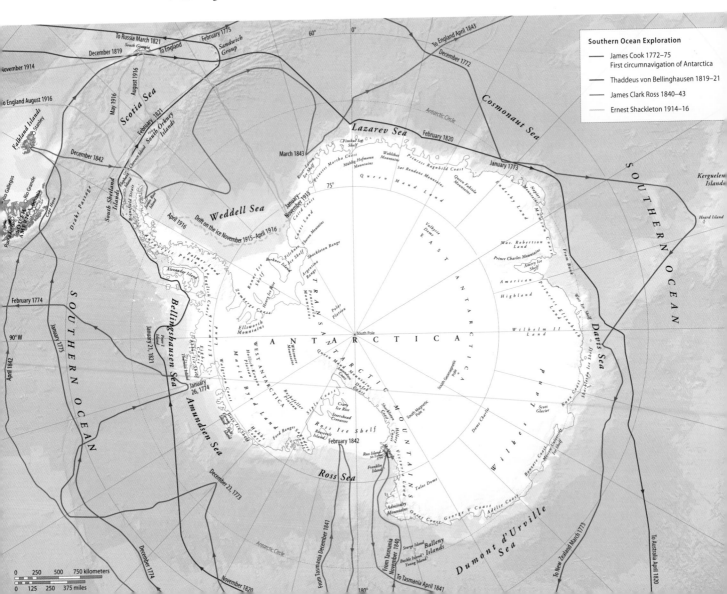

Southern Ocean Exploration
— James Cook 1772–75
First circumnavigation of Antarctica
— Thaddeus von Bellinghausen 1819–21
— James Clark Ross 1840–43
— Ernest Shackleton 1914–16

plants, the latest compasses, and, most importantly, the new sea chronometer (Larcum Kendall K1)—the first timepiece to measure time accurately at sea. Cook sailed as far south as he dared, supported by his crew, who trusted in the man who had led many of them successfully around the world a few years earlier. Weaving between icebergs, the two ships were the first to cross the Antarctic Circle on January 17, 1773. He crossed the circle twice more, reaching 71'10"°S on January 31, 1774. Cook was wise enough to attempt these pushes south during the summer months. In winter, he enjoyed the warmer Pacific Islands. Cook and Furneaux were separated in the infamous Antarctic fog; Furneaux decided to head north, but Cook stayed south all the way to the Atlantic.

The result was that Cook circumnavigated Antarctica, coming to within 80 miles (130 km) of the land mass itself. What he had done was traverse what would later be called the Southern Ocean. Cook had sailed some of the stormiest seas on the planet. The Roaring Forties might be windy with a heavy swell, the Furious Fifties might produce great storms, but the Shrieking Sixties—as they are called today—pound ships with hurricane-force winds. They certainly make for fast sailing, if you can manage to stay afloat. More than one modern around-the-world yacht has come to grief here. James Cook managed them all with his customary skill and perseverance.

SIGHTING TERRA AUSTRALIS

It was abundantly clear that no fertile and temperate land existed far to the south. Cook had come across a series of wind-swept and icy islands such as South Georgia, but there was nothing further to colonize. Forty-five years would pass before another explorer crossed the Antarctic Circle. It was to be a Russian, Fabian Gottlieb von Bellingshausen, who finally saw the famed Terra Australis, or Antarctica. After plenty of experience in sailing through Russia's icy seas, von Bellingshausen took two Russian navy ships south on an extended expedition (1819–1821), carefully circumnavigated the continent, and sighted the icy shoreline on January 28, 1820. Von Bellingshausen's momentous discovery passed almost without notice. He returned home and took up regular navy duties, gaining fame only after his death.

However, the rush was now on. Just two days after von Bellingshausen, the Irishman Edward Bransfield pushed through the Southern Ocean and noted "high mountains, covered with snow" from his ship, *Williams*. Unlike von Bellingshausen, Bransfield charted what he saw. Then in November of the same year (1820), a 21-year-old American seal hunter, Nathaniel Palmer, sailed

Shackleton and the Voyage of *James Caird*

The most remarkable voyage over the Southern Ocean was that of Ernest Shackleton in *James Caird*, described as "one of the great boat journeys ever accomplished." In an open whale boat no more than 22½ feet (7 m) long, Shackleton and five companions sailed 800 nautical miles (1,500 km) through the mountainous seas of the wintry Southern Ocean.

It began promisingly enough. Shackleton had set out with the Imperial Trans-Antarctic Expedition in 1914. After his heart-breaking failure to reach the pole first in 1908–1909, Shackleton decided to conquer the last great challenge—crossing the Antarctic mainland. However, his ship *Endurance* became locked in the ice of the Weddell Sea. He and his crew decided to winter on the ice only to watch the ship being crunched into pieces with the onset of spring. Their effort to stay on an ice floe until they came close to land was unsuccessful, so they set out in three lifeboats to reach the desolate Elephant Island. From there, Shackleton decided to sail for help, leaving part of his crew on the island. They set out in the sturdiest of the three boats for the whaling station at South Georgia Island, 800 nautical miles (1,500 km) away.

Between April 24 and May 10, they plowed through the gales of an early Antarctic winter. As Shackleton wrote, "We felt our boat lifted and flung forward like a cork in breaking surf." They furiously bailed out the water that was washing in, managed to cook, chipped off the ice spray in shifts, became water-logged and raw, tried to rest, but, astonishingly, they navigated successfully to South Georgia. But then, within sight of land, a gale struck and they had to wait off shore until it passed. When they did land, it turned out to be on the wrong side of the island. So Shackleton and the two strongest men set off to cross the rugged mountain range and glaciers, without a map, to Stromness, the Norwegian whaling station. After 36 hours non-stop (they had no tents), they skidded on their behinds down the other side of the mountains to the welcome sight of Stromness. The following spring, Shackleton rescued the crew left behind on Elephant Island.

his small sloop, *Hero*, deep into the Southern Ocean in search of seals. He made for the shore and became the first person to set foot on Antarctica.

Palmer was followed by James Clark Ross in the heyday of the British Empire. After long experience in the Arctic, Ross spent almost four years in the Southern Ocean (1839–1843). Instead of the single sightings of the earlier explorers, he charted much of the Antarctic coastline, no mean feat in itself. The Ross Ice Shelf, a low flat shelf of ice, is named is his memory. To weather the turbulent seas and the perpetual ice, Ross made what turned out to be a wise choice of ship. *Erebus* and *Terror* were originally naval bomb vessels, designed to fire mortars rather than track through icy waters, but

Ross knew that they had extraordinarily strong hulls. Meant to withstand the recoil from mortars, they turned out to be excellent at withstanding ice.

THE HEROIC AGE

The target now became the land itself. Although the expeditions got off to a slow start, by the "heroic age" of Antarctic exploration, so-called because the daring explorers still used basic materials and methods before advanced mechanization, there were 16 expeditions from eight different countries.

These all happened between 1897 and 1922. They had their sights firmly set on the land, but a good number also mapped and explored the seas.

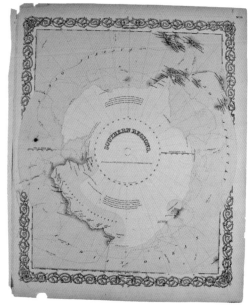

ABOVE In 1838, en route south to the Weddell Sea, the ships of French explorer Jules Dumont d'Urville, *L'Astrolabe* and *Zélée*, became stranded in pack ice. Although his mission was unsuccessful, a French research station, Dumont d'Urville Station in Antarctica, is named for him.

LEFT A mid-nineteenth-century map drawn by American cartographer Joseph Colton, showing the routes taken by a number of Antarctic explorers.

During the heroic age, many explorers came and went, often with ships that had been specially built to endure the incredibly rough conditions. There was *Discovery*, used by Robert Falcon Scott on his first expedition (1901–1903) and which survived two years in the ice before it was released through controlled explosives. There was also *Fram*, which was first used by Fridtjof Nansen in crossing the Arctic, and then used by Roald Amundsen in his successful bid for the South Pole. The desire that burned deep in the hearts of all these men—especially Roald Amundsen, Carsten Borchgrevink, Robert Falcon Scott, Ernest Shackelton, and Wilhelm Filchner—was to reach the South Pole, and then, when that objective was finally achieved in 1912, to cross the entire continent. All their energies were directed to attaining these goals.

But there were others who preferred to explore the seas around Antarctica. These include the Belgian, Adrian de Gerlache, who was the first person to winter in the Southern Ocean when his ship was caught in the ice (1897–1899), as well as ocean explorers such as the Scotsman, William Bruce (1902–1904), Jean-Baptiste-Charcot from France (1903–1905 and 1908–1910), and Nobu Shirase from Japan (1910–1912).

The Southern Ocean and Antarctica still present formidable challenges, but with modern technology, the area is opening up more readily to sailors, scientists, adventurers, and even tourists.

The Search for the Northeast Passage

The idea of reaching East Asia by sailing around the northern rim of the Eurasian landmass was well accepted in medieval Europe. Unlike the search for the Northwest Passage, the history of the Russians' Arctic endeavors was one of gradual but continuous success. By the mid-seventeenth century, evidence from their expeditions confirmed that Asia and North America were separated by a large strait. Economic factors first stimulated the quest toward the East, but were soon replaced with attempts for Russian geopolitical dominance over northern Asia.

ABOVE In 1553, English explorer Hugh Willoughby (c. 1500–1554) sailed across the Barents Sea to Novaya Zemlya. Although he and his crew perished, the voyage proved that a Northeast Passage was certainly possible.

VENTURE INTO THE UNKNOWN

As western European nations grew in strength, their economic aspirations extended from a regional to a global scale. In the fourteenth and fifteenth centuries, the East was out of reach. The Venetians monopolized trade in the eastern Mediterranean, and the Arabs controlled the Indian Ocean's trade routes. The New World was as yet undiscovered. The perception that Africa and an unknown southern land (Terra Australis Incognita) formed a single landmass proved a barrier to the south. A northern route, however, could allow access to the riches of China and the spice-producing islands of Southeast Asia.

The northern coastal area of present-day Russia, the longest coastline in the world, represented an unknown world to westerners. Although inhabited since prehistoric times, this vast coast was home only to isolated hunters and gatherers. The Russians, traditionally not a seafaring people, ventured only rarely northward to the tundra. The Russians had to focus their attention on a successful campaign against the Mongol khanates, which controlled central Russia for several centuries. But as they managed to conquer lands previously held by the Golden Horde, the Russians pushed eastward across the Siberian plains. As early as the end of the sixteenth century, the road to the Pacific coast became wide open. It was then that Russian leaders realized the importance of controlling the Arctic from the influence of other European powers.

Then, as today, the North Atlantic Gulf Stream was a vital contributor to climate on the European side of the Arctic. It warms the Barents and White seas and prevents their freezing, even during winter months. This is the reason why Murmansk and Archangelsk still serve as two leading ports in northern Russia. Farther east, climatic conditions deteriorate. Ice-free waterways on the Siberian coast are a seasonal occurrence and last two or three summer months. Compared with a search for the Northwest Passage, however, explorers encountered fewer islands near the Russian coast. Numerous archipelagos in the Canadian Arctic and their shallow waters created constant danger.

The eastern Arctic had few such barriers, but the thousands of miles of frozen ocean were impenetrable for three-quarters of the year. In summer, ice recedes northward, and the rivers that flow from central Asia to the Arctic are open for traffic for several months. Although these periods of uninterrupted travel are short, the ability to travel to Siberia by water had a potentially high economic and geopolitical importance.

GREAT MANGAZEYA ROUTE

An exploration of Siberia from the north by water initially had only peripheral importance to the Russians. Usually they would cross frozen rivers and keep moving eastward, but only until early summer. Siberian summers, when the upper layer of permafrost begins to melt, create sometimes unbridgeable physical barriers to travelers—a sea of mud, high air temperatures, and millions of mosquitoes combine to slow any advance. Even today, ground travel in the Asian part of Russia is difficult during the summer. Roads—few of which are paved—and railroads require constant repairs. In such conditions, rivers have to serve as major highways. Unfortunately, only a few rivers in Siberia flow in the

LEFT In 1594, Dutchman William Barents (Willem Barentsz) and his fleet arrived at Novaya Zemlya. He hoped to enter the Kara Sea and find the Northeast Passage.

nt hadde/ dat van over de zee op Nova Sembla was comen drpven/ twelck wp gheftadich met fleden haelden ter plaetfe daert hu
werden/wel twee mplen ging ende weder/tweemaels daechs/met vp naeft onuptfprekelijcken arbept/geduerende wel 1 5. dagen la
be ong int werck volherden/want fo wijt een weeck of t'wee later begonnen hadden/fo waere ong niet doenlijck gheweeft.

west–east direction; most major rivers flow toward the northern coast of Russia. In order to reach southern Siberia, the Russians, of necessity, needed to explore the Arctic. The Great Mangazeya Route, linking the watersheds of Ob-Irtysh and Yenisey with ports on the White Sea, was one of the early attempts.

Significant steps in search of the Northeast Passage began with Hugh Willoughby's expedition across the Barents Sea to Novaya Zemlya in 1553. Although Willoughby died on this trip, his backers in England learned that navigation along Russia's coast was possible, but how far was not yet confirmed.

ADVANCEMENT TO THE PACIFIC COAST

The exploration of the northern coast went slowly. By the end of the sixteenth century, the Kara Sea between Novaya Zemlya and Taymyr Peninsula was only partially charted. In 1597, Dutch expeditions under William Barents (Willem Barentsz, c. 1550–1597) ended an era of western European attempts to find the Northeast Passage. In his third trip to the region, Barents's expedition fell victim of the natural environment near Novaya Zemlya—Barents and most of his crew perished. Dutch explorers then abandoned trips to the northeast. During the next several decades the Russians remained the lone explorers of northern Asia.

An amazing paradox in the history of world maritime explorations followed. In order to confirm the existence of the Northeast Passage, the Russians chose an alternative route, but not by sea. They focused on land travel that eventually—if geographic calculations proved correct—could bring them to the Pacific and

ABOVE On his third voyage to the Arctic in 1597, Barents's ship became stranded in the gripping ice. He and members of his ever-weakening crew set out in two small boats, but died at sea.

A late twentieth-century photograph of the unforgiving icy seascape of Cape Dezhneva in northeastern Russia. Jutting into Bering Strait, the cape is named for Semyon Dezhnev, the Russian explorer who found that the continents of Asia and North America are not connected.

became immediately integrated into the empire. In 1619, the Great Mangazeya Route was permanently closed to prevent possible penetration by Westerners through the northern sea routes. The Cossacks, fierce protectors of the empire's boundaries, accompanied these early expeditions and established numerous settlements. In the 1630s, the Russians already had settled on the Sea of Okhotsk's shores. Only Kamchatka, a long southward-stretching peninsula, remained as a major landmass to conquer before fully entering the waters of the North Pacific.

Rather than sailing around Kamchatka, the Russians decided upon a less complicated option. In a few stages during the 1647–1648 expeditions, they used small boats and navigated downstream on the Kolyma River, which discharges into the Arctic Ocean. From there, they went east and finally navigated around the Chukchi Peninsula, sailed through the as-yet-unnamed Bering Strait and reached Kamchatka. Historical evidence of the first expedition through the Bering Strait is sparse. Scholars agree, however, that Semyon Dezhnev (c. 1605–1673) was indeed the first European to accomplish this mission. It proved all speculation concerning the Northeast Passage to be correct. It did little, however, to make immediate inroads in terms of its initial intent—global economic expansion and developments of permanent sea routes.

the northeastern end of Asia. It was risky, yet the only option. Nature provided a window of time simply too short for ships to sail around Russia's northern coast before the autumn season. Sea maps did not extend farther than one-third the length of the Arctic coast. Amazingly, it would take less than half a century to accomplish the task. The stimulus from Moscow for land exploration satisfied the hunger for scientific knowledge. More importantly for the tsars, the search for the Northeast Passage became the vanguard of imperial expansion. Each new territory discovered

CONQUEST OF THE LAST FRONTIER

When Peter I "the Great" came to the throne in 1682, the exploration of waters around the Russian Empire

gained much support. He wished to make Russia a powerful naval force. Lacking harbors with exits to warm seas, Russia was for all practical purposes a landlocked country. Sweden controlled the Baltic Sea, and the Ottoman Empire blocked a Russian exit from the Black Sea. Peter the Great funded the Russian Navy and employed foreigners as military assistants. Among them was Vitus Bering (1681–1741), a Danish seaman chosen to conduct an expedition to the Far East and to explore further territories that Dezhnev had discovered. At that time most of Russia's northern coast was

fairly well known, but the same transportation problems still remained. Bering had to travel to Okhotsk by land, then to Kamchatka, in order to assemble a vessel and gather a crew. Between 1728 and 1741, Bering conducted several voyages that confirmed Dezhnev's findings. He sailed through the strait that now bears his name and reached North American shores in Alaska. On return to Kamchatka, Bering's health deteriorated, and he died from scurvy in 1741.

The historical importance of Peter the Great's era, and the subsequent cultural impact of the Russian settlement of North America, makes Vitus Bering, without much doubt, one of the eighteenth century's leading mariners. Several decades later, Captain James Cook sailed north through the Bering Strait and acknowledged, for the western Europeans, the existence of the Northeast Passage.

THE FIRST TO SAIL THE PASSAGE

In 1878, the Finnish-born explorer and scientist, Adolf Erik Nordenskiöld, sailed east in his steam ship, *Vega*, from northern Norway. He reached the Bering Strait in September 1878, where his ship remained frozen in the ice for 10 months until the following July. When the thawing of the ice released the ship, Nordenskiöld and his crew touched the coast of Alaska and sailed on to Yokohama, becoming the first people to sail the length of the Northeast Passage.

However, it was only when the Soviet Union introduced nuclear ice-breakers to the region that the northern route was fully conquered.

LEFT Finnish-born scientist and explorer Adolf Erik Nordenskiöld (1832–1901) with his ship *Vega*. In 1878–1879, Nordenskiöld and his crew became the first people to sail through the Northeast Passage.

BELOW The Russian nuclear-powered ice-breaker *Rossiya* on its way to the Lomonosov Ridge in the Arctic Ocean in 2007. Nuclear ice-breakers made the northern routes more accessible.

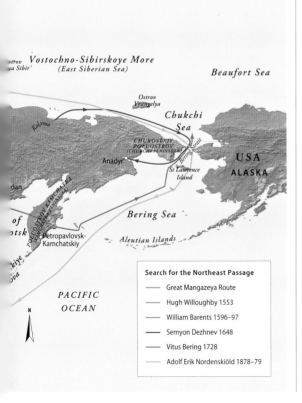

Vostochno-Sibirskoye More
(East Siberian Sea)

Beaufort Sea

Ostrov
Vrangelya

Chukchi Sea

Kolyma

CHUKOTSKIY
POLUOSTROV
(CHUKCHI PENINSULA)

Anadyr'

St Laurence
Island

USA
ALASKA

Bering Sea

Petropavlovsk-
Kamchatskiy

Aleutian Islands

PACIFIC OCEAN

N

Search for the Northeast Passage
— Great Mangazeya Route
— Hugh Willoughby 1553
— William Barents 1596–97
— Semyon Dezhnev 1648
— Vitus Bering 1728
— Adolf Erik Nordenskiöld 1878–79

The Search for the Northwest Passage

Not long after Europeans discovered the Americas, explorers began their search for an oceanic corridor to Asia. The Spanish and Portuguese dominance over Latin America prevented other European nations from traveling west without interruption. In the 1520s, the remote and stormy Strait of Magellan was the only sea route between the Atlantic and Pacific Oceans.

OPPOSITE *HMS Investigator,* commanded by British explorer Robert McClure, set out to find the lost Franklin expedition and became trapped in the ice for three winters before being abandoned in 1853.

ABOVE Martin Frobisher (1535–1594) made three unsuccessful voyages to Arctic waters in search of the Northwest Passage.

RIGHT Seeking the Northwest passage, Henry Hudson led an expedition to North America and discovered what is now known as Hudson Bay in 1610. But Hudson's freezing crew mutinied and set him adrift in an open boat in 1611. He was never seen again.

In the late sixteenth century, the English started to explore the Arctic realm in search of an alternative westward route—the Northwest Passage. But it would take nearly four centuries and numerous expeditions to finally prove that such a route indeed existed.

INITIAL ATTEMPTS

The dream of sailing westward from Europe to China and other East Asian locations did not come to an end with Christopher Columbus's discovery of the Americas in 1492. In the early sixteenth century, Portugal controlled the East Asian spice trade, and Spain had established a monopoly in much of America. To reach China, other European powers would have to rely on the lengthy and costly route around the tip of Africa and through the Indian Ocean. In London, the desire to find a shorter route that would allow the British to gain a trade monopoly became an obsession. Although many envisioned such a possibility, none knew whether a Northwest Passage actually existed.

The uncharted waters of the Arctic Ocean lying to the west of Greenland allowed plenty of room for imagination. With each new attempt, speculation about a water corridor grew. The French entered the search, and discovered that the St Lawrence River that led to the Great Lakes. They found very lucrative fur trading opportunities, which gradually shifted their economic interest to Canada. European mariners knew little

about navigating in dangerous polar waters. During the short summer, the ice melts and opens new waterways, but in early autumn, sea-ice returns with a vengeance. In 1576, the English sent a three-ship expedition, under the command of Martin Frobisher, to explore the waters beyond Greenland. He undertook further voyages in 1577 and 1578, both of them unsuccessful.

To minimize the possible dangers, exploration into the uncharted region and its treacherous waters was conducted in small steps. The news that the ocean extended farther north and northwest encouraged sponsorship of further expeditions.

The English speculated that one could sail northward, then turn west, therefore bypassing the northern extension of the North American continent, avoiding the shallow waters, and allowing detailed mapping of the unknown region.

The next explorer of note in the region was John Davis. Beginning in 1585, he explored a large expanse located between the Arctic Circle and 70°N latitude. The sixteenth century ended, however, with only very limited knowledge of merely a small portion of this vast and hostile region.

Explorations were expensive, but wealthy financiers in London were well aware of potential profits. They sponsored several other fruitless attempts to find the Northwest Passage. Henry Hudson's ill-fated voyage westward in 1610, between Labrador and Baffin Island, led only to the discovery of the vast bay later named after him. Although he did not realize his original goal, Hudson's discovery opened doors for the British to bypass the St Lawrence valley and engage in a lucrative fur trade centered in far northern Canada. This shift of economic attention was instrumental in reducing costly London-sponsored Arctic explorations.

Five years after Hudson's crew returned, William Baffin became the first European to prove that straits indeed separated the far northern islands. He reached nearly 80°N latitude and discovered the straits that, although frozen and impenetrable, could eventually lead to an Asian passage. The interest in Hudson Bay and the lucrative returns on fur-related investments overshadowed initiatives for further exploration in the seventeenth century. Further, because of the wealth generated by the fur trade, exploration became increasingly secret. The British were making inroads in India, settling in Madras (Chennai), where they built Fort St George in 1639. New possessions in the Indian Ocean area also diverted interests from costly Arctic endeavors.

Search for the Northwest Passage

- Martin Frobisher 1576
- John Davis 1585
- Henry Hudson 1610–11
- William Baffin 1616
- James Cook 1778–79
- John Franklin 1845
- Roald Amundsen 1903–06
- Modern country borders

ARCTIC OCEAN

Ellesmere Island

Kane Basin

GREENLAND

Smith Sound

Lancaster Sound

Baffin Bay

Beaufort Sea

Banks Island

Prince of Wales Island

Victoria Island

Amundsen Gulf

Gulf of Boothia

King William Island

Baffin Island

Davis Strait

ICELAND

Arctic Circle

NORWAY

Oslo

USA ALASKA

Nome

Foxe Basin

Cape Farewell

Hudson Strait

ICELAND

NORTH Sea

North Sea

CANADA

Hudson Bay

Labrador

Gulf of Alaska

New Albion

James Bay

N

ATLANTIC OCEAN

Plymouth

London

Dartmouth

PACIFIC OCEAN

USA

Newfoundland

Gulf of St Lawrence

EUROPE

1,000   2,000   3,000   4,000 kilometers
500   1,000   1,500   2,000 miles

ABOVE The polar explorer Roald Amundsen and his intrepid crew in Nome, Alaska, aboard the Norwegian ship that was the first to navigate solo through the Northwest Passage in the expedition of 1903–1906.

THE NEXT STAGE

For over a century, there was very little news about the Northwest Passage. When fur trade revenues in the Hudson Bay area began to decrease and the Russians reached the Pacific Ocean by land and sea, perceptions in London began to change. Aware that Asia and North America were separated only by a narrow strait, the English renewed their search. Between 1740 and 1800, a plethora of new information provided many clues for mapmakers and sailors. Captain James Cook sailed through the northern Pacific to the Bering Strait in 1778, a half century after the Russians accomplished the task. This time the English had irrefutable evidence that the continents were not connected.

While all this was happening, overland exploration of North America was extending northward. Alexander Mackenzie set off on foot in 1789, between Canada's interior and the Arctic's Beaufort Sea. His expedition proved that the continental landmass eventually gave way to a northern ocean. One decade earlier, Samuel Hearne had also reached the northern Canadian coast. Slowly but surely, a realistic picture began to emerge of what lay in these high latitudes. At the beginning of the nineteenth century, there was growing agreement that the Northwest Passage existed. Only the exact route required confirmation, and whether it was adequate for maritime transportation. In spite of the improvements in navigational and shipbuilding technologies, the reasons for concern remained identical—narrow and shallow straits, rapidly expanding ice barriers, and the changing patterns of the weather.

THE FRANKLIN EXPEDITION

By the early 1800s, the mighty Royal Navy controlled the global sea and an empire that stretched around the world. Yet the question about the Northwest Passage remained unanswered. The best efforts of numerous explorers had fallen short. For his final return to the Arctic Ocean, Sir John Franklin, a veteran of two previous trips in 1819 and 1827, received extraordinary funding for an 1845 expedition. This time, authorities believed, possible success was based upon the size of his ship, his crew, and immediate access to abundant food and necessary utilities.

Franklin set off with two ships, 127 crew members, and several hundred tons of food and supplies. Unfortunately, environmental reality erased all optimistic visions of success shortly after the ships passed beyond Baffin Island. The ill-fated expedition ventured into Arctic waters and became imprisoned by advancing ice near King William Island. At the same time, the crew

members, unaware that the lead lining in tin cans was poisonous, became seriously ill after eating canned meat. Franklin died in 1847. After it became clear that advancement was impossible, the remaining members tried to reach civilization by foot, across unforgiving land and frozen sea. One by one, all the crew members perished, making this expedition the single largest loss of life in any British scientific or geographic exploration. The lack of any news of the Franklin party over a three-year period led to dozens of search missions. The consensus was that there were no survivors, and this eroded support for further expeditions.

SUCCESS AT LAST

It is very difficult to imagine, but at the dawn of the twentieth century no one could yet present conclusive proof that a Northwest Passage existed. After centuries of costly attempts, the British had been unsuccessful. Ultimately, it was the Norwegian explorer, Roald

Amundsen, who, in his epic 1903–1906 voyage with a small boat and a crew of only six men, successfully navigated the Northwest Passage. A great deal of his success was based upon his understanding of the Inuit (Eskimo) way of life. These hardy Arctic people had lived in this region for millennia, and practiced survival methods that Franklin and his crew had ignored. Amundsen chose to board sleds and dogs and travel light and fast on land if necessary. He soon learned to hunt like the Inuit and realized that their animal-skin clothing and food preservation techniques were superior to those of the Europeans in the bitterly cold environment. After spending a year among locals on King William Island, Amundsen's crew continued westward in the summer of 1905. Not long after their departure, they encountered an American whaling ship that had passed through the Bering Strait. After more than four centuries, the long search for the Northwest Passage was over, and the Norwegians had won.

ABOVE Amundsen negotiated a passage through the Beaufort Sea and into Bering Strait, finding the Northwest Passage in the process. It was when he encountered a whaling ship in Arctic waters that he knew his dream had been realized.

Modern Day Exploration

The advent of modern ships and navigational methods has made sea voyages relatively easy. The bridge of most modern vessels today contains GPS screens, radar, computers, telephones, and a range of up-to-date equipment that can access the latest ocean and weather information. Yet these developments have also increased the fascination with the way people used to sail before these technological advances. So adventurers looked to the oceans and wondered how to build ships and sail using traditional methods.

OPPOSITE Thor Heyerdhal's papyrus-reed boat *Ra* is swamped by a wave. The Norwegian adventurer soon launched a successor to this boat. Called the *Ra II*, in 1970, it sailed across the Atlantic.

THOR HEYERDAHL

In 1947, the Norwegian Thor Heyerdahl thrilled the world by crossing the Pacific on a balsa-wood raft he named *Kon-Tiki*. Heyerdahl and five others traveled 4,300 miles (7,000 km) from Peru to the Tuamotu Islands in Polynesia in a little over three months. He had based the design of the raft on ancient legends and old descriptions by the Spanish colonists. He used traditional materials for binding the logs and making the sails. The balsa logs were left green so that the sap repelled water, and the large sail caught the prevailing winds. They encountered dolphins and whales, ate seafood that gathered in between the logs of the raft, and used fish for moisture when rain was scarce.

Many others have emulated that epic journey, among them Heyerdahl's grandson, Olav, in 2006. But Heyerdahl combined his daring with a flair for publicity and controversial theories. The book *Kon-Tiki* was an international bestseller, the motion picture won an Academy Award, and he was a popular speaker. But he also championed alternative theories of the origin of peoples and their migrations. By examining the plants, language connections, archeological sites, and above all by treating ancient myths as literal historical records, he suggested that fair-skinned peoples migrated from Europe to South America, and then across to Easter Island and Polynesia. Heyerdahl began a fashion for similar theories that are popular today.

BELOW In 1976, Irish explorer Tim Severin recreated a sixth-century currragh and sailed it from Ireland across the North Atlantic to Newfoundland.

Fired up by his first great success, Heyerdahl's next project was the *Ra* expeditions. He set out to construct an Egyptian papyrus reed-boat, using traditional methods and information taken from drawings and inscriptions, to sail across the Atlantic. The first boat began to take on water, so he built another, *Ra II*, this time using craftsmen from Bolivia rather than Lake Chad. It arrived in triumph in Barbados in 1970.

By now Heyerdahl's concern for world peace and the environment had become more public, especially as he had a worldwide reputation. The third ship, *Tigris*, left Iraq in late 1977 en route for the Red Sea and Egypt. Its purpose was to show a possible connection between the ancient Indus Valley civilization, Mesopotamia, and Egypt. But when the expedition reached Djibouti in early 1978, Heyerdahl and the crew burned the boat in protest at the wars raging in the Middle East.

IN ST BRENDAN'S WAKE

Heyerdahl's theories about the sea-borne movements of ancient peoples remain controversial. However, his spectacular recreated voyages with traditionally built ships inspired others. One was Tim Severin, an Irish writer of fiction, who sailed a currragh (a small, leather-covered boat) from Ireland to Newfoundland. Like Heyerdahl, Severin assumed that ancient legends about sea voyages should be taken as historical works. Severin designed his currragh by following the instructions in an eleventh-century work, *The Voyage of St Brendan the Abbott*, that describes in fantastical terms the voyage of sixth-century monk, St Brendan.

It must have been a strange sight to see the tiny vessel with a Celtic cross on its two sails turning up in the islands of the North Atlantic. During 1976–1977, Severin sailed to the Hebrides, Faroes, Iceland, and then Newfoundland, passing by icebergs, whales, and porpoises. For Severin, this was proof that the legend of Brendan's sixth-century voyage to the Isle of the Blessed (North America) described an actual journey along the very same route.

After his first success, Severin dug out some other legendary stories, built boats according to ancient instructions, and recreated them: Sinbad's voyage from Oman to China; Jason's voyage from Greece to Georgia; Ulysses' journey from Troy to Ithaca; and the China voyage, sailing on a bamboo raft that did not quite make it across the Pacific.

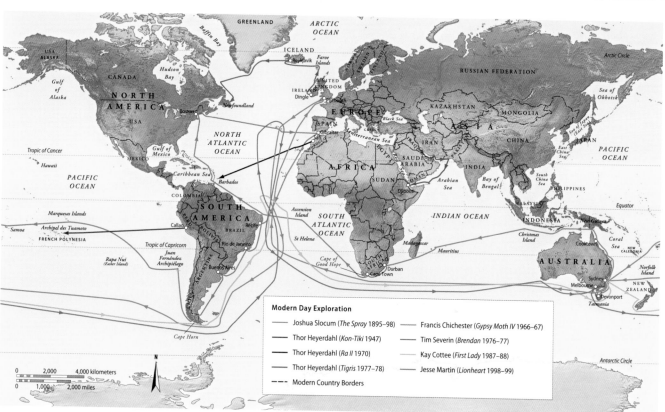

Modern Day Exploration

———— Joshua Slocum (*The Spray* 1895–98)

———— Thor Heyerdahl (*Kon-Tiki* 1947)

———— Thor Heyerdahl (*Ra II* 1970)

———— Thor Heyerdahl (*Tigris* 1977–78)

‐ ‐ ‐ ‐ Modern Country Borders

———— Francis Chichester (*Gypsy Moth IV* 1966–67)

———— Tim Severin (*Brendan* 1976–77)

———— Kay Cottee (*First Lady* 1987–88)

———— Jesse Martin (*Lionheart* 1998–99)

RIGHT Joshua Slocum (at left) on his boat *The Spray* in Cape Town, South Africa, where he stopped briefly in 1897. Slocum was the first person to circumnavigate the world single-handedly. He chronicled his 1895–1898 travels in a book called *Sailing Alone Around the World*.

BELOW Dr Robert Ballard (center) and assistants consult various charts in their search for the wreckage of the *Titanic* in 1985.

Robert Ballard

Robert Duane Ballard (born June 30, 1942, in Wichita, Kansas) is a modern day deep-sea explorer. Using submersibles outfitted with lighting, cameras, and manipulator arms remotely controlled from a surface ship, he discovered numerous shipwrecks including the *Titanic* in 1985. On other missions, he has explored seafloor hot springs or "black smokers" and documented the strange marine communities that thrive on them in total darkness. His boyhood interest in underwater exploration was sparked when he read Jules Verne's novel *Twenty Thousand Leagues Under the Sea*.

Dr Ballard founded the JASON Project in 1989 to share his love of the deep sea. The submersible *Jason* broadcasts video signals from its missions, live via two-way satellite, to students in schools around the world, enabling them to take part in the expeditions in real time without leaving their classrooms. He is also the founder and president of the Institute for Exploration, which is involved with deep-sea archeology. With just 1 percent of the ocean explored, Ballard is passionate about the future of underwater exploration. He also believes that "the students of today are the key to the discoveries of tomorrow … [E]ducators need to encourage students to follow their dreams and uncover the places we have yet to explore."

SOLO AROUND THE WORLD

Following in the wake of legendary seafarers was not the only path open to modern explorers. Other challenges remained. Could one man or woman make it all around the world using only wind power? And what lay beneath the surface of what is really a water planet?

To be alone in the middle of an ocean for months on end requires an inner calm and strong personality, not to mention significant sailing skills and presence of mind when tossed into the water by a raging sea. Four names stand out in the stories of solo, round-the-world sailing: Joshua Slocum, Francis Chichester, Kay Cottee, and Jesse Martin. Each tried to outdo the other, first sailing solo around the globe, and then non-stop, unassisted, and via the great capes—Cape Horn and the Cape of Good Hope.

THE MEN OF THE SEA

Joshua Slocum was the very first person to sail solo around the world from Boston to Newport, Rhode Island, USA. It took him more than three years (1895–1898). He made numerous stops along the way, but he managed it on his own. Slocum was a unique man, more at home on the water than on land. Running away from home at 14, he spent most of his remaining 51 years at sea. The boat in which he completed the journey, *The Spray*, became his home until he was—fittingly perhaps—lost at sea in 1909.

In contrast to Slocum's leisurely voyage, Francis Chichester completed his circumnavigation at break-neck speed. Not content to better Slocum, Chichester set out to beat the times of the fastest sailing ships in history, the tea clippers in the last great age of sail. He sailed from Plymouth, England, traveling from west to east, with the prevailing winds (in contrast to Slocum). He followed the clipper routes in the Roaring Forties, and made only one stop, in Sydney, Australia. He completed the voyage single-handedly in 226 days—from August 27, 1966 to May 28, 1967. He was 66 years old when he returned to England.

FIRST LADY

As yet a woman had not completed this great challenge, since the sea has traditionally been a man's world. It fell to the Australian, Kay Cottee, to achieve that dream. Cottee in her boat, *First Lady*, outdid Chichester on a number of counts. She completed the voyage in 189 days, setting out from Sydney on November 29, 1987, and returning home on June 5, 1988. Apart from being the first woman, she also sailed non-stop and did so without any assistance. Perhaps the greatest test in such a journey is to be able to rest in a tossing boat. Cottee managed with short spells of sleep in between the continuous tasks of sailing.

THE YOUNGEST

An old man and a woman had so far completed the world voyage, so it was left to a teenager to become the

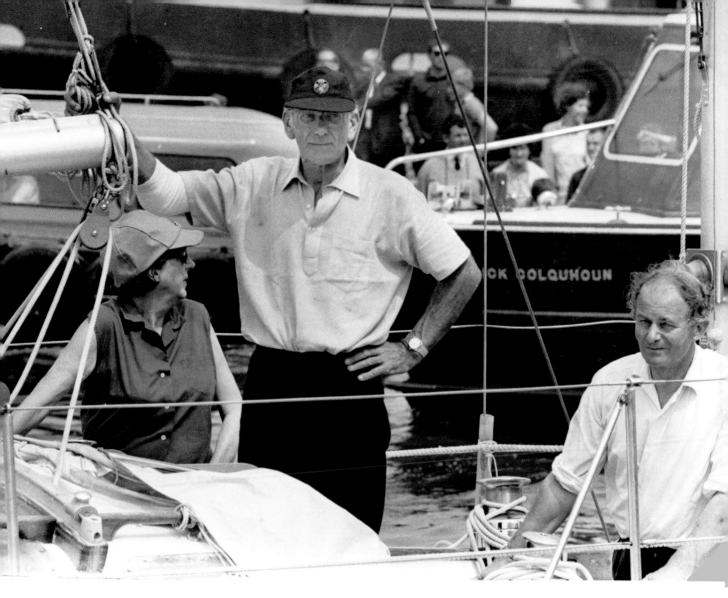

youngest. This was another Australian, Jesse Martin, who set sail from Melbourne on December 7, 1998. While at sea, he wrote copious notes about his inner feelings, the realization of a dream, of his fears and hopes, of almost being run down by a tanker, of being hit by a whale, and of becoming tired of prepackaged food. Nearly one year later, on October 31, 1999, he sailed back into Melbourne. His hair hung down to his waist as he had not stopped at all on his journey. A modest man, Martin commented, "I do not consider myself as the world's best sailor; I have never been in a yachting race in my life. I've just put up a bit of sail and done four knots all the way around the world—that's nothing special."

BENEATH THE OCEAN

As these sailors were meeting new challenges on the surface, the Frenchman Jacques-Yves Cousteau and his colleagues were exploring beneath the waves. Cousteau pioneered the way and many others have followed in the short time since he and Émile Gagnan, developed, in 1942, the aqualung, enabling divers to carry their own air supply with them.

ABOVE English yachtsman Sir Francis Chichester (1901–1972) took nine months to sail around the world in his ketch *Gipsy Moth IV*, returning to England in May 1967.

LEFT Jesse Martin was just 17 years old when he sailed out of Melbourne in 1998 in his yacht, the aptly-named *Lionheart*.

Jacques Cousteau

Jacques-Yves Cousteau stands as a hero figure to many an aspiring explorer of the oceans. He had an intense passion for exploring the undersea world combined with an amazing ability to share the beauty and mystery of that world with the average person. During his long lifetime (June 11, 1910–June 25, 1997), Jacques Cousteau was highly regarded as a French naval officer, explorer, ecologist, filmmaker, innovator, scientist, photographer, author, and researcher who studied the sea and all its life forms.

ABOVE Jacques Cousteau was honored with membership of the Académie Française in 1989. Four years earlier, President Ronald Reagan awarded him the US Medal of Freedom.

RIGHT Cousteau and a diving companion are lowered into the waters off Abu Dhabi in 1954. The cage went down 250 ft (76 m) and kept the undersea explorers safe from shark attack.

SCUBA DIVING

Prior to the invention of the modern "aqualung," which Jacques Cousteau co-developed with Émile Gagnan during the 1940s, most underwater exploration was carried out using "standard diving dress." This older system—hardhat diving—had been in use since 1837. Divers wore cumbersome weighted suits with heavy metal helmets and were fed air from compressors on a boat. Hardhat divers were restricted to walking on the sea bottom, and any problems on the surface usually meant that they died from suffocation.

The new aqualung freed divers from these restrictions, allowing them to move about freely, suspended in the ocean's transparent blueness. Indeed, one of the most thrilling experiences for first-time divers is experiencing this ethereal feeling of gravity-defying

weightlessness. In the new system, divers carried compressed air cylinders on their backs and breathed air through a regulator that delivered air at ambient pressure. The used air was simply expelled out of the regulator into the surrounding water. Fins worn on the feet allowed divers to propel themselves through the water with the ease of a dolphin, and as time went on, neoprene suits of various thicknesses were developed—these are worn for warmth and protection.

As overhead compressors and hoses were no longer needed to supply air, the new equipment soon became known as "Self-Contained Underwater Breathing Apparatus," or SCUBA for short. Cousteau describes experimenting with the first aqualung prototypes in his 1953 book, *The Silent World: A Story of Undersea Discovery and Adventure.* By the 1960s SCUBA diving had became extremely popular as a sport, bringing the upper part of the undersea world into easy reach of all who undertake a certified diving course.

FILMING THE UNDERSEA WORLD

Jacques Cousteau's desire to explore the undersea world took root during his childhood on the Gironde estuary at St-André-de-Cubzac, near Bordeaux, France, and continued to develop during his service in the French Navy. He was involved in mine clearance work, underwater archeology, and salvage operations, including the rescue in 1949 of the FNRS-2, a bathyscaphe that Professor Jacques Piccard was using to explore the ocean's deepest regions.

Cousteau was a founder member of the Group of Study and Underwater Research (GERS) with Philippe Tailliez, Frédéric Dumas, Jean Alinat, and the writer/film director Marcel Ichac. This group sailed the sloop *Élie Monnier* to Mahdia, Tunisia, to explore underwater Roman remains. SCUBA gear was used, paving the way for scientific underwater archeology. Movie cameras in waterproof housings allowed Cousteau and Marcel Ichac to record underwater film footage of the expedition, which was shown at the Cannes Film Festival.

CALYPSO

Jacques Cousteau left the French Navy in 1949 and founded the French Oceanographic Campaigns. He built an underwater laboratory in his ship, *Calypso,* which became the support base for his diving, filming, and research. Cousteau and his team used *Calypso* to explore the planet's most interesting oceans and rivers, combining scientific research with adventure. He also developed the two-person mini-submersible, *Denise.* It was the first such craft designed specifically for underwater research, and could dive to 1,150 ft (350 m), staying submerged for up to five hours.

In 1968, Cousteau was asked to make a television series, and for the next eight years, *The Undersea World of Jacques Cousteau* brought the amazing world of dolphins, sharks, whales, coral reefs, and sunken treasure into people's homes.

THE COUSTEAU SOCIETY

The more Cousteau explored, discovered, and filmed the underwater world, the more he became an environmentalist. In 1973, he founded the Cousteau Society, headquartered in the United States. It was born out of his desire to protect the ocean, and grew as his films, books, and publicity campaigns instilled a sense of wonder and adventure in people. This non-profit group, with its sister organization Equipe Cousteau, is currently restoring the original *Calypso* and raising funds to build a new research vessel, *Calypso II.*

ABOVE In 1964, Cousteau's film *World Without Sun* was released in France. It won the Academy Award for that year's best Documentary Feature.

TOP Cousteau was rarely away from the ocean. His dedication to the marine environment raised public awareness of the need to protect our oceans.

Modern Vessels

The surface warship has two possible dates of origin: The oared ship dating back thousands of years, and the fighting sail, which, some historians argue, began with the Battle of Sluys in 1340 when the English navy defeated the French.

OPPOSITE The dreadnought was the quintessential battleship of the early twentieth century. Depicted here is the *USS New York*, which was built in 1911 and carried 14-in (35-cm) guns.

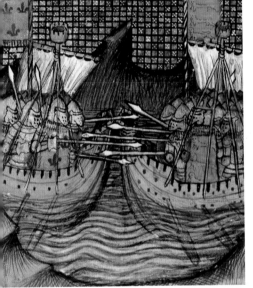

ABOVE A late fourteenth-century illustration depicting the Battle of Sluys, where the English navy scored a decisive victory over the French fleet. Having maneuvered their ships to advantage, English archers attacked before soldiers boarded French ships to engage in hand-to-hand combat.

THE FIRST SURFACE WARSHIPS

The oared ship was usually rowed by its crew and—rarely—by galley slaves. Among the types of oared ships were the bireme and the trireme, the latter with three banks of oars. The ships were unarmed except for a ram projecting underwater from the bow. Weapons consisted of the small arms of the embarked soldiers. These were either missile weapons—the short bow, spear, trident, javelin, and sling—or edged weapons—sword, knife, battle-ax, and club. The common method of fighting was to ram the enemy, shower the ship with missiles, and then board, with hand-to-hand combat deciding victory.

Fighting sail was first successfully employed at the Battle of Sluys in 1340. The battle took place between basic sailing warships, which had three or four masts, and square-rigged sails. Over time decks were added to the open hull arrangement. From around 1450, guns were fired from the ships' sides, with small numbers of bow and stern chasers. Additional decks were then built on and the vessels became bigger and heavier. One ship possibly too big for her design was *Mary Rose*, the pride of Henry VIII's fleet. It capsized in windy conditions.

The fighting tactics of sail ships were the same as those used by oared ships. However, "cannonade to sink" gradually overtook the "close, grapple, and board" school until it became the preferred tactic. The weapons of the surface fleet became the "great gun," inaccurately known as "cannon." Many classes of great gun existed, firing varying weight shot, including culverins, sakers, and falcons.

LINE OF BATTLE SHIPS

Ships in the Royal Navy were divided into first to sixth "rates." The term "battleship" comes from the concept of fighting in the line of battle, devised as a naval offensive in the seventeenth century. Of the six rates, only the first three usually fought in the line of battle. A ship's rate was determined by the number of guns it carried, but the criterion changed over time. The 64-gun *HMS Resolution*, launched in 1610, was dubbed a first rate, but later first rates carried 100 guns, and from 1810, 110 guns.

Battleships fired broadsides, with decks of guns firing together or in a ripple effect, from either the port or starboard sides. The one-sided firing was for good reason. The shock of complete decks of guns all firing together might cause damage to the ship, or a target might not be seen by all of the guns at the same time, as the weapons projected through gunports, allowing only a little sideways variation. Manpower was another reason for limited firing—a gun needed several men to work it, and with the operation of sails a ship's available manpower was seldom enough to have all guns fully manned. Gun captains "borrowed" from the crews on the unengaged side to help operate their weapons, which required loading, aiming, firing, swabbing out, reloading, running up, and firing again.

NINETEENTH-CENTURY DEVELOPMENTS

Steam appeared as propulsion after the Napoleonic wars. There was antipathy toward it in various quarters, and for many years ships used both steam and sail. One of the chief attractions of mechanized propulsion was that it supplemented muscle power, formerly the only method for hoisting sails or raising anchors. In 1778 *HMS Victory* carried approximately 1,000 men, most of whom performed physical tasks. By comparison, 200 years later, destroyers with enough firepower to wipe out a large city are operated with only a few hundred personnel.

Capital ships—a navy's primary craft—gradually expanded in all dimensions. For example, *Mary Rose* was 126 ft (38.5 m) in length at the waterline; *HMS Victory* was 226 ft (70 m); *HMS Dreadnought* 528 ft (160 m); and the *Yamato*, the Imperial Japanese Navy's super-battleship, was 840 ft (255 m). Further experiments of the mid-nineteenth century included iron cladding ships, with the French building *Gloire* in 1858 and the British *HMS Warrior* in 1859. Ironclads could maneuver well in calm conditions and also overtake wind-powered vessels.

Breech loading guns—much easier to handle and also providing more firepower—appeared, as well as the revolving turret, which allowed fire from more angles. Guns changed from being measured by the pound-weight of the ball they could throw to the diameter of their muzzle bore.

A new ship evolved—the monitor. Named after the *USS Monitor*, this was a shallow draft vessel for use in coastal waters to bombard an enemy's defenses. The inconclusive American Civil War confrontation between *Monitor* and *Merrimack* was significant. After

an engagement where neither ship was able to break through the other's armor, both sides retired to give naval architects decades of thought and experiment.

THE TWENTIETH-CENTURY APPROACH

HMS Dreadnought in 1906 signaled a return from coastal monitors to sea-keeping ships, and made every other capital ship obsolete overnight. The new-style dreadnoughts joined big guns (12 by 12 in [30 cm]) with heavy armor 12 in (30 cm) thick. They were true creatures of the waves, with very good maritime qualities, and a high speed of 24 knots (45 kph). There was no vessel to match the dreadnought, and a building race between nations commenced. The term eventually was discarded and replaced by "battleship."

Britain's First Sea Lord, Admiral Sir John Fisher, was the creator of the dreadnought. He was also responsible for modifying battleships into "fast armored cruisers." The alteration removed some armor which made the ships faster so they could function as scouts ahead of the main fleet. The term "battlecruiser" led commanders to think that such ships could be used in general fleet battles. The concept of a "super battlecruiser" came with the building of the 42,000 ton (41,000 tonne) *HMS Hood*, armed with eight 15-in (38-cm) guns in 1920. However, in World War II she was outclassed and sunk by the German *HSK Bismarck*, 20 years her junior—thinly armored ships were no match for the modern 15-in (38-cm) guns.

The term "frigate" dates back to sail, and refers to fourth and fifth rate vessels designed with an unarmed lower deck; their guns were carried higher; they could heel more, and carry more sail in rough conditions, not having gunports open to the sea. Known as "the eyes of the fleet," the frigates had more than a scouting role: They pursued merchantmen, battled other frigates, or snapped up smaller vessels. The modern frigate is smaller than a destroyer, and can operate aggressively in anti-submarine, anti-surface, or anti-air warfare.

ABOVE An 1883 painting by Ebenezer Wake Cook of *HMS Victory*, one of England's most famous warships. *Victory* was commanded by Lord Nelson at the Battle of Trafalgar.

The word "destroyer" comes from the phrase "torpedo-boat destroyer," which was a vessel that was designed to counter torpedo-boats (small, fast ships deploying self-propelled torpedoes). Motor torpedo boats were armed with upper deck torpedoes. Missile patrol boats sheltered in coastal radar shadows before they swarmed out to overwhelm larger warships with missiles. Gunboats (small, shallow-draft craft) enabled river system penetration, bringing guns to bear on fortifications based on shore.

Corvettes, originally sailing vessels that were smaller than frigates, re-emerged during World War II; they were designed to escort convoys and also to carry out anti-submarine attacks. Modern navies also employ minelayers and mine hunters; collectively they are referred to as mine warfare vessels.

BELOW At a little over 1,120 ft (340 m) in length, *USS Enterprise* is the longest naval vessel in the world today. More significantly, it is also the world's first nuclear-powered aircraft carrier.

AIRCRAFT CARRIER—KING OF THE SEA

Taking aircraft to sea gives advantages to ships. At first, their reconnaissance showed the enemy's whereabouts, or spotted artillery's fall of shot, but soon they were used in attack or defense roles. There were many initial obstacles to overcome. Test pilot Eugene Ely took off from *USS Birmingham* in 1910, but recovery of water landings proved difficult. In World War I, the battle-cruiser *HMS Furious* was converted into an aircraft carrier and the first deck landing occurred in 1917.

The carrier was much experimented with after the Great War. The "big gun" battleship was still very much the ambition of all seamen officers, and the carrier was seen as an aid—its aircraft useful for finding ships and submarines, but not a key element of sea power. Aircraft had many problems. The early machines were slow and fragile, with machine-gun fire often proving fatal. Aircraft also presented other issues—they needed wind over the deck to become airborne; flammable fuel, specialized mechanics, and aircrew to fly them; and were these new seamen officers or ratings?

In 1939 Britain, the battleship was still king of the sea, but over the next five years this role was shattered. Significant carrier combat events proved the pre-eminence of that class of combat vessel. The defeat of *Bismarck* in May 1941 showed the usefulness of carrier aircraft in reconnaissance and in the strike role—aerial attack wounded the German vessel sufficiently to enable her destruction by Royal Navy ships.

In the Pacific, the attack by Japanese aircraft on Pearl Harbor was launched from carriers, as well as the raid on Darwin in northern Australia, which bypassed shore gun defenses designed for use against battleships. The sinking of *HMS Repulse* and *HMS Prince of Wales* off Malaya in December 1941 demonstrated the folly of not having sufficient anti-aircraft guns or accompanying aircraft to repel attackers.

The Coral Sea and Midway battles saw carriers as the most important warship. Battleships were relegated to the role of floating gun batteries lacking the destructive range, measured in hundreds of miles, of carrier-launched aircraft. As the war against the Japanese was concluding, the strategic concern was to capture land bases such as Saipan. Bombardment before landing was necessary, and aircraft utilized rockets and bombs to great effect; they also gave support to infantry.

Carrier types evolved the designations "escort," "light," and "fleet". The role of escort carriers was to attack submarines, or to support amphibious landings; the others provided fleet protection and assault roles. The concept of an amphibious assault carrier, complete with hovercraft and close attack aircraft, continued after World War II. Carriers proved their usefulness in the Korean War, where few convenient airbases were available for flying operations. The Royal Navy used carriers as the mainstay of its victory in the 1982 Falklands War—the amphibious assaults would have been impossible without them.

SUBMARINES

The first operational submarine was *Turtle*, designed in 1775 by American David Bushnell. Navigated through a small window at the top of the vessel, she was more a submersible than a submarine. During the American War of Independence, *Turtle* made an unsuccessful attack on *HMS Eagle* in New York Harbor.

The first successful attack submarine was a railway boiler converted into the Confederate vessel *H. L. Hunley*. In the American Civil War this unwieldy craft, powered by internal cranking and manned by a crew of nine, attacked the Union *USS Housatonic* using a spar torpedo. Although *Hunley* sank her victim, its crew was killed in the process.

Submarine development was by then in full flight in the United States. Two inventors stand out. Simon Lake's design utilized the concept of negative buoyancy; he also invented the periscope. John Holland's endeavors used a petrol engine while the submarine is on the surface and an electric motor when submerged.

This new weapon in sea combat quickly proved its worth. On September 5, 1914, the German submarine *U-21* fired the first torpedo of World War I, sinking the British cruiser *HMS Pathfinder*. On September 22, *U-9* sank three cruisers off Holland: *HMSS Aboukir*, *Hogue*, and *Cressy* were lost along with the lives of 1,460

British sailors. In counter attacking, surface ships rammed the submarines, used their guns, or employed the depth charge, invented by the British in late 1915.

By World War II, torpedo tubes had been fitted to fire rearward and sideways. Some Japanese submarines

ABOVE German submarines, or U-boats, photographed in 1936. Up to and during World War II, Germany had a large fleet of submarines, and they played an important role in destroying Allied shipping routes.

LEFT An illustration from a 1903 edition of the Italian newspaper *La Domenica del Corriere* of a submarine called *Battello Lavoratore*, which was invented for underwater exploration.

RIGHT Container and cargo ships carry goods from one port to another. Made of steel, these massive vessels transport vehicles, machinery, furniture, oil and gas supplies, and countless other materials across the world.

had waterproof hangars for small aircraft. The snorkel allowed air replenishment while submerged.

By 1945 the number of submarines in world navies was an indication of the enormous scope of the new weapon. In World War II, the United States Navy lost 52 submarines out of 288 vessels; the Japanese 128 from 186; the Germans 785 of 1,158 constructed. But submarine successes were also immense—the Germans had sunk 2,828 merchant ships and 187 warships, including six aircraft carriers and two battleships.

After the war, new roles emerged with the ability to attack land with intercontinental ballistic missiles. Modern submarines, some powered by nuclear energy, retain their original task of striking enemy shipping, and coupled with land-attack capabilities, remain one of the most potent weapons on the planet.

MERCHANT SHIPPING

A miscellany of vessels is afloat on today's oceans. Apart from craft involved in the fishing industry, many ships belong to the area of merchant-marine, carrying goods from one location to the other. These include enormous oil tankers with tonnages of 100,000, cargo container ships, and liquid natural gas carriers—one of the more unusual sights on the oceans with enormous bulbous containers atop the weather deck. Car-carriers transfer new automobiles by the hundred. Passenger ferries range from small vessels to those capable of carrying many hundreds of passengers and their cars in air-conditioned comfort.

The passenger liner has become a unique vessel over the last century. People go to sea not to be merely transported overseas—rather the liner itself becomes the attraction. Many of the larger ships are similar to luxurious land-based resorts.

The seas of the twenty-first century are home to all of these vessels, carrying the produce of a busy world while simultaneously guarding it. Modern commerce and warfare cannot possibly be supplied by air—the seas are still the world's biggest highway.

BELOW The *Queen Mary 2*, the world's largest cruise ship, in Brooklyn, New York. This luxury passenger liner is more than 1,100 ft (335 m) long and over 236 ft (72 m) high.

Conflict on the Ocean

For as long as seafaring nations have been in contact with one another, conflict on the water has been a fact of life. Naval warfare has been occurring in many parts of the world for thousands of years. The earliest recorded sea battle occurred in 1210 BCE on the Mediterranean Sea, when the Hittites defeated a force from Cyprus.

The primary purpose of sea power has always been to protect territory, natural resources, or trade routes by putting a halt to enemy advances. So naval warfare can justifiably be considered a nautical projection of political power. Sometimes this protection involved pre-emptive action to strike a foe before it became powerful enough to be a threat.

For a very long time, naval activities were just as important as land warfare for achieving objectives. The transport of troops and arms, the supply of goods, and the denial of the use of the sea to opposing forces served the same ends as land combat. In some ways, naval operations were even more effective—the speed of advance could be greater than that of land-based soldiers, and retreat could often be achieved more effectively by sea than across enemy-held territory.

The Mediterranean Sea was particularly prone to maritime conflict, with many seafaring nations living in close proximity to each other. It was only natural that warfare would escalate from land onto water as territories clashed over resources and security.

ABOVE Xerxes, king of Persia, watches the Battle of Salamis. Despite superior numbers, the Persians were defeated by Greek forces, led by Themistocles.

BELOW The Spanish warship *Santissima Trinidad*, part of the combined French–Spanish force, surrenders to British ship *Neptune* during the Battle of Trafalgar, on October 1, 1805.

During the Middle Ages, naval power became increasingly important in many regions of the world, including Asia. Over the centuries, new kinds of ships were designed and constructed, not just to transport land forces to the scene of a battle, but also to engage directly with opposing fleets. Innovations in weaponry included primitive torpedoes and cannons. Many new combat techniques were developed, including ramming, hand-to-hand fighting, and firing broadsides from the extended lines of sailing ships.

Ships became heavier and more maneuverable. Navigational techniques improved as engine-powered propulsion took over from sail. More sophisticated weaponry was developed. In many ways, the history of sea warfare is also the history of technological change.

SMOKE ON THE WATER

History has seen some famous clashes between mighty naval forces, from the Battle of Salamis in 480 BCE—where fewer than 400 Greek ships defeated a Persian fleet of more than twice the size—to the internal Chinese conflicts of Red Cliffs in 208 CE, and Lake Poyang in 1363 CE, the latter involving over 100 ships and 800,000 personnel. The 1916 Battle of Jutland, where huge German and British fleets faced off, was the largest naval battle of World War I.

In terms of massive firepower, sea battles reached their peak in the World Wars of the twentieth century.

This was still the age of gun battles, where ships would blast away at each other, albeit at much greater ranges than in the days of sail and cannon. Many nations employed huge naval forces, able to project power in many places around the globe simultaneously. Intense battles took place at strategic points such as Leyte Gulf off the Philippines, the Coral Sea, Midway, and the North Atlantic. Entire military campaigns were won or lost on the ability of a navy to destroy an enemy's forces or deny them passage.

THE FUTURE OF NAVAL WARFARE

The last major ship-to-ship naval conflict took place during the Falklands War between Britain and Argentina in 1982. This can be partly explained by the fact that most of the world's military forces had allied with either the Soviet bloc or the western camp during the Cold War, with the prospect of major conflict between the two sides being too awful to contemplate. This deterrent effect, known as MAD ("mutually assured destruction"), was integral in successfully maintaining an uneasy peace during the Cold War.

In the twenty-first century, most nations are more concerned with protecting their own boundaries and resources, rather than starting fights far from home. Even in conflicts such as the Gulf War of 1990–1991, and the continuing campaigns in Afghanistan and Iraq, naval assets were employed mainly to attack land targets, and transport troops and supplies.

The power and precision of modern weaponry, such as sea-skimming anti-ship missiles launched from

ABOVE The Battle of Manila Bay, fought in the Philippines in May 1898, was part of the Spanish–American War, a conflict sparked by Cuba's efforts to achieve independence from Spain.

small fast ships, has greatly increased the likelihood of a kill. Navies therefore take great care not to jeopardize their highly expensive warships. While naval forces will always be an essential part of an overall defense capability, future sea battles are likely to be small, quick, surgical operations designed to prevent a enemy from achieving its larger aims.

Early Navies

Mighty empires of old relied on naval strength to protect and secure their borders and their trade. Unavoidably, a great many conflicts erupted between them. The areas encompassing modern-day Europe, the Mediterranean, and the Middle East were fertile areas for the establishment of naval forces. With numerous nations founded on coastlines, and bordering each other, it was natural that military activities would take to the water.

OPPOSITE The Battle of Mylae (Milazzo), in Sicily, was fought in 260 BCE during the First Punic War. Having destroyed about 50 Carthaginian ships, Rome was victorious, marking the start of their naval supremacy.

BELOW A Roman galley equipped with a corvus, a long hooked plank that could be dropped onto the deck of an enemy ship. This ingenious boarding device was used during the First Punic War.

One of those was the Phoenician civilization, which was based on the shores of the eastern Mediterranean, encompassing parts of modern-day Israel, Lebanon, and Syria. The Phoenicians were a seagoing people who traded with Europe and Africa using their galleys (oar- and sail-driven vessels). Although they enjoyed a lengthy period of ascendancy, they were eventually supplanted by Hellenistic Greece. However, their legacy lived on in their descendants in northern Africa—the Carthaginians.

THE ROMANS

The Romans were not originally a great naval power—their military force was centered on their infantry, or legions, with land warfare their specialty. During the early years of the republic they would often seek ships and crews from Greek city–states.

Yet in 265 BCE, Rome moved against Sicily and then Carthage. The Carthaginians had become the maritime rulers of the western Mediterranean, so Rome set about

building a fleet of 120 ships. These ships were equipped with a device known as a corvus—essentially a long plank with a hook on the far end—with which to snare enemy ships and provide a means for the centurions to board and take up hand-to-hand fighting. The corvus was later dropped in favor of a ram.

This period of combat with Carthage became known as the First Punic War (264–241 BCE). Initially the Romans were the underdogs, but they soon gained the upper hand. The Battle of Ecnomus, fought some time around 256 BCE, is considered to have been one of the largest sea battles in history, with almost 700 Roman and Carthaginian vessels taking part. The Romans won the day.

For the next few decades, Rome turned its attention elsewhere, notably becoming involved in the Illyrian Wars. However, in 218 BCE, Rome and Carthage once again locked horns, beginning the Second Punic War, which saw Hannibal lead his land force on an unprecedented overland march to the Italian peninsula. Throughout this war, Rome's naval forces were fully occupied both in protecting its homeland and with harassing Carthaginian shipping ventures along the North African coast. By 201 BCE, Rome was once again victorious and the war came to an end, by which time the Carthaginian fleet was disbanded.

Yet during this same period, Rome had also been in conflict with the Macedonians. The First Macedonian War (214–205 BCE) resulted in a stalemate, but the two sides would meet once again in the Second Macedonian War (200–197 BCE).

By the second half of the second century BCE, Rome had conquered the Mediterranean. Feeling safe, Rome reduced the size of its navy, and left much of the security work to her Greek allies.

ROME VERSUS THE PIRATES

This decision opened the door for piracy to take hold. And take hold it did—at one point, the pirate raiders made it as far as Ostia, Rome's main port. For more than a quarter of a century, Roman sea trade—especially the import of grain from Africa—was at the mercy of pirates. The Romans fought back, but it wasn't until the military leader Pompey was given special authority in 67 BCE that a large enough force was raised to conquer the pirates. Pompey's campaign to rid the region of pirates was successful.

THE GRADUAL DECLINE OF ROME'S NAVY

When civil war came to Rome in the last half of the first century BCE, naval forces attached to the different generals came into conflict with one another. The Battle of Actium (31 BCE), where a Roman force of 400 ships under Octavian fought with an Egyptian force of 500 ships under Mark Antony and Cleopatra, was the final battle of the Roman Republic's civil war, and at stake was the future of what would become the Roman Empire. Octavian was victorious and Rome's navy dominated the region for a long time to come.

Roman naval forces extended their reach far and wide, including into modern-day Britain. Skirmishes

BELOW This Roman mosaic, dates from c. second century BCE, and depicts a galley with a single bank of oars and two sails.

erupted in various parts of the empire over the coming centuries, but Rome retained its dominant position. Paradoxically, however, this was the beginning of its downfall, as Rome became complacent about its might. During the third century CE, the empire came under attack from all sides, and lost some very important parts of its territories.

Over the next two centuries, Roman naval forces declined in both number and expertise. By the fifth century CE, it was written that Rome no longer had a worthwhile navy in its Western sphere of influence. But in the East, Rome's Byzantine successors and their naval forces survived for many centuries.

Fighting Ships of Old

Warship design and technology evolved steadily throughout ancient times. The galley was the main naval combatant, comprising a narrow long vessel with rows of oars on either side. The purpose of a galley was to ram enemy ships, or it could be brought alongside to enable troops to board an enemy's vessel to conduct hand-to-hand combat. Catapults of various kinds were introduced in the fourth century BCE.

Galleys took various forms, such as the bireme, which had two sets of oars on either side. Triremes had three rows, one above the other. Other variations on the number of oars and oarsmen existed as well, such as quadriremes and quinqueremes, both of which were considered far superior vessels to triremes.

GREEK VICTORIES

Initially, Greek military ships were utilized solely for transporting the armies' troops to their many various destinations, but by around the middle of the seventh century BCE, they began to be used as warships to fight off the navies of their enemies.

The Greeks came into conflict with the Persians on a number of occasions, as Persia sought to extend its influence in the region. The Greeks realized that they would be outnumbered in a land battle, so they chose to build up their naval fleet. Persian forces were repulsed at the Battle of Marathon (490 BCE), and the Greeks had a decisive victory over a far larger Persian fleet at the Battle of Salamis in 480 BCE, when they fielded around 370 ships against the Persian fleet of over 1,200 vessels. Having tempted the Persians into battle in the tight confines of Straits of Salamis, the huge Persian fleet became disorganized, enabling the Greeks to attack and sink or capture 200 ships. The Persians thereafter withdrew.

The Peloponnesian War (431–404 BCE) saw Athens and Sparta fight ferociously. Athens was besieged on land, but kept its port open to supplies, safeguarded by its navy. The strategy was a success. But a quarter of a century later, in 405 BCE, the Athenian fleet was decimated—it had been drawn up on the beach and was a sitting duck for a surprise attack by the Spartan navy, which burned all the Athenian ships.

THE VIKINGS

Scandinavian raiders and pirates, the Vikings roamed northern waters for three centuries until the middle of the eleventh century CE. Their agile longships could be driven by both oar and sail, and carried them as far east as modern-day Russia, as far west as Greenland and Iceland, and even to North America. Rather than operating as a navy, Viking activities were led by individual chiefs. Their motives for expansion into surrounding territory are not known with certainty, but it is speculated that they had outgrown their coastal territories, and rather than clear areas of inland forest, it was easier to grab lands from weaker regions.

CHINESE CONFLICTS

The Mediterranean wasn't the only place where naval conflicts occurred. In China, several enormous naval battles took place, such as the Battle of Red Cliffs (also known as the Battle of Chibi) on the Yangtze River south of Wuhan in the winter of 208–209 CE. Pitted against each other were the naval forces of the northern warlord Cao Cao, and a combined force commanded by southern warlords Sun Quan and Liu Bei. The former is thought have fielded around 220,000–240,000 men, while the latter are believed to have had around 50,000 marines. The southern warlords won a surprising and decisive victory, proving that weight of numbers is not the only thing that counts in a naval war.

ABOVE The Battle of Actium, fought in 31 BCE, was a decisive battle in the Roman civil wars. The defeat of Mark Antony by Octavian effectively ended the Roman Republic. Octavian, who changed his name to Augustus, became Rome's first emperor.

The Royal Navy

The creation of Britain's Royal Navy dates from the time of King Alfred the Great in the ninth century. Formed to deal with Viking attacks, the navy became, of necessity, a semi-permanent service—it needed trained men and equipment in permanent readiness. As Britain did not have a standing army until Cromwell's time in the seventeenth century, but rather relied on trained bands of called-up personnel, the Royal Navy became the "Senior Service," its nickname today.

ABOVE Eleven centuries ago, to counter Viking attacks on England, Alfred the Great (849–899) built a small fleet of ships. From these modest beginnings grew the mighty Royal Navy.

EARLY BATTLES

In a history of over 1,000 years there have been many victories and defeats for the Royal Navy. One of the most notable early successes was the Battle of Sluys on June 24, 1340, when the English fleet won the day against a combined French, Castilian, and Genoese force. Although numbers vary, the English are said to have had around 400 ships, their enemy some 250. Other than a small number of large vessels such as *Christopher*, most of the ships were diminutive, carrying crews of around 25 sailors and fighting men.

One of the most famous battles the Royal Navy fought was against the Spanish Armada in 1588. The Spanish fleet sailed up the Channel, while the English forces under Admiral Howard held back, bombarding their enemy from the windward side. Fire-ships and a storm finished off the Spanish effort, leaving the stragglers to limp back to Spain.

During the seventeenth century, the navy grew rapidly. In 1642 when it declared itself for Parliament on the outbreak of the Civil War, it consisted of 35 vessels; in 1688 it numbered 151. Over the succeeding centuries, its enemies were mainly European, but its ships sailed all the world's oceans, and engaged not only in enlarging the British Empire, but also in furthering knowledge of hydrography, coastline charting, and contact with other nations.

A SAILOR'S LIFE

In popular fiction, British seamen are often depicted, inaccurately, as inhabiting a floating hell where they were routinely flogged, ate poor rations, and lived in appalling conditions. In reality, their lives compared not unfavorably with life ashore; at least they were given a steady diet and a daily allowance of beer, wine, or rum. Order was imposed by the Articles of War, and there was also the possibility of sudden wealth from prize money. They were often volunteers, but sometimes pressed, and they could be the victims of naval sharp practice—having their pay withheld to prevent them from deserting. They were generally loyal, but not above rebellion when severely mistreated, and although insurrection could be savagely repressed, in some circumstances, such as the Spithead Mutiny of 1797, food, medicine, and leave were all improved as a result.

Known as "the people," seamen were organized into three main groups according to skills—topmen who went aloft, idlers who performed basic laboring tasks on deck, and the mariners whose warrants recognized their higher skills and rendered them immune from flogging. These included the cooper who made barrels, the master gunner, the sail maker, and the carpenter. The sea-going soldiers known as marines were formally organized from 1740; by 1801 the Royal Marines numbered 30,000 of around 145,000 men within the Royal Navy. All men on board were expected to engage in combat when necessary, manning the guns or the sails, and boarding enemy vessels.

AN OFFICER'S DUTY

Officers were originally appointed because of their social status, but this gradually changed with more formalized training culminating in the lieutenants' exam. This started a midshipman on his way up the

LEFT The Battle of Sluys in 1340 resulted in a decisive victory for the English, who were pitted against the combined naval might of France, Castile, and Genoa.

promotion ladder. Lieutenants were rated according to their seniority. A first rate ship of the line might have six or more, who commanded sections of the ship, usually gundecks, in battle. A lieutenant's aim was to be given a command, often of a prize, especially one that might see him promoted "master and commander" of the vessel, and eventually to be made a post-captain.

As well as officers who were primarily connected with the sea and command, there were several others who were also welcome in the wardroom—the officers' mess—because of their skills and status, the ship's surgeon being a notable example, as well as the chaplain, when one was carried.

The Admiralty expected a great deal of its officers: Admiral Russell's *Sailing and Fighting Instructions* of 1691 emphasized a number of doctrinal tactics, but these were no substitute for leadership, courage, and initiative. Mistakes such as groundings could lead to being beached and reverting to half-pay. Cowardice in the face of the enemy or even failing to do one's utmost could result in being immediately struck off the Navy

List, or worse: Admiral John Byng was shot on his own quarterdeck in 1757 for this latter offence.

THE CHANGING NAVY

In the eighteenth century, the American Revolution set cousin against cousin, and the Royal Navy was to fight again against the United States in 1812. But a titanic struggle against the French dominated the Navy for decades. Trafalgar was a victory comparable to the defeat of the Armada centuries before, and enabled the defeat of Napoleon at Waterloo a decade later.

The change from sail to steam following Trafalgar saw the lessening of reliance on muscle power and a growth in skilled sailors. A seaman of the 1600s would have been at home on a Trafalgar ship, but he would have been completely mystified by *HMS Warrior*, the fleet's first iron warship. Shells had replaced solid shot, vessels could move without wind power, and the guns were housed in rotating turrets. But it was not until the completion of *HMS Dreadnought* in 1906 that the shape of major warships was set.

ABOVE The great Spanish Armada, constructed with the aim of overthrowing Queen Elizabeth I of England in 1588, was unable to defeat English naval forces.

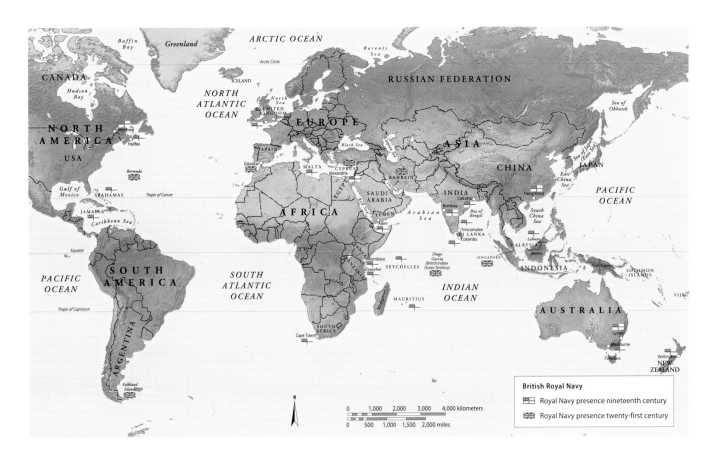

British Royal Navy

Royal Navy presence nineteenth century

Royal Navy presence twenty-first century

The Royal Navy was characterized not only by major battles in the nineteenth century, but also by protection of colonies. The Navy also battled against slavery after the British government declared it illegal, and was a key agent in the war against piracy.

TWENTIETH-CENTURY ROLE

World War I saw the Royal Navy in yet another great battle—at Jutland in 1916— but it was not the next Trafalgar. A tactical victory for the German Navy, it was a strategic one for the British, as they kept command of the seas for the rest of the war.

After the war, the battleship reigned supreme, but the use of naval aviation had proved so useful that aircraft carriers were employed by the Royal Navy with guarded enthusiasm. The Royal Navy entered World War II under-equipped—naval spending had been neglected, and personnel numbered 89,000, compared with 380,000 in 1919. Early campaigns showed a lack of understanding of the latest military technology—the carrier *Glorious* was lost off Norway along with her two destroyers, with not one aircraft flying in support. The lack of anti-air defense led to the losses of *HMS Repulse* and *Prince of Wales* early in the war against Japan.

Although it is popularly supposed that the Battle of Britain, fought in the skies by fighters against bombers, saved Britain, in reality during 1940 the German army could not have crossed the Channel with the Royal Navy afloat in such strength.

In the majority of surface engagements, the Royal Navy was successful. It engaged with the Italian fleet on several opportunities, with an especially telling engagement at Taranto in November 1940, when the Fleet Air Arm proved its value. The victorious engagement against battleship *SMS Scharnhorst* in December 1943 was the last big-gun engagement between such surface units in the Navy's history.

In 1944, there was a new effort by U-boat wolf-packs but the Royal Navy eventually overcame the submarine threat by a combined approach of aircraft carrier-escorted patrols. They were backed up by skilled surface work, complemented by Coastal Command's long-range Anti-Submarine Warfare aircraft. The Arctic convoys were undertaken in freezing and perilous conditions, but the Royal Navy ensured the safe passage of vital materials for the Russian Eastern Front.

RIGHT The forward guns and bridge of *HMS Queen Elizabeth*, a dreadnought battleship and the flagship of the British fleet, at Gallipoli in the Dardenelles in 1915 during World War I.

In the latter stage of the war, scores of vessels were employed in the Pacific against the Japanese, the Royal Navy carriers, with their armored flight decks, having an advantage over the US Navy's timber equivalents.

AFTER WORLD WAR II

Following the war, there was a steady decline of force units, but the Royal Navy continued to evolve. Innovations such as the angled flight deck and the catapult appeared on carriers. The Navy embraced the nuclear age, with reactors both for power—the Royal Navy submarine fleet eventually became entirely nuclear-powered—and weapons.

The Falklands War in 1982 saw the culmination of centuries of fighting skill—a Royal Navy task force centered around two carriers sailed some 6,000 miles (9,650 km), fought off attacks from a missile-equipped enemy, and made a successful amphibious assault to take back the Argentine-occupied islands. However, it was a near-run thing. The then British government had decided to divest the Navy of aircraft carriers, but basing the task force around the remaining two meant that the loss of one would have denied the necessary air coverage for the landings.

The British withdrawal from colonial possessions saw a gradual naval retraction from overseas basing. In

the twenty-first century, the Royal Navy maintains a presence in the Falkland Islands, Diego Garcia (in the Indian Ocean), Cyprus, and Gibraltar, with some smaller facilities in Singapore, Bermuda, and Bahrain.

The force has become more balanced with a wider range of roles. It is now formed around two 66,000-ton (60,000 tonne) aircraft carriers—the largest vessels ever operated by the Royal Navy.

Great Britain's respected Royal Navy is the oldest navy in the world, and it certainly retains its position as one of the world's most professional navies.

ABOVE HMS Invincible, an anti-submarine aircraft carrier, was launched in 1977.

TOP A British submarine chaser, c. 1939. These small vessels were intended for anti-submarine engagements, and were used to patrol coastal areas.

European Navies

When Christopher Columbus set foot on San Salvador in 1492, he heralded in a new age of European sail. With the opening up of the New World, the majestic European fleets became the sinews of trade and empire. Portugal, Spain, France, the Netherlands, and England—Europe's maritime powers— were poised to take advantage of this discovery.

OPPOSITE The French flagship *Redoutable* at the Battle of Trafalgar in 1805. This major naval action saw the French soundly defeated by the English, who were commanded by the famous admiral, Lord Nelson.

BELOW In June 1667, Dutch naval forces made a successful raid on a major English naval base on the Medway River near Chatham. The victorious Dutch attack precipitated the end of the Second Anglo–Dutch War.

Land trade routes from the East were monopolized by the Ottoman Empire, and the mark-up on goods paid by the western European countries was prohibitive. Economic opportunity in the New World beckoned Europe's seafaring nations.

SPAIN

While Portugal initially sailed south and east, Spain, the financer of Columbus's journeys, took the lion's share of the New World. It took the mineral wealth of this vast empire, then packed it away for transit across the Atlantic to Europe. It was the value of the cargo of the famous Spanish "treasure fleets" that attracted unwelcome attention from other parties. Piracy was already rife in the Caribbean when Elizabeth I of England began to hand out Letters of Marque. These documents gave selected pirates a free hand to attack Spanish trade shipping as privateers in English employ. Francis Drake was the most famous privateer; in 1581 he brought half a million pounds' worth of Spanish loot back to England, and was promptly knighted.

In 1588, in a gallant attempt to put an end to these activities, Phillip II of Spain resolved to invade England, and amassed a fleet of 130 vessels carrying over 2,000 guns and 26,000 men. The Spanish Armada

sailed into the English Channel and anchored off Calais, waiting to launch its invasion. The English scared the Armada out of port with fire-ships, and then attacked it near Gravelines, between Calais and Dunkirk. Scattered by this engagement, the remnants of the Spanish Armada fled north, then west into the North Atlantic, before returning to Spain. With that test of arms, Spanish sea power was shattered.

THE DUTCH REPUBLICS

At the same time that Spain was counting on the success of the Armada, the Dutch were securing their independence from Spain. By the late seventeenth century, the Dutch controlled a vast trading empire, much of which it had taken from Portugal, the Hanseatic League, and Spain. The Dutch owned few imperial possessions, but they were spread far and wide, from New Amsterdam in North America to Indonesia in the Pacific. As Dutch merchants became rich carrying trade goods between the East Indies and Europe, it was England that laid down a naval challenge by passing the Navigation Act of 1651, which banned foreign ships from carrying trade into English ports. A series of naval conflicts between the Dutch Republics and England soon followed, culminating in the Dutch sailing a fleet into the Thames estuary and burning seven English ships. This action secured the repeal of the Navigation Acts.

In 1688, the English Parliament's dislike of the Catholic monarch, James II, caused it to invite the Dutch William of Orange and his wife Mary—James's Protestant daughter—to "invade" England. They sailed across the English Channel with an army and James capitulated without a fight. However, Dutch sea power eventually diminished after the Dutch Republics became entrenched in war with France from 1672 to 1678. Money earmarked to maintain its powerful fleet was spent instead on the army.

FRANCE

France had aligned itself with James II against both the Dutch and the English in the war of English succession. As the Dutch receded as a threat, England and France readied themselves for another clash of arms. France had established its empire late, but thanks to the reforms of Jean-Baptiste Colbert, France took possession of much of what is now the eastern United States, as well as the east coast of India. Throughout the 1700s, France clashed with England in Europe, the Caribbean,

and the Indian Ocean. The French sided with the Americans during their revolt against England.

However, the French navy was bedeviled by two significant problems. First, with both Atlantic and Mediterranean coastlines, it was forced to split its fleet. Second, as a continental land power, France was also less reliant on maritime trade than its rivals. Unlike Britain and the Dutch, France did not have a large merchant marine and its navy was often lacking in experienced seamen. After the French Revolution, Napoleon attempted to reform the navy into a powerful fighting force. Although he had many ships, the revolution had stripped him of his most skilled officers, many of whom were nobles. After Trafalgar in 1805, the French navy was in decline, and the seas belonged to the British Empire for the next century.

RIGHT The capture of the French frigate *La Réunion* by the English ship *HMS Crescent* on October 20, 1793. France had declared war on Britain in February of that year.

The Chinese Navy

As a vast land empire, China was unaccustomed to the need for a navy. The Silk Road was a well-established and lucrative overland trade route to Europe. Threats of invasion from the north and west were usually far more pressing than from the sea. Successive Chinese emperors flirted with naval reform, but thought only of the needs of the moment, and allowed the navy to slip into decline when it was no longer useful.

OPPOSITE Chinese emperor Yang Ti is shown riding through the Grand Canal in China, in this painting on silk dated to around the eighteenth century.

FIRST NAVIES

The Song Dynasty established the first standing navy in 1132. The Mongols were invading from the north, supporting their ground troops with substantial sea power. Kublai Khan eventually conquered China, beginning the Yuan Dynasty. The Chinese turned inland, constructing a series of canals to facilitate land trade. The navy, along with the many coastal provinces, was allowed to decline.

The Ming Dynasty, which replaced the Yuan, faced a number of new problems. China's sea trade routes extended east to Java and west to the Middle East. By

RIGHT Timur, the great Muslim leader, is shown enthroned in this Arab script dated to around 1563. Timur died during a winter campaign against the Ming Dynasty, and his tomb still stands in Samarkand, Uzbekistan.

the 1380s, pirates were rife, operating from bases in Japan and Vietnam. The Ming emperors set up trading licenses to prevent Japanese pirates selling stolen goods in Chinese ports. The Chinese invaded Vietnam in 1406 in order to quell the pirates. These measures did not prove sufficient to protect merchant shipping against piracy, so the Ming emperors were forced to reform and rebuild the navy.

GREAT EXPEDITIONS

The Ming emperor Yongle (or Chengzhu) was faced with problems beyond piracy. The Muslim warlord Timur the Lame had conquered most of Asia, and was slowing the trade to Europe through Asia Minor along the Silk Road. Timur's 200,000-strong horde was too great even for China, so the Chinese turned again to maritime trade. Yongle ordered construction of a huge number of vast "treasure ships"—powerful warships with spacious holds that would sail along China's existing sea trade routes as a show of strength.

A number of now famous maritime expeditions occurred under the command of Admiral Cheng Ho, traveling as far afield as Africa, the Middle East, and Southeast Asia.

After Timur died and his empire wasted away, the Chinese focused again on land trade routes. In 1411 the Grand Canal, largest of the inland highways, reopened, revitalizing inland trade and redirecting ships and sailors away from the coast. Another protracted war in Vietnam, and another invasion by the resurgent Mongols in the 1420s, reinforced the Chinese belief that the army was more essential than the navy. The old doctrine of ignoring the coast in favor of the inland empire meant that, once again, China's navy was allowed to waste away.

OPIUM WARS AND FOREIGN INTERVENTION

The next naval threat to China was a long time coming, but was the most substantial yet. In 1839, China went to war with the Royal Navy. The British had found the Chinese prickly trading partners—the Chinese would only accept silver in return for their goods, and the British could only trade through Chinese government intermediaries, not directly with their customers. They started paying for goods in opium, shipped over from India. The Chinese tried to ban this arrangement, and their action precipitated war with Britain. British ironclads and guns were vastly superior to the almost non-existent Chinese navy.

BELOW The port of Foo Chow was one of the first ports opened for trade after the Treaty of Nanjing in 1842.

The Treaty of Nanjing in 1842 that ended the first Opium War gave Britain improved trading rights with China. Additional treaties soon followed with France and the USA, and eventually with Germany, Russia, and Japan. These treaties gave the foreign powers a free hand in China and helped topple the weakened Qing Dynasty. It was the lack of naval power that left China so exposed to foreign nations and with the need to make treaties. This was a telling blow and it was not until after 1948 that China could once again look to rebuilding a modern navy.

The Dowager Empress's Marble Boat

In the closing years of the nineteenth century, the Qing Dynasty was ruled by the Dowager Empress Cixi. In 1893 she was overseeing the restoration of the Summer Palace in Beijing, which had been destroyed by Anglo–French forces during the Opium Wars. There was an elegant, wooden pavilion built out into one of the lakes in the palace grounds. It was shaped like a boat, and the Dowager Empress was able to convince the First Prince Chun, Controller of the Admiralty, to grant her money from naval funds to restore the "boat." It was painted to look like marble, hence the name "the Marble Boat." This incident highlights the corruption of late imperial China, and also the indifferent approach by Chinese officials to maritime affairs.

Pirates and Buccaneers

Pirates of old bore no allegiance to a sovereign nation, but plundered the sea at will, paying no heed to nationality. Buccaneer was the name given to backwoodsmen on the island of Haiti in the mid-1600s. It came to be applied to the mainly English and French raiders of the Spanish territories in the Caribbean basin, and northern coast of South America—the Spanish Main.

PRIVATEERS

In addition to pirates and buccaneers, there were the privateers; among the most famous of these were Sir Walter Raleigh and Sir Francis Drake. Privateers were "legitimate" pirates, in that they captained privately owned warships, and carried a Letter of Marque (a commission) authorizing them to attack merchant (or military) vessels of an enemy nation in times of war.

The Barbarossa ("red beard") brothers, Aruj ad Din and Khair ad Din were Turkish Muslim privateers who attacked Spanish ships and holdings in the Mediterranean region in the early sixteenth century. They had started as pirates, plundering Spanish riches and

BELOW Khair ad Din, one of the Barbarossa brothers, Turkish privateers whose main targets were Spanish vessels carrying gold and other treasures. Khair later became an admiral in the Ottoman navy.

territories on their own behalf, but in 1517 they agreed to assign their assets, including Algiers, to the Ottoman Sultanate in return for soldiers, ships, and armaments. Aruj ad Din was killed in 1518, but Khair continued his successful plundering on land and sea, often attaching sails to cannons to power them across land. In 1532, he was granted command over the Ottoman holdings in North Africa, including Algiers, as well as several Mediterranean islands. He fought the Spanish until his death in 1546 in Istanbul.

Welshman Henry Morgan, one of the most formidable Caribbean pirates, traveled to British Jamaica following Oliver Cromwell's 1655 invasion of Wales. In 1662, he was named commander of a privateering vessel, and attacked Spanish shipping and towns along Mexico's Yucatan Peninsula. His band of bloodthirsty brigands tortured and killed anyone who stood in their way. Morgan befriended the governor of Jamaica, Sir Thomas Modyford, who supplied him with ships, troops, and governmental authority. In 1671, he looted a Spanish fortress in San Lorenzo, Panama, but by then Britain and Spain were at peace. Modyford was soon dismissed, and the following year the new governor arrested Morgan and sent him to England. But Morgan had friends in high places. He was not imprisoned; instead he managed to have the governor replaced. He was also knighted and installed as Jamaican deputy-governor. He served until 1682, without returning to his buccaneering ways, and was buried with full military honors in 1688.

William Kidd made only one voyage and achieved only one plunder, but he caused a major political scandal. He was employed by the British governor of New York as a privateer, charged with hunting pirates (and the French) in the Indian Ocean. In January 1698, Kidd attacked and plundered the *Queddah Merchant*, which, unfortunately for him, was carrying cargo for the British-owned East India Company. He returned to Boston where he attempted to make a deal with the governor, but he was branded a pirate, arrested, and shipped to England in chains. The opposition tried to make him reveal his secret backers in Parliament, and the government narrowly avoided a political disaster by "losing" incriminating documents. The case was dropped, but by now Kidd was a dangerous liability to the government; it tried and convicted him of murder and piracy. He was executed in 1701, and his body placed in a cage on the banks of the Thames as a warning to budding pirates.

ABOVE Pirates attack an English vessel. They were not always after "treasure." Often they stole essential supplies such as food, clothing, and weapons.

LEFT English privateer and adventurer Sir Francis Drake attacks a Spanish treasure ship. Privateers were given official sanction by their governments to sack and plunder enemy vessels during times of war.

PIRATES OF THE CARIBBEAN

Blackbeard is perhaps the most infamous pirate of all
time. Blackbeard's real name was Edward Teach, or
perhaps Drummond, and his hunting ground was
the Caribbean and southern North America, where he
plundered English naval ships and French vessels. His
career was short, beginning in 1716, and ending when
he was killed in a duel with an English pirate-hunter
in 1718. His nickname comes from the burning hemp
twine he twisted into his hair and beard, thus impart-
ing a further intimidating air of ferocity to his generally
fearsome demeanor. He fought with six pistols slung
around his neck, and was wont to assert his authority
by occasionally shooting one of his own crew members.

In the early eighteenth century, English buccaneers
Jack Rackham and Anne Bonny sailed the Caribbean

and Atlantic in *Revenge*, concentrating their piratical
efforts on smaller, poorly defended vessels. Anne had
been unhappily married to another pirate, James
Bonny, and jumped at the chance to escape for a life of
adventure with Jack. They captured a transatlantic ship,
one of whose passengers was Mary Read, traveling to
England dressed as a man in an attempt to claim an
inheritance. She had been serving in the English navy,
but was happy to hook up with the pirates. In 1720,
Revenge was ambushed, and the crew captured by the
pirate-hunter Jonathan Barnett. The men were in a
rum-induced stupor and too drunk to resist, but the
women gave a good account of themselves before being
overwhelmed and taken prisoner. The women were so
disgusted at the inability of their male colleagues to
mount a defense that they shot several of them just
before their capture. Jack was sentenced to death, but
the women were spared because they were (or claimed
they were) pregnant. Mary died in prison shortly
afterward, but Anne escaped, and after learning that
Jack Bonny had been killed, she later married Dr
Michael Radcliffe. She did not return to piracy.

OFF THE COAST OF AFRICA

Edward England plundered the African coast and
Indian Ocean from 1717 to 1720. Unlike most pirates,
he rarely killed his victims. He built up a large fleet of
captured ships, although he allowed others to depart
after robbing them. Most of his targets were English,
or vessels belonging to the Dutch East India Company.
In 1720, his crew mutinied after he refused to kill
members of the captured English trading boat *Cassan-
dra*, marooning him on the island of Mauritius. He
managed to build a raft and escape to Madagascar,
but died of starvation in 1720.

Bartholomew Roberts ("Black Bart") was a Welsh
buccaneer who plundered Portuguese convoys off the
coast of Africa, then English fishing fleets off Newfoundland, before heading to the Caribbean where he
attacked anything he could find. Black Bart returned
to Africa, capturing numerous European slave ships
bound for the New World. In a highly successful career
lasting only 30 months (June 1719 to February 1722),
he captured more than 200 ships. Most unusually for
a member of his profession, Roberts did not swear,
always observed the Sabbath, and drank nothing
stronger than tea. His agreement with his crew stated:
"The musicians shall have rest on the Sabbath Day only
by right. On all other days by favor only."

Black Bart was killed during a skirmish with British
warship *HMS Swallow* off the coast of French Equatorial Africa (now Gabon) in 1722.

THE JOLLY ROGER

The pirate flag was used to intimidate a prospective
victim or enemy into surrender. If the potential enemy
ship could be coerced to heave-to, danger to the pirate
crew would be diminished, and the ship and bounty

could be taken intact, thus increasing its value. It was an integral part of a pirate's psychological warfare, especially if he (or she) had a reputation for being totally ruthless. The first-known record of the classic "skull and crossbones" appears in 1700, when French privateer Emmanuelle Wynne displayed a black flag featuring a skull, two crossbones, and an hour-glass. This was also the first-known use of the term "Jolly Roger." Until then, privateers often displayed a red flag alongside their national flag. The French named this flag Jolie Rouge ("Pretty Red"), which probably evolved over time into "Jolly Roger."

Various different symbols were used on the Jolly Roger, including complete skeletons, dancing skeletons, spears, swords or crossed swords, wings, hearts, and raised drinking glasses. In an era where emblematic art was commonplace, these images carried a symbolism that was immediately apparent to all. Raised glasses were a toast to death, weapons signified imminent slaughter, dancing skeletons indicated that the flag-flyer was unconcerned about his own life and thus fearless, wings and hourglasses denoted the passing (or flying) of time—and the victim's life! All the symbols featured in contemporary allegorical paintings and gravestones.

ABOVE Dutch ships encounter Barbary pirates in the seventeenth century. Barbary pirates were privateers based in northern African ports such as Tunis, Tripoli, and Algiers, an area known as the Barbary Coast.

Pirate Songs

Pirates, along with more legitimate seafarers, employed a variety of songs to raise morale and help ease the burden of the numerous arduous and tedious tasks required to keep a ship afloat. These "sea shanties" were usually chanted rather than sung, the repeated words of the chorus accompanied by a repetitive action such as a "heave" to raise an anchor. One famous example is quoted in Scottish author Robert Louis Stevenson's 1883 novel *Treasure Island*:

> *Fifteen men on a dead man's chest,*
> *Yo ho ho and a bottle of rum!*
> *Drink and the devil had done for the rest,*
> *Yo ho ho and a bottle of rum!*

The "fifteen men" were members of Edward (Blackbeard) Teach's crew. He left them stranded on "Dead Man's Chest"—a tiny Caribbean island in the British Virgin Islands group—as punishment for attempted mutiny and desertion.

LEFT A map of Treasure Island as envisioned by the Scottish writer Robert Louis Stevenson for his famous book of the same name, first published in 1883. The pirate protagonist, Long John Silver, is one of the most recognizable characters in English literature.

Piracy in East Asia

When we think of piracy, we tend to imagine well-known pirates like Blackbeard, the skull and crossbones flag, and European-built galleons manned with heavy cannons. However, East Asia has historically been one of the most active centers of world piracy.

For approximately 400 years—from 1250 to 1650—groups of pirates based in Japan terrorized the waters of East Asia, and the coastlines of Korea and China. So notorious did these pirates become, that Japan started to appear on contemporary maps as Ilhas dos Ladrones, or the Isle of Pirates.

DWARF RAIDERS

Within East Asia, these pirates are usually referred to by a two-character compound word that is pronounced as *wakô* in Japanese, *waegu* in Korean, and *wokou* in Chinese. The first part of the compound (wa) can be translated literally as "dwarf," but in this period it was used primarily as a derogatory term for the Japanese people. The second part, kô, means "robber," "raider," or "pirate." Put together, the word *wakô* is normally translated as "Japanese pirates," or sometimes as "dwarf raiders." In fact, these groups may have been based in Japan, but they were essentially multi-ethnic, consisting of Chinese, Japanese, and Korean mariners. They have been referred to as marginal men, as it would appear that they existed on the maritime peripheries of East

Asian society. As such, they moved freely across the region, sailed in hybrid vessels that joined multiple shipbuilding traditions together, and may have developed their own language for easy communication.

The initial impetus for piracy was a prolonged drought and resultant famine in Japan. The first groups of pirates came from Kyushu. One Korean envoy who visited the island in 1444 wrote that "the people's dwellings are miserable; land is ... utterly barren, so that they do not pursue agriculture and can scarcely escape starvation." Although the first pirates were probably desperate peasants, they were quickly succeeded by more organized groups eager to pillage. Wakô groups were aided by a collapse in central authority in Japan, which enabled them to operate without fear of government punishment.

ASIAN VIKINGS

European pirates based in the Atlantic and the Caribbean used powerful cannons that enabled them to bombard their targets from a safe distance before boarding. Wakô pirate groups, who relied on light weapons like swords and bows, did engage in ship-to-ship warfare, but they typically used their vessels for transport rather than as platforms of attack. Once they had landed, wakô bands besieged vulnerable settlements, bringing their plunder back to their ships. Because of this tactic, they have been called the Vikings of the Far East.

Although piracy continued at a low level for four centuries, there were two clear peaks of activity in the fourteenth and sixteenth centuries. The first surge of pirate activity was directed against Korea. In 1373, one dismayed Korean official sent the following report to his superiors: "[Since 1350], Japanese pirates have raided continuously. Troops are sent to pursue and capture them, but the troops have not yet been able to seize and restrain them. Within recent years their violence has increased greatly ... Coastal prefectures

BELOW A sixteenth-century European illustrated map of the Isle of the Pirates, the name by which Japan was known. Piracy in East Asia was rampant for around 400 years.

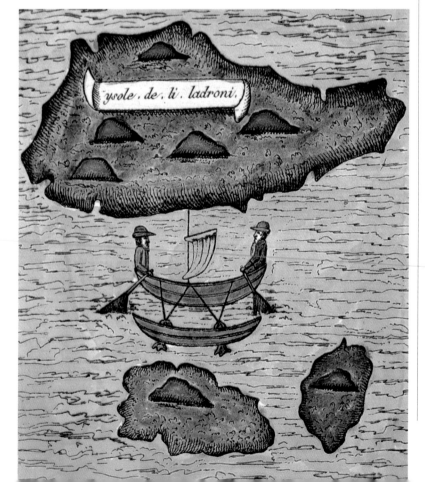

ysole. de. li. ladroni.

and subprefectures, near and far, are agitated. They have twice invaded the capital area. There is no place for which they have any respect or dread."

WANG ZHI

In the sixteenth century, the wakô started to launch attacks against the Chinese coast. The most famous pirate captain of this period was Wang Zhi, a Chinese commander who was known in Japan as the "king of Hui." Wang established his base in Hirado, a small port in Japan that was transformed from a minor fishing village into a global center for piracy. Wang used the wealth earned from piracy to build up a huge force of ships and sailors that he then employed in devastating raids against his homeland.

ANTI-PIRACY TACTICS

As the Chinese government's anti-piracy measures became increasingly successful in the 1560s, the wakô started to voyage to Southeast Asia, where they became well known for their reckless violence.

An English captain, who encountered a group of these pirates in 1605, wrote that "the Japons are not suffered to land in any Port in India with weapons: being accounted a people so desperate and daring, that they are feared in all places where they come." These far-ranging attacks proved to be the last phase of wakô activity. The Tokugawa regime, which assumed power in Japan around 1600, moved to suppress the wakô, bringing at last a conclusive end to four centuries of organized piracy in Japan.

ABOVE A Portuguese ship arrived in Tanegashima, Kyushu, Japan, in 1543, where, some sources suggest, it was boarded by Chinese-born pirate Wang Zhi, thus marking an early contact between Europe and Japan.

Modern Piracy

With more ships plying the seas than ever before, and with war, famine, and disadvantage creating discord in many parts of the world, recent years have seen a rise in maritime piracy. When one thinks of pirates, images of swashbuckling figures, buried treasure, and majestic sailing ships bristling with rows of cannon come to mind. But today piracy is rife in many regions, and there's nothing swashbuckling about it.

BELOW Following its release by Somali pirates, *MV Golden Nori* refuels with the US Navy dock-landing ship *USS Whidbey Island*. *Whidbey Island* was deployed in support of Maritime Security Operations.

Modern pirates have become increasingly sophisticated in their methods, equipment, and operations. They are heavily armed, often carrying automatic weapons and rocket-propelled grenades. They operate in small, very fast boats, sometimes launched from mother ships, giving them the ability to conduct their activities far from shore—and for victims, far from the possibility of any assistance.

Piracy has destructive consequences, including financial losses arising from ransoms, increased insurance premiums, counterpiracy operations, stolen and damaged vessels, and interruption to shipping schedules. There are also more serious immediate consequences, such as injury or death to hostages, rescuers, or the pirates themselves.

Reported rates of piracy incidents decreased during the early 2000s, reaching a plateau in 2007. Authorities attribute this to better countermeasures employed by shipping operators, as well as the direct involvement of naval forces for protection. But now piracy is once more on the rise.

PIRACY HOTSPOTS

There are several regions where piracy has become a critical problem. The waters off Somalia in Africa are perhaps the worst hotspot, but piracy also occurs in many parts of Asia, such as the Strait of Malacca and the South China Sea. Pirates operate in the Mediterranean Sea, off the northern coastline of the African continent. Piracy has also been a serious problem in the Caribbean Sea, but vigorous antipiracy operations by various countries' authorities have seen rates of piracy fall quite dramatically, although drug-running by boat remains a major concern.

In the Gulf of Aden, armed pirates have been boarding ships and sailing them to the Somali coast, where they demand a ransom for the release of the crew and vessel. Many ransoms have been paid by shipping companies, who often consider it easier and cheaper to give in than to risk the loss of their vessels, cargo, and crews.

High-profile examples of piracy include the seizure of the largest vessel so far, the supertanker *MV Sirius Star* carrying US$100 million of crude oil. Seized by Somali pirates off the coast of Kenya in November 2008, it was eventually released on January 9, 2009, after a ransom was paid. The pirates tried to escape in a small boat, but it capsized and five drowned.

Another notable recent example was the capture of the *MV Maersk Alabama*, a large cargo ship carrying emergency relief supplies for Kenya, Somalia, and Uganda. An altercation between *Maersk Alabama*'s

LEFT Armed Somali pirates stand on the bow of the merchant vessel *MV Faina* after a US Navy request to check the welfare of the ship's crew who were being held as ransom.

crew and the pirates saw the latter take to a covered lifeboat with the ship's captain as hostage. A US Navy destroyer arrived on the scene and, after a few days of tense standoff, the pirates were killed by US Navy Seal snipers when they believed the captain's life was in danger. He was rescued safely.

FIGHTING BACK

What can be done to deter or prevent piracy? In recent times, various navies have begun operating warships in piracy-prone areas, sometimes escorting convoys of ships to their destinations. Two task forces maintain a permanent presence in the Horn of Africa region, and off the Somali coast. But even this protection has failed to deter some pirates.

Shipping companies carry out various strategies to protect against attacks. Captains are advised to increase speed and take a zigzag course in order to evade fast boats. Firefighting water cannon are often used, and ropes and nets are sometimes trailed in an attempt to foul propellers.

More sophisticated measures include a device called Secure-Ship, a 9,000-volt electric fence surrounding the ship. Another device emits a very concentrated sound blast, which is used to warn pirates at a distance, and to harass and deter them at close range with a painful, deafening pulse of noise. In addition, satellite tracking systems send out a signal notifying a ship's owner of a vessel's whereabouts at all times.

The International Maritime Bureau maintains an antipiracy unit that gives advice to operators and maintains a 24-hour hotline for operators to report acts of piracy.

ABOVE A Landing Craft Air Cushion (LCAC) comes ashore on a beach during exercises in the Gulf of Aden. The *USS Boxer* Expeditionary Strike Group is supporting Combined Task Force-151 that is conducting antipiracy operations in the Gulf.

SEA BATTLES

Although the nature of naval warfare has changed over the centuries, the fundamentals remain the same—the use of surprise and firepower to achieve political and territorial ends. The fate of many a nation has rested upon the fortunes of naval warfare.

Conflict on the waters has accompanied the growth of empires and the pursuit of scarce resources, as well as being used as defense from such opportunism. Although there have been changes in sea warfare over the centuries, much remains the same. Sea power has been used to transport troops for land battles, resupply those troops, and defeat opposing fleets to clear the way for land forces to take territory.

WEATHERING THE STORM
Weather often played a major role in ancient sea battles. In the era of oared vessels and sailing ships, a capricious wind or tide could spell disaster. Conversely, a change in the weather could lead to a victory, or perhaps an escape. The introduction of powered vessels saw the influence of weather diminish, although often it was still a factor. For instance, weather can play havoc with radar, and provide cover—ships can "hide" under clouds to avoid detection by aircraft or even satellites.

THE GOLDEN AGE OF SAIL
Some of the mightiest sea battles occurred during what is sometimes called the golden age of sail. Vast opposing forces would meet in close proximity to blast away furiously with cannon and smaller weapons. The English, French, and Spanish operated large armadas, which often came into conflict with one another.

Naval warfare played a major role in the American Revolutionary War (1775–1783), when American privateers and naval ships, sometimes in league with French, Spanish, or Dutch naval forces, harassed England's Royal Navy and made it difficult for the English to supply its land-based troops.

A famous sailing ship battle took place in 1805 off Cape Trafalgar in Spain, when the English fleet led by Admiral Lord Nelson fought a combined Spanish and French fleet led by French Admiral Pierre Villeneuve. The English emerged victorious, losing not a single ship; their opponents lost 22 vessels.

THE TWENTIETH CENTURY
The two world wars of the twentieth century saw an enormous use of sea power and many large naval battles. Although this was still a time of ship versus ship, or fleet versus fleet, the range of modern guns meant that the fights could be conducted at a greater distance. The world's ocean floors are littered with the remains of vanquished ships and their crews.

Sea battles also marked some of the major turning points in the course of those wars. If Japan had been victorious at Midway, the Pacific war might have lasted much longer. If the Allies had not been victorious in the Coral Sea, Australia might easily have been invaded. If the German U-boat menace had not been negated in the Atlantic and North Sea, at great cost, Britain may have fallen to the Nazis.

THE MODERN ERA
The nature of naval warfare has changed in the modern era. No longer do vast opposing forces line up within visual range of each other, to blast away with guns and torpedoes. Today's naval warfare is much more remote, and it is rare for naval vessels to come into direct conflict—such proximate actions are now generally confined to smaller vessels operating in littoral waters where, for instance, border disputes get out of hand. Recent examples include the small actions in the Iran–Iraq War (1980–1988), and the conflict in Sri Lanka between government forces and the Tamil Tigers.

Navies now rely on long-range weapons to accomplish their goals. Surface-to-air and surface-to-surface missiles can eliminate foes over the horizon many miles away; cruise missiles can attack targets hundreds of miles away.

Since World War II, aircraft carriers have been the kings of the sea, able to project massive firepower for hundreds of miles in every direction. A carrier task force is the most potent power afloat, able to take on all comers. Below the surface, long-range submarines are silent killers, able to remain submerged and undetected for months at a time.

The modern navies of large countries are most concerned with the protection of shipping routes and the projection of military might in distant regions. And although naval warfare has always relied upon surprise, precision, and overwhelming force to gain advantage, the modern navies can achieve their aims at greater distances and with deadlier firepower than ever before.

LEFT Clouds of smoke engulf a burning tanker hit by an Iranian rocket in December 1987 during the Iran–Iraq War.

RIGHT The Battle of Trafalgar, 1805, as depicted by Joseph Turner in his painting. Nelson's semaphore message to his fleet was: "England expects that every man will do his duty."

BELOW RIGHT *USS Louisville*, a *Los Angeles*-class submarine, conducted war patrols during Operation Desert Storm against Iraq. It was the first American submarine to launch Tomahawk cruise missiles in combat.

BELOW British warships landing their troops in the old town of Boston, USA, are shown here in an engraving by the famed Paul Revere. He is honored as a patriot for his role in alerting John Hancock and Samuel Adams of the impending movement of British troops.

Battle of Salamis

The Battle of Salamis in September 480 BCE saw the Persian navy suffer a defeat at the hands of a smaller but well-led Greek fleet. This cost Persia its command of the sea and contributed significantly to the Persian defeat when they invaded Greece for the second time.

ABOVE Xerxes, king and commander of the Persian fleet. The Greek victory at Salamis was a huge setback for the Persians.

BELOW Greek and Persian warships at Salamis. The ships were equipped with battering rams and many armed men.

King Xerxes invaded Greece by crossing the Hellespont and advancing southward by land and water. The Greeks, led by the city–states of Sparta and Athens, attempted to block the Persians at Thermopylae and Artemisium. Defeat at Thermopylae in August 480 BCE saw most of the peninsula north of the Isthmus of Corinth fall to the Persians.

The island of Salamis blocks the entrance to the Bay of Eleusis, west of Athens, with access only by eastern and western straits. The Greek fleet of around 360 to 380 ships concentrated on the eastern strait. The fleet was commanded nominally by the Spartan Eurybiades, but effectively by the Athenian Themistocles.

Xerxes needed to destroy the Greek fleet in order to ensure he could use his navy to outflank the Greek armies and keep his sea communications open. He had a numerical advantage with some 600 to 800 ships, but this would be greatly reduced by being forced to attack through the narrow straits. However, Xerxes was apparently tricked by misinformation—planted by Themistocles—that the Greeks were not united and

that their fleet would splinter if attacked. The Persian fleet sailed to bring them to battle but further reduced their numerical advantage by dispatching a squadron of Egyptian ships to the western straits.

THE GREEKS ARE VICTORIOUS

Details of the battle itself are unclear from the evidence that survives. It appears the Greeks were in two ranks, arrayed north from Cape Vavari. The Persians entered the straits in three lines, steering north. Then they pivoted on Cape Vavari to face the Greeks. In the course of this action their fleet became disorganized. The Greeks attacked and as maneuver was impossible in the cramped waters, the battle was likely decided by boarding. Here the Greeks had the advantage of heavier armed men and soon defeated the Persian fleet. Xerxes sent the remnants of his navy back to Persia.

Xerxes then withdrew the bulk of his army to Asia. The smaller remaining army was defeated at Plataea the following year. This brought to an end both the war and the threat of further invasion.

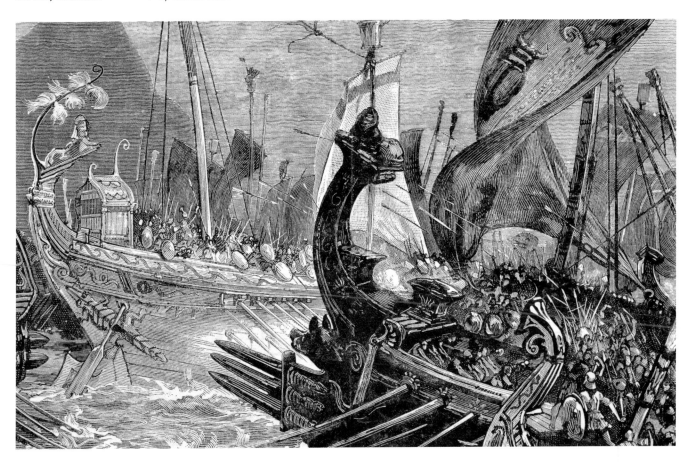

Battle of Dan-no-ura

The Battle of Dan-no-ura off southern Honshu in 1185 saw the defeat and ultimate destruction of the Taira clan, and the rise of their bitter rivals, the Minamoto. The Minamoto established the shogunate, which became the dominant form of government in Japan until 1867.

For many years the Taira and Minamoto had struggled with one another for supremacy in the Japanese court in order to gain control over Japan. In 1177, the Taira were dominant, but there was no trust between the Emperor Go-Shirakawa and the Taira. Shirakawa had failed in his attempt to oust the Taira prime minister Kiyomori, and in 1180 Kiyomori installed his two-year-old son Antoku as emperor.

GENPEI WAR

This unpopular move, which Shirakawa's son opposed with the assistance of the Minamoto, resulted in what became known as the Genpei War. Initially successful, the Taira suffered severe defeats in 1183, which forced them into western Honshu.

Throughout the following year, the Minamoto further pushed the Taira, who established themselves on the island of Yashima in the Inland Sea. In 1185, their fortress was attacked and the Taira took to their ships with the Emperor Antoku, now six years old. A Minamoto fleet was sent to engage them.

THE IMPORTANCE OF THE TIDES

Although the Minamoto fleet was larger, the Taira were considered superior sailors and were far more familiar with the tides of the local waters, which were part of their traditional homeland. Battle began on April 25, 1185. The Minamoto advanced in a single mass, while the Taira divided their fleet into three, attempting to use the tides to outmaneuver their opponents. The archers of both sides came into action at long distances but, as the two forces closed, fierce hand-to-hand fighting ensued when the ships were close enough to board.

The tides, which had first assisted the Taira, now started to change, and the Minamoto began to gain the upper hand. This advantage was compounded when a Taira general defected and revealed to the Minamoto generals which ship carried the emperor. The Minamoto then concentrated their fire-power on that particular vessel and, realizing defeat was inevitable, the emperor and his warriors commited suicide by drowning.

Dan-no-ura was the final battle of the war between the clans and placed the Minamoto in the seat of power.

RIGHT Minamoto Yorimoto (1147–1199), one of the founders of the shogunate in Japan. His brother led Minamoto forces against the Taira.

ABOVE The emperor's mother is discovered by Minamoto Yoshitsune during the battle for supremacy between the Taira and the Minamoto.

Battle of Lepanto

As the largest galley engagement of the gunpowder era, the Battle of Lepanto checked Ottoman ambitions in the Mediterranean. While it did not halt Ottoman expansion, the battle gave a much needed morale boost to the Christian allies of the region and blunted the edge of Ottoman naval power.

BELOW Pope Pius V organized the Holy League of the Papal States that resulted in victory at the Battle of Lepanto. He was canonized in 1712.

THE OTTOMANS INVADE CYPRUS

Since the fall of Constantinople in 1453, the Ottoman Empire had conducted a steady successful campaign of expansion in the Mediterranean, and many of the long-standing Christian states had come under its suzerainty. In 1570, the Ottomans demanded that the city-state of Venice surrender Cyprus. While the Venetians sought allies, the Ottomans invaded Cyprus.

A fleet of allied galleys reached the Turkish coast opposite Cyprus in September 1570. It achieved nothing, as the Spanish contingent withdrew when its admiral, Gian Andrea Doria, informed the remaining allies that it was too late in the season to attack.

THE HOLY LEAGUE

Pope Pius V oversaw the formation in May 1571 of the Holy League of the Papal States—Spain, Genoa, Venice, and the Knights of St John from Malta.

Although relations between the many commanders were strained, a fleet was assembled at Messina, Sicily, under Spanish leader, Don John of Austria. Uncertain as to the fate of Cyprus (which had just fallen to the Ottomans), the Holy League sailed with a fleet of 207 galleys and six larger galleasses.

The Ottoman force, comprising some 230 galleys and 70 smaller galliots under the command of Muezzinade Ali Pasha, was based at Lepanto—in modern-day Greece—on the northern shore of the Gulf of Corinth. As the allied armada entered the Gulf of Corinth from the Gulf of Patras, the Ottomans approached from the opposite direction. Both sides were keen for battle, and each underestimated the strength of their opponent. At first, both sides hugged the shoreline, before the Ottoman fleet extended south in three squadrons.

Don John also deployed in a line north–south in three squadrons. He stationed the heavily gunned galleasses in pairs in advance of each squadron and formed a reserve squadron of 38 galleys. The allied forces were distributed throughout the four squadrons, so that none could withdraw its contingent en masse.

RIGHT This painting by Luca Cambiasso (1527–1585) depicts the four squadrons set up by the allied forces of the Holy League. As commander of the allied forces, Don John distributed all the the ships between the four squadrons to prevent any one State from removing their individual forces.

THE BATTLE

The fighting began around noon on October 7, 1571. The heavy armaments of the galleasses tormented the lighter-built Ottoman galleys. Close to the shore, the Ottoman right, under Mehmet Suluk, broke ranks under the gunfire. Clever maneuvering by Antonio Barbarigo, commander of the League's left, enabled it to push the Ottomans against the beaches, although at the cost of Barbarigo's life.

The Ottoman center also suffered losses from the galleasses as it attacked Don John's force. The ships came together in a riot of carnage as fighting raged from deck to deck with muskets, pikes, swords, and arrows. In action with Don John's galley, Ali Pasha was killed and his head displayed on a Spanish masthead. Encouraged by this, the Christian galleys, with a height and weight advantage over their opponents, eventually overwhelmed and destroyed the Ottoman center.

In the south, there was much maneuvering as Uluj Ali took his squadron south to outflank the galleys of the League's right under Doria. Doria also rowed south to keep pace, opening a gap between himself and Don John's center. Uluj Ali swiftly took advantage, steering for the gap, and had initial success, overwhelming a

number of Christian galleys. However, Don John's wisdom of maintaining a reserve bore fruit. Its commander, the Marquis of Santa Cruz, saw the danger and interposed his 35 galleys. This checked the Ottomans until the squadrons of Don John and Doria could combine and crush Uluj Ali, who escaped with only 35 vessels.

The Holy League's triumph was complete. The Ottomans lost 200 galleys, and counted 20,000 dead. The Allies suffered 7,500 dead with 15,000 wounded. A bonus was the release of about 10,000 Christian galley slaves. The League, however, found Cyprus was beyond reclamation.

The League itself dissolved under disagreements between Spain and Venice on future operations against Tunis and Algiers. Philip II eventually came to a truce with the Ottomans to allow him to deal with problems with England, Portugal, and the Netherlands.

But the almost inevitable loss of Crete was postponed for 90 years and, most importantly, the Ottoman navy, although rebuilt, was gutted of its trained manpower and was never again to wield the power and prestige in the Mediterranean that it had before the Battle of Lepanto.

ABOVE This wall fresco captures the height of battle at Lepanto as Ottoman and Holy League fleets fire on each other. Flames from burning ships, crew falling overboard, and hand-to-hand combat are all evident.

The Armada Battles

For many years, Spain and England had been in a state of quasi-war caused by commercial, religious, and strategic differences. When the English executed the Catholic Mary, Queen of Scots, in 1587, Spain's Philip II commissioned the invasion of England by the "invincible Armada." He wanted to return England to Catholic rule.

To achieve his goals, Philip financed the construction of a mighty fleet, comprising warships and merchant-men to carry combat troops. When completed, his fleet consisted of 130 ships, mounting over 2,400 guns, and carried a force of 26,000 men.

By 1588, the Spanish fleet set sail. Philip II also hoped that the fleet would put an end to the attacks on the Spanish commercial empire in the Americas being perpetrated by English buccaneers with covert government approval. He hoped it would also cut English assistance to rebels in Spain's Netherlands territories. The fleet was to take control of the English Channel, and embark Spanish troops commanded by the Duke of Parma from Flanders to invade England.

However, the English were aware of the Spanish scheme—in April 1587, Sir Francis Drake carried out a pre-emptive strike on Cadiz. He "singed the King of Spain's beard," destroying a number of Spanish ships and vital stores. But the outfitting of the Armada continued, and it sailed on May 4, 1588, from Lisbon under the command of the Duke of Medina Sidonia, an able soldier but an inexperienced seaman. Early on, storm damage caused the fleet to put into Corunna in northern Spain for refitting, but eventually, on July 19, it entered the English Channel.

BELOW The defeat of the Spanish Armada off Plymouth, England, in 1588. The once-great Spanish fleet was scattered to the winds and the remaining ships limped back to Spain.

SKIRMISH IN THE CHANNEL

England had assembled a naval force under Lord Howard of Effingham, assisted by some of the more notable buccaneers, among them Sir Francis Drake and Sir John Hawkins. Two-thirds of the fleet were at Plymouth and quickly sailed to gain the weather gage (the most favorable position) when the Armada was sighted. Medina Sidonia continued up the English Channel with his ships disposed in a loose crescent formation. The English pursued with 118 ships and engaged in a running fight.

Generally, the English ships were more maneuverable than the Spanish ships. They were able to avoid close contact, which would have led to boarding action by the superior numbers of Spanish soldiers. Instead, they used their maneuverability to engage with gunfire—at a distance. However, in this first important battle in history where broadside guns were deployed in a major fashion, they proved ineffective. Only two Spanish ships, damaged by accidents, were lost in the Armada's progress up the Channel. No English ships were lost to Spanish gunnery.

THE BATTLE OF GRAVELINES

On July 27, the Armada anchored off Calais to embark the troops from Flanders. However, the Duke of Parma's forces had not yet arrived. On the night of July 29, the English released eight fire-ships into the tightly packed Spanish fleet. While no ships caught fire, all formation was lost as anchors were hurriedly cut. The Armada became a collection of groups of ships and stragglers, gathering off Gravelines, just along the French coast.

Taking advantage of the disorganization, the English now attacked, again using fire power rather than close combat. These tactics were more successful than previously, with three Spanish ships lost and many more damaged. By the time lack of ammunition caused the English to break off the action, the Armada had left Gravelines without embarking the Flemish army—invasion had been thwarted.

"HE BLEW AND THEY WERE SCATTERED"

Southerly winds obliged the Armada to sail northward. The English fleet followed until they reached the River Tyne, where they left the Spanish in a devastated condition, in damaged ships, exhausted, and short of water. Prevailing winds forced the Armada to return to Spain via northern Scotland and western Ireland. Relentless Atlantic storms savaged the fleet, scattering it and driving the battered ships and exhausted crews

ABOVE Philip II of Spain reigned from 1556 until 1598. His well-thought out plans for invading England came to naught, and Spain and England remained at war for years to come.

ABOVE Sir Francis Drake (1540–1596), one of England's most successful naval men. The Spanish regarded Drake as a pirate, with Philip II of Spain reportedly offering a handsome reward for his capture.

onto the coasts of Scotland and Ireland, where the wrecks have since provided a rich archeological harvest. Of the once mighty fleet, only 67 ships and some 10,000 men survived to return to Spain.

The defeat of the Armada saved Protestant England from invasion but did not stop hostilities. The English attempted an unsuccessful assault on Spain in 1589, but in 1595 attacked Cadiz successfully. Subsequent Spanish armadas in 1596 and 1597 were also defeated by the weather. English attacks on ships carrying treasure from the Americas continued, as did support for the Dutch Revolt. The English Navy was right on course to play a significant role in British colonial expansion over the following centuries.

The Anglo–Dutch Wars

The three Anglo–Dutch Wars (1652–1654; 1665–1667; 1672–1674) arose from commercial competition between the Netherlands and England. Tactical innovations developed during these wars set the character of naval battle until the introduction of steam in the mid-nineteenth century.

The first half of the seventeenth century saw a growth in Anglo–Dutch rivalry involving trade with the East and the countries of the Baltic, and fishery competition in northern waters. Anti-Dutch feeling in English led to the Navigation Act of 1651: It promulgated English dominion over the Channel, and restricted trade in English ports to English vessels.

FAILURE TO SALUTE THE ENGLISH FLEET

The spark that ignited the First Anglo–Dutch War occurred off Dover on May 19, 1652 (Old Style dates). A Dutch fleet refused to recognize England's suzerainty of the Channel by failing to salute an outnumbered English squadron under the command of General-at-Sea Robert Blake. In the ensuing action the Dutch lost two ships. War was declared on July 8, and that month saw 12 Dutch ships lost in a storm while in pursuit of the English fleet. Admiral Tromp was replaced by Admiral Witte de With. On August 16 the Dutch had the better of an action off Plymouth.

At Kentish Knock on September 28, Blake defeated a Dutch fleet under de With's command. Tromp was recalled and ordered to escort a convoy through the Channel and return with another. On November 30 he defeated a small English fleet off Dungeness, ensuring safe passage of the convoy. The English reinforced their fleet and intercepted the return convoy. The 3-day Battle of Portland in February 1653 resulted in the convoy's escape, but at the cost of 12 warships and 43 merchantmen.

THE LINE OF BATTLE

To date, seventeenth-century naval battles were confused melees at which the Dutch excelled, having smaller, more maneuverable ships. Blake, a master tactician, drew up his "Sailing and Fighting Instructions" which formally introduced the "line of battle." This formation optimized English artillery power and negated the Dutch superiority in a melee.

Tromp was soundly beaten at Gabbard on June 2–3 as the English employed their new tactical system. When the English blockaded the Dutch coast, Tromp emerged to fight off Scheveningen on July 31, but was killed in battle. The demoralized Dutch retreated, but damage to the English fleet saw it unable to continue the blockade. Although the Dutch had later success in the Mediterranean, and cut off English access to Baltic

resources, they had lost 1,500 merchant ships and their economy was ruined. Both sides were now war-weary and welcomed peace—however, the Treaty of Westminster of 1654 favored the English as the Navigation Acts remained in force.

THE SECOND ANGLO–DUTCH WAR

Anglo–Dutch commercial rivalry continued, exacerbated by the financial needs of the newly restored English monarchy under Charles II. Fighting overseas in North America in early 1665 precipitated the second war. The English won the first naval engagement, at Lowestoft on June 3. Conflict continued on land while the Dutch rebuilt their fleet. In May 1666, French involvement led to a division of the English fleet and the Dutch took advantage. The resulting Four Days' Battle, despite the return of the detached squadron, saw a Dutch victory.

ABOVE Michiel Adriaenszoon de Ruyter (1607–1676) was one of the most famous naval commanders in Dutch history, and played a pivotal role in all three stages of the Anglo-Dutch Wars.

On July 25, the English countered by winning the Battle of St James with a well-disciplined line. They exploited the victory with a devastating raid on Dutch merchant shipping. However, the Dutch exacted their revenge. In 1667, de Ruyter sailed up the Medway on June 12, burning three great ships and capturing two others. Peace was concluded on July 31, 1667, with the signing of the Treaty of Breda: The Dutch gained trade concessions and Surinam, while the English were given the territory of New Netherland (including New York).

THE THIRD ANGLO–DUTCH WAR

Charles planned a renewal of hostilities and concluded an alliance with the French. War resulted in March 1672 when Admiral Robert Holmes attacked a Dutch convoy. The English supported a French invasion of the Netherlands but their amphibious operations were disrupted on May 28 by the Battle of Solebay, tactically an Allied victory, but leaving the Dutch fleet intact. Two battles off Schooneveld in May and June 1673 were drawn, but again Anglo-French landings were foiled. A further battle, off Texel on August 11, was also drawn.

Both sides sued for peace, which was signed in February 1674. The wars left England the stronger commercial power, while the Dutch withdrew from naval conflict.

LEFT Edward Montagu (1625–1672), 1st Earl of Sandwich, served in the English fleet, losing his life at the Battle of Solebay during the Third Anglo–Dutch War.

BELOW There was no victor at the Battle of Texel, with the battle ultimately being declared a draw. This 1683 artwork by Willem van de Velde shows the Dutch ship *Gouden Leeuw* engaged in battle.

Battle of Trafalgar

As the British fleet headed toward its French and Spanish opponents on the sunny morning of October 21, 1805, few on board would have realized the significance of the battle they were about to fight, a battle that was the culmination of a long campaign to thwart French imperialism.

THE ADMIRABLE NELSON

Lord Horatio Nelson, the British admiral who led the fleet, had proved himself a unique man, a warrior who understood both tactics and strategy, and he inspired great loyalty in his followers. There was an invasion to be stopped, and the British way of life needed to be preserved from the French. Lord Nelson had repeatedly demonstrated his mastery of strategy, and he had an understanding of international affairs. He had been recognized by one of the great admirals of the age, Sir John Jervis, later Lord St Vincent, to be "more an associate than a subordinate officer." Before the Battle of Cape St Vincent in 1797 he noted: "A victory is very essential to England at this moment." He was truly an instrument of his nation rather than himself.

Nelson was the supreme naval tactician. At Cape St Vincent, commanding *HMS Captain*, Nelson—working without orders—positioned his ship across the advancing line of Spanish warships. His two-decker of 74 guns faced a four-decker of 136 guns—which was then the biggest ship afloat. In this way, he slowed the progress of Spanish ships, allowing the remainder of the British fleet to join the battle.

Nelson was a man of courage, honor, and action and, being a commander who led from the front, he suffered terrible wounds. His right arm was amputated after being hit by grapeshot during the Battle of Santa Cruz de Tenerife in 1797. On the way back to his ship *HMS Theseus*, Nelson was lying in the bottom of a boat barely conscious. Once on board he gave orders for the surgeon to be called, saying: "… I know I must lose my arm, and the sooner it is off the better."

Nelson was a man who knew when to fight and when to seek peace. Having defeated the Danish fleet at Copenhagen in 1801, he negotiated with Denmark's Prince Royal, seeking to stop the country from allying

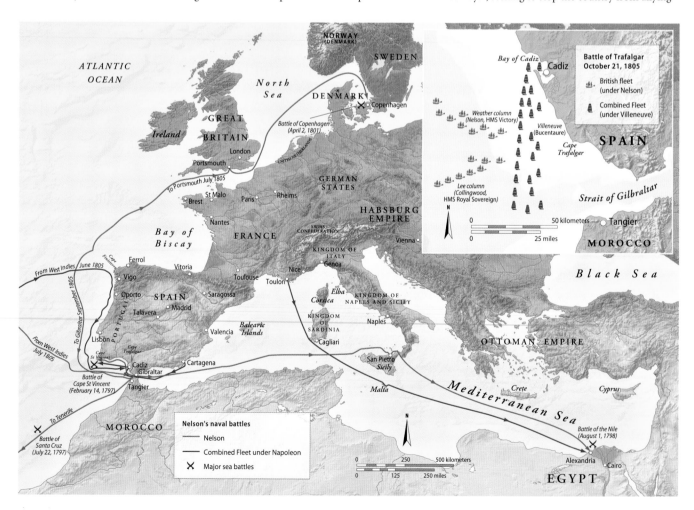

itself with Napoleon Bonaparte. A successful armistice was concluded, demonstrating his mastery of statesmanship and strategy. A vote of thanks in the House of Commons noted that "Lord Nelson had shown himself as wise as he was brave, and proved that there may be united in the same person the talents of the warrior and the statesman."

RULE BRITANNIA

On October 21, 1805, Admiral Lord Nelson's British fleet, after months of pursuit, met the combined fleet of French and Spanish forces under Admiral Villeneuve off Cape Trafalgar, just north of the Strait of Gibraltar. The British sailed to cut the enemy's line of battle. In the late morning, Nelson directed that an encouraging signal be hoisted. The flags on *HMS Victory*'s masthead read: "England expects that every man will do his duty." At 11.45 AM, battle was joined. On *Victory* the band played "Rule Britannia" and "Britons Strike Home" as, followed by *HMS Temeraire* and *HMS Neptune*, she opened fire. The combined fleet fought valiantly, but the British, more practiced by years at sea rather than blockaded in harbor, were the more dominant force, and gradually the battered ships of the combined fleet either surrendered or sailed away.

At 1.35 PM, Nelson, pacing his quarterdeck amid the crash of the broadsides, was giving his orders quietly and firmly. A French sharpshooter, stationed in the rigging of *Redoutable*, fired at the distinctively uniformed figure. Nelson died a little later in *Victory*'s cockpit, but not before he was brought news of the complete success of the battle.

THE IMPORTANCE OF TRAFALGAR

The Battle of Trafalgar was a decisive battle because its outcome changed the future of Britain and the world Britain ruled over. Once the result was sealed and the enemy fleet destroyed, the country no longer needed to safeguard against a French invasion from across the English Channel. With no need to patrol the Channel, the British navy could concentrate its energies on commanding the seas, and Napoleon's ambitions would be limited by the land he could control. He could not attack America, and he could not use the sea to transport an army to new conquests. He would not have access to materials from overseas— timber, metals, and all the other resources he would need to continue expanding his field of conquest.

After Trafalgar, the Royal Navy became the world's paramount naval force for the next 100 years.

ABOVE The Battle of Trafalgar on October 21, 1805, was one of England's most decisive victories, with Lord Nelson's ships gaining the upper hand over the combined French and Spanish fleets.

The Spanish–American War

Decades of tension over Cuba—a Spanish possession since the early sixteenth century—exploded in the Spanish–American War of 1898, which saw the end of the Spanish empire in the Caribbean and the Pacific, and the foundation of American authority overseas.

ABOVE Most of the crew perished when an explosion sank *USS Maine* in February 1898.

BELOW The Battle of Manila Bay was the first major battle in the Spanish–American War. It was a decisive victory for the US.

In a bid for independence, Cubans rose up against Spanish oppression in 1895. Spain would not entertain American concerns at its suppression of the revolt, nor complaints about disruptions to US interests. The destruction of *USS Maine* in Havana harbor on February 15, 1898 was blamed on Spain, and America went to war.

BATTLE OF MANILA BAY

On the declaration of war on April 25, Commodore George Dewey, Asiatic Squadron commander, was ordered to eliminate the Spanish Philippines Squadron. Dewey steamed into Manila Bay with four cruisers and two gunboats. The Spanish commander, Rear-Admiral Patricio Montojo, concentrated his ships under the guns of the Cavite naval base. On May 1, Dewey attacked, taking an elliptical course five times around Manila Bay. His superior gun power devastated Montojo's force. Dewey took control of Cavite but lacked the strength to do more until more American troops arrived to occupy the Philippines.

CUBA LIBERATED

In the Atlantic Ocean, the Spanish had sent a squadron of four cruisers and three destroyers commanded by Rear-Admiral Pascual Cervera to Cuba. The US North Atlantic Fleet (under Rear-Admiral William Sampson), and the Flying Squadron (commanded by Commodore Winfield Scott Schley) searched for Cervera but he evaded them, reaching the port of Santiago de Cuba on May 19. The American fleet of five battleships, two cruisers, and two converted yachts massed off Santiago on June 1. Their attempt to block the harbor by sinking the *USS Merrimac* failed.

With the fall of Santiago de Cuba to US land forces imminent, Cervera sortied from the harbor on July 3, taking advantage of the absence of two of the American battleships. The Spanish ships fled westward with the remaining American ships in pursuit. Despite poor American gunnery, the Spanish were overwhelmed and all their ships driven ashore or sunk, with 323 sailors killed. The Americans suffered only one fatality.

The collapse of Spanish power saw the United States emerge as a world power. The new US Navy had proved itself in war and was launched on its rise to become the pre-eminent navy of the twentieth century.

Battle of Jutland

On May 31, 1916, Britain's Grand Fleet, commanded by Admiral John Jellicoe, and Germany's High Seas Fleet, under Admiral Reinhard Scheer, met in the North Sea off Jutland in one of the largest naval battles of all time. The Grand Fleet heavily outnumbered the German fleet, which the British were determined to destroy. The Germans aimed to sink part of the Grand Fleet, thereby eroding British numerical supremacy.

At 1.00 AM on May 31, the German fleet sailed into the North Sea, hoping to draw out the British battle cruisers commanded by Vice-Admiral David Beatty, over a submarine trap. Warned by intelligence, however, the remaining British fleet sailed south from Scapa Flow in the Orkney Islands.

BATTLECRUISERS ENGAGE

Both searching ahead of their main fleets, the German battle cruisers under Admiral Franz Hipper met Beatty's squadron at around 3.30 PM. A savage battle left the honors with the Germans.

Beatty's battle reports to Admiral Jellicoe lacked detail, so with only a limited knowledge of the whereabouts of the High Seas Fleet, Jellicoe deployed in line ahead of the German ships. In very poor visibility, the Grand Fleet was perfectly positioned across the head of the German ships and, opening fire at 6.17 PM,

inflicted heavy damage. Admiral Scheer attempted to turn away but Jellicoe steered to cut him off.

NIGHT FIGHTING

Scheer turned back and again blundered into Jellicoe at 7.10 PM. Taking heavy punishment, the High Seas Fleet again turned away, covered by its battle cruisers. A torpedo attack caused Jellicoe to veer off course, but he soon set a course to keep Scheer out of his Wilhelmshaven base. Jellicoe was hampered by a lack of intelligence from the Admiralty and also by his own light forces, which fought a confused night action and sank an old battleship. Eventually, Scheer slipped by and returned his battered fleet to Wilhelmshaven.

The British navy lost more ships and men than the Germans and were bitterly disappointed in not having achieved a decisive victory. Yet after Jutland, Germany no longer controlled the North Sea.

ABOVE The British battlecruiser *HMS Lion*, Vice-Admiral Beatty's flagship, joins the action in the Battle of Jutland, the biggest naval battle of World War I.

Battle of River Plate

The first major naval battle of World War II took place off the River Plate estuary, located between Uruguay and Argentina. The battle saw the destruction of an important German warship, and provided a boost to Allied morale.

ABOVE *HMS Exeter* shows its battle scars after combat with the *Admiral Graf Spee*. *Exeter* was completely refitted after the battle, and in 1942 was sunk in the East Indies by the Japanese.

RIGHT The *Admiral Graf Spee* lies burning off Montevideo, Uruguay. Much of the super-structure of the ship remained visible after sinking. In 2004, a salvage team began the task of raising the wreck, which will take some years.

The pocket battleship—Panzerschiffe—*Admiral Graf Spee,* under Captain Hans Langsdorff, sailed from Germany just before the outbreak of war. Armed with 11-inch (28 cm) guns and with a speed of around 25 knots (46 km/h), she could outgun any single Allied cruiser, and outrun most battleships. The battleship sank nine merchant ships before steaming to disrupt Allied shipping off the River Plate located between Uruguay and Argentina, arriving on December 13, 1939.

Commodore Henry Harwood, commanding the Royal Navy's cruisers *HMS Ajax, Achilles,* and *Exeter,* had anticipated the move and sailed his ships to the area. Around 6.14 A.M. they sighted *Graf Spee.* The British force divided, attempting to split the fire of *Graf Spee*'s guns. The 8-inch (20 cm) gunned *Exeter* turned west, while the two 6-inch (15 cm) gunned cruisers circled to the German ship's other flank.

Initially, *Graf Spee* concentrated her firepower on *Exeter* and damaged her severely, knocking out all but one turret. *Exeter,* in turn, hit *Graf Spee* three times. The light cruisers engaged at 6.25 A.M. Under cover of smoke, *Graf Spee* turned away, and *Ajax* and *Achilles* came around to follow. They hit her frequently, but attempts to concentrate their guns' fire, controlled by *Ajax*'s catapult aircraft, were marred by communication difficulties. At 7.30 A.M. *Ajax* had two turrets knocked out; shortly after, the crippled *Exeter* was dispatched to the Falkland Islands.

BLOCKING THE GRAF SPEE

Langsdorff now misread the battle. Instead of pressing home his advantage, he made for Montevideo, with the British cruisers shadowing him. As *Graf Spee* entered port, the British ships, reinforced by heavy cruiser *HMS Cumberland,* took station to block her. There followed complex diplomatic maneuvers as the British attempted to delay the departure of *Graf Spee* until reinforcements could arrive.

Langsdorff broke the impasse on December 17 by steaming into the middle of the estuary and scuttling *Graf Spee,* having had his crew transported safely to Argentina. His motives remain unknown, as he committed suicide shortly afterward.

The loss of the powerful German raider came, in Winston Churchill's words, as a "flash of light and color" in a "somber, dark winter."

Naval Battles of Guadalcanal

Two desperate naval battles saw the Americans, at heavy cost, sink two battleships and nullify a Japanese attempt to shore up their forces on Guadalcanal in the western Pacific. Henderson Field, the small airfield on the island, became a strategic battleground in the war in the Pacific.

On the night of November 12, 1942, the Japanese attempted to run a convoy of 11 troop transports escorted by destroyers to Guadalcanal. A squadron consisting of battleships *Hiei* and *Kirishima*, escorted by cruiser *Nagara* and 11 destroyers, covered the troop convoy and was to bombard Henderson Field. The Japanese strategy was to neutralize Henderson Field and thus gain the upper hand.

On the opposing side was an American cruiser and destroyer force commanded by Rear Admiral Daniel Callaghan, supported by Rear Admiral Norman Scott, consisting of cruisers *San Francisco*, *Portland*, *Helena*, *Atlanta*, and *Juneau*, and eight destroyers. The force sailed ahead with destroyers preceding and following the cruisers. Callaghan had issued no battle plan to his ships, a number of which had just joined his force.

COLLISION COURSE

The opposing forces collided early in the morning of November 13. The action quickly dissolved into a confused skirmish lit by gun flashes, explosions, and searchlights, fought at very close range, and resulted in the Japanese force being turned back, with *Hiei* left dead in the water to be sunk by aircraft the next day.

The Japanese also lost two destroyers, and sustained damage to other vessels. American losses were a cruiser and four destroyers, with only *Helena* and a destroyer undamaged. Callaghan and Scott were killed. *Juneau* was later sunk by a submarine. However, the Japanese convoy was temporarily halted.

Early on the morning of November 14, a Japanese cruiser force bombarded Henderson Field and the convoy recommenced its approach. But air attacks that day sank a cruiser and seven transports. That night, the battleship *Kirishima*, four cruisers, and nine destroyers approached, to again bombard Henderson Field while the remaining transports unloaded.

The Americans sent the battleships *Washington* and *South Dakota* with four destroyers to intercept the Japanese. In a confused night action, *Kirishima* heavily damaged *South Dakota*, but in turn she and a destroyer were so heavily damaged by radar-controlled gunfire from *Washington* that they had to be sunk the next day. Three American destroyers were also lost.

The four transports beached themselves on Guadalcanal but lost much of their loads to air and naval bombardment. Despite these heavy losses, American forces had saved Henderson Field.

ABOVE This photograph taken from *USS President Adams* off the coast of Guadalcanal on November 12, 1942, shows *Jackson* making a 90-degree turn to the left to avoid further bombardment. Flack and smoke from other battleships can be seen across the sea.

Battle of the Coral Sea

The Battle of the Coral Sea, fought in May 1942 off Australia's east coast, was a significant engagement between units of the Imperial Japanese Navy and those of the United States Navy and the Royal Australian Navy.

Although the battle was not decisive, its result carried consequences affecting the later Battle of Midway. Further, it signaled the demise of the battleship as the most important element of naval fleets, and heralded the arrival of the aircraft carrier as its replacement. It was the first battle in which the opposing ships did not sight each other, nor come within gun range.

JAPANESE SUCCESSES

Following the attack on Pearl Harbor, the Japanese forces had achieved remarkable success. They had attacked down the Malaya Peninsula and seized Singapore. The Philippines had fallen to their forces, and General MacArthur, the supreme general of the Allied effort, had retreated south to Melbourne. The Japanese had achieved landings and consolidation through the islands of today's Indonesia.

Emboldened by their achievements, the Japanese commanders planned to take New Guinea. This would allow them to control the eastern seaboard of Australia, and thus deny this strategically placed continent to be used as an "aircraft carrier" by Allied forces. Australia was considered too weak to stand by itself and would eventually fall to the Japanese.

BELOW Rear-Admiral Frank Fletcher was commander of the joint US–Australian force at the Battle of the Coral Sea in 1942.

RIGHT US Navy recruiting strategies, such as this poster, were utilized throughout the years of the war in the Pacific.

NEW GUINEA INVASION

An invasion from the north, to land in Port Moresby, was planned. A Japanese task force, focused on the light carrier *Shoho*, was stationed to stop any interception. Two heavy carriers, *Shokaku* and *Zuikaku*, were also placed to intercede where necessary.

Two Allied task forces under Rear-Admiral Frank Fletcher, centered on the carriers *Yorktown* and *Lexington*, maneuvered to engage this force and stop the landings. However, due to a combination of weather and poor scouting, both forces had difficulty locating each other. Reconnaissance at sea was notoriously difficult in those days—ships seen from enough height for the searching aircraft to stay out of gun range were often misidentified. This characterized the early phases of the engagement: For three days the Allies searched for the Japanese, achieving little except an attack on May 3 on the island of Tulagi, which was under assault by their enemy.

On May 7 both sides made serious errors. The Allied task force was split, with eight ships led by the battlecruiser *Australia* sent off to destroy any invasion fleet. The remainder of the force, unaware of the true size of the enemy ranged against them, sent off an aerial strike force against what was reported to be "two carriers and four cruisers." By sheer good fortune, the aerial forces spotted *Shoho* and her covering force and attacked. The ship was hit by 13 bombs and 7 torpedoes, and soon sank. Meanwhile the Japanese force had sent off a strike element against what their reconnaissance had told them were "a carrier and a cruiser" but actually were a US refueling ship and a destroyer. Both vessels were sunk.

THE BATTLE PROPER

By now the Japanese had become aware of their danger and withdrew the landing force. Their carrier group continued to hunt for the main Allied units, and sent out an aerial strike force in the late afternoon. In poor weather, the Japanese planes could not find their target, and had to jettison their weapons to make it back to the carriers. They flew straight over the top of their enemy with predictably disastrous results. Only 7 of

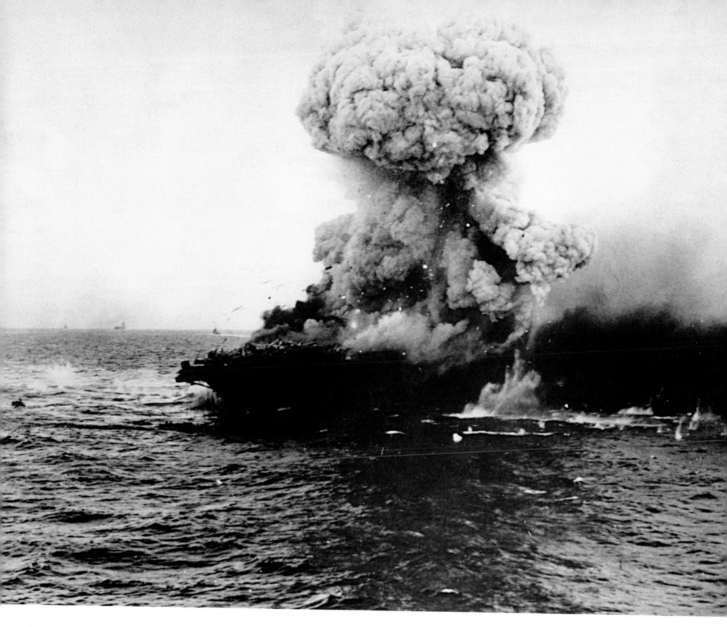

the 27 aircraft returned to their ships. The morning of May 8 saw the first true carrier battle in history.

Aircraft from both sides soon found their targets. *Shokaku* was hit by two bombs—her flight deck was damaged while a fire broke out in her bow. Japanese pilots hit *Lexington* with two torpedoes and two bombs, setting her on fire, and *Yorktown* was hit by a heavy bomb. *Lexington*'s fires could not be controlled and she eventually sank. The Japanese lost 42 aircraft, and the Americans lost 33 aircraft.

The result of this long and rather patchy fight was significant. The Japanese attack on Port Moresby had been prevented. However, the Japanese could claim a tactical victory: *Lexington* was a much greater loss than the far less capable *Shoho*. They also thought that their planned invasion of Midway Island would be strengthened by the Americans' loss. But neither *Shokaku* nor *Zuikaku* would be able to participate in this battle—the Japanese check at the Battle of the Coral Sea was to turn to disaster at Midway, and mark the beginning of the end of their fortunes.

ABOVE The Japanese bombing of *Lexington* on May 8 caused large fires on board. Damage control measures were ultimately unsuccessful and the vessel sank.

LEFT Survivors from *Lexington* abandon ship after the attack on the US carrier. Although many men managed to escape, over 200 crew members were killed in the explosions.

Battle of Midway

Before the Battle of Midway, Japanese wartime ambitions were riding high. They had carried all before them since Pearl Harbor, and they possessed naval superiority over the Allied forces. Despite the check delivered by the Battle of the Coral Sea in early May 1942, they could still field more aircraft carriers and battleships than the United States, their main adversary.

By taking Midway Island, northwest of Hawaii, Japan could reduce the United States to operations emanating from their west coast. But, in a battle measured in mere hours, their ambitions would be shattered.

AMERICAN ADVANTAGE

The Americans had one advantage—they could read substantial amounts of Japanese code, and they knew that an attack on Midway was planned. They rushed essential supplies to the island—ammunition, barbed wire for beach defenses, and B-17 bombers.

Meanwhile to the west, the Japanese force gathered, confident that they would be facing inferior numbers. The Battle of the Coral Sea had lost them one small aircraft carrier—*Shoho*—but they had sunk the far more capable *Lexington*, and they believed the battering handed out to *Yorktown* would ensure its absence from any conflict. They expected to fight no more than two US carriers.

However, the heroic dockyard workers at Pearl Harbor labored non-stop repairing *Yorktown*. In three days they completed repairs that normally would have taken three months. The carriers *Hornet* and *Enterprise* sailed on May 29, and *Yorktown* the next day. The early departure ensured that the US fleet of eight cruisers and 14 destroyers avoided the 12 Japanese submarines that were massing for attack. The US forces made their way to a rendezvous north of Midway. Rear-Admiral Frank Fletcher, the overall commander, had a very simple strategy—find and destroy the Japanese carriers.

ATTACK ON MIDWAY ISLAND

On the morning of June 3, the Japanese fleet was spotted by a PBY Catalina flying boat. A strike force of B-17s was sent out from Midway to attack. They reached their target in the evening but failed to hit anything. A follow-up strike by PBYs armed with torpedoes hit a tanker but failed to sink it. Meanwhile, the Japanese were readying their first strike—an assault by half their aircraft against Midway itself. The rest of their planes were held as insurance against the need to attack the US fleet. The defenders of Midway were lucky. They had assembled every aircraft they had for another strike against the enemy, so none were caught on the ground when the raid hit.

AMERICAN AIR STRIKE

Knowing that a second strike on Midway was needed, Admiral Nagumo ordered the ordnance on the remaining aircraft to be changed for that of land targets. At the same time, a reconnaissance aircraft spotted the US fleet. The Japanese wheeled to the attack, but it was too late—the US aircraft were on the way.

The American torpedo bombers fared badly at the hands of the defending Zeros—35 out of 41 did not make it back to their ships. The dive bombers did better hitting three of the Japanese carriers—*Akagi*, *Kaga*, and *Soryu*. *Hiryu* managed to launch aircraft and these found *Yorktown*, scoring three bomb hits. The fourth Japanese carrier was also struck—*Hiryu* burned through the night of June 5 and then sank. Pearl Harbor was avenged—all four carriers had been used in that attack some seven months previously.

AFTERMATH

Admiral Nagumo still had a formidable force under his command, although it lacked strike aircraft. Only if the US ships were brought within gun and torpedo range did he have a chance. Admiral Fletcher had been on board *Yorktown*, and he had passed tactical control to Admiral Spruance. He had no intention of losing his carriers, thus handing a Pyrrhic victory to the enemy.

Nagumo could have bombarded Midway, but he would have been exposing his ships to attacks from Midway aircraft. He retreated instead. American aircraft gave chase, sinking the cruiser *Mikuma* on June 6. Behind them the *Yorktown* was beginning a tow back to Pearl Harbor, but the Japanese submarine *I-168* caught her, and sank both it and the destroyer *Hammann*. They were the only US ships lost at Midway. The Japanese would be forced steadily backward for the next three years and would be beaten into surrender. The decisive Battle of Midway, Japan's first defeat at sea for 350 years, was the beginning of the end for them.

BELOW *USS Yorktown lists badly after bombardment by Japanese aircraft and torpedoes during the Battle of Midway in June 1942. An American destroyer stands by to offer assistance.*

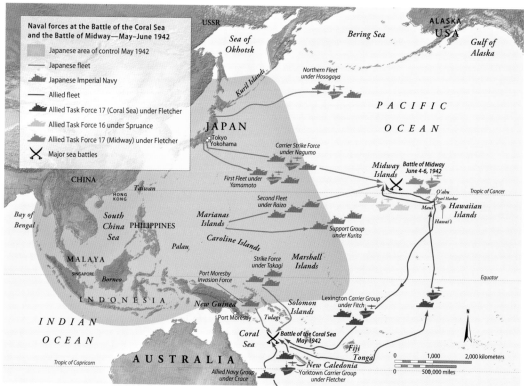

Naval forces at the Battle of the Coral Sea
and the Battle of Midway—May–June 1942

Japanese area of control May 1942

Japanese fleet

Japanese Imperial Navy

Allied fleet

Allied Task Force 17 (Coral Sea) under Fletcher

Allied Task Force 16 under Spruance

Allied Task Force 17 (Midway) under Fletcher

Major sea battles

ABOVE A squadron of Douglas "Devastator" torpedo bombers aboard *USS Enterprise* unfolds its wings in preparation for takeoff. The Americans suffered heavy losses from Japanese aircraft during the Battle of Midway, but the US forces held their ground and defeated the Japanese.

Battle For Leyte Gulf

The battle for Leyte Gulf in the Philippines—October 23–26, 1944—was the last gasp of the Imperial Japanese Navy during World War II. Despite enormous *bushido* fighting spirit, it lost through dismal strategic planning, along with failure to concentrate forces and consolidate possible success.

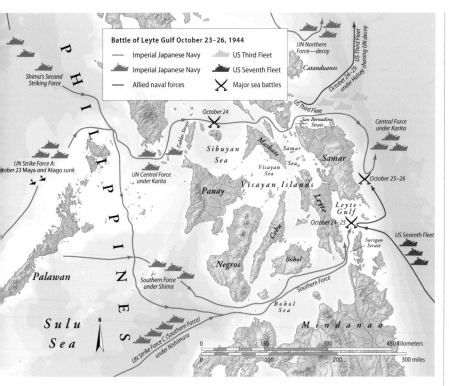

THE STRATEGY

Nearly three years after Pearl Harbor, the Japanese navy was critically short of aircraft pilots. So they devised a strategy using aircraft carriers as a lure, in an effort to split the Allied forces attempting to land in the eastern Philippines. With carriers deploying from Japan as the bait, three flotillas would converge from the south and west and annihilate the enemy landing forces.

ENGAGEMENT

In the initial engagement, two cruisers of the IJN Strike Group A, *Maya* and flagship *Atago*, were sunk at dawn on October 23 by the submarines USS *Darter* and USS *Dace,* and the Japanese admiral, Kurita, was forced to swim for safety. The following day, land-based aircraft attacked the US Third Fleet. The light carrier USS *Princeton* was lost. In reply, American planes sank the super-battleship *Musashi.*

Group C under Admiral Nishimura then entered Surigao Strait on October 24 with two battleships, a cruiser, and four destroyers. Met by Allied battleships, cruisers, destroyers, and PT boats, only one of the Japanese ships survived.

To the north, US Admiral Halsey's force had sighted the aircraft carrier decoys, and turned after them, which allowed Admiral Kurita to emerge from San Bernadino Strait. The Japanese had the upper hand: The US force of six light carriers under Rear Admiral Sprague was caught by surprise and fled. Kurita was nearing victory, having sunk the carrier USS *Gambier Bay,* when he called off his ships, believing he was about to be trapped by a returning Halsey.

KAMIKAZE

The Americans were soon under assault by a dramatic new tactic—Zero pilots acting as suicide kamikazes. The carrier USS *St. Lo* was lost and other US ships damaged. But the Japanese carriers were destroyed by massive air strikes. The loss of 3 battleships, 4 carriers, 10 cruisers and 9 destroyers was a terminal blow to the Imperial Japanese Navy.

Leyte Gulf was possibly the last great naval battle. With modern-day guided weapons and more powerful attacking aircraft, it is doubtful naval commanders would expose their forces to such devastation.

LEFT Firefighters aboard USS *Intrepid* battle the fires caused by a kamikaze strike during the Battle for Leyte Gulf in the Philippines.

The Falklands War

On April 2, 1982, under the grip of a military dictatorship, Argentina invaded the Falkland Islands, a group of islands off its coast it claimed as the Malvinas. However, the islanders were fiercely British, and Britain reacted by dispatching a maritime task force. Initial combat saw the island of South Georgia retaken on April 26, with the Argentines losing the submarine *Santa Fe* in the process.

BRITISH TASK FORCE

Centered on two aircraft carriers that were to fend off the Argentine airforce, the British task force sailed to the Falkland Islands, carrying with it an amphibious assault group. Argentina possessed a powerful navy and airforce—34 British Harrier aircraft faced 220 Argentine aircraft—but Argentina was outclassed by British military experience.

Argentina's aircraft carrier battle group, including *25 de Mayo*, approached the British force from the north. Coming from the south, to catch the British in a pincer movement, was the cruiser *General Belgrano* with two destroyers. However, *Belgrano* was being shadowed by the nuclear submarine *HMS Conqueror*, which sank the cruiser. Poor weather prevented the Argentine carrier from deploying her aircraft.

The war now became one essentially of Argentine aircraft against those of the Royal Navy fleet. The Argentines sank the destroyer *HMS Sheffield* with an Exocet missile on May 4. Seventeen days later, amphibious forces made the first landing, although the frigates *HMS Ardent* and *HMS Antelope* were also lost. Many Argentine aircraft were shot down, with not a single Harrier of the British force downed in combat.

LAND BATTLE

The amphibious assault force embarked on a tortuous campaign to win back the land. This element of the war should have gone in Argentina's favor, as they had the numerical strength of soldiers and prepared fixed defenses. However, they were without the professional thoroughness of the British. The Argentines were also

using conscripts at the troop level, many of whom were unwilling to fight, and whose morale had been further lowered by the failure of their navy and airforce to stem the attack. Despite the loss of another four ships, the British force overwhelmed its opponents, and the Argentine forces surrendered on June 14, 1982.

The Falklands War showed the ability of the Royal Navy to fight—and win—a war waged 8,000 miles (12,880 km) from home, a great logistical success.

ABOVE British commandos aboard *HMS Hermes* prepare to be transferred to other ships to await deployment to the Falkland Islands in April 1982.

LEFT The bombed remains of an Argentine base on Thule Island in the South Sandwich Islands during the Falklands conflict.

Untamable Waves

Three-quarters of our planet is covered with water, so it's only natural that the gradual expansion of mankind and the exploration of Earth have long encompassed the seas. For many thousands of years, sailors have explored, traded, and come into conflict on the waves. The greater the distances traveled, the more sophisticated have watercraft needed to be, and the more knowledgeable and experienced have sailors grown. But no amount of sophistication or experience is enough to handle all that the world's oceans can throw at us.

The seas, oceans, shores, and rivers of our globe are littered with the wrecks of literally millions of vessels that have come to grief in one way or another, mostly by coming off second-best in a clash with the elements. Nature is never concerned with the plight of miniscule man-made specks fighting their way through her storm-tossed seas—she is concerned only with the rhythms of the planet, the ceaseless ebb and flow of the seasons, and the slow majesty of the world's great water cycle.

SUCCUMBING TO THE ELEMENTS

Many kinds of natural disasters can strike a ship at sea. Squalls, gales, and cyclones (hurricanes) are the most destructive. Vessels of earlier ages were essentially defenseless against the most powerful of these storms,

ABOVE Shipwrecks reveal the history of those adventurous early sailors. Here, divers raise an iron cannon from the seventeenth-century Spanish ship, *Nuestra Senora de las Maravilles*. The English-made cannon bore the seal of Henry VIII and was dated 1543.

and entire fleets have been known to disappear into their awful chaos. Unlike the modern age, early ships' captains had limited ability to predict a storm's coming, or the path it would take. Yet even today, storms are no laughing matter even for the largest ships, and captains will often make wide detours to avoid them.

Other dangers lie on the waves. Icebergs have claimed many a vessel, most famously the *RMS Titanic*. Despite being billed as the most iceberg-proof passenger ship afloat, *Titanic* hit an iceberg on its maiden voyage and quickly sank, with a dreadful loss of life. This was, no doubt, a testament, perhaps, to man's often overconfident approach to the perils of the sea.

Tsunamis, and freak, or rogue, waves are other sources of destruction. Tsunamis, such as the one that devastated parts of Southeast Asia in 2004, are generally caused by earthquakes or volcanoes, while the precise origins of freak waves remain to be fully determined. The famous ocean liner *RMS Queen Elizabeth 2* was hit by a rogue wave in 1995—the wave was reported to be almost 100 ft (30 m) high.

DEFYING THE ELEMENTS

Even for those vessels strong enough, well-sailed enough, or even just lucky enough to withstand the sea's ferocity, other dangers lurk. An uncounted number of vessels have been driven ashore, or onto

CONFLICT ON THE WAVES

Sadly, a great many vessels, and countless lives, have been lost during maritime battles. For over 2,000 years, nations have used raised navies to patrol their borders, protect (or capture) trading ships, and to transport troops and equipment. Unavoidably, naval forces have come into conflict, and upon the result of maritime clashes have the fates of nations sometimes rested.

The outcome of the major wars of the twentieth century were largely determined by the ability of navies to achieve strategic supremacy in order to ensure the continued supply of men and raw materials, or to deny that ability to the opposing side. But the cost in lives lost and ships sunk is almost beyond imagining.

rocks or reefs, during the fury of a storm. To help prevent such occurrences, lighthouses—and other signals such as bells—have long been used to warn sailors of dangerous coasts or the tricky approaches to harbors and safe anchorages.

In the modern age, satellite navigation, radar, and electronic communications have largely supplanted lighthouses, at least for major vessels, and have made safe navigation much easier. But that hasn't stopped collisions and sinkings from happening—some regions of the world have seen an explosion in the number of shipping movements, and more ships means more potential for disaster.

ABOVE Tsunamis are among the most destructive forces that the sea can unleash on the land. Here, fishing craft have been pushed inland well away from normal moorings.

BELOW The awesome power and energy of the sea is seen here as waves crash against the rocky shore. The tops of the waves are breaking due to intense wind.

LEARNING FROM HISTORY

For all their tragedy, shipwrecks, whatever their cause, have attained their own importance in several ways. Firstly, some wrecks, or at the very least their cargoes, can be salvaged, minimizing the loss. Others, deliberately sunk, have become a way to dispose of unneeded ships and create artificial habitats for marine creatures.

But perhaps the most important aspect of many shipwrecks—particularly the most ancient of them—is that they've become time capsules, windows into distant and exotic pasts. Such wrecks can provide us with unique insights into the lives and dreams of those who came long before us, and who died in the pursuit of their dreams… something, perhaps, that they would never have imagined possible.

SHIPWRECKS AND TRAGEDIES

Ever since humans began to venture from shore in the flimsiest of wooden vessels to catch fish or trade with neighbors, shipwrecks have been an inevitable part of maritime life. The frightening forces of nature, sometimes combined with human error and the inadequacies of shipbuilding, conspire to make the sea a treacherous place.

TOWARD THE UNKNOWN

For most of maritime history, captains and crews have been alone, far from land, and with no chance of assistance. They had nothing to rely on but their skills and experience to navigate safely from one port to another. Until recently, mariners explored without the aid of accurate charts—or indeed, any charts at all. It's no wonder that so many came to grief in unfamiliar waters.

FORCES OF NATURE

The dangers at sea are many and varied. Nature has many weapons in her arsenal to throw at those bold enough to take to the oceans and seas—storms, hurricanes, pounding swells, tidal waves and tsunamis, blinding fogs that suddenly materialize as the temperature drops, freak waves, and "the doldrums," those extended patches of windless calm that can last for weeks in the tropics. Obstacles like icebergs, rocks, reefs, whales, and flotsam can hole and sink a boat without warning.

Human errors such as navigational miscalculations, mechanical failures, fires, poor decision-making, inadequate nutrition and hygiene, warfare, mutiny, and piracy have also boosted the death toll. With all these factors conspiring against the seafarer, it's a wonder anyone ever took to the sea at all!

The sea has wrought its wrath on mariners from all seafaring nations, on vessels large and small, from close to shore to the depths of the oceans. The United Nations has estimated that there are around three million shipwrecks lying on the bottom of the world's oceans.

BEFORE THE WIND

Sailing ships, with their limited ability to move independently of the wind, are especially vulnerable to stormy weather. The introduction of steam power, then diesel, meant that ships could steer toward the direction that was safest in a storm. The advent of steel hulls meant that vessels were much stronger. But weather, combined with rocks and reefs close to shore, still makes navigating a dangerous activity. The introduction of lighthouses and other navigational devices has greatly improved safety for mariners, their passengers, and cargo.

HUMAN ERROR

Unfortunately, many maritime disasters are the result of human error rather than nature's fickle fury, encompassing many things, from design faults, to mistakes or shortcuts in manufacture, to errors in navigation or lack of knowledge of the sea.

Such errors have led to terrible maritime losses, perhaps the most famous of which was the *RMS Titanic*. On her maiden voyage in April 1912, the supposedly unsinkable ship hit an iceberg and quickly sank in the frigid waters of the North Atlantic Ocean. Only 706 of her 2,223 passengers and crew survived, and her wreck remained undiscovered until 1985.

Wars have taken their toll too, of course. The oceans are littered with the wrecks of thousands of combatant, cargo, and passenger vessels, sunk by enemy weapons. Many are time bombs, full of oil and other toxic substances just waiting to break through their slowly rusting tanks and hulls.

TREASURE HUNTS

Out of tragedy, success often comes. Such is the case with the very occasional discovery of ancient shipwrecks, which tell us much about the lives of those who came before us. Many are well preserved, containing all manner of artifacts that give us a window into ages past—coins, sealed bottles of oil, jewels, fabrics, arms, and so on.

And in modern times, new treasures are sometimes created when decommissioned ships are deliberately sunk. Surplus or outdated vessels are often sent to the bottom to become artificial reefs and diving attractions—a more dignified end than the scrap wreckers.

CRUEL MISTRESS

Despite its dangers, the sea has always been vital for civilization and human progress. Exploration, trade, the opening of new lands, and contact with other cultures have all led to the development of a globally connected, and better understood, world. Today, with the use of the GPS—Global Positioning System—as well as radar and computer technology to predict weather and plot courses, the sea is a safer place. However, the world's oceans and seas always maintain the element of surprise, and an unpredictable sea can be a cruel mistress.

ABOVE A large cruising yacht approaches a massive iceberg near South Georgia Island, off Antarctica. The iceberg has been sculpted by waves and wind, and by the effects of global warming accelerating the melting action.

ABOVE The single-hulled oil tanker *Prestige* sank off the Galicia coast of Spain in 2002, with thousands of tons of oil on board. It is believed that one of the 12 oil tanks split during a storm.

BELOW In 2005, the tall ship *Irving Johnson* ran aground at the entrance to Channel Island Harbor in southern California, USA.

ABOVE This 1822 hand-colored engraving entitled *Scenes in England* shows scavengers laying claim to anything they can, after luring a ship to run aground using torches.

RIGHT In 2008, the Filipino ferry *MV Princess of the Stars* capsized after passing through a typhoon. Of the 825 passengers listed, only 52 survived. A US Navy rescue boat is seen approaching the upturned hull.

The Pride of the Fleet is Lost

The *Mary Rose* was the pride of the English fleet, a modern vessel of war and the flagship. Yet it was to sink so rapidly that hardly any of its crew survived. Watched by Henry VIII, the sinking was a devasting blow to the nation and a loss never forgotten by the public.

HERITAGE

The warship *Mary Rose* has acquired fame on several levels during the past 500 years, first as a state-of-the-art naval combatant, and lately as the only sixteenth-century warship to be preserved and put on public display in its own museum.

BELOW Located in Magdalene College, Cambridge, this painting is the only surviving picture of the *Mary Rose*.

EARLY CAREER

The *Mary Rose* began its life around 1510 as a 78-gun Tudor carrack vessel, and served as English flagship under several admirals, with distinction in wars against the Italians and the French. Displacing 500 tons and 126 ft (38.5 m) in length, it carried a crew of 200 sailors and 36 gunners, as well as 180 soldiers. The *Mary Rose* was one of the first Royal Navy ships to be built from scratch as a warship. Upgraded in 1528 and 1536, it gained 200 tons in displacement and a further 13 guns. Part of the weight increase was caused by the installation of an extra upper deck, making it top-heavy and perhaps contributing to her ignominious end.

A SINKING FEELING

In 1545, France attacked England, with King Francis I leading an invasion force of 225 ships carrying 30,000 soldiers. The English countered with a much smaller naval force—12,000 soldiers in 80 ships.

The French fleet entered the Solent Channel, which runs between the Isle of Wight and the English county of Hampshire. On July 19, 1545, the English fleet sailed forth and the two sides exchanged fire at long range, with neither suffering large losses. During the calm weather of the following day, the French used galleys to attack the English ships.

It was during this confrontation that the *Mary Rose*, watched proudly from nearby Spithead by English king Henry VIII, suddenly capsized and sank in less than a minute. Only 35 of the crew survived.

To this day, no one knows exactly why the ship sank, and in particular why its demise was so sudden. One theory is that, being much heavier than when originally designed, its lower gun deck was much closer to the waterline. While making a tight turn, water was able to gush in through the gun ports, flooding the ship. The ports should have been closed during such a turn, but may have been left open in the heat and confusion of battle. A second hypothesis is that the hull had been holed by French cannon fire, again leading to an inflowing of water during a tight turn, which doomed the ship.

In an experiment carried out for a television program, a scale replica of the *Mary Rose* was subjected to the conditions of the battle and was able to turn without capsizing. But eyewitness accounts from 1545 indicate that a breeze had sprung up during the conflict, and when this possibility was added to the scenario, the model heeled over too far during the turn, flooded through the gun ports, and quickly sank.

It seems the *Mary Rose* was lost through a mixture of top-heavy overloading, failure to close her gun ports, and plain bad luck.

RECOVERING THE WRECK

The wreck of the *Mary Rose* was found by a fisherman in 1836, and some artifacts were recovered. But her location was soon forgotten. It wasn't until 1971 that the wreck began to be uncovered by tides and winds. The ship was found to have been lying almost on her side, and consequently only half of her remained—the half that had been solidly buried under the mud was relatively intact, but the other half had rotted away.

The site of the wreck became officially protected in 1974, and in 1979 efforts were begun to raise her. In 1982 all the hard work paid off, as the *Mary Rose* was lifted from the water and placed into a temperature- and humidity-controlled dry dock.

Preservation efforts began immediately. The remains have been impregnated with a wax-like substance. They will then be dried out in the final stage of the preservation process.

PRESERVED FOR POSTERITY

Today, what's left of the hull of the *Mary Rose*, together with thousands of other artifacts recovered from the wreck, such as guns, tools, cooking utensils, and so on—is on display in a museum at the existing naval base in Portsmouth, UK.

Millions of pounds have been raised to build a new museum for the *Mary Rose* in Portsmouth, where the wreck and the recovered artifacts will be housed. The *Mary Rose* will then become a time capsule for future generations to study, and to learn more about English naval life in the sixteenth century.

ABOVE This carving of an angel is part of an ivory artifact recovered from the wreck of the *Mary Rose*. It will be part of the display at the specially-built museum.

LEFT The historic lifting of the *Mary Rose* took place on October 11, 1982. A giant 500-ton crane was used to lift the special cradle that had been placed under the wreck. The ship was lying on its side and only the underside of the ship which had been buried in mud for 437 years was still intact. The upper side—exposed to the sea—had completely rotted away. News and photographs of the lift were broadcast across the world.

Ghost Ship Mary Celeste

It is the most baffling maritime mystery of all—a ship found drifting in almost perfect
condition with cargo intact, but with no sign of the crew and no evidence of foul play.
And so began one of maritime's greatest mysteries.

VOYAGE TO THE UNKNOWN

Maritime history is full of stories of so-called "ghost
ships"—vessels seemingly abandoned and drifting at
sea. But none is more mysterious or intriguing than
the story of the *Mary Celeste*.

The *Mary Celeste* was a 100-ft (30 m) brigantine
built in Canada in 1861. After an accident-prone early
career that saw it involved in a collision with another
vessel, and after running aground in 1867, it was
eventually sold to new owners in the United States.

According to reports, the ship departed New York
Harbor on November 5, 1872, bound for Italy with a
cargo of 1,701 barrels of industrial alcohol. Its captain
was Benjamin Briggs, and there were seven crewmembers. Also on board were the captain's wife Sarah and
two-year-old daughter Sophia. There was no inkling
that the voyage would be anything but uneventful.

A month after setting sail, the *Mary Celeste* was
spotted by another ship, the *Dei Gratia*, drifting in
the Atlantic. The *Dei Gratia*'s crew boarded it and
found it deserted, with no sign of a struggle or foul
play. In the words of the *Dei Gratia*'s captain, the *Mary
Celeste* was a "wet mess," with around 3 ft (1 m) of
water in the hold and water between decks. Two large
top hatches were open, the compass was damaged
beyond repair, and the navigation instruments were
missing. Most importantly, the ship's only lifeboat was
gone—it appeared to have been intentionally launched

rather than swept overboard. The *Dei
Gratia*'s crew sailed the *Mary Celeste*
to Gibraltar, where they put in a
claim for salvage, and an official
inquiry was launched.

CONTROVERSY AND COURT

Various hypotheses were put forward
to explain the mystery. Some proposed that pirates boarded the ship
and murdered the crew, but there
is no positive evidence to imply this.
Another suggestion was that the crew
mutinied, murdering the captain and
his family. But again, there was no
evidence to support this, and what
is known of the crew does not lend
credence to this theory. Perhaps a
fierce storm arose, leading Captain
Briggs to believe that the vessel was
in danger of sinking, and causing
those on board to jump into the
lifeboat and abandon it.

At the court of inquiry, the
prosecutor suggested that the *Dei
Gratia*'s crew had taken over the *Mary Celeste* and then
killed its occupants. But there was no evidence of this,
and the proposal was quickly dismissed.

But another proposal was put forward at the official
inquiry—the one that is now considered to be the most
likely. The cargo of alcohol could have been slowly
emitting fumes into the hold of the *Mary Celeste*. In
fact, nine of the barrels were empty by the time the
vessel was found. With a low flash point, the fumes
could have ignited, causing an explosion. The blast
would have violently blown the top hatches open, and
could easily have convinced the captain that his ship
was on fire, or at least in danger of catching fire and
exploding. One can readily imagine him ordering
everyone into the lifeboat.

A torn rope was found dangling from the *Mary
Celeste*, and a storm was known to have passed through
the area—hence the water found in the ship. Perhaps
they secured themselves to the ship with the rope, the
rope broke in the storm, and the ship drifted away,
leaving them to die of thirst.

A recent experiment lends support to this theory.
A model of the ship was constructed, and its hold filled
with butane gas. When ignited, the gas blew the hatches
off the model with a roar of flames, but left no sign of

BELOW This painting is the
only known image of the *Mary
Celeste*. It was painted in 1861,
when the ship was named
Amazon. It's said by many an
old sailor that it's bad luck to
ever rename a ship. Perhaps
they are right.

fire damage. Another possibility implicates nature. A seaquake can cause an enormous eruption of water on the surface and smash a ship to pieces, or throw it around. Perhaps the captain was panicked by such an event and ordered the ship to be abandoned.

THE MYSTIQUE

The *Mary Celeste* served for another 12 years for at least 17 different owners. On January 3, 1885, the ship was deliberately wrecked on a Caribbean reef in an effort to claim an extravagant insurance payment. When the ship failed to sink as planned, the captain attempted to burn it, but the scheme failed and his fraud was uncovered. The marooned *Mary Celeste* was deemed beyond repair or salvage, and it gradually broke up and disappeared. The crew's disappearance from the *Mary Celeste* will always remain one of the great mysteries of the sea.

ABOVE This engraving shows New York Harbor in 1872, the year the *Mary Celeste* sailed from its shore. The *Dei Gratia*, the ship that found the *Mary Celeste*, also departed from this bustling port.

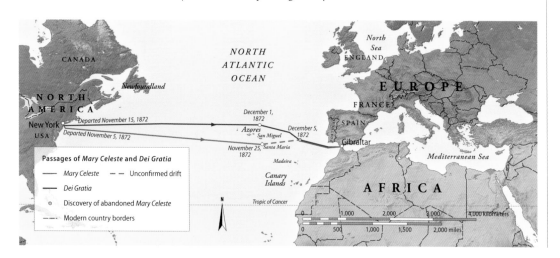

The Unsinkable

The loss of the liner *Titanic* has captivated the imagination of millions for nearly 100 years. The sinking of the ship on its maiden voyage in 1912; scenes of tragedy, courage, and despair as it slowly sank; the many mysteries surrounding its loss, the finding of the wreck—all combine to make the ultimate maritime disaster.

RIGHT The unsinkable *Titanic* departing on its maiden voyage. Its four boiler stacks are its most famous trademark. The forestay running from the mast to tip of the bow was held in place by a giant shackle, which can be seen fallen forward on the wreck.

CONSTRUCTION

Titanic was built in the Harland and Wolff shipyard in Belfast, Northern Ireland, beginning in 1910. The vessel was built alongside its sister ship *Olympic*, which was launched first. The ships were virtually identical, which later gave rise to the possibility that in fact it was *Olympic* that met its end on an iceberg in the Atlantic some two years later.

Weighing in at 52,310 tons (46,705 tonnes) displacement, the two liners were the biggest in the world, and were primarily designed for the lucrative trans-Atlantic passenger trade—their owner, the White Star Line, intended the two ships to be fierce competition for their main rival, Cunard.

The two vessels were very strongly built, and were specifically designed to withstand collisions. They each had 15 so-called watertight bulkheads fitted across the hull—these were actually open across the top, not meeting the deck above. The ships were referred to in *Shipbuilder* magazine as "practically unsinkable." This was a phrase much repeated, often with the first word omitted. A new process of hydraulic riveting, which gave much more strength than the old hand-riveting method, was employed.

Considerable expense was lavished on the comfort of the passengers, which in first class included a squash court, Turkish bath, and pool. Twenty lifeboats were fitted on board, to carry 1,178 people—approximately one third of the 2,425 passengers and 900 crew that *Titanic* was licensed to carry. The number of lifeboats carried was actually more than the number that was mandatory at the time.

ICEBERG!

On April 14, 1912—four days into her maiden voyage—the liner was running through calm, nighttime seas at over 20 knots (37 km/h). Just before midnight her lookouts saw an iceberg ahead, called for action, but the ship struck. The impact seemed minimal but was actually fatal and the captain gave the order to abandon ship. Wireless operators sent out the international distress signal with several responses—the *Carpathia* being the closest ship.

In 2 hours 40 minutes *Titanic* settled and sank, at around 2.20 A.M. on April 15, 1912. Over 1,500 people lost their lives. The Cunard liner *Carpathia* arrived about four hours after hearing the distress call—too late for most passengers in the icy waters of the North Atlantic.

WHY?

The enduring fame of the *Titanic* tragedy lies in the myriad mysteries surrounding the sinking. They range from the conspiracy, to carelessness, to just puzzling. Why was Captain Edward Smith entrusted with the command when he had a track record of collisions and carelessness, the latter borne out by his failure to

BELOW *Titanic* was the ultimate in shipboard luxury. Its wide decks and furnishings allowed first class passengers to enjoy a slow amble or a comfortable seat on the famed "deckchairs."

arrange for women and children to be evacuated first? The "abandon ship" routine was semi-organized chaos—the seas were calm and many lifeboats were launched at half capacity. Why was *Titanic* going so fast in seas where Captain Smith had been warned continually of dangerous ice?

Then there is the stuff of tragedy. The ship's band is reliably reported to have played continually during the evacuation, and went to their deaths as one. It seems that Captain Smith did not commit suicide, although he would have had to carry much of the blame. Several male passengers ignored the precedence order and managed to gain places in the lifeboats—some suffered ignominious fates in the two subsequent inquiries. Several ships enacted a rescue, but there is also a well reported "mystery ship" which failed to help. This is believed to have been a fishing vessel or sealer who saw the lights of *Titanic* but its radio operator was in bed for the night.

FINDING THE WRECK

The wreck of *Titanic* was found by Robert Ballard on September 1, 1985, in water 2½ miles (4 km) deep. The wreck has been explored countless times since,

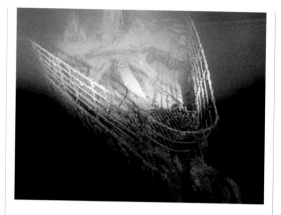

and around 3,600 items recovered. But examination of the vessel has caused even more questions—one of the most puzzling is a large hole near the bow suggesting an explosion. There is speculation that the ship's steel was brittle, and that millions of rivets were popped by the collision. Countless books, films, and millions of hours of research have dealt with this most famous of shipwrecks. For years *Titanic* represented the biggest loss of life at sea, until surpassed by a ferry collision in the Philippines in 1980, which took 4,375 lives.

LEFT The bow of *Titanic* at rest in the North Atlantic Ocean with its forestay shackle fallen forward. The hull split in two, with the stern section—very badly damaged and torn apart from the descent—found almost 2,000 ft (600 m) from the bow section, which is relatively intact.

BELOW This painting depicts what probably happened after the "Abandon ship" command was issued. Lifeboats were launched, but as the ship began to wallow and tilt, panic among the passengers and crew no doubt led to mistakes and loss of life.

Mystery of World War II

The disappearance of *HMAS Sydney II* is one of the most enduring mysteries of World War II. The loss of 645 men—more than Australia saw fall in action in the Vietnam War—was a major blow to a country that was slowly starting to realize it was in a major conflict. But *Sydney*'s disappearance was more than just the loss of a light cruiser—it was a maritime mystery.

ABOVE This painting by Frank Norton, shows the *Sydney* in action against *Bartolomeo Colleoni* off Crete, in 1940.

How could a ship that had seen victory the previous year in the Mediterranean, vanquishing an Italian cruiser, fall victim to an inferior-powered German raider? How was it there were 300 survivors from *HSK Kormoran*, and none from *Sydney*? Were there external, suspicious, factors at work?

THE ACTION

The story, as related by the Germans, soon became famous. They encountered *Sydney* on November 19, 1941, off the West Australian coast, where it was en route back to Fremantle from a convoy escort. *Sydney* had returned some months previously from a highly successful period in the Mediterranean theater of war where it had taken part in several battles—in one case sinking the Italian cruiser *Bartolomeo Colleoni* in July 1940. Now, with a new captain, it was stationed in a relatively benign part of the world.

Sydney sighted a ship, as happened frequently. It closed to within signaling range—radio was usually kept silent to avoid giving possible enemy vessels information—and interrogated *Kormoran* by flashing light. The German ship replied that it was a Dutch vessel, *Straat Malakka*. *Sydney* was unconvinced and approached, now using signal flags. *Kormoran*, flying

a false flag, struck it, hoisted its true colors, and then opened fire. It succeeded in hitting *Sydney* in the bridge area with its third salvo. *Sydney* hesitated, and then replied. The two ships fought each other for just under an hour, *Sydney* taking a torpedo hit, and *Kormoran* beginning to sink, its survivors taking to their lifeboats.

Sydney, on fire, and having taken a tremendous battering, moved off. The Australian cruiser was never seen again, and there appear to have been no survivors, although wreckage was found, and a body in a Carley float presumed from the ship, was later recovered near Christmas Island and buried there.

UNSOLVED QUESTIONS

There were many controversies associated with the action. Why did *Sydney* not stand off at the extreme range of *Kormoran* where it would have had the disguised raider under fire from its own more effective weapons? Why did it not deploy its embarked Walrus aircraft for overhead inspection? The result of the engagement should have been very different.

The light cruiser was a dedicated warship, its firepower was much more directed than *Kormoran*'s, its guns reached further—it "outranged" its enemy—and it had armor over vital sections. In summary,

Sydney should have been well able to deal with a converted merchantman such as *Kormoran*.

Some allegations made over the years range from the possible to the extreme. Did *Kormoran* open fire under the German flag as it should have? Were the Japanese forces—perhaps a submarine—involved, although this action took place several weeks before they entered World War II with the Pearl Harbor attacks? Were *Sydney* survivors machine-gunned in the water to prevent their speaking out about "war rules" being broken? Over 60 years the controversy was the subject of inquiries, books, fanciful articles, and hoaxes, and claims the ships had been found.

WRECKS DISCOVERED

Finally, in 2008, using a vessel hired by the Finding *Sydney* Foundation, renowned wreck hunter David Mearns—the finder of *HMS Hood* sunk by the German battleship *Bismarck* in 1941—and a team of researchers and technicians scoured the ocean roughly 150 nautical miles (280 km) off the West Australian coast.

The starting point was the information advised by *Kormoran*'s captain, Theodor Detmers, some 66 years previously. Using this information as the best-possible note of the location, Mearns and his team deployed a

towed sonar system that gave a picture of the seabed. They located *Kormoran* first, torn into several large pieces by the detonated blast of mines, set by the crew as they left the ship. The location was important. The Germans had said *Sydney* was last seen steaming in a southeasterly direction.

Within days the cruiser was found. It showed signs of massive bow damage from a torpedo, and having been heavily battered by scores of shells from the German guns. Although some theorists will never be satisfied, it looks as if the Germans were telling the truth—*Sydney* was sunk by surprise and subterfuge.

ABOVE Actual (undated) photograph from the Royal Australian Navy Historic Archive of the *Sydney II* passing under the Sydney Harbour Bridge on her return to port.

LEFT Photographed by the RAN at the wreck site, this picture shows a 36-ft (10 m) motor pinnace (large tender) and a 27-ft (8 m) whaler (motor boat) from *Sydney*.

Disaster in the Deep

It was a nightmare, the ultimate deep-sea tragedy—a disabled submarine on the bottom of the sea with some crew possibly alive, then a failed rescue attempt resulting in the loss of 118 lives—all played out in full view of the world's media.

EXPLOSION

Working beneath the ocean waves is a very dangerous endeavor at the best of times. When explosive weapons are involved, it becomes all the more perilous. And that peril was no better illustrated than in the awful tragedy that befell the K-141 *Kursk*, a Russian Oscar II-class nuclear cruise missile submarine.

On August 12, 2000, during a Russian naval exercise in the Barents Sea north of Norway, a massive explosion occurred inside the *Kursk*. It is believed that HTP, an extremely dangerous form of highly concentrated hydrogen peroxide used as a propellant, leaked through the rust inside an aging torpedo. The resulting massive explosion immediately killed or disabled all the men in the forward few compartments of the submarine.

Smoke and flames spread quickly, and the captain was overcome before he could issue the order to surface the submarine. By this time, the *Kursk* was plummeting toward the bottom of the ocean. When it hit the sea floor, a second explosion occurred as other torpedoes detonated under the impact. This second explosion was so powerful that it was picked up by seismographs around the world, registering 4.2 on the Richter scale.

DARK SILENCE

The surviving crew members made their way to the aft-most compartment of the *Kursk* to await rescue, not knowing if it would come in time. The submarine's emergency buoy, designed to automatically detach, surface, and begin broadcasting in the event of a

BELOW The ominous hulk of the submarine *Kursk* floats on the surface at Roslyakovo Harbor, 14 months after the explosions that caused it to sink, with all 118 crew members lost.

catastrophe, had been intentionally disabled during earlier naval exercises. Consequently, it wasn't until much later that day that anyone noticed that the *Kursk* was missing.

The Russian Navy immediately dispatched a rescue ship, the *Rudnitsky*, carrying two small rescue subs. It reached the accident site the next morning, and over a few days, several unsuccessful attempts were made to attach one of the rescue subs to *Kursk*'s escape hatch.

INTERNATIONAL AID

By now the disaster had become public knowledge around the world. The governments of the UK, USA, and Norway all offered assistance in the form of their own sophisticated deep-sea rescue vehicles and divers. This help was initially rejected, but in the face of mounting international pressure, the Russian government relented, and on August 16 accepted aid from Britain and Norway. A Norwegian rescue ship reached the rescue area on August 19, and divers from Norway and the UK made it to the *Kursk*'s escape hatch the next day. But they soon learned that all the sub's compartments were fully flooded.

It is not known how long the *Kursk*'s remaining crew survived, but it probably wasn't long. Emergency power soon ran out, water was leaking in, and a flash fire had occurred when a canister that was being used to replace carbon dioxide in the air with oxygen exploded upon contact with sea water, quickly using up the last of the oxygen. There could be no survivors. Help had arrived too late for the crew of the *Kursk*.

MEDIA CRITICISM

The Russian government and navy came under intense criticism for the way they handled the rescue efforts. Initially downplaying the accident, they only slowly and reluctantly conceded the seriousness of the situation. It soon became a major public relations disaster for the Russians.

AFTERMATH

With no concrete evidence as to the cause of the *Kursk* disaster, the catastrophe brought out many conspiracy suspicions directed toward the US Navy.

The US had two submarines—*Memphis* and *Toledo*—shadowing the Russian naval exercise. Some suggested that one of those submarines had been trailing *Kursk* and accidentally collided with it. But *Memphis* and *Toledo* reached friendly ports soon after the *Kursk* accident, and neither showed any sign of collision damage.

POSTHUMOUS AWARDS

In 2001, most of the hulk of the *Kursk* was raised from the sea floor and towed to a Russian naval shipyard for inspection and dismantling. The remains of all the crew members were buried, and all were posthumously awarded the Order of Courage. The *Kursk*'s captain, Gennady Lyachin, was made a Hero of the Russian Federation. The official investigation confirmed that the disaster was caused by a faulty torpedo.

ABOVE The captain and crew of the *Kursk* line up on parade one week before heading to sea for the last voyage. Some crew members survived the first explosion and left notes for their families on their bodies.

ABOVE Families of the deceased crew of the *Kursk* gathered on August 24, 2000, in the Barents Sea to pay their last respects to lost relatives. They scattered red carnations on the water.

Shipwreck Coasts

The storm-tossed seas know no boundaries, and reefs and rocks are as oblivious to whom they claim. No coast has remained untouched by the wrecks of ill-fated voyages with the world's coastlines and oceans holding the resting places of an estimated 3 million shipwrecks. Ranging from antiquity to the modern day, they take us on explorations into exotic pasts.

OPPOSITE The Atlantic Ocean continues to pound against this shipwreck on the beach near Slea Head, on the Dingle Peninsula, County Kerry, Ireland.

BELOW The Greek luxury liner, *Oceanos*, sinks off the coast of South Africa, in 2001. Deck chairs and life jackets can be seen floating on the water.

BELOW RIGHT This beautiful manuscript shows Henry I of England mourning the loss of his only legitimate son, William the Aethling, who drowned on the *White Ship* in 1120.

THE MEDITERRANEAN

Shipwrecks in the Mediterranean span the ages from some of the earliest recorded times to the present day, and comprise some of the most valuable—particularly in archeological terms—wrecks.

A very ancient shipwreck is that of the *Uluburun*, a fourteenth-century BCE late Bronze Age vessel, found off the coast of Turkey. The ship was carrying a variety of goods including copper and tin ingots, wood, glass, gold, jewels, bowls, jugs, and weapons.

Another valuable wreck known as the *Kyrenia* ship, was found off Kyrenia, Cyprus. Dating from the fourth century BCE, it is the only Greek vessel from that period to have been found. A merchant ship, it was carrying jars of almonds, as well as wine amphorae.

The *Antikythera* wreck, discovered in 1900 by divers off the Greek island of Antikythera, dates from around 86 BCE, and contained bronze and marble statues of people and animals, and many other valuable artifacts. But perhaps the most important find in the wreck was a device that was at first thought to be part of a clock, but is now known to be the earliest extant example of an astronomical "computer."

Although the Mediterranean has a reputation of being a sun-drenched paradise, the weather is just as capable of turning nasty here as in other seas.

Tragically, to this day all manner of ships continue to founder, including those carrying refugees fleeing to another country in boats of dubious seaworthiness.

EUROPEAN SEAS

European nations—especially England, Portugal, France, and Spain—have been among the world's greatest seafaring countries, with their ships reaching most parts of the globe. It is no surprise, then, that wrecks of their ships are scattered throughout the oceans and seas, including close to their home shores, where North Atlantic weather conditions can quickly turn the seas treacherous.

A famous wreck is that of the *White Ship*, which sank in 1120 off the coast of Normandy. All but one on of those aboard was killed—among the dead was William the Aethling, the only legitimate son and heir of Henry I of England. His death led to civil war in England, and the eventual seizure of the throne by the family of Plantagenets.

OPPOSITE The Cape of Good
Hope, at the southernmost tip
of South Africa, is a very dangerous rounding for any sailor.
Although not as treacherous
as Cape Horn, it still demands
skill and respect of the sea as
the ship moves from one
ocean to another.

Another notable wreck is known as the Pepper
Wreck, which sank off Lisbon, Portugal, in 1606. This
was a Portuguese galleon, *Nossa Senhora dos Mártires*,
with a cargo of peppercorns and other precious spices
from India—within sight of land it struck a rock and
sank. This wreck is particularly important to archeologists as it is one of the few Portuguese vessels of
that era that has been discovered.

THE AMERICAS

The waters surrounding the North American continent
are littered with the wrecks resulting from centuries of
exploration and trade. The famous Spanish Treasure
Fleets returning to Spain with riches from the New
World plied these waters, many coming to grief during storms. Their remains—including many parts of
their precious cargo—are still being discovered in the
twenty-first century.

The Caribbean was also notorious for piracy—one
of the most famous pirates was Blackbeard, Edward
Teach (or Drummond). His ship, named *Queen Anne's
Revenge*, is thought to have been wrecked on the shore
of North Carolina in 1718, though the wreck has yet
to be discovered.

The coasts of the United States and Canada were
also the scene of many naval battles, especially during
the American Revolutionary War and the two World
Wars. In 1864, the *USS Housatonic*, a sail- and steam-
powered sloop, became the first ship to be sunk by a
submarine—the Confederate vessel *H.L. Hunley*. Its
remains were located in 1995.

In December 1941, a tanker, *SS Emidio*, was sunk
by a Japanese submarine about 185 miles (300 km)
from San Francisco. The tanker was the first casualty
of Japan's Pacific submarine force.

Like its northern counterpart, South America has
very different oceans on its two sides—the treacherous
South Atlantic on the east and the more placid South
Pacific on the west. Where the two oceans meet at the
southernmost tip of the continent is well-known for
its dangers to shipping. The Straits of Magellan and
Drake Passage have claimed numerous casualties over
the centuries—the opening of the Panama Canal,
though, reduced the number of vessels having to
make the hazardous journey south.

AFRICA AND ASIA

In 1907, a Roman vessel, known as the Mahdia wreck,
was discovered in only 128 ft (39 m) of water by a
sponge diver off the coast of Mahdia, Tunisia. It was
carrying marble columns and bronze artifacts, which
are thought to have originated in Greece. The ship
is believed to date from around 100 BCE, and is still
being excavated and examined.

While Cape Horn at the southern tip of South
America is notorious for its sudden deadly storms,
the misnamed Cape of Good Hope, at the southern
end of the African continent, is just as fickle. *HMS
Sceptre*, a 64-gun ship-of-the-line of the Royal Navy
was anchored off the coast on November 5, 1799,
when its anchor cables broke and it was driven onto
a reef. Only 38 people survived the wreck—the rest
of the crew of 358 drowned.

To the east, across the Indian Ocean, the Chinese
had long had a vigorous maritime merchant fleet. One
of those vessels came to grief around the second half of
the twelfth century. The 100-ft (30 m) long *Nanhai 1*
was found in 1987 and raised in 2007. It contained tens
of thousands of precious artifacts, including blue- and
green-glazed porcelain. The vessel itself is considered
as valuable an archeological find as its treasure—it is
one of the few examples of the Chinese ships that sailed
the "Marine Silk Road."

The wreck of a fifteenth-century Vietnamese cargo
vessel, *Hoi An*, was found by fishermen in the South
China Sea in the 1990s. This wreck was considered a
unique find, as the cargo was the first to contain only
Vietnamese ceramics.

AUSTRALIA

The Australian coastline is one of the longest in the
world, and has collected its fair share of wrecks over
the centuries. In addition to wartime wrecks, there are
many examples of early explorers coming to grief. A
famous wreck is that of *Batavia*, a Dutch East India
Company ship that ran aground in the Abrolhos
Islands off Western Australia in 1629. *Batavia* was on
its maiden voyage to the Dutch East Indies (Indonesia).
Following the wreck, most of the passengers and crew
were killed in a bloody period of savagery instigated by
a mutineer. Only 68 of the 341 people survived.

An intriguing tale comes from the Victorian town
of Warrnambool, on the "Shipwreck Coast" of southern Australia. Legend has it that the wreck of a Portuguese caravel made of mahogany was once seen there.
But despite many searches over the years, the ship has
not been found. If the putative wreck—perhaps hidden

BELOW On February 17, 1864,
the sloop-of-war *USS Housatonic*
was sunk by a Confederate submarine. It was the first successful
submarine attack on a warship.

from view by the shifting sand dunes—is located, it might show that the Portuguese discovered Australia centuries before James Cook.

THE POLES

Earth's Polar regions are probably some of the most inhospitable areas on the planet. They have claimed many lives and vessels in mankind's quest to explore the frozen wastes. The waters of the Arctic were once crowded whaling ships hunting marine mammals for their oil and meat. Given the often treacherous conditions in this part of the world, it is not surprising that many ships came to grief, often with terrible loss of life. Icebergs, uncharted rocks, and fierce storms all took their toll. Ships were also wrecked during the exploration of the northern Polar region, in particular during searches for the famed Northwest Passage.

RIGHT Considered by sailors as the most dangerous passage in the world, Cape Horn, at the southernmost tip of South America, is known for its violent storms. Here, the massive waves generated by the wind and currents wash over the deck of a ship.

The most famous of these expeditions, led by John Franklin, left England in 1845. The two ships, *HMS Erebus* and *HMS Terror*, became trapped in ice off King William Island in Baffin Bay, and all the crew perished.

The southern Polar region, too, has had its share of shipwrecks, from both commercial and exploration voyages. The most famous shipwreck of the region was that of *Endurance*, Sir Ernest Shackleton's three-masted barquentine, in 1915. The aim of Shackleton's expedition was to cross Antarctica from coast to coast via the South Pole. The explorers never reached land—*Endurance* became trapped and crushed by pack ice in the Weddell Sea. Shackleton and his crew were forced to make a series of arduous journeys by foot and by

lifeboat, with part of the team reaching South Georgia Island. A rescue mission was mounted for the remaining crew and, in the end, all 27 men survived.

Modern technology has not meant that the Southern Ocean is without inherent dangers. On November 23, 2007, the specially built Antarctic passenger liner *MS Explorer* struck a submerged object near King George Island in the Southern Ocean and began sinking. Luckily, all its passengers and crew escaped in lifeboats and all were picked up only hours later by another ship.

WARTIME WRECKS

Ever since mankind extended its land conflicts to the water, the oceans and seas have become hosts to a multitude of naval shipwrecks. Many military shipwrecks are ticking time bombs, containing cargoes of oil and other pollutants that will spill out once the vessels' hulls have corroded.

Wrecks of military vessels, where loss of life has occurred, are usually considered to be war graves, and many countries have legislation that forbids interference with them. Wrecks from ancient times are often protected by laws that aim to preserve culturally valuable items—one such is the UNESCO 2001 Convention on the Protection of the Underwater Cultural Heritage.

A tragic World War I sinking was that of *RMS Lusitania*. Carrying almost 2,000 passengers and crew from New York to Liverpool in May 1915, it was sunk by a German submarine off Ireland, with the loss of almost 1,200 lives. Although considered a war crime by many, it has recently been shown that *Lusitania* was secretly carrying munitions, making it "fair game" under wartime conditions.

ACCIDENTAL AND INTENTIONAL

With the introduction of modern navigation methods—satellites, real time weather observations and forecasting, radio communications—maritime accidents should be a thing of the past. Unfortunately they are not, as events in the past few decades have proved.

On March 24, 1989, the massive oil tanker *Exxon Valdez* ran aground on Bligh Reef, Prince William Sound, in Alaska. Immediately her cargo—1.26 million barrels of oil—began to leak out. Almost 11 million barrels of oil spread throughout the pristine waters and caused tremendous damage to the environment. Largely as a result of this disaster, singled-hulled oil vessels such as the *Exxon Valdez* have been banned from European ports.

Even in this day and age, sea tragedies occur that appear preventable, such as collisions between ships at sea. On December 14, 2002, a Norwegian car carrier, *Tricolor*, collided with *Kariba*, a cargo carrier, in the English Channel. *Tricolor* sank and settled on the bottom, with its superstructure just below the wave tops; fortunately no lives were lost. But despite many

BELOW Many of the victims of the sinking of the *Lusitania* by a German U-boat, in 1915, were buried in mass graves along the shore of Ireland. Here, mourners stand in silence over the many caskets.

RIGHT This aerial view shows the *Exxon Valdez* with its massive oil spill spreading across the once crystal clear waters of Prince William Sound, Alaska. In 1990, the ship ran aground on Bligh Reef in the sound.

warnings, guard ships, and a lighted buoy, the following night a German ship, *Nicola*, collided with the wreck of *Tricolor* and had to be towed free. Two weeks later *Tricolor* was struck again, by the Turkish vessel *Vicky*, which was ultimately freed on a rising tide. Not before time, *Tricolor* was salvaged.

Not every wreck is accidental. In recent years there has been a trend to create artificial reefs, by the deliberate sinking of surplus vessels. These ships then provide a home for numerous sea creatures, and they can also become popular tourist spots with divers. However, it has to be said that the decision to sink a ship is not always as altruistic as it seems—often, the cost of removing toxic materials from a ship before it can be broken up for scrap is a lot more than the cost of preparing it for sinking. Economics rule the waves.

SEARCH, SALVAGE, AND PRESERVATION

The action of wind and waves can break a wreck apart, and decay can set in quickly. The state of decay and how long the wreck survives depends on the length of time the wreck has been submerged, how salty the water is, how exposed it is to marine organisms, temperature, and the fabric the vessel is made from, be it wood, steel, or other material.

Modern search methods have made it possible to find wrecks that would have been considered lost forever only decades ago. An example is the finding of the wreck of Australian warship *HMAS Sydney*, sunk off the Western Australian coast in World War II. Analysis of records, and weather and ocean current information, led a search team to the site in 2008. Sophisticated sonar mounted on a submersible craft spotted the wreck on the ocean floor.

Salvaging of wrecks is sometimes undertaken to recover valuable materials that might be involved, sometimes for the purpose of hunting for treasure, and sometimes for archeological investigations. No matter what reason is chosen for searching them out and studying them, shipwrecks provide us with priceless windows into the past—unintended time capsules in their watery graves.

ABOVE Not just ships make good artificial reefs. This Boeing 727 is about to be sunk off Key Biscayne, Florida, USA, to form a fascinating home for fish and crustaceans and a unique dive spot for tourists.

PILLARS OF FIRE

For millennia, lighthouses have been the savior of seafarers.
Without these beacons, mariners would have found it much
harder to explore the seas.

SIGNAL FIRES

The earliest lighthouses were nothing more than signal fires situated on
the top of hills. Protective enclosures were later added, and ultimately,
the light was placed on raised platforms so that it could be seen far out
to sea. At first, the primary purpose of lighthouses was to mark the
entrance to ports. Only later were they used to warn of dangerous
reefs and rocks, and to serve as signals for coastal navigation.

Most lighthouses were built on cliffs or hills on the shore, but they
have been also constructed on offshore rocks or even placed in the
shallows, anchored to the sea floor by piles, to warn of reefs.

A few ancient lighthouses survive today. The oldest example in the
United Kingdom was built by the Romans in the first century CE, and
its remains can be seen in Dover Castle.

On the Estonian island of Hiiumaa stands the Kõpu lighthouse,
the world's third oldest operating lighthouse, dating from 1531. Its
light stands 330 ft (100 m) above sea level.

SOLAR RAYS

Lighthouse technology has evolved markedly over the years. Ancient
beacons burned wood or various oils. These fuels eventually gave way
to kerosene, and finally to gas and electricity, and more frequently
nowadays, to solar power.

Reflectors were introduced to focus the light, later followed by
sophisticated lenses. The lenses rotated around the stationary lamp,
concentrating the light into a thin beam that would sweep around a
full circle. The arrangement of the lenses and speed of rotation would
give the light a unique pattern of flashes called a "characteristic." By
these characteristics, mariners could distinguish one lighthouse from
another and safely navigate from point to point.

While almost all lighthouses used to be staffed round-the-clock,
most have now been converted to automatic operation, substantially
reducing their running costs.

In the modern era, many lighthouses use aviation-style strobe
beacons, which give off very powerful flashes of light. Some lighthouses are also painted with distinctive patterns—"daymarks"—so
that they can be told apart visually from other nearby lighthouses.
Others have radar reflectors built into them, providing a means for
radar-equipped vessels to locate them in poor weather.

One lighthouse device even garnered its inventor a Nobel Prize.
The Dalén light used a system of rods heated by the sun to operate a
fuel valve—when night fell, the valve opened and the light began to
operate. Swede Nils Gustaf Dalén was awarded the Nobel Prize for
Physics in 1912 for this apparatus.

In addition to traditional solitary lighthouses, other lights are used
for specialized marine navigation purposes. One such is the range light,
where a pair of lighthouses is arranged one behind the other, with the
posterior light raised higher. By keeping both lighthouses in a line of
sight, a sailor can follow a safe channel. They are often used in rivers
and at entrances to harbors and give navigational guidance to a deep
and safe channel during daylight hours as well.

DYING LIGHT

Modern navigation systems, such as the satellite-based, Global Positioning System (GPS), are reducing reliance on traditional methods
of navigation and obstacle avoidance. But modern electronic systems
can fail, leaving a ship's captain with no choice but to fall back on tried
and trusted manual methods.

It is hard to conceive that there will be a time when lighthouses
will disappear completely. Even if they are not retained as operational
facilities, many will be preserved in one fashion or another.

Scores have already become museums, while others have been sold
into private hands to become homes. These majestic lonely sentinels
on windswept coasts are constant reminders of the role the sea plays
in humankind's history.

ABOVE Each lighthouse in the world has a distinct pattern of flashes, or characterisic, that allow ships to know which light they are observing.

BELOW Finished in 1887, Phare de la Vieille stands on a solitary rock, illuminating the Raz de Sein, in Bretagne, France. Due to its remote position, the lighthouse was automated in 1995.

ABOVE The awesome power of the sea is evident in the waves crashing around Longships lighthouse on Land's End, Cornwall, UK.

LEFT Solar power is rapidly becoming the most economical way to keep lighthouses going. This one is on the Greek island of Lesvos (Lesbos).

Mariners' Beacons

Since the time of the ancient world, beacons have been used to guide ships through dangerous passages and into safe harbors. Originally simple signal fires lit when needed, these beacons' importance was soon evident, and permanent guides were needed. And thus lighthouses were born—each having an individual "characteristic" or light pattern—allowing sailors to know where they are and how to find safe anchorages.

BELOW This sixteenth-century painting by Maerten van Heemskerck depicts Egypt's Pharos of Alexandria. Its masonry was so strong that some of it was used to construct Fort Qait Bey that stands there today.

THE PHAROS

The most famous of the ancient lighthouses was the Pharos of Alexandria. From it, we get the word *pharology*, the study of lighthouses. Constructed in the third century BCE, it stood offshore from Alexandria in Egypt, on the island of Pharos. Egypt's flat topography made navigation difficult, as there were few landmarks. Thus the Pharos was erected initially to serve as a daylight landmark for sailors. But by the first century CE, with the addition of a reflector—which used the sun's rays during the day and a fire at night—it had become what we would call a lighthouse.

The Pharos stood well over 330 ft (100 m) high, making it, for centuries, one of the tallest built structures in the world. Indeed, it is considered one of the Seven Wonders of the ancient world.

PHAROS

Although no drawings exist that date from its construction, over the years travelers have given descriptions of the Pharos that make it possible to get an idea of its magnificence. It was built in three layers—a square base, on top of which was an octagonal central section, and the whole topped by a circular section. Roman coins depict a statue of a triton erected on each of the four corners of the base, as well as a statue of Poseidon on the top of the tower. The Pharos's height meant that its light could be seen far out to sea, as much as 35 miles (56 km) in some claims. Legend also has it that its light could burn enemy ships as they approached port.

As strong as it was, the Pharos could not withstand the elements forever. It was damaged by an earthquake in 956 CE, and again in the years 1303 and 1323.

Travelers described the building in ruins and very dangerous to enter. Eventually, in 1480, a fort was erected on the site, using some of the original stonework in its construction. This fort, known as Citadel Qait Bey, still stands today. Remnants of the original lighthouse have been found on the seabed.

TOWER OF HERCULES

Another beacon of the ancient world is the 1,900-year-old Tower of Hercules in A Coruna, Spain. Built by the Romans before the second century CE, it overlooks Spain's Atlantic coast and, amazingly, is still in use today. It is the oldest Roman-built lighthouse still operating, and is also considered the world's oldest operating lighthouse.

The design of the Tower of Hercules is believed to have been inspired by the Pharos of Alexandria. The massive structure is built of granite and once had an external ramp winding its way around and up the tower, giving access to its different levels, and enabling wood for fuel to be transported to the top of the tower. Originally standing 110 ft (34 m) tall, a fourth 69-ft (21-m) high story was added in 1788. Modification works have been carried out on its base, but visitors to the Tower can see examples of the ancient Roman and Medieval sections in special galleries.

The Romans chose that site for the tower, believing at the time that it stood at the edge of the earth. The coastline there was then, and continues to be, treacherous, and has earned itself the name of Costa da Morte, or "Death Coast."

EDDYSTONE LIGHTHOUSE

The design of the third lighthouse to stand on Eddystone Rocks—off the United Kingdom's Cornish coast—set the building standard for future light towers.

The current structure is actually the fourth lighthouse to be built on this site, indicating the hazardous nature of these rocks to navigation.

The original structure was built of wood and was known as Winstanley's Light, after its builder, Henry Winstanley, an English engineer.

LEFT The Tower of Hercules, *Torre de Hercules*, at A Coruna on the Galicia coast of Spain, stands like a sentinel watching over a massive tiled mosaic compass rose set on the flatlands between the lighthouse and the coast.

BELOW The laying of the new foundation stone of the current Eddystone Lighthouse, in 1879, was a huge event attended by the Duke of Edinburgh, as Master of the Trinity House Corporation responsible for lighthouses, and the Prince of Wales.

OPPOSITE In 1999, when Cape Hatteras Lighthouse looked in danger of being washed away, an engineering plan was conceived to lift it onto a massive platform. It was then dragged at 1 ft (30 cm) per minute over the half-mile journey inland.

ABOVE Eddystone Lighthouse has been rebuilt four times. This version was the first built in granite blocks. However the rock it was built on began to crumble and the lighthouse was dismantled.

BELOW Cape Byron, in the state of New South Wales, is the most easterly point in Australia. The lighthouse on Cape Byron has the most powerful "characteristic" in the Southern Hemisphere.

Erected between 1696 and 1698, Winstanley's Light operated only until 1703, when it was destroyed by a severe storm. Its replacement also was made of wood, but it had a core of concrete and bricks. Known as Rudyerd's Tower, it went into operation in 1709 and lasted until 1755, when it was destroyed by fire.

The third iteration of the lighthouse marked a new era of lighthouse construction. Modeled on the shape of an oak tree, it was built of large interlocking granite blocks set with hydraulic lime—a type of concrete that sets in water. Called Smeaton's Lighthouse after its designer, it was 59 ft (18 m) high. It began operation in 1759 and served until 1877, when it was found that the rock on which it was built was being eroded by the sea. Smeaton's Lighthouse was dismantled—apart from the foundation—and rebuilt on the mainland in Plymouth as a memorial to its designer.

The current Eddystone Lighthouse, also known as Douglass's Lighthouse, began operation in 1882 and is still in use to this day. Standing 160 ft (49 m) tall, its light can be seen for just over 25 miles (40 km). It also has a powerful fog horn that will sound every minute when necessary. A helipad was built on its tower to allow easy access for maintenance crews.

THE ROCK

The Bell Rock Lighthouse stands in the North Sea, 11 miles (18 km) off Arbroath, on the east coast of Scotland. It is one of the marvels of modern construction, being a "sea-washed" structure that has stood for two centuries, and is widely considered to be one of the seven engineering marvels of the modern world.

Legend has it that a bell was installed as a warning to sailors, but that it was stolen by a pirate. In a case of poetic justice, that same pirate came to grief on the rock some time later for lack of a warning bell.

The engineer in charge of the Bell Rock Lighthouse was Scotsman Robert Stevenson—grandfather of the author Robert Louis Stevenson. Work on the lighthouse began in 1807. At first, the construction crews had to live aboard a ship moored just off the Rock,

accessing the site daily only during the four hours of low tide. First, they built a raised wooden house for their accommodation. Once this was completed, the workers were able live on the Rock and thereby carry out their job more efficiently. During the next three years, over 2,800 granite blocks were laid in position. The difficult conditions and treacherous weather led to many injuries and one death. The lighthouse stands at 115 ft (35 m) and went into operation in 1811.

SPIRAL BEAUTY

One of the most visually striking and famous lighthouses is the Cape Hatteras Lighthouse in North Carolina, USA, built between 1868 and 1870, from over one million bricks. Visible more than 19 miles (30 km) out to sea, it is powered by a 250,000-candlepower rotating aviation beacon and stands 208 ft (63 m) high.

Over the years, the Cape Hatteras Lighthouse became threatened by encroaching seas, until by 1935 the surf was lapping at its base. The lighthouse was withdrawn from service and a skeleton steel tower was raised a short distance inland to replace it. But engineering works carried out over the following decade managed to reclaim land from the sea, and the brick lighthouse was re-commissioned in 1950.

Perhaps the most striking feature of the Cape Hatteras Lighthouse is the angled, spiral black-and-white pattern that adorns its exterior. Although it is still a fully functioning lighthouse, it is also a tourist attraction. Thousands of people visit every year, making the long climb up the 268 steps to the top. Between 1999 and 2000, the lighthouse was moved to safer ground in a mammoth engineering operation.

EASTERN TIP

The coastline of the great southern continent of Australia stretches for tens of thousands of miles, much of it treacherous due to weather conditions or rocks and reefs. The easternmost point on the Australian mainland is Cape Byron, where the Cape Byron Lighthouse was erected in 1901. It is only 59 ft (18 m) tall but stands on the edge of a 300 ft (100 m) high cliff, which gives it great height. It has the most powerful light in the Southern Hemisphere, making it visible far out to sea.

DOWN SOUTH

Another notable Australian lighthouse is the Wickham Lighthouse on King Island, in Bass Strait, between the Australian mainland and Tasmania. At 157 ft (48 m) high, this is not only the tallest lighthouse in Australia but also the tallest in the Southern Hemisphere.

There are even lighthouses in Antarctica, although they are quite small and only in use when ships are expected. The best known is the Arctowski Light on King George Island, sometimes cited as the southernmost lighthouse in the world.

Sunken Treasure

Precious metals, priceless antiquities, and historical artifacts have all been recovered by maritime treasure hunters. The lure of forbidden gold, jewels, and other riches has led many a treasure hunter on a wild goose chase, but some have been lucky. The result has been a heady blend of fact and myth that has captivated hearts and minds for centuries.

SPANISH TREASURE FLEETS

For almost 300 years, until 1790, Spain operated a series of convoys known as the Spanish Treasure Fleets. The *Flota de Indias*, or Spanish Caribbean fleet, sailed from ports in the Caribbean to Spain. An additional fleet, the *Galeón de Manila* or Manila galleons, took treasure from the Philippines to Mexico. From there goods were carried to Caribbean ports for the journey to Spain. The fleets consisted of cargo vessels, which carried the precious metals, spices, silk, tobacco, and other goods, escorted by heavily armed warships. The Spanish crown took one fifth of the goods as payment for their protection.

Although there is a lot of folklore concerning attacks on the Treasure Fleets, very few in fact fell prey to pirates, privateers, or foreign navies. Only in 1628, 1656, and 1657 were fleets captured or destroyed. There was another fleet destroyed—in 1702 in the Battle of Vigo Bay—but it had already landed most of its precious cargo. Many ships were also lost in storms, including substantial losses in 1622 and 1715. The last Treasure Fleet sailed in 1790. However, by this time, other nations had established bases in the regions, and Spain decided to open her colonies to free trade.

SALVAGING THE FLEETS

One of the Spanish fleets sank off the Florida Keys in 1622, constituting a huge loss to Spain. A delayed departure meant the fleet ran into bad weather and foundered. Prime among the vessels lost was *Nuestra Señora de Atocha*, which was carrying precious metals, jewels, and tobacco. Although Spain managed to salvage some of the lost bounty, they could not find the wreck of *Nuestra Señora de Atocha*. That had to wait until 1985 when American bounty hunters found it and recovered much of the cargo and other artifacts. Although the US government claimed the wreck and took legal action, eventually a court ruled in favor of the salvagers.

Another of the Spanish fleets, that of 1715, also was lost off the Florida coast during bad weather. This was Spain's worst maritime loss, comprising a huge amount of money and around 1,000 lives. Although the Spaniards spent years retrieving what they could, it wasn't until the 1960s and the advent of modern technology that the majority of the cargo began to be recovered.

REMARKABLE FINDS

There have been many astonishing treasure finds over the years, notable both for the difficulty of locating the wrecks, and also the sums involved. There still remain many surprises waiting to be found beneath the waves.

In 2007, a private shipwreck hunting company discovered the wreck of a Spanish galleon off the coast of Spain, with an estimated $US500 million in gold coins. The ownership of the wreck and the rights to the bounty are presently being fought out in the courts.

Similarly, in early 2009, the same company announced that it had found the wreck of *HMS Victory*, a British warship that sank in 1744 in the English Channel. *Victory* had been carrying around 4 tons (3.5 tonnes) of Portuguese gold, and over 1,000 sailors lost their lives when she went down. The claim to this wreck, too, is before the courts.

TREASURE AND THE LAW

Although finding sunken treasure might seem like the most difficult part, the legal battles that ensue can often be more protracted than the discovery process itself.

BELOW This painting depicts a vessel of the Spanish Treasure Fleet leaving port, laden with treasure and bound for Spain.

International law generally holds that when a vessel is abandoned, it can be claimed by anyone who finds it. If the wreck hasn't been formally abandoned it can be salvaged by someone other than the owner, but there is no automatic right to keep what has been found. Negotiations usually follow.

Some countries, such as the United States, have adopted formal positions of never officially abandoning vessels unless specifically stated, no matter how old they are. The United States, in fact, has an agreement with Spain which states that any Spanish wreck found within the territorial waters of the United States will be accorded the same status as a US vessel.

Many countries have also enacted laws that prohibit unauthorized interference with sunken wrecks, primarily in order to preserve their archeological integrity, but also to prohibit looting. There are also statutes that recognize sunken warships as war graves, and therefore untouchable.

ABOVE The Battle of Vigo Bay took place on October 23, 1702, when the Anglo-Dutch fleet got news of the Spanish Treasure Fleet returning to Vigo Bay at Cadiz, in Spain.

LEFT These gold and silver coins were recovered from the wreck of the Spanish ship, *Conde de Tolosa*, in the Dominican Republic.

FORCES OF NATURE

Earth's global sea is as dynamic and powerful as its terrestrial forces, and these forces are often interlinked. Wind, for example, creates waves and drives currents; ocean currents, on the other hand, strongly influence the temperature and moisture on land. Warm water creates storms that can unleash their power on land.

OCEAN CURRENTS

Oceans are vast sources of energy. At sea, wind-created ocean currents flow as huge rivers, some moving at a velocity measured by miles per hour. Those flowing from equatorial regions transfer heat energy toward the poles. Nowhere is this shown more dramatically than in Western Europe, where the warm Gulf Stream and North Atlantic Current contribute to extremely mild temperatures.

Most currents that flow in the opposite direction—toward the equator—transfer cold water that influences temperatures, precipitation, and relative humidity of the coastal regions they bathe. Many west coastal, desert regions bordered by a cold current, such as areas of western Peru and Chile, experience rather cool temperatures and high humidity, though little rain. South-flowing currents from the far north also carry icebergs southward where they create navigational hazards if they enter shipping lanes.

TIDES

Tides are variations in sea level resulting from the gravitational attraction of the Moon (54 percent) and Sun (46 percent). Tidal influences are most evident along coastal zones that experience a considerable range of water level. This is particularly noticeable in Canada's Atlantic-facing Bay of Fundy, where tides range up to 53 ft (16 m).

Many North Pacific locations also experience a large tidal range. Alaska's Turnagain Arm, an eastward extension of Cook Inlet south of Anchorage, experiences a bore tide, one of 60 such tides in the world. Around the full and new moons, the bore tide produces a wave that can reach 10 ft (3.5 m) high, and travel at speeds between 10–15 mph (16-24 km/h) up the 40-mile (64.5 km) long arm.

WAVES

A wave crashing onto shore is one of nature's most spectacular sights. Most waves are formed by the frictional drag of wind on the ocean's surface. Wave magnitude depends upon the velocity, direction, duration, and fetch—distance of the wind.

Some places are well known for their large waves, attracting surfers from far and wide to ride the waves. Along low-lying coastal zones, storm waves create—or remove—sandy beaches, sand spits, offshore sandbars, and tombolos. With assistance from the wind, they also contribute to coastal dune formation. Waves also create littoral drift—slow-moving currents that flow parallel to the coast.

Some waves grow to a huge size. The best known of these are tsunamis—sometimes incorrectly called "tidal waves". These waves are caused by seismic—or some other—shocks on the ocean floor. They are notorious for the destruction they create when striking low-lying coastal areas. Much of the damage from the devastating 1964 Alaska earthquake was actually caused by the tsunami it created, wrecking a number of coastal Alaskan communities. More recently, the December 2004 earthquake in the Indian Ocean created a tsunami that sent a wall of water up to 100 ft (30 m) tall rushing ashore in what

was one of history's most deadly and costly natural disasters. By the time the water subsided, the toll was nearly one-quarter of a million people dead in 11 countries, and trillions of dollars in economic losses.

Gigantic "rogue waves" out at sea have featured in sailors' tales for centuries. Recently, scientists have begun to realize that they are not just figments of imagination, although how they form is still debated.

TROPICAL STORMS

Warm ocean water also creates the spawning grounds for tropical storms. Hurricanes, typhoons, and cyclones are the same storms with different regional names. For a variety of reasons, they form in the warm waters of the North Atlantic, North Pacific, and Indian oceans, but not elsewhere. As long as they remain over warm water, these storms generally gain or maintain their strength. Winds, rain, and accompanying storm surge can cause massive destruction in low-lying coastal areas, and even inland wind and flood damage can be extensive.

PROTECTING COASTS

Today, more than half of the world's population lives on or near coasts. As coastal populations grow, people, settlements, and economic development become increasingly vulnerable to the ravages of the sea. Over time, however, a number of methods have been developed to protect coastal environments. These include hard engineering structures, such as breakwaters and seawalls, as well as the more environmentally friendly processes of dune building and vegetation planting.

LEFT This satellite image taken December 25, 2008, shows Cyclone Billy off the Western Australian coast. Formed a few days earlier, it traveled across several hundred miles of coastline before crossing the Kimberley region.

BELOW The fantastic formations along the Namib Desert coastline, in Namibia, are formed by wind and sea erosion. It's rare to see ocean waves washing onto a desert.

ABOVE The waves along the coast of Hawaii are coveted by experienced surfers. Here a board riders loses his board as it shoots from under him taking its own course to shore.

LEFT Fundy Bay at Fundy National Park, New Brunswick, Canada, is renowned for its range of 53 ft (16 m), causing waves to rush in and out twice a day.

Tsunami

A tsunami is a series of waves that is created when a large volume of water is rapidly displaced. Tsunamis were sometimes referred to as tidal waves. However, this term is no longer accepted, because the processes that produce tsunamis have nothing to do with processes that produce tides. Tsunamis are usually generated by tectonic forces.

RIGHT A mosque is all that's left standing after the tsunami hit Banda Aceh on December 26, 2004. The wave surge wiped out everything in its path.

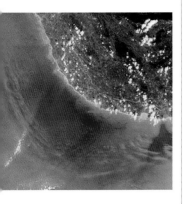

ABOVE The ripples in the ocean on this satellite image are the series of waves approaching the Sri Lankan coast, only hours after the tsunami hit Banda Aceh on December 26, 2004.

PHYSICAL CHARACTERISTICS

Tsunamis are caused by water displacement, and are shallow-water progressive waves with long wavelengths that travel very fast in the open ocean. Shallow-water waves are waves that interact with the ocean bottom. Most wind waves and swell waves have short wavelengths, and wind waves that are formed out at sea do not interact with the ocean bottom in deep water. This means that a wind wave with a wavelength of 65 ft (20 m) can pass over water 30 ft (10 m) deep and not be affected by the ocean bottom.

However, once the depth to the ocean bottom is shallower than one twentieth of the wavelength, the wave begins to interact with ocean bottom. This causes the wave to slow down. The wavelength then shortens and wave height increases. The wave period—time between the waves—remains constant.

Tsunamis formed by deep ocean seismic events typically have wavelengths that range from 60 to 125 miles (approximately 100–200 km). A tsunami with a relatively short wavelength of 60 miles (96 km) would interact with an ocean bottom 3 miles (4.8 km) deep. The deepest of the world's oceans is the Pacific Ocean, which averages around 2.65 miles (4.3 km) in depth. Only those deepest areas, like deep ocean trenches, would cause a tsunami with a relatively short wavelength not to interact with the ocean bottom.

In the deep waters of the open ocean, a tsunami's wave height may only be 4–40 in (10–100 cm). The average wave period for a deepwater tsunami is typically about 8 to 20 minutes. Such waves can go unnoticed by ships at sea due to normal wind wave

Shaking the Planet

On the morning of December 26, 2004, at 00:58:49 UTC—Coordinated Universal Time—a large earthquake with a magnitude between 9.1 and 9.3 occurred off the west coast of northern Sumatra, Indonesia. The epicenter was at a depth of 18.6 miles (30 km). An estimated 994 miles (1,600 km) of fault line slipped about 50 ft (15 m) in two phases along the tectonically complex region composed of both a subduction zone and a strike-slip fault zone. Here the Indo-Australian Plate collides with the Burma Plate and forms the Sunda Trench.

The resulting tsunami struck 11 of the nations bordering the Indian Ocean. Northwest Sumatra was closest to the epicenter and received the highest waves. An International Tsunami Survey Team (ITST) investigating the damage on Sumatra documented wave heights of 65–100 ft (20–30 m) at isolated locations along the island's northwestern end. Estimates place the death toll for the surrounding regions affected by the tsunami at near 230,000.

RIGHT The peaks around Lituya Bay, Alaska, show the scars of the massive tsunami that caused a wave to run up the opposite shore reaching 1,720 ft (525 m).

activity, and because of their very long wavelengths and periods. A ship will rise slightly on the crest of the wave and then descend gradually into the trough.

WALL OF WATER

The long period between tsunami waves has resulted in many deaths. People often mistakenly believe that the first wave will not be followed by a second or third. As a tsunami approaches a shoreline, it begins to slow down and its wave height increases.

When the shoreline is close to the large tectonic movements that caused the tsunami, the waves can reach heights of 100 ft (30 m). The wave does not have the appearance of a plunging breaker. Instead, it appears more like a surging wall of water that continues flowing inland until its energy is dissipated; then it slows and recedes.

CAUSES

The most common cause of water displacement is shallow earthquakes in subduction zones at the edge of tectonic plate boundaries. Here two tectonic plates converge and the heavier—denser—plate plunges beneath the lighter—less dense—plate. As the subducting plate sinks, it occasionally becomes locked in place for long periods of time before it is suddenly released. The release triggers the subducting plate to thrust downward and the lighter plate to lurch upward.

These sudden movements affect the overlying water mass and cause changes in sea level. Energy from the earthquake is passed on to the water column and a tsunami is generated. At the surface, energy radiates away from the source in the form of long period waves.

VOLCANOES

Volcanic eruptions can displace large volumes of water and generate extremely destructive tsunami waves in the immediate source area. A volcanic explosion can cause a large portion of a volcano slope to slide off—slump—into the ocean.

Other explosive eruptions result when water enters a collapsing volcano's magma chambers—phreatomagmatic explosions. One of the largest tsunamis ever recorded occurred on August 26, 1883, after the explosion and collapse of Krakatoa in the Sunda Strait between Java and Sumatra. The tsunami waves generated were up to 120 ft (40 m) high. The combined

Warning Signs

One or all of these signs may be evident before a tsunami reaches the shore:
- Ground shaking from local earthquakes near the coast.
- Water receding from the coast exposing the ocean floor, reefs, fish, and stranding anchored boats.
- A wall of churning water may sometimes be visible on the horizon.
- A loud "roaring" sound similar to that of a train or jet aircraft.
- Unusual behavior of animals in coastal areas such as fleeing to higher ground or restlessness—many animals can hear the ultra low frequency sound waves or "infrasound" created by large waves and earthquakes many miles away.

The Numbers

The speed of a tsunami can be calculated by the formula used for a shallow-water wave: $C = \sqrt{gd}$, where C is the speed of the tsunami, g is the acceleration due to gravity—32.2 ft (9.8 m) per second—and d is the average depth of the ocean—14,000 ft (4,267 m). Solving for C shows that the tsunami would travel at an average of 458 mph (737 km/h). In deeper water the speed of these waves can be more than 500 mph (800 km/h). This allows tsunamis to travel thousands of miles across the open ocean in only few hours.

effects of the tsunami and pyroclastic flow destroyed coastal towns and villages along the Sunda Strait, killing 36,417 people.

LANDSLIDES

Underwater landslides or slumps can be triggered by earthquakes, coastal volcanoes, and coastal landslides, and are another process that generates tsunamis. When a large volume of rock detaches and slides downhill, water is dragged in behind it from all sides and collides in the middle. This energy radiates out in a great wave. On July 9, 1958, a magnitude 7.9 earthquake on the Fairweather Fault triggered a rock avalanche at the head of Lituya Bay, Alaska. The landslide generated a wave that ran up 1,720 ft (525 m) on the opposite shore. Eyewitness accounts state that the wave was close to 100 ft (30 m) tall near the mouth of the bay. The wave sank two fishing boats and killed two fishermen.

PALEO-TSUNAMI EVIDENCE

Large tsunami events tend to be rare and therefore very few modern records are available. Geologic records allow us to extend the historical and instrumental records and provide us with a better understanding of tsunami hazards for a location. The study of paleo-tsunami includes identification, mapping, and dating of tsunami deposits. These increase our knowledge of recurrence intervals, estimates of tsunami size, and inundation extents. Evidence from past tsunamis is derived from core samples taken along coastal zones that show sand deposits between soil layers. Other evidence comes from marine deposits such as coral or large boulders that are transported far inland.

Meteorite impacts are known to have produced a tsunami but are extremely rare. Earth is impacted by meteorites every day but most of these cause little damage. Large meteorites, however, have struck Earth in the past.

In 1992, an impact crater was discovered near the small village of Chicxulub on Mexico's Yucatan Peninsula. Dating of the impact showed that it had occurred 65 million years ago at the end of the Cretaceous Period, and paleo-tsunami evidence showed the impact resulted in mega-tsunami waves hundreds of feet high.

WARNING NETWORKS

Tsunami warning systems have been in place for many decades in the Pacific and Atlantic oceans. After the 2004 tsunami, a similar network was installed in the Indian Ocean. The current system is known as the Deep-Ocean Assessment and Reporting of Tsunamis (DART). It consists of a platform that lies on the seafloor monitoring seismic activity and sending signals to a buoy floating on the surface. The buoy then uses satellite communication to pass on the information to tsunami warning centers.

New methods to monitor tsunami areas are in development. One of these uses GPS stations near the earthquake epicenter to measure horizontal and vertical displacement of the seafloor.

ABOVE This very early sketch shows Krakatoa beginning to explode in 1883. The blast was so powerful that the island was almost destroyed. The resulting tsunami caused devastation across the region.

Eye of the Storm

The terms hurricane, typhoon, and cyclone are regionally-specific names for a strong tropical cyclone—the generic term for a deep low-pressure system without a front attached. Tropical cyclones are among the largest and most violent weather systems on Earth and perform an important function by helping to regulate Earth's temperature.

ABOVE Called a supercell, cloud formations like this are almost always associated with the onset of violent weather.

BELOW This cross-section of Hurricane Katrina shows rain areas. Blue has ¼ in (6 mm) of rain p/hour; green ½ in (12 mm) p/h; yellow 1 in (25 mm) p/h; and red over 2 in (50 mm) p/h.

CREATING THE ATMOSPHERE

The development of intense tropical cyclones requires several key ingredients. The first ingredient is warm ocean water—at least 80°F (26.6°C)—at the surface along the path of the disturbance. The necessary depth of this warm water is unclear but approximately 160 ft (50 m) appears sufficient. These warm waters provide fuel and are the heat engine of a tropical cyclone.

The second ingredient is a location of between 8° and 15°N or S, as the Coriolis effect is least near the equator and greatest at the poles. The Coriolis effect is an apparent deflection of moving objects as seen by an observer on Earth's surface—a rotating reference frame. Objects in the Northern Hemisphere are deflected to the right and objects in the Southern Hemisphere are deflected to the left. Because of this deflecting force, tropical cyclones rotate counterclockwise in the Northern Hemisphere and clockwise in the Southern Hemisphere.

A third ingredient is light winds at middle and high altitudes, allowing convective clouds to build vertically. Strong winds aloft shear away the tops of developing cumulonimbus clouds.

The fourth ingredient is a steep temperature lapse rate that allows for latent heat of condensation. This means the temperature decreases rapidly with height. Under these conditions the atmosphere becomes very unstable and is favorable for cloud development. Latent heat released into a developing tropical cyclone provides additional energy to the system.

The fifth ingredient is some type of disturbance to cause the system to begin to rotate. This could occur when an upper level jet stream passes to the northwest of the disturbance. The system begins to rotate as divergence aloft increases, and inflow at the surface increases. Pre-existing cyclonic systems, orographic (mountain) obstructions, and diurnal influences, are also sources that provide rotation to a developing system.

The sixth ingredient is abundant moisture in the lower-to-mid troposphere. The tropical ocean is a source region for abundant amounts of moisture and is essential for convective cloud formation and tropical cyclone development.

BUILDING STRENGTH

Easterly waves—weak troughs of low pressure—are migratory wavelike disturbances that are pushed along by the trade winds and move slowly from east to west. Divergence at the surface to the west of the trough line produces fair weather. Cloudiness and heavy rain showers are located to the east of the trough line and result from convergence at the surface. Easterly waves form asymmetric weather patterns that occasionally intensify into tropical depressions.

Tropical depressions are assigned a number by hurricane, typhoon, or tropical cyclone weather centers. These may further intensify into tropical storms, when the system is given a name for identification and tracking purposes. Short distinctive names are easier to remember and lead to fewer errors than the more cumbersome methods like latitude-longitude identification.

If the system continues to intensify and wind speeds are greater than 73 mph (63 knots, 117 km/h), it is classified as a hurricane, typhoon, or cyclone, depending on where it formed.

PHYSICAL STRUCTURE

Tropical cyclones are non-frontal synoptic scale low-pressure systems, typically 300 miles (480 km) wide but sometimes more than 500 miles (800 km) wide. One of the most distinctive features of these systems is the eye that often appears when the tropical cyclone matures and becomes fully developed. It is located in the center of the storm and ranges from 12 to 40 miles (20–65 km) wide. The edges of the eye are made up of swirling clouds that spin around the eye and form the eye wall—a region of intense cloud development, heavy rainfall, and the strongest winds.

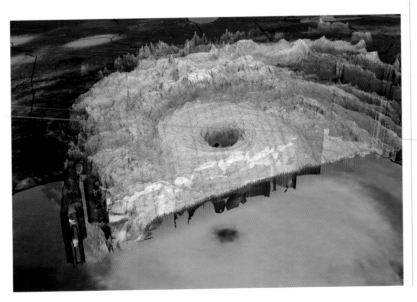

Spiraling winds shoot warm air up through the hurricane and release latent heat that adds energy to the system. Spiral bands—rain bands—are composed of cumulonimbus clouds that surround the eye wall and radiate outward away from the center. Strong winds, although not as strong as those around the eye wall, are most intense near the storm center, and gradually diminish toward the outer margins.

Dangerous thunderstorms produce torrential rainfall and tornadoes along these bands and the eye wall. In many situations several of the bands may pass over a location, bringing a period of heavy rain showers, followed by brief clearing, and then another period of heavy rain showers as a second spiral band passes overhead. These heavy precipitation regions within the storm cause the flooding that sometimes occurs inland as a storm passes.

WHERE AND WHEN
Tropical cyclones form over the warm waters in most of the tropics. There are, however, several locations in the tropics where they do not develop, like the southeastern Pacific Ocean, South Atlantic Ocean, and off the coast of northern Africa. These special regions have relatively cool ocean temperatures—lower than 80°F (26.6°C)—or the presence of temperature inversions that inhibit cyclone formation.

Tropical cyclones are not restricted to the tropics. They frequently move into middle latitude locations and perform an important function by carrying heat energy surpluses from the tropics to the middle and sometimes higher latitudes. This movement helps to regulate Earth's temperature.

Tropical cyclones begin to dissipate when they move away from warm tropical waters or over a large land mass. The most favorable time of the year for cyclone development occurs in summer, when the water has had the opportunity to warm up. The season usually extends into late autumn. Globally, September is the most active month and May is the least active. Each ocean basin, however, has its own seasonal pattern.

BAD EFFECTS
Tropical cyclones have direct impacts on ecosystems. High wind speeds uproot and blow down trees and other vegetation. Heavy rainfall causes inland flooding, which leads to soil erosion and desalination of coastal saltwater estuaries. Storm surges often result in extensive beach erosion, damage to coral reefs, and can send sea water well inland. Pollution in the aftermath of a tropical cyclone comes from household chemicals, motor oil, pesticides, and building materials. These contaminate waterways and water supplies. Biogeochemical and ecological changes can last for years.

ABOVE An unusual and frightening sight for a sailor, a waterspout is actually a whirlwind caused by heavy air turbulence that sucks up water as it reaches the sea. This one was photographed over the Wadden Sea, near the Netherlands.

ABOVE In December 2008, Cyclone Nargis hit the village of La Put Tar in Myanmar (Burma), causing massive floods across the low-lying landscape.

RIGHT This satellite image shows the structure of twin tropical cyclones over Iceland. Moving in a counterclockwise motion they paralleled each other as they crossed the land.

...AND GOOD

Tropical cyclones provide many beneficial functions to natural habitats in the tropics and subtropics where most species have developed adaptations for living in this type of an environment. High winds and storm surges increase sediment and dissolved oxygen content that support fish and other aquatic species. High soil runoffs flow downstream and replenish sediments in estuaries that may have been eroded through wind and wave action. Many plant species found in the tropics have shown that they can rapidly grow back due to the stimulation of new nutrients. Powerful waves often cause significant beach erosion but this can open up new habitats for dune and seagrasses. These storms are an important source of annual rainfall for many locations. They replenish inland wetlands and reduce the occurrences of wild fires. Although the negative and positive effects from tropical cyclones are abrupt, their changes to ecosystems can last for decades.

All the Same

Systems are called hurricanes if they form in the Atlantic and eastern Pacific Oceans. They are called typhoons if they form in the western Pacific Ocean, and cyclones if they form in the Indian Ocean.

The intensity of a tropical cyclone is usually determined using the Saffir-Simpson Scale, although other terms are sometimes used to describe tropical cyclone intensities. A "major hurricane" is used by the National Hurricane Center for hurricanes that reach maximum sustained 1-minute surface winds of at least 111 mph (96 knots/179 km/h). This is the equivalent of category 3, 4, and 5 on the Saffir-Simpson scale. A "super typhoon" is used by the US Joint Typhoon Warning Center for typhoons that reach maximum sustained 1-minute surface winds of at least 150 mph (130 knots/240 km/h). This is the equivalent of a strong Saffir-Simpson category 4 or category 5.

Saffir-Simpson Scale

CATEGORY	WIND SPEED MPH (KNOTS; KM/H)	STORM SURGE FT (M)
Tropical depression (TD)	0–38 (0–33; 0–62)	
Tropical storm (TS)	39–73 (34–63; 63–117)	0–3 (0–0.9)
1	74–95 (64–82; 119–153)	4–5 (1.2–1.5)
2	96–110 (83–95; 154–177)	6–8 (1.8–2.4)
3	111–130 (96–113; 178–209)	9–12 (2.7–3.7)
4	131–155 (114–135; 210–249)	13–18 (4.0–5.5)
5	greater than 155 (135; 249)	greater than 18 (5.5)

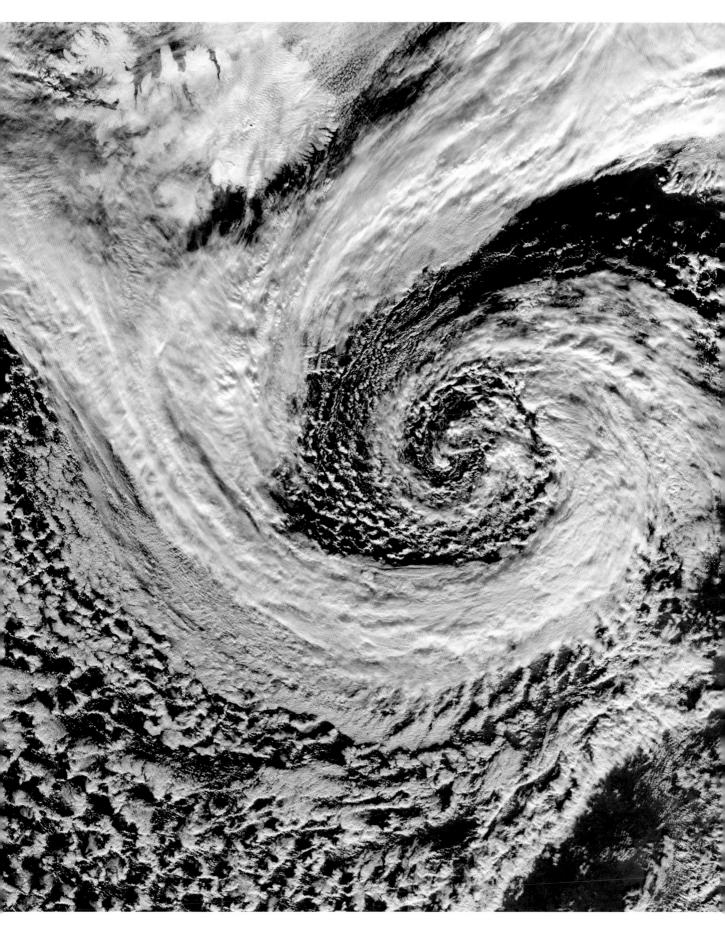

Saving Land from Sea

Humans, since they first began to occupy the coastal zone, have been involved in modifying it through various endeavors including fisheries, agriculture, transportation, housing, industry, recreation, and protection.

COASTAL CAPTIVATION

The attraction of the coast is evident in that more than half of the people of the most populous nations of the world live on or near the sea, and that 70 percent of the world's largest cities are located on the coast. Although population density and development along the coastline are already great, they continue to grow rapidly, adding an ever-increasing amount of pressure on the coastal system—a system that is among the most variable and fragile on Earth. Coastal change, whether caused by earthquake, volcanic eruption, sea-level rise, hurricane, or some other natural force and, indeed, by human endeavors such as beach mining, can alter the very reason that humans were drawn to the coast in the first place. As a result, once manmade structures are in place, major efforts—often at very great expense—are made to stabilize and protect them.

PERMANENT WAVE PROTECTION

Although there are many reasons to modify a coastal region—reclamation for agriculture, a housing development, or an industrial complex; artificial nourishment of a sand beach for recreation; or the creation of a marina—most also include some method of protection from the natural forces that impact shorelines. The primary objective of most structures is to keep waves from impacting the zone to be protected. Because of the great variability in the type, intensity, and frequency of waves along shorelines, engineers have devised a variety of forms of wave protection that are now found along many coastal sectors, especially those in the developed countries.

Probably the most common forms are hard-engineering structures, such as revetments, seawalls, and breakwaters. In general, the type used reflects

the anticipated intensity of the waves reaching the shore. These types of protection are constructed parallel to the zone to be shielded, and are made from a variety of materials including rubble, sheet metal, interlocking blocks, and especially concrete.

SEAWALLS

Revetments—structures designed to absorb the waves' energy—are designed for the least severe conditions. Seawalls are constructed in regions where very intense action such as typhoon- and tsunami-type waves and surges can be expected. Seawalls take many different forms—they may be vertical, sloping, stepped, or curved. They modify the natural land/water interface by converting the former contact zone into a cliff of various heights and forms. In Japan, seawalls have been constructed for protection against typhoons, some as high as 40 ft (12 m).

BREAKWATERS

Breakwaters, as the term implies, serve to reduce the intensity of the waves reaching the shore. The earliest breakwaters were used mainly for harbor protection; however, with the rapid increase in tourism, they are now common offshore from many recreational beaches. Offshore breakwaters may be exposed or

BELOW This surge of water over the levee in New Orleans was caused by Hurricane Gustav in 2008. This is the same area that had the first levee breach by Hurricane Katrina three years earlier.

LEFT The ancient wall around Talmont sur Gironde has protected it from sea erosion. Talmont sur Gironde has been voted the most beautiful village in France.

ABOVE A lighthouse marks the end of the breakwater off Long Beach, California. The wall protects the coast from savage waves crashing in from the Pacific.

BELOW Following a hurricane in Cancun, Mexico, workers pour sand to reconstruct the beach.

submerged, fixed or mobile, impermeable or permeable, all of which affect their function. Although the most common materials used are rubble—country rock—and concrete; armor, or interlocking blocks of various sizes and shapes are also present.

JETTIES

Groins and jetties contrast with seawalls in that they are oriented more or less at right angles to the shoreline and serve slightly different functions. Groins are designed to trap longshore drift and prevent erosion; jetties help prevent drift from entering a river mouth and are usually located updrift from a navigable channel. As groins trap sand on their updrift side, they invariably cause erosion downdrift. Because such a result is repetitive, groin fields are usually the result of this type of protection, and along some coasts of the world, these extend for miles.

There are, however, many extreme or longterm events from which protection may not be possible. Typhoons and tsunamis are two examples. In addition, there are the issues of coastal subsidence and sea level rise. The latter, if the projected glacial melting and ocean water warming materialize, will impact the entire coastline and will bring a new dimension to the need for coastal protection.

Enhancing Nature

In addition to the rigid structures used to protect the coast, there are the many so-called "environmentally friendly" procedures of beach fill, dune building, and vegetation planting. Their advantage is that they are compatible with the natural processes of wind, waves, and biology, in contrast to hard structures that permanently affect shoreline materials, forms, and processes. These procedures and structures are aimed, at least partially, at providing some protection from the more or less normal shoreline processes.

Icebergs

Icebergs are large pieces of floating freshwater ice that have calved (broken away) from a glacier or ice shelf. Ninety-three percent of all icebergs are found in the Southern Ocean surrounding Antarctica. Another 6 percent originate from the Greenland ice cap, the great majority of which are formed by west Greenland glaciers. A small number originate from glaciers on Baffin Island or other islands in the Arctic Ocean.

OPPOSITE This impressive iceberg is drifting in the iceberg graveyard, an area where many icebergs from the Weddell Sea end up after circulating with the Antarctic Circumpolar Current. The current is the strongest in the world, moving more than 4.8 billion cubic feet (0.1 billion m³) of water per second.

BELOW Eco-tourists from a research vessel in Antarctica approach a massive iceberg in Wilhelmina Bay off Enterprise Island.

TIP OF THE ICEBERG

Ice floats because it is less dense than water. Typically, up to 90 percent of an iceberg is submerged, making it impossible to know the size or configuration of the underwater portion. This can cause serious problems for vessels—or anything—that encounter an iceberg.

The size of icebergs varies from small chunks the size of a refrigerator to huge masses. Most of them rise from between 1 ft (30 cm) to about 250 ft (75 m) above the water. One giant discovered in the North Atlantic measured 550 ft (168 m) above sea level, the height of a 55-story building. The largest icebergs have calved from Antarctica's Ross Ice Shelf. In 2000, a mass of ice identified as B-15 broke away from the shelf. It measured 23 x 183 miles (37 x 295 km), and covered an area of 4,250 square miles (11,000 km²).

Icebergs also are classified by their shape. Many Antarctic icebergs are tabular—they resemble a plateau with a flat surface, steep sides, and a width-to-height ratio greater than 5:1. Icebergs in northern waters tend to be non-tabular in form. Shapes vary, and are identified by terms such as blocky, dome, dry-dock, pinnacle, and wedge.

FORMATION AND DISTRIBUTION

Most icebergs form during the warm season, because the higher temperature accelerates the rate of movement of glaciers, and subsequent calving. When the edge of the moving glacier reaches water, chunks break off and float away as icebergs. Each year as many as 35,000 icebergs are produced in the Northern Hemisphere, while several hundred thousand form in the Antarctic region.

Once formed, icebergs are moved around by ocean currents. It may take 3,000 years for a west Greenland iceberg to exit Baffin Bay, pass through the Davis Strait, and enter the Labrador Sea. Throughout its journey, the iceberg is carried by the cold water of the Labrador Current. An estimated 99 percent of all Greenland icebergs melt long before they reach the Atlantic. Once there, the warm waters of the Gulf Stream and North Atlantic Current melt the ice within a matter of weeks. In both hemispheres, the extreme limit of icebergs is determined by water currents. Forty-eight degrees of latitude, both north and south, is generally regarded as the limit, although exceptions do occur, particularly in the Indian Ocean where cold waters of the West Wind Drift can transport ice masses as far north as 35°S off Africa's southeastern coast. In the North Atlantic, an occasional iceberg will drift as far south as 35°N.

HUMAN FACTORS

Each year, several hundred icebergs drift south of 48°N and enter the North Atlantic shipping lanes where they pose a potential hazard to navigation.

In 1912, there was no system to track icebergs. On April 14 of that year, during its maiden voyage, *RMS Titanic* struck an iceberg. In less than three hours, the supposedly unsinkable vessel sank, taking with it 1,517 of its 2,223 passengers. The tragedy resulted in an immediate demand for a system to locate and monitor icebergs and their movement within shipping lanes.

Since 1914, various groups have tracked these ice hazards. In 1995, the US National Ice Center (NIC) was created to observe icebergs and map their distribution worldwide. Today, about 95 percent of all data used to locate and track icebergs is obtained from satellites equipped with several types of remote sensors.

Clearly, large icebergs can inflict the most damage to a vessel. But they are more easily detected by a ship's radar or satellite imagery. Smaller icebergs are more difficult to detect, and therefore pose a greater hazard to ships of all sizes.

Icy Profits

Icebergs have spawned new industries. Iceberg tourism is growing in popularity; so many tourists are now visiting Antarctica that they pose a threat to the continent's fragile ecosystem. In Canada, the Newfoundland Labrador Liquor Corporation is making vodka using water from icebergs drifting off the coast. It was once even suggested that Saudi Arabia could solve at least part of its chronic water problem by having plastic-wrapped icebergs towed into the Red Sea!

Historic Ocean Trade Routes

Maritime trade was well established in many parts of the world by the second millennium BCE, by which time the Sumerians, Indians, and Chinese had been practicing oceanic navigation for over a thousand years. By 1500 BCE, Phoenician galleys were plying the waters of the Mediterranean, and through the Pillars of Hercules (Strait of Gibraltar) and beyond. As early as 1900 BCE, the Egyptians had constructed a canal that linked the mighty Nile River to the Red Sea. By 1500 BCE, Egyptian vessels (perhaps crewed by Phoenician sailors) were sailing southward along Africa's east coast to the legendary Land of Punt in the Horn of Africa.

BENEFITS OF MARITIME TRADE

Over time, shipbuilding techniques and navigational skills improved enormously. The land-based trade routes were dangerous, time-consuming, and costly. Shipping, although hazardous, was faster and much cheaper than land travel.

Avenues of waterborne trade developed between the sources of exotic goods and their markets. Luxury goods such as spices, incense, gems, precious metals, and amber brought huge profits to traders. The value of some items—such as spices from the islands of Southeast Asia—increased by as much as ten thousand percent by the time they reached European markets.

Much of the world's contemporary distribution of cultural practices can be traced to early trade, much of

ABOVE A seventeenth-century Venetian arsenal or shipyard. Venice was well-known for its many maritime exploits.

BELOW A nineteenth-century view of Victoria, Hong Kong, from the harbor. Strategically situated, Hong Kong became a British colony in 1841 and soon became an important trading base for English interests.

it by water. Some early centers of waterborne trade included east Asia, south Asia, southwest Asia, and the Mediterranean region. By the fourteenth century, northwestern European countries around the North and Baltic seas were engaged in trade.

EUROPEAN AGE OF EXPLORATION AND ITS IMPACT

Prince Henry of Portugal ("Henry the Navigator") reshaped the world in many ways. Although he did not sail widely, he supported and promoted oceanic navigation. Shipbuilding, sail making, and navigational

skills all advanced under his direct or indirect tutelage. Within a century of the opening of his school of navigation, European sailors ventured out to sea and discovered the "New World" in the process. By the dawn of the sixteenth century, the world order was on the brink of a massive human and cultural transformation.

Soon after Christopher Columbus's epic voyages, the Americas were almost completely drawn into the western European sphere of influence. Spain had laid claim to much of what is now "Latin America." The Portuguese had established a foothold in Brazil. The Spanish, British, French, and Dutch claimed lands within North America and the Caribbean region. As a result of these early contacts, trade links were established between New World holdings and Old World imperialistic nations. In order to protect their economic interests and trade monopolies, Europeans soon colonized the new lands.

Throughout the New World (including Australia and New Zealand), European languages are spoken, southwest Asian and European religions are practiced, and Old World crops, livestock, and poultry dominate the agricultural landscape. Many New World peoples, particularly those of British descent, prefer tea over coffee. This taste is a legacy from British south Asian colonial holdings and the tea trade. In many Latin American countries, the Caribbean, and parts of Central America, most of the population can trace their ancestry back to Africa and the dreaded slave trade. In response to trading opportunities, major shipping routes developed. On both sides of the Atlantic, port cities developed and prospered. A great

ABOVE The West India Docks in London, built at the turn of the nineteenth century by merchant Robert Milligan, were the delivery point for produce from the West Indies, such as coffee and sugar.

deal of new world architecture, dress styles, law, and other aspects of culture can be traced back to early European maritime trade, along with subsequent developments such as mass migration.

It is often said that sailors have vivid imaginations. As a result of their imaginations, maritime legends abound. The earliest documented strange occurrences are found in Homer's *Odyssey*, written about 900 BCE. From ancient mermaids and monsters to the mysterious disappearances in the Bermuda Triangle in the northwest Atlantic Ocean, the sea has always been a fascinating mosaic of intrigue, romance, and legends.

Spice Trade

Since ancient times, exotic spices have held economic significance usually reserved only for precious metals. The quest for spices served as a catalyst for oceanic exploration with the search for direct trade routes to the Indian Ocean. The spice trade also stimulated cultural interaction between southern and southeastern Asia and Europe on a scale not surpassed until the sixteenth-century exchange between Europe and the Americas.

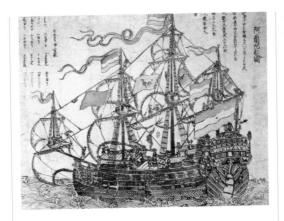

RIGHT A seventeenth-century Japanese engraving of a Dutch ship of the Dutch East India Company, a trading company that flourished for almost two hundred years.

RIGHT As well as peppercorns and cardamom, India has long been an important source of cinnamon. This photograph from 1922 shows Indian laborers drying the popular spice.

BELOW A nineteenth-century painting of an English executive from the East India Company riding in an Indian procession. The English trading firm also traded textiles, tea, and opium.

A SYMBOL OF WEALTH

Pepper, nutmeg, and cloves, among other spices, had always been highly prized in Europe, and were used in food preparation and preservation, as well as medicinally. Climatic conditions precluded their cultivation in Europe as the most valued spices came from the tropics. Other than salt and locally grown herbs, European cuisines relied on spice imports from Asia. India, particularly its southern tip, played a vital role as the chief producer of peppercorns and cardamom. Conveniently, the country also was a midway point between Europe and the nutmeg- and cloves-growing islands of today's Indonesia.

During medieval times, the Arabs were deeply involved as middlemen in the spice trade, particularly from India westward. Spices eventually found their way to the Mediterranean region and from there, with the help of Venetian traders, to the rest of Europe. As with any rare and exotic product, only the wealthy could afford spices. The culinary distinction of having a dash of pepper on meat served to guests was a sign of luxury. The markup on the price of pepper in Europe, for example, was 10,000 percent that of Asia. Those who could afford such spices—or indeed fine Chinese silk for clothing—were perceived as being wealthy and socially significant individuals.

TWO-WAY TRADE

The spice trade was never one directional. Archeological finds in India's Tamil Nadu state include first century BCE Roman artefacts, coins, and amphorae filled with olive oil and wine—all Mediterranean products. East–West exchange during Roman times was a continuation of even earlier connections between Ancient Greece and the East. Developments in navigation and shipbuilding improved connections between civilizations, while sailing across the Indian Ocean became routine, as long as mariners understood the monsoon winds. These winds allowed continuous travel in one direction only in a season; this limitation extended the time between shipments.

Many cultural traits "traveled" to other regions on ships loaded with spices. During Arab expansion, Islam reached the Spice Islands (the Moluccas and Banda Islands), and the shores of the Pacific. It was this trade that explains why the world's most populous Islamic nation, Indonesia, lies outside the Middle East. Chinese merchants, too, became involved in the spice trade, adding another dimension to this global interaction.

PORTUGUESE DOMINATION

It was only when the Portuguese captain Bartolomeu
Diaz navigated around the southern tip of Africa in
1488—and his successor, Vasco da Gama, sailed on
to India in 1498—that the previously unimaginable
happened: a direct sea route between Europe and the
spice-producing areas of the East was proven. With
this new link, the cultural pendulum swung toward
the European side. Without middlemen, and with the
seas open for business, transportation obstacles became
minimal. The price of pepper in Lisbon dropped to a
fifth of what it had been!

To keep the peace between the powerful Catholic
trading nations of Spain and Portugal, the pope had
divided the world into two spheres of interest. Under
the 1494 Treaty of Tordesillas, Portugal was granted
"rights" to the Eastern hemisphere, Spain to the Western. Portuguese colonial enterprises soon stretched
from Africa to India to New Guinea, and for the first
time, the spice trade was in the hands of one power.

In 1505, the first European, Italian explorer Ludovico
de Varthema, reached the Moluccas. This was the only
place in Asia that grew cloves, a crop of immeasurable
value. The information he gathered provided the
Portuguese with exclusive knowledge of the area.

By 1512, the Portuguese controlled ports in Goa
(India) and Malacca (Malay Peninsula), which allowed
them to oversee trade and shipment. However, this
early monopoly did not last long. Before the end of the
sixteenth century, the Portuguese were already overshadowed in the East Indies (Indonesia) by the Dutch,
who, in 1602, created the Dutch East India Company
to solidify their control of the region.

The British began their expansion in the 1630s in
India, and soon after became a dominant European
force in South Asia. Although the spice trade continued
to grow during the seventeenth century, making many
merchants extremely wealthy, Asian spice production
lost its prominence as new plantations in Africa and
the Americas were established.

ABOVE Indian women walk on
a trail through drying chillies.
Introduced to India by Portuguese traders in the sixteenth
century, chilli is an integral
ingredient of many traditional
Indian and other Southeast
Asian dishes.

Slave Trade

When one thinks of the slave trade, images of the trans-Atlantic shipment of Africans to the Americas typically come to mind. In reality, the history of slavery is much more complex and involves many cultures, races, and oceanic routes. Slave-carrying vessels plied many waters, including the Mediterranean and Red seas, and those of the Atlantic, Indian, and even Pacific oceans.

Nearly 4,000 years ago, Egyptians enslaved African peoples. The Code of Hammurabi (c. 1760 BCE) refers to slavery in ancient Babylon and throughout Mesopotamia and beyond. Slavery is mentioned in Homer's poems (c. tenth century BCE), and Aristotle supported slavery on philosophical grounds. Centuries before the

RIGHT Brazil was one of the most likely destinations for these slaves taken from west Africa. Here, and in parts of the Caribbean, slaves were made to work on Portuguese sugar plantations.

dawn of the Atlantic slave trade, about 1.25 million Europeans were captured by North Africans (Barbary pirates) and sold into bondage. Most of these Christian slaves were captured in settlements in coastal areas of the Mediterranean, Iberia, and northwest Europe. In some coastal regions of Spain, Portugal, and Italy, slave raids were so common that the coastal zone became nearly depopulated. These captives were sold to slave owners scattered throughout much of the Arab world.

Through time, the Old World slave trade involved nearly all of Africa, much of Europe, most of Southwest Asia, large portions of coastal southern Asia, and even China, where African slaves were reported in Canton in the twelfth century.

ARAB SLAVE TRADE

Over a millennium before Europeans became involved in the African slave trade, Arabs had developed a vast

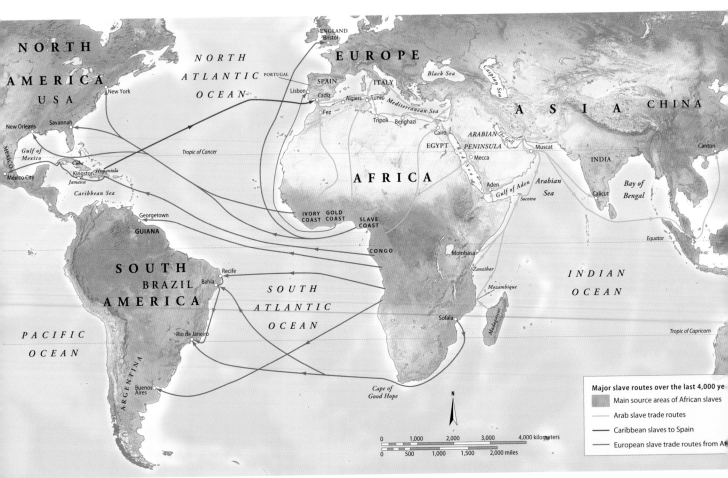

Major slave routes over the last 4,000 ye...

- Main source areas of African slaves
- Arab slave trade routes
- Caribbean slaves to Spain
- European slave trade routes from A...

Slave Numbers

Although no less brutal, the Atlantic slave trade paled in numbers compared to that of the Old World. Over a period of more than three centuries, around 6.3 million Africans were documented as having been transported to the Americas. Allowing for perhaps several million more whose records were lost through time, the total number enslaved is believed to have been between 9 and 10 million. In terms of destination, estimates vary widely. Based upon a variety of sources, it appears that they were distributed as follows:

Caribbean islands[1]	40%	3,800,000
Portuguese Brazil	38%	3,650,000
Spanish America[2]	16%	1,550,000
British North America	4%	400,000
Elsewhere in Atlantic Basin	2%	200,000

[1] British, French, and Dutch colonies
[2] Includes Spanish-held islands in the Caribbean

LEFT An eighteenth-century engraving of a group of slaves being taken to a ship. Slave ships were usually cargo or merchant ships that were converted so they could carry large numbers of slaves. The plan for stowing this human cargo is shown at bottom.

slave-trading network. Millions of Europeans and Africans (mostly from East Africa) were taken to countries that stretched from Morocco to the Middle East and on to southern and eastern Asia. Estimates of the human numbers involved in the Arab slave trade run as high as 25 million.

Although some land routes existed, most Arab slave trading involved routes in the Mediterranean, Red Sea, and the Indian Ocean. Little documentation exists to provide specific details of Arab sea routes. The slave-carrying ships were dhows, traditional Arab sailing vessels with one or more lateen sails. Some of these ships were large enough to carry a substantial human cargo. The Arab slave trade in the Indian Ocean and adjacent waters peaked during the nineteenth century.

ATLANTIC SLAVE TRADE

The Atlantic slave trade began in 1495. On his second voyage, Christopher Columbus captured more than one thousand Taino Indians on the Caribbean island of Hispaniola. He attempted to ship about 500 of them to Spain, although some 200 died en route. The several hundred American natives who survived the voyage to Spain were then sold as slaves.

In the Americas, nearly all slavery was associated with tropical and subtropical plantations. Europeans were not accustomed to the tropical heat and humidity and often had a cultural antipathy toward manual labor. For a variety of reasons, indigenous Americans were poorly suited to performing slave labor. So the European colonists turned to Africa and thus began a heinous trade in human beings that lasted from the early sixteenth century until well into the 1800s. Most slaves toiled as laborers on sugar plantations; others worked on cotton, coffee, cacao, indigo, or tobacco plantations, or as domestic servants.

The Atlantic slave trade developed into what is often referred to as a "Triangular Trade." First, slaves

were taken from various coastal areas of West Africa to tropical and subtropical America. Second, New World slave-produced agricultural commodities such as sugar, rum, and cotton found their way to European ports. Third, various manufactured goods—such as trinkets, cloth, firearms, and alcohol—were taken to African slave-trading ports by European slave merchants who used the items for the purchase of more slaves from black slave dealers or from African kings.

Britain and the United States both banned the slave trade in 1807, but slavery itself continued well into the nineteenth century. Brazil was the last country—in 1831—to abolish the Atlantic slave trade.

ABOVE Conditions on board slave ships were deplorable. Many hundreds of slaves were crammed into spaces far too small for their numbers. The hold was hot, the air was fetid, and the unhygienic setting meant that many did not survive the long voyage.

Tea Trade

Although the exact date for the brewing of tea as a beverage is unknown, many scholars regard the Chinese as the pioneers of tea as long as 5,000 years ago. The earliest instance of tea drinking has been attributed to the Chinese emperor, Shen Nung (Shennong), who promoted the development of agriculture and the extraction of the medicinal properties of herbs around 2730 BCE.

OPPOSITE The *John Wood* arrives in Bombay, India, in the early 1850s. Vast quantities of Indian-grown tea were sent to Britain in the nineteenth century.

BELOW Japanese women in the kitchen make preparations for the tea ceremony. The tea ceremony is not only a social event, it has religious overtones and there is a strong emphasis on esthetic principles.

EARLY TEA TRADE

From that time, tea became Imperial China's favorite beverage. By the eighth century CE, it was popular all over China, partly as a result of Lu Yu's seminal work, *The Classic of Tea*, which praised tea as a "grand plant." During this period, Buddhist monks, coming from northern India into China and onward into Japan and the Korean Peninsula, spread the habit of tea drinking while also disseminating their religion.

By the mid-twelfth century, teahouses had been established all over China. However, with the conquest of China by the Mongols, tea fell out of favor with the Imperial court, although it continued to flourish in Japan. The first instance of tea cultivation in Japan was recorded in the town of Uji to the south of Kyoto. Uji's rich alluvial soil permitted green tea cultivation. Green tea remains one of Japan's favorite beverages. By the beginning of the sixteenth century, the brewing and serving of tea—the traditional tea ceremony—assumed semi-religious status among Japan's Zen Buddhists.

EUROPEAN COLONIZATION AND THE GLOBAL TEA TRADE

By the mid-1600s, China was the main producer of tea in the world. During this time, European colonial outposts in East and Southeast Asia, which were already trading spice, silk, and pepper, now looked to tea as another commodity. The Portuguese colony of Macau in southeastern China was already trading tea with the Dutch East Indies town of Batavia (present-day Jakarta, Indonesia), and tea drinking had become popular in the Netherlands. However, the Dutch East India Company had limited early success in the tea trade because China was closed to them.

In the early 1700s, the British East India Company began to think of Chinese tea as a lucrative form of commerce. The British outpost in Canton, situated adjacent to Portuguese Macau, began to load their ships bound for London with tea. Initially this was the beverage of the wealthy, but by the middle of the eighteenth century, tea had replaced ale and gin as the drink of choice of the British.

The tea trade had crossed the Atlantic with the Dutch in the 1650s, and by 1664, when the British took over New Holland (renaming it New York), tea drinking was well established in the colonies. In 1770 the British parliament imposed a tax on all tea imports that were not bought from the British East India Company. This instigated protests—the most famous being the Boston Tea Party in 1773—which ultimately led to the birth of the United States of America.

As demand in Europe increased in the eighteenth century, other European nations—Denmark, France, and Sweden—also became involved in the tea trade. The Russians increased their overland trade routes to China in order to meet the growing demand for the beverage in their country.

NEW AREAS OF GROWTH

The Opium Wars, fought in the 1830s between Britain and China over the trade of opium for tea, provided the impetus for Britain to seek other areas for the cultivation of tea. Northeastern India's Assam district was seen as a favorable tea-producing region. Tea was also introduced into southern India's Nilgiri Hills. With the creation of the Assam Company, tea from Assam, together with that from China, reached London in large quantities and reinforced the British East India Company's role as the leading tea trader. The loss of its monopoly in the mid-nineteenth century, however,

RIGHT A trading card, c. 1900, from the Thomson & Taylor Spice Co., purveyors of fine tea, whose primary source of tea leaves was the Dutch East Indies.

opened up the trade, and led, each harvest time, to the "race" between British and American tea clippers to be the first to reach the London Tea Exchange from China.

In 1876, the failure of the coffee crops in Ceylon (present-day Sri Lanka) prompted the introduction of tea plants to the island. These were cultivated by indentured labor from India's population of Tamils. From the foothills of Assam in northeastern India to the Central Highlands of Ceylon, British India's tea trade became one of the more successful colonial experiments in South Asia.

However, tea cultivation and trade were not just restricted to China and India. Tea was also planted in East Africa in what is today Kenya, Malawi, and Zimbabwe, and the region is still considered to be Africa's home of tea.

Now, in the twenty-first century, more people in the world drink tea than any other beverage.

RIGHT Workers in Ceylon pack and weigh tea for the British tea market. This illustration dates from 1905. Tea from Ceylon is popular with tea drinkers to this day.

Myths and Superstitions About the Sea

Whether you are on a large supertanker or a small fishing boat, the myths of the sea are alive and well. Sailors have many sayings that convey their superstitions. "Red sky at night, sailor's delight; red sky in the morning, sailor's warning"—this had its origins in the Bible. A expression used by mariners from at least the eighteenth century employs a euphemism: If a sailor dies at sea, he is said to go to "Davy Jones's Locker." Above all, for a sailor, the sea governs life and death: "What the sea wants, the sea gets."

ABOVE The Ancient Mariner, who, in Coleridge's famous poem, shoots an albatross with his crossbow, bringing a curse on the ship. All the sailors die, the Mariner the only survivor. His punishment is to wander the Earth telling his sad tale.

ANCIENT MYTHS

For the Greeks, Poseidon was king of the sea. The philosopher Plato, spoke of Atlantis, a kingdom from outside the Pillars of Hercules that dominated the world and then disappeared into the sea. Many still seek the lost Atlantis today. The ancient Israelites had Leviathan, a monster that swam the oceans well into the Middle Ages, as well as Jonah, who was swallowed by a great fish. In Greenland, there was the Mother of the Sea—should a taboo be broken, she would gather all sea-life to her. To release the animals, a shaman had to untangle her hair.

TABOOS AND SAYINGS

Some myths have biblical origins, such as unlucky Friday. Sailing on the day Christ was crucified is said to bring danger. So do the first Monday in April (the day Cain killed Abel), the last day of December (Judas Iscariot committed suicide on this day), and the second Monday in August (when Sodom and Gomorrah were destroyed). By contrast, Sunday is the best day—"Sunday sail, never fail"— since this is the day that Christ rose from the dead.

Many sailors' beliefs are well known. A woman on board was often thought to bring bad luck, for unless she has her breasts bared, she would make the sea angry—hence the nude female torsos carved on the bows of ships.

Equally known for bringing bad luck are red-haired, cross-eyed, or flat-footed people; clergymen; black bags; flowers; left foot first on the boat; the cutting of hair and nails; throwing stones overboard; whistling on the first day of sail; looking back; saying the word "drowned;" and wishing good luck. On the other hand, good luck is said to come from a ring in the ear; a silver coin under the masthead; a stolen piece of wood in the keel; pouring wine on the deck; dolphins; swallows; the feather of a wren killed on New Year's Day; and keeping a black cat on board ship.

MERMAIDS AND ALBATROSSES

One of the most persistent myths about the seas concerns mermaids and mermen. Triton, the son of Poseidon, was said to be a merman—half-man and half-dolphin. The race to which he gave birth—the Tritons—played tricks on sailors. Then there is the mermaid, a woman with the tail of fish. A mermaid has long green or gold hair, and is seen on moonlit nights combing her hair while looking into a mirror. She may sing beautifully, luring ships close to the rocks, or may howl like the wind to bring on a storm.

Another belief involves the royal albatross. With a wing span of more than 5 ft (1.5 m), and an ability to fly for weeks over the ocean without touching land, the albatross is a potent symbol of life. Killing an albatross brings ill luck. Samuel Taylor Coleridge immortalized this myth in his poem *The Rime of the Ancient Mariner*.

LEFT A Southern Royal albatross (*Diomedea epomophora*). Dead sailors were said to be reincarnated as albatrosses, and seafarers considered it bad luck to harm one of these birds.

FERDINAN. MAGALA.

The mariner kills one of these birds and has to wear it around his neck until he learns how to pray for forgiveness. But by then all his shipmates are dead.

DEVIL'S TRIANGLES

A more recent maritime myth has its supporters and skeptics. On December 5, 1945, five US Air Force bombers went missing off Florida. A search aircraft also disappeared. Stories surfaced of earlier disappearances in a "triangle," with its points at Florida, Puerto Rico, and Bermuda, so the idea of the Bermuda or Devil's Triangle arose. Theories abounded, including that the triangle was caused by equipment left behind by aliens; or perhaps demons from Atlantis; or paranormal activity; magnetic fields; methane eruptions; piracy; storms, or human error.

In the Pacific Ocean south of Tokyo, there is the Devil's Sea, or Dragon's Triangle. Stories of lost ships and planes abound—even a possible reason for the

disappearance of the aviator, Amelia Earhart. Theories too are legion, including an extra-gravitational hole that connects the two triangles.

What is clear is that the sea holds such a sway over those who sail on her that fear—and respect—will always need to be evident.

ABOVE This sixteenth-century painting is an allegory of the voyages of Ferdinand Magellan. It shows some of the more fantastical characters and animals associated with the sea.

LEFT This nineteenth-century Thai mural depicts a formidable ogress who guards the ocean, fighting Hanuman, the monkey king. The story comes from the Hindu epic the *Ramayana*, known as *Ramakian* in Thai.

The Economic Importance of the Ocean

With 71 percent of Earth's surface covered by the global sea, it is little wonder that people have long been involved with the ocean and its varied resources. As recently as the mid-twentieth century, many viewed the ocean as an infinite source of resource wealth. Today, we know that this is not true.

WHO CONTROLS MARINE RESOURCES?

Competition for, and control over, marine resources have long been contentious issues. As early as the 1600s, a "freedom of the seas" policy limited national rights to 3 nautical miles (5.7 km) from a nation's coast. This distance, not surprisingly, coincided with a cannon's range. Beyond that limit, waters were considered to be international and free for all.

During the twentieth century, the human population soared and maritime (including fishing) technology greatly improved. Demands placed upon the global sea and its resources increased greatly, and led to over-exploitation. Stocks of commercially valuable fish, whales, many crustaceans, and other marine resources have been in sharp decline for decades, some to the point of near-extinction.

Faced with the prospect of increased competition for resources in nearby waters, many countries sought to extend their claims. Some claimed a 12 nautical mile (22 km) limit. A few, including the United States, laid claim to all resources on their continental shelf. By

BELOW Dockworkers unload sacks of imported sugar at the port of Umm Qasr, in southern Iraq. Umm Qasr is the country's only deepwater port.

BELOW Oil is an economically significant resource, and oil companies invest huge sums in oil exploration and exploitation, both on land and in the oceans. Here, an offshore oil exploration rig in the North Sea burns off some of the oil and natural gas it has just tapped.

1950, most coastal nations claimed control of waters within 200 nautical miles (370 km) of their shore. Today, the limits are established by the United Nations Convention on the Law of the Sea. Under this agreement, coastal countries can exercise control over all waters within 12 nautical miles (22 km) of their shore.

The convention also established an Exclusive Economic Zone that extends 200 nautical miles (370 km) from the shore. Finally, a country may claim mineral rights to its continental shelf, but not beyond 350 nautical miles (650 km).

HARVESTING THE SEA'S BIOTIC RESOURCES

Geographer Carl Ortwin Sauer believed that the seashore of eastern Africa was the original home of humankind. There, Sauer reasoned, early humans harvested the abundant edible marine life found in tidal pools, including fish, crustaceans, shellfish, seaweed, and other marine life. Since the dawn of human history, the ocean has been a source of biotic resources. Marine fur-bearing animals such as seals and otters have been hunted for centuries. The phrase, "burning the midnight oil" originated with the widespread use of whale oil lamps during the first half of the nineteenth century. By mid-century, the oil sold for as much as US$1,500 a barrel. Fortunately, for the

rapidly declining whale population, by the 1860s kerosene offered a much cheaper and more efficient alternative source of fuel. Pearls have long been a valuable marine resource in many coastal locations. Through time, oceanic fishing has provided humans with a major source of protein-rich food. However, as stocks of natural fish, shrimp, mussels, and other prized marine delicacies dwindle, supplies increasingly come from "farmed" stocks.

MINERAL RESOURCES

In addition to salt (sodium chloride), seawater contains at least 60 chemical elements, only about a half-dozen of which are being exploited today. Salt, which amounts to about 80 percent of the mineral content of seawater, is the primary chemical element extracted from the sea.

Magnesium is the only metallic element that is taken directly from ocean water. Gold, diamonds, and several metals including tin and titanium, are taken from the ocean floor. Eventually, it may become feasible to extract manganese nodules from the ocean bed.

Fresh water is being produced through the process of desalination. As technology improves and costs are lowered, a growing and thirsty coastal population will no doubt increase its dependence upon the sea for much of its domestic water supply.

ENERGY FROM THE SEA

The movement of water resulting from tidal changes, waves, or currents, can be harnessed to produce clean

RIGHT A desalination plant in Spain. Desalination is the chemical process whereby salt is removed from seawater, making it suitable for drinking.

BELOW Fish has always been a very important part of the human diet. Here, frozen fish, ready for export, are being loaded onto a ship.

energy, and this is already being done on a limited basis. The primary energy sources that are being extracted from off-shore deposits on continental shelves are petroleum and natural gas.

Today's technology allows rigs to drill ever deeper. Test wells have been drilled in 7,100 ft (2,165 m) of water and then through another 16,000 ft (4,877 m) of sand, rock, and salt off the coast of Brazil.

THE SEA'S MAGNETIC ATTRACTION

A considerable percentage of Earth's population lives within a short distance of the sea. Some of them harvest the various marine resources. Others depend upon ocean-based commerce. And still others come to the sea as tourists. Today, a rapidly increasing number of people are attracted to the world's many beautiful seacoasts, drawn by their natural splendor, as well as the amenities, and myriad recreational options.

Hunters and Gatherers

Since the dawn of time, hunting and gathering have been the traditional methods for humanity to obtain food and other essential materials. The sea has always produced a bountiful harvest for those who live near it, and for those who venture out into its waters. Yet today, the outlook is less promising, with over-fishing and excess harvesting of sea creatures.

PEARLS

Pearls, long treasured by humans all over the world as a precious gem, are produced by several species of aquatic mollusk including the oyster, freshwater mussel, and occasionally the abalone. Pearls are produced when a grain of sand, grit, or other irritant lodges inside the host shell while it is open during feeding. The intruding particle becomes surrounded by a substance called nacre that gradually builds up in layers to form a protective coating that eventually becomes a pearl.

Traditional pearl hunting was a very hazardous activity, involving a great deal of luck and guesswork. Divers would descend to depths up to 125 ft (45 m) on a single breath, manually collect large numbers of shellfish, then return to the surface where the shells, occasionally revealing a pearl, were searched. Divers risked shark attack and encountering other hostile marine creatures, as well as waves, storms, and even drowning—often as a result of nitrogen narcosis.

In 1916, the Japanese entrepreneur Kokichi Miki-moto patented a technique to produce cultured pearls, whereby a round smooth irritant is artificially introduced into the gonad of an oyster and allowed to mature. This innovation transformed the pearl industry because it allowed the large-scale production of perfectly formed, high quality pearls. Cultured pearls can be distinguished from more valuable natural pearls by x-rays, which reveal the gem's inner nucleus.

Nowadays, almost 100 percent of pearls sold are cultured—large aquatic farms are found all over the world, including Japan, China, Mexico, Tahiti, New Zealand, and Australia.

SEALS

Seals, particularly the harp seal, are hunted commercially in Canada, Greenland, Russia, Norway, and Namibia for their pelts, blubber, and meat, and to ensure that populations do not increase to the extent that they endanger other species. They are also an important source of food and income in some small coastal settlements where other options are limited.

For millennia, aboriginal people have used seal skins to make waterproof clothing. In the twentieth century, seal hunting became an important industry, resulting in a major decline in populations. Annual quotas are now based on recommendations of the International Council for the Exploration of the Sea. Canada harvests the vast majority of the world's seals, including baby seals, which are seasonally clubbed to death. This practice is highly controversial, attracting considerable protests and wide media coverage.

Seal blubber is used to make oil, which is used in lamps, some medicines, and dietary supplements. Pelts make up over half the value of a seal, fetching prices that often exceed US$100. Some meat is sold to various Asian fodder and pet food markets.

High levels of mercury are now being found in the blood and tissues of seals and their predators, including sharks, polar bears, and humans—particularly the Inuit populations of the Arctic region.

WHALES

For thousands of years, humans have hunted whales, primarily for food and oil. Populations remained stable until the seventeenth century, when efficient fleets and factory ships began to harvest them in ever-increasing numbers. This resulted in a dramatic decline in the numbers of most whale species.

BELOW Japanese pearl divers, c. 1939. The divers collected the oysters, put their catch in the wooden tubs, and later handed them over to the collection boats. These female divers averaged about 300 oysters a day.

The International Whaling Commission (IWC) was formed in 1946, with a brief to manage conservation, resource management, and the conflicting needs of stakeholders. In 1986, it introduced a moratorium on commercial whaling, with mixed success.

Some whaling countries, including Canada, refused to join the IWC, and so are not bound by its decisions. Some member countries, including Japan and Norway, continue to harvest whales in the name of "scientific research." The stated aim is to determine the numbers and migratory movements of whale populations. But anti-whaling organizations claim that these programs are a front for commercial whaling, and point out that large amounts of whale meat are sold in local supermarkets. They also assert that the annual sample size (Norway around 1,000, and Japan 1,330 minke whales) is unnecessarily large, and that the required information can be obtained by harmless methods such as studying small samples of whale tissue or excrement.

Small-scale whaling also occurs in several regions, including Indonesia and some Caribbean countries, where whale hunting by non-automated methods has long been a traditional pursuit.

The International Whaling Commission sanctions these activities and imposes annual quotas.

LEFT A nineteenth-century hand-tinted engraving showing whalers harpooning a whale by hand—a perilous operation. The carcasses were taken back to the ship for processing.

BELOW A pearl farmer inspects his oyster shells. Today's cultured pearl industry is not only very profitable, it is also reliable— growers can decide the shape and size of the pearls produced.

The Fishing Industry

The fishing industry involves the catching, farming, preserving, transporting, and selling of fish or seafood products. The largest sector of the industry is commercial fishing, including aquaculture (farming), but many millions of people around the world participate in smaller-scale subsistence fishing or recreational fishing.

TYPES OF FISHING

Commercial fishing provides large quantities of fish and other marine products for human consumption, or for use in other manufacturing purposes. The larger companies run their own fishing fleets and fisheries; their products are sold to grocery chains, or agents.

Subsistence fishing is carried out by Aboriginal individuals (or groups) who harvest marine products in accordance with their traditions. Techniques include rod and reel; arrows, spears, and harpoons; and various kinds of net, including drag nets and throw nets.

The recreational sector is made of those who participate in fishing for recreation, sport, or sustenance, and who do not sell their produce. It includes the manufacture and sale of fishing tackle, specialist books and magazines, and recreational fishing boats. It also covers the provision of accommodation and charter vessels, and the payment of license fees.

THE OCEAN'S FOOD RESOURCES

The oceans contain the world's largest resources of living matter. The average yield per acre is almost exactly the same as that on land, although it varies greatly from one region to another.

Most oceanic seafood is harvested in the photic zone, from the surface down to around 160 ft (50 m), where sunlight stimulates photosynthesis (the transformation of energy from sunlight by plants such as plankton, seaweed, and other algae). Small schooling species are the most plentiful fish in this surface layer, with pilchards, herring, sardines, anchovies, and small mackerel making up more than one quarter of the world's fish harvest. These fishes often travel in enormous schools measuring several miles in length and width, and sometimes comprising many thousands of individuals. Cod and similar fish such as haddock and whiting are the next most prolific group.

BELOW A fisherman in the Kerkenah Islands, off the coast of Tunisia, uses a traditional fish trap made of staked nets. This is the most common method of fishing in these islands, and is the same as that used by the Phoenicians millennia ago.

The main types of shellfish (mollusks) consumed are oysters, mussels, clams, scallops, whelks, and snails, including the abalone, which is prolific in many warm and temperate waters. The United States is the major consumer of shrimp and prawns, importing them from more than 60 countries. The cephalopods—octopus, squid, calamari, and cuttlefish—are popular in the Mediterranean region, Asia, and Australia.

Shark meat is a common food in warm latitudes but generally not consumed elsewhere—except for the controversial use of their fins, consumption of which in celebratory soups in Asia is considered a sign of wealth. Some conservation groups believe the shark population to be endangered with between 100 and 200 million sharks killed each year for their fins alone. Atlantic cod is the most important food fish in North America and Europe. Australia and South Africa have developed an international market for rock lobster (crayfish), while Japan and Russia are the largest consumers of king crab.

Fish provides around 16 percent of the world's total protein consumption. The UN Food and Agriculture Organization estimated the 2005 commercial wild fish catch at 93.3 million tons (84.5 million tonnes), with a further 63 million tons (57 million tonnes) harvested from aquaculture. This equates to approximately 55 lbs (25 kg) per year for every person on Earth. The highest harvesting countries are China, Peru, Japan, the United States, Chile, and Indonesia, with China accounting for a third of the world's entire consumption.

ADDITIONAL USES OF AQUATIC RESOURCES

As well as being a valuable food source, fish and other marine life are used for other purposes. Sharks and rays provide high quality leather; starfish, sea urchins, and sea horses are used in Chinese medicinal preparations; marine snails, squid, and cuttlefish provide pigments for dye; isinglass (a type of collagen processed from the bladders of sturgeon or cod) is used to clarify wine and beer; and fish emulsion, produced from the remains of fish that have been processed for fish oil and fish meal, is processed into fertilizer.

By contrast, freshwater fish comprise about 5 percent of the world's total harvest of water products. Although some rivers produce as much as 180 lbs per acre (200 kg per hectare) annually, and some lakes yield up to 145 lbs per acre (160 kg per hectare), the world average is only about 20 lbs (8 kg) per hectare.

It is becoming increasingly evident that large-scale commercial fishing has severely depleted stocks of many ocean fishes, endangering such species as cod, Atlantic herring, West African sardine, and South Atlantic pilchard, among others.

Aquaculture, where fish such as cod, trout, salmon, catfish, carp, and tilapia are bred and raised in tanks, canals, or other enclosures, is increasingly being employed in order to satisfy the growing worldwide demand for fish and fish protein.

TOP Alaska has a thriving commercial fishing industry. Among the fish harvested are salmon, herring, halibut, and shellfish.

ABOVE Bermeo in northern Spain is the most important fishing port of the Basque Country.

LEFT A Japanese fisherman with a fresh catch of mackerel. Every year, the Japanese consume about 175 lbs (80 kg) of fish each per person.

Minerals of the Ocean Floor

The little-explored depths of the ocean floor have remarkably uniform geology, consisting of mostly cooled basalt lava that oozed along meandering mid-ocean fractures or spreading ridges. In recent decades, deep-ocean submersibles have revealed an exciting range of mineral resources hidden in the depths. Seawater is also a useful resource—it contains about three or four percent dissolved solids that are made up of over 60 chemical elements.

OPPOSITE Each year, the salt works at Walvis Bay, Namibia, processes millions of tons of seawater to produce 650,000 tons (590 tonnes) of salt, much of it sent to other parts of Africa.

ABOVE About a quarter of the world's manganese comes from Groote Eylandt, a small island in the Gulf of Carpentaria in northeastern Australia.

RIGHT A hydrothermal vent on the ocean floor. The warm waters around this geological phenomenon are home to tubeworms, shrimps, and a variety of microorganisms.

BLACK AND WHITE SMOKERS

Perhaps the most bizarre feature of the ocean floor is the metal-sulfide "black smoker" chimneys, continuously belching smoke-like plumes of tiny black sulfide particles. Substantial groups of these smokestacks, reminiscent of industrial-age England, sit in the inky blackness, slowly building up immense deposits of copper, lead, and zinc.

Black smokers form when young volcanic rocks near the mid-oceanic ridge heat subsurface water. This super-hot water (at temperatures up to four times the normal boiling point) contains high concentrations of dissolved metals. These metals pour out of fractures into the near-freezing waters of the ocean floor. Precipitation of the metals as tiny mineral crystals is almost instantaneous and they fall to the ocean floor forming a rim around the vent. The rim builds up into a chimney that continues growing, rapidly becoming taller and more unstable, before it finally collapses and starts again. "White smokers," the cooler cousins of the black smokers, are a build-up of the white-colored minerals barium, calcium, and silicon.

Although investigations are under way to look at the economic feasibility of mining these chimney complexes, it must be noted that they are also home

to a unique marine ecosystem, which derives its basic energy from the heat of the black smokers rather than the Sun. Most of the creatures that live here, such as shrimps and tubeworms, lack skin pigment and eyes, which are not necessary in the blackness.

LIVING NODULES OF MANGANESE

Manganese is found in abundance on certain parts of the ocean floor, growing as spherical, black nodules. Deep-sea exploration carried out by *HMS Challenger* found good quantities of manganese nodules in most of the world's oceans. These lumps of metal oxide are actually living communities of metallogenium, a type of bacterium that removes dissolved manganese, iron, and other elements from seawater and deposits them around its cell wall. Organic nodules commence their growth around a nucleus, such as the shell of a marine microorganism or perhaps a shark's tooth. The nodules slowly grow bigger in a series of concentric rings over thousands of years and can eventually reach the size of a football. There were plans to harvest these nodules in the Pacific and Indian oceans, where strong ocean currents have rolled them into depressions and formed considerable minable concentrations. These plans have not been put into effect as yet. This is because there are sufficient resources of manganese that are more readily accessible on land.

DIAMONDS, GOLD, TIN, AND SALT

Heavy minerals are also in abundance on the ocean floor, especially near the mouths of large rivers that drain basins containing mineral-laden rocks. At the present time, however, underwater mining is limited to diamonds, gold, tin, and titanium, considered to be the highest value gemstones and metals. Although it is still prohibitively expensive to explore for and extract minerals directly from the ocean floor, it is common to mine minerals that once formed in the ocean but are now conveniently located on dry land. The most common of these are salt and other soluble "evaporite" minerals that contain potassium, magnesium, and calcium. Evaporites are deposited when seawater evaporates within a closed basin, similar to today's Dead Sea, leaving behind its dissolved minerals as a solid residue. Ancient evaporite deposits are far easier and cheaper to mine that trying to extract the dissolved elements directly from seawater.

A LIMITLESS SUPPLY OF FRESH WATER

Extraction of resources directly from the ocean may become economically feasible if the Earth's accessible land-based mineral deposits become depleted and population (and hence demand) continues to grow. This extraction will not only include precious gemstones, gold, and other important metals, but also construction sands and gravels, limestone, and even fresh drinking water, which is becoming increasingly scarce in polluted and populous areas. Seawater can be stripped of its dissolved minerals and turned into fresh water by means of a filtering process known as reverse osmosis, although this requires a great deal of energy. One day the sea may become our prime source of fresh water—our most valuable commodity.

RIGHT At a salt factory in Hon Khoi, Vietnam, shallow ponds are flooded with seawater and then allowed to evaporate in the sunlight. Workers remove the salt in baskets. This salt factory has been in operation for over a century.

Undersea Oil and Gas

All of our planet's oil and gas is produced from ancient sedimentary basins that lie (or at one stage lay) beneath the sea. Trapped within the rock strata, oil and gas accumulates for many millions of years until discovered during exploration drilling.

MILLIONS UNDER PRESSURE

Petroleum begins as millions of tiny marine organisms that flourish in the warm waters of shallow ocean basins. Vast numbers of these zooplankton and algae reproduce and die, then fall to the bottom of the sea where they rapidly accumulate. Here, when quickly buried in the absence of oxygen, they decompose into the light organic liquids and gas that are collectively known as hydrocarbons. Layer upon layer of organic-rich sediments can accumulate over time, eventually building up a thick sequence of hydrocarbon source rocks. These liquids rise through the overlying porous sandstone rock layers until they meet an impermeable capping layer that traps the hydrocarbons in an underground reservoir. Gas, being lightest, rises and sits on top of the denser liquid hydrocarbons. Petroleum differs from coal, which forms on land from the accumulation of vegetation in freshwater swamps.

LIQUID "BLACK GOLD"

Utilizing specially designed vessels with seismic geophysical capabilities, explorers trawl the oceans looking for geological structures that contain oil and gas. Compressed air guns send explosive shock waves down into the earth. These seismic waves bounce off different rock strata then return to the surface and provide geophysicists with a map of the underground layers. Areas where the rock layers have been folded up

BELOW Oil tankers are massive ships designed to transport oil around the globe. Oil is pumped on and off the ships through a complex system of connections devised to minimize risk from dangerous fumes.

ABOVE Oil is found on land as well as deep in the ocean. Here, pipelines lead to the separation plant of Saudi Arabia's Shaybah Oil Field, which produces 550,000 barrels of oil per day.

into domes are promising locations to drill because it is here that petroleum accumulates in rich pools. Oil and gas pumped from beneath the sea floor is then transferred via pipelines or tanker ships to nearby refineries on the land.

The crude petroleum is separated into its different components—from the lightest most volatile gases, such as methane, ethane, and propane, through the liquid fuels such as gasoline and dieseline, down to the heaviest and thickest tars and asphalts that are used for the construction of roads.

In order, the world's top ten producers of oil are Saudi Arabia, Russia, the United States, Iran, Mexico, China, Canada, United Arab Emirates, Venezuela, and Norway. Each day, Saudi Arabia alone produces over 10 million barrels from its proven reserves of some 262 billion barrels. Most of the global oil production is exported to the United States, which is the world's greatest oil consumer, burning more than 20 million barrels of oil each day.

GOING, GOING, GONE

Although oil is an excellent source of energy, and one to which we have all become very accustomed, it is important to keep in mind that what has taken millions of years to form is now taking just a matter of decades to extract and use. It will not be long before this energy source runs out. Oil and gas are referred to as non-renewable energy sources. Also, because hydrocarbons are burnt to release their energy, they give off carbon dioxide and other gases that have been proved to be contributors to global warming. It is therefore critically important that as a global community we invest some of the profits generated by the sale of petroleum into the research and development of environmentally friendly, renewable energy sources, for example, solar and geothermal power.

Cities in the Sea

Offshore petroleum drilling platforms, such as the one pictured above, are self-contained islands or "cities in the sea." They house workers and all the equipment needed to drill oil wells into the sea floor. They are either floating platforms or fixed decks anchored directly onto the seabed by steel or concrete legs. Most platforms are located on the oil-rich continental shelves, although advances in technology are making it possible to drill in much deeper waters.

Drilling platforms accommodate more than 100 workers at a time, from the captain in charge, to the laborers on the drill floor. Life on the platform continues 24 hours a day with two rotating 12-hour shifts. Replacement crews are flown in and out by helicopter every four weeks. Conditions are physically demanding and sometimes very dangerous for the workers, with heavy, greasy, equipment, often terrible weather conditions, and long working hours. In 2001, the Brazilian Petrobras 36 Oil Platform exploded, killing 11 people. The platform sank five days after the explosions. On the positive side, workers are extremely well paid and receive holidays equal to time worked offshore. Platform crews eat international-standard meals in kitchens open 24 hours a day, and during their off-shift time can relax in the recreation room, work out in the gymnasium, use the internet, or watch latest-release movies.

The Ocean's Relentless Energy

The oceans of the world have the very real potential to provide us with our everyday energy needs. There is prodigious energy in the waves of the oceans and in the forces of the tides, and this energy can now be tapped using exciting new technologies.

TIDAL POWER

Tidal power transforms the energy of the tides into electricity and other types of power. Tides are totally predictable, an advantage that this form of energy has over solar and wind power.

Tides are generated by the combined actions of the Earth's rotation and the gravitational pull of the Sun and the Moon. Most locations are semidiurnal, that is, they have two high and two low tides each day. Some locations are diurnal, having only one high and low

tide each day. In either case, the regular movement of the seas provides a source of energy when tapped.

HARNESSING THE FORCE

There are a number of ways to harness tidal power. Building a large dam, called a barrage, at the mouth of a tidal basin is one form. Some barrages completely span the basin opening and others only partially cover the mouth. This key location helps capture the movement of the tides in both directions as the sea moves toward and away from land. This type of tidal power also has difficulties, however, because it impacts on the environment in quite complex ways. In addition, the cost for building the barrages is high, and potential coastal sites around the world are limited. The largest tidal power site of this type is the Rance Power Station in France, which opened in 1966. Rance has 24 turbines that produce 240 megawatts of power, enough to power 240,000 homes.

A second way of generating tidal power relies on the kinetic energy of the tides and power turbines. These turbines capture the movement of the water with underwater fans that work much like windmills. Tidal fences are another variation of the same theme. The idea of underwater wave farms has been advanced in recent years and experiments are being conducted in the Bay of Fundy in Canada, an area that has the world's highest tides. This form of tidal power generation is cheaper than using barrages and presents fewer environmental challenges.

Many other tidal projects of both types are currently in the planning stages, with additional projects planned in Australia, Canada, Argentina, the United Kingdom, the United States, Russia, Norway, Chile, South Africa, Mexico, India, South Korea, and China. Scottish Power Renewables plans to have the world's largest tidal power project completed by 2011, one of many new efforts.

WAVE POWER

The oceans provide another possible source to feed humankind's increasing thirst for clean and renewable energy. Power generated by surface waves has received greater attention in recent years. Like the tides, ocean waves are predictable and everlasting. Harnessing this form of energy has been advanced by many projects, and experimentation

with more efficient, wave power generators is occurring in a number of places, such as Portugal, Oregon in the United States, and Australia.

Offshore and onshore systems now exist for wave power generation. The offshore systems are typically located in waters of more than 130 ft (40 m) and use the up and down motion of waves to create electricity. In 2008, Portugal opened the world's first wave farm, called the Agucadoura Wave Park, 3 miles (5 km) off its coast. This wave farm uses sausage-shaped buoys that are partially submerged in order to capture the power of surface waves.

Onshore systems rely on the waves as they break on land. Three systems are commonly used, including TAPCHAN (tapered channel systems), oscillating water columns, or pendulum box devices. Both the on- and offshore systems usually have more reasonable costs than common tidal systems. Environmental impact is also lessened, but not totally eliminated, because some detractors believe that these structures are a source of visual pollution and beach erosion. The challenges include durability issues in the face of occasional harsh climate conditions and saltwater corrosion. Some of the devices are noisy, but this problem is usually offset by placement in remote locations.

The advantages of wave power are numerous. No fuel is needed because energy is supplied by the waves, the systems are easy to maintain, and they produce large amounts of energy. Renewable energy experts estimate that waves could provide nearly 2 terawatts of electricity annually—more than enough to power the countries of Japan and Russia. The potential of ocean wave power can provide the world with a staggering amount of renewable energy.

ABOVE The tidal power station on the Rance River in Bretagne, France, was the first power station in the world to use tidal energy. This form of energy works by harnessing the energy of the tides and converting it into electricity.

LEFT Tidal farms utilize underwater turbines to generate electricity from the flow of the tides. The propellers are anchored to the sea floor and can be raised for necessary maintenance.

Ocean Tourism

The call of the sea beckons millions every year to embark on a marine adventure. Marine tourism is not only valuable in monetary terms, but also has benefits for education and recreation. Direct experience of the ocean's wonders instructs in a way that is simply not possible by reading a book or watching a documentary.

ABOVE Diving has changed markedly in recent decades. Here, divers driving submersible vessels explore the sea around Nassau in the Bahamas.

BELOW Marine eco-tourism is becoming increasingly popular. These tourists in Antarctica enjoy a close-up view of a majestic humpback whale (*Megaptera novaeangliae)* that has surfaced for air.

CRUISING THE WORLD

Marine tourism creates hundreds of thousands of jobs and is worth billions of dollars in revenue for the cruise industry and the many communities around the world that benefit from their business.

Today's ocean explorers need not travel in the torrid and life-threatening circumstances that were familiar to Magellan, Columbus, or Cook in order to experience the world's wonders. In centuries past, the oceans were viewed as a major barrier to human interaction, but today the seas serve to link people together, with cruise liners providing luxury travel for up to 5,000 passengers on the open seas, including visits to many exotic ports along the way.

Venturing onto a cruise ship today is an amazing experience in itself. The cruise industry has moved far beyond ships such as the ill-fated *Titanic*, offering passage on modern megaships that are more like floating cities, complete with swimming pools, basketball courts, jogging tracks, golf and other games, dance clubs, karaoke, beauty salons and spas, internet cafes, libraries, multiple restaurants, cinemas, casinos, and world-class entertainment. The cabins are plush and comfortable, and stabilizers and other technologies keep passengers from experiencing the true effects of harsh seas and inclement weather. Tourism on the seas has also become more affordable, with costs considered more reasonable than they have been in the past.

Today's seafarers can now visit some of the world's most amazing sites in both comfort and safety. Indeed, there are international regulations governing health and safety issues on board. Cruise ships carry tourists to all seven continents, and their surrounding islands and ports. Regular destinations include the Greek Isles, the volcanic Hawaiian Islands, the Great Barrier Reef, the Rock of Gibraltar, the Amazon River, Alaska's Inside Passage, the Panama Canal, and even as far south as Antarctica. Passengers are now able to experience voyages that could only be imagined in bygone times—venturing to Tasmania or Greenland or through the Strait of Magellan, as well as to most of the world's major cities, is now commonplace and within the reach of everyday tourists.

While cruise tourism is a pleasant experience for most people, unfortunately it can also result in harmful effects on the ocean environment. Cruise ships create sewage (often called black water) and gray water, which comes from soapy water used for showering, laundry, and dishes. The average cruise ship generates over 1 million gallons (3,785,400 l) of black and gray water each week. These ships are also major sources of air and waste pollution.

PORT TOURISM

Port communities reap the economic benefits of cruise tourism. Cities such as Barcelona, Athens, and Alexandria, for example, give cruise tourists their entry point for exploring the community and spending money. Guides with comfortable buses carry the voyagers onto land, where they can explore the history and culture of significant sites. Port cities assess docking fees on the cruise ships, and tourism provides jobs for workers in restaurants, museums, souvenir shops, guide services, transportation services, and, in many places, street vendors selling their array of wares.

MARINE RECREATION

Marine recreational tourism includes a wide variety of activities, ranging from surfing, snorkeling, scuba diving, sailing, windsurfing, and fishing, to dolphin encounters, whale watching, and sandcastle building. Each year, millions of tourists participate in these activities and pay large sums of money to do so.

However, ocean tourism also has a negative impact on fragile marine environments, such as coral reefs. Construction works for ports and piers takes a toll on the shoreline, as does the harvesting of shells, many of which still contain living animals, for souvenirs.

SUSTAINABLE MARINE TOURISM

The United Nation's World Tourism Organization (UNWTO) promotes responsible and sustainable tourism that is accessible to all. UNWTO acknowledges and promotes the positive economic, social, and cultural importance of tourism, but also recognizes that work needs to be done if we are to keep our tourism treasures intact for future generations.

The vastness of the oceans has encouraged humans to take for granted our collective impact on it. Tourism is only one of the potential culprits having an effect on the well-being of our oceans, but its impact can be devastating if left unregulated and unchecked. Coral reefs, plants and animals, and the chain of life that depends on a healthy marine environment are reliant on the tourism industry becoming sustainable and stakeholders making a concerted effort to minimize any long-term negative effects. As marine tourism increases, this challenge becomes more important.

ABOVE The 90,000-ton (82-tonne) *MS Queen Victoria* in Sydney Harbour in February 2008. Among its many grand features, this massive luxury cruise ship boasts three swimming pools, a large ballroom, a museum, and a library containing more than 6,000 books.

Sea Change

Widespread attention is focusing upon such problems as piracy; a sharp increase in the number of "dead zones," where marine life cannot survive due to depleted oxygen levels; "red tides" caused by harmful algal blooms; and the ever-growing spiral of litter known as the "Pacific garbage patch." Other topics for debate include the possibility of the Arctic Ocean becoming an open shipping lane, the need to widen the Panama Canal to accommodate larger ships, various political conflicts over territorial waters and their potential riches, and the depletion of valuable marine biotic resources.

PLAYING POLITICS

Today, the ocean has become a hotbed of contested political claims. With improvements in off-shore drilling technology, many countries are engaged in heated political debate over marine territorial claims and exploitation rights. Arctic Ocean countries are vying for control of potential shipping passages.

Rapid depletion of vital marine resources due to over-harvesting is a concern that begs for international monitoring and cooperation, as does the widespread pollution of oceans, and the rampant piracy in the international waters of the Indian Ocean, off the coast of Africa, and elsewhere. In future, the focus of political, strategic, legal, and perhaps military attention will shift from land-based conflicts to those related to control of the sea and its resources.

ABOVE A large grain ship enters the Gatun Locks in the Panama Canal. These locks are almost 2 miles (3.3 km) long and can raise a ship over 82 ft (25 m).

MARINE ECONOMY

The sea is a tremendous source of wealth. The value of a country's annual harvest of fish can be easily documented in monetary terms, but how does one place an economic value on the warm climate, exotic culture, spectacular scenery, coral reef, and the pristine sea surrounding a tropical island? Figures can attest to the value of a particular shipping route—for example, miles traveled compared with fuel cost—but how can we calculate a value for the influence of warm north-east Atlantic waters on the climate and economy of northwest Europe? What is uncontestable is that the ocean's value continues to increase.

OCEANIC SUPERHIGHWAY

The map of global shipping reveals the relative importance of a small number of major routes—the oceanic superhighways. Many of the world's largest centers, including Tokyo, London, and New York, owe a great deal of their prosperity to their function as seaports.

As the global economy changes, so does the relative importance of all ocean routes. Today, a major trans-Pacific cargo route carries manufactured goods from East Asian manufacturers to ports on the US West Coast. Timber, agricultural products, other resources, and raw materials flow in the other direction. Another major route links the oil-rich Middle East with the energy-hungry countries in Europe and East Asia. Each of these routes is relatively new.

Today's ships, particularly petroleum supertankers, are so huge that the Panama Canal is being enlarged to allow their passage, impossible at present. Begun in 2007 and scheduled for completion in 2014, this expansion will double the canal's capacity.

As Earth's climate continues to warm, the currently-icebound Arctic Ocean is expected to become a major shipping lane. A route between western Europe and eastern Asia, passing through the Norwegian or Greenland Sea, then across the Arctic Ocean and through the Bering Strait to the North Pacific Ocean, would shave thousands of miles from today's routes.

PROTECTING THE MARINE ENVIRONMENT

We used to believe that the ocean was indestructible, an unlimited cornucopia of food and other resources. Today we know this is not true.

RIGHT The oceans are there for all to enjoy, just like these tourists at Alicante in Spain. Thousands flock there daily during summer to cool off in the gentle surf.

ABOVE Marine life suffers daily from human interference and neglect. This seal has been caught in a fishing net and without help, would drown.

BELOW Villagers gather each morning to collect the early catch at Mui Ne, on the south-central coast of Vietnam.

The ocean is as vulnerable to pollution, depletion of resources, and endangerment to species as the terrestrial realm. The North Pacific Ocean now contains two huge "garbage patches" nearly as large as the United States. Fishing banks in the Pacific, Atlantic, and Indian Oceans are producing a mere fraction of their former yield. Marine resources are so depleted that many scientists question whether they can ever rebound. The exploding populations of jellyfish—like an oceanic "canary in the mine"—forewarn of growing environmental problems, as does the widespread decline in coral reefs. If we are to rescue and preserve the oceanic environment, we must act immediately.

Sea Power

The British King Offa (757–796) once said, "He who would be secure on land must be supreme at sea." The political and strategic importance of the ocean is most apparent on an island, but its principles apply elsewhere. Around two-thirds of the planet is covered by water, and the concern for the ocean is part of the first duty of government—safety of the realm.

RIGHT Selected as one of the best pictures of World War II, this aerial shot shows Marines in landing craft as they hit the beach at Iwo Jima on February 19, 1945. Transmitted by radio, the image appeared in US newspapers within 15 hours of the assault.

LAND CONTROL

There are oft-repeated dogmas of strategic studies that emphasize the importance of land forces. The fact that only an army can hold ground is often cited as the reason air forces and navies are support services. While the maxim is true, it is simplistic, and more suited to the nineteenth century than the twenty-first.

As humans conduct their central business on land the need to control ground seems obvious. However, if that ground is encircled by water, and the forces cannot support themselves from the land, the maxim is negated. The situation of Australia in World War II is an example—if it had been cut off from support from the rest of the Allies it would have been doomed. Similarly if the ground is being completely bombarded, as was Iwo Jima when held by the Japanese in the same war, control of the land does not amount to much.

COMMAND OF THE SEA

Therefore, to fully understand the strategic situation of a country, the sea surrounding it must be taken into account. Britain, invaded twice by the Romans, failed to take account of Roman domination of the English Channel. The British could muster plenty of troops, but they were no sea power—they could not prevent the Roman transports and galleys from commanding the water. It was the Romans' sea power that enabled the victory for their army.

It was a lack of sea power that harried Britain over the next 1,000 years. The island was attacked by Saxons, Vikings, and eventually by William the Conqueror's force in 1066. It was the last time Britain was to be

BELOW Japan has a show of strength by parading its Maritime Self Defense forces in a military exercise just after North Korea's nuclear test in 2006.

invaded. England fended off attacks from Spain in 1588 by competently using sea power to destroy the Spanish Armada, and from Napoleon centuries later when, at Trafalgar, the annihilation of French/Spanish fleet prevented invasion of Britain.

MOBILITY, REACH, PRESENCE

The sea, therefore, can be both an enemy and an ally. It can form a moat, but it can also give an enemy fleet mobility that they would not have on land—the freedom to move swiftly along a coast; to hold off landing where opposition is evident; to rush in forces where defenses are weak. The value of amphibious assault is at once evident, but in many cases forgotten.

In 1991, it gave Coalition forces the ability to make a landing in Kuwait, but the landing was a feint—the forces did not beach. However, they created a gap in the defending Iraqi Republican Guard and the gap was exploited to begin the assault.

The sea gives reach, not often matched by land movement. Movement by sea gave armies in World War I the ability to land at Gallipoli—a bold thrust, which, if successful, would have opened up a massive new front to divert the land enemy. Similarly, by the covert use of submarines, an aggressor can reach the very openings of harbors, sinking vessels that emerge. This cannot be done with land troops, and it can only be achieved temporarily by air power.

The sea gives presence in a way unmatched by armies. Ships concentrated off a coast, seen but not targetable, send a message of potential force by their presence. This potential force of presence can last for months if necessary—as proven by the Coalition forces in the Gulf waters from the 1980s.

MODERN STRATEGIES

Modern navies practice sea control and sea denial. The first means to control an area of sea, below the surface, on the water, and above it, for a certain time. Denial does not require a physical presence, but other forces are denied access. This can be seen at a choke point—such as outside the Suez Canal. Any force sailing in the area can be warned off by the use of missiles, or mines, or aircraft. Blue water big gun engagements are probably in the past: Leyte Gulf was the last such battle. Modern navies are too powerful to expose themselves to similar forces.

Today's use of the sea is related to the land with amphibious assaults into the enemy's vulnerable areas likely to be standard in the future. The sea is of prime political–strategic importance in controlling the land.

ABOVE A diesel submarine from the Pacific Fleet heads out to sea from its naval base at Vladivostok, Russia.

LEFT On February 8, 1984, *USS New Jersey* fired almost 300 shells at Druze and Syrian command positions east of Beirut. This was the heaviest bombardment since the Korean War.

Ocean Economics

Despite the rapid growth in the use of planes, trains, and automobiles, ships still transport the vast majority of traded goods. Many of the world's largest cities are located on the coast and their ports are a major source of income. Oceans are the prime source of food for many people. In Asia, over one billion people rely on seafood as their main source of protein. People also use the ocean and shoreline for recreational activities. Beneath the ocean floor lie the vast resources of oil and natural gas that supply energy for the global economy.

The majority of people in Asia, Australia, Africa, and the Americas live near the coast, largely because proximity to the ocean facilitates economic activity, especially trade and fishing. Indeed, leading economies today are often those with large coastlines.

For example, half of the gross domestic product of the United States, worth US$4.5 trillion per year, is generated by ocean-related and coastal-based activities, which provide around 60 million jobs.

BELOW India, with its vast population, is heavily reliant on fish and seafood. Veraval, in Gujarat, India, has the largest fishing fleet in the country.

ECONOMIC EXCLUSION ZONES

Due the economic importance of coastal areas, in 1982 countries developed Exclusive Economic Zones (EEZ). Extending beyond the traditional 12 nautical miles (22 km) of territorial waters, the EEZ covers all waters up to 200 nautical miles (370 km) from the coastline. Within that zone each country has the right to manage marine affairs and resources such as fishing, mineral extraction, and oil drilling. International shipping is permitted to pass through an EEZ, but the importance of controlling isolated islands throughout the world's oceans has dramatically increased. Ownership of an island or two in the Pacific or Atlantic means that a significant stretch of water and sea floor is also available for exploitation by that country.

Coastal waters also generate significant income through recreational boating and other activities. Sailing, fishing, swimming, surfing, sightseeing, and

LEFT Container terminals now exist in all the major ports of the world. With highly computerized systems, the terminals can locate an individual container, and transport it to the right truck or ship by remote control.

diving, especially to view marine life such as whales and coral reefs, have become the primary economic source for many coastal communities.

INTERNATIONAL TRADE

To enable a sense of the sheer quantity of goods carried by ship, consider a small freighter vessel. Each standard container of 20 ft (6 m) may legally hold up to 33 tons (30,000 kg), although many are overloaded. The ship holds up to 500 containers, making a total of almost 16,500 tons (16,764,774 kg). By contrast, the longest freighter—currently the *Emma Maersk*—can carry up to 15,200 containers. Given that there are more than 9,000 container ships in the world, one can see that they carry an immense amount of freight. That figure does not include the 26,000 other commercial, non-container ships. The total capacity of these ships is over one billion tons (1,016 billion kg), and in 2007 they carried over seven billion tons of freight. Most of these ships are tankers, carrying liquids such as oil, or bulk carriers for wheat, coal, iron ore, and so on.

FISHING

Recent estimates put the world's fishing fleet at around four million vessels, of which over 99 percent are small fishing boats based in coastal towns and villages. The vast majority of fishers—almost 90 percent of about 15 million—live in these towns and villages and fish not for commercial reasons, but for their own livelihood. Yet, of the world's total catch of approximately 90 million tons per year, these small boats take less than half. The remainder of the catch is harvested by around 40,000 large commercial vessels. European fleets trawl the Atlantic, while ships from Russia, Japan, South Korea, the USA, and other countries traverse the Indian and Pacific Oceans.

NEW ECONOMICS

Since Earth is primarily a water planet, the oceans have long been acknowledged as one of our important natural resources. Their sheer size has made them appear inexhaustible resources of food, transportation, minerals, and recreation. However, we now understand the oceans' limits. Pollution, over-fishing, and mining have left their mark. Recent studies of the economic value of the oceans for welfare and health have moved beyond the traditional trade, fishing, and recreation, to include such factors as air quality, and the ability to process waste and food.

ABOVE Commercial fishermen haul in a massive catch of cod from the Atlantic. Seabirds hover overhead waiting for scraps after the fish have been cleaned.

Modern Shipping Routes

Although there are hundreds of shipping routes on the world's oceans, most ships travel along well-established straits and passages on routes linking the major economic centers of the world.

ABOVE On a busy day, the Suez Canal has hundreds of ships passing up and down its length, cutting thousands of miles off the journey between Asia and the Mediterranean Sea.

ABOVE This lovely old poster advertises a cruise line that carries mail to and from Canada and Europe.

MAJOR ROUTES

The oldest trading route passes from the Mediterranean, through the Middle East and Asia Minor, then across the Indian Ocean to China. For thousands of years Egyptian, Greek, Roman, Arab, Indian, and Chinese traders have used this route. With the opening of the Suez Canal in 1869, the route became a major thoroughfare. Much of its traffic today carries petroleum products from the Middle East.

The second-oldest route runs between Europe and the Indian Ocean, via the Cape of Good Hope in South Africa. Opened up by Vasco da Gama in 1498, it was, for centuries, the shortest route to Asia and Australia from Europe. Today it is used by ships too large for the Suez Canal, and those that wish to avoid Somali pirates near the mouth of the Red Sea.

The Atlantic crossing from Europe to North America began with Christopher Columbus in 1492. Since then it has competed with the Indian Ocean as the busiest route in the world, largely because it links the economic power-houses of Europe and North America. The Pacific Ocean routes between Asia and Australia were the last to develop. With the rise of China as a manufacturing power, trans-Pacific traffic has increased dramatically. Raw materials are imported by China, manufactured into various products, then exported around the world.

CUTTING THROUGH

Modern shipping has been revolutionized by two major engineering feats—the Suez and Panama canals. The Suez is a 119-mile (192 km) canal linking Port Said on the Mediterranean Sea and the Gulf of Suez on the Red Sea. Completed in 1869, the canal is steeped in history. The Egyptians built an east–west canal linking the Nile and the Red Sea in the 2nd millennium BCE. It enabled Egyptian access to the Red Sea and the east African coast, and opened up an indirect link between the Mediterranean and the Red Sea. Over the centuries these canals silted up, were re-opened, fought over, and extended when the Red Sea retreated.

Despite initial international skepticism and active opposition from the British, the canal has fundamentally changed the rhythms of world trade. Today, there are almost 20,000 ships a year passing through the Suez Canal, carrying around 7.5 percent of the world's trade.

In contrast to the flat terrain of the Suez Canal, which required no locks, the challenges posed by the three-lock Panama Canal were immense. Although only 48 miles (77 km) long, malaria, yellow fever, and landslides killed around 27,500 workers during its

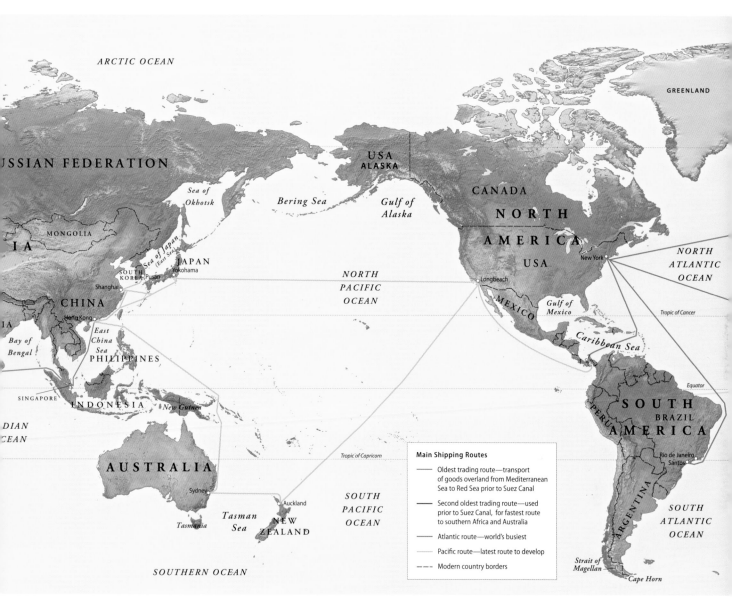

Main Shipping Routes

——— Oldest trading route—transport of goods overland from Mediterranean Sea to Red Sea prior to Suez Canal

——— Second oldest trading route—used prior to Suez Canal, for fastest route to southern Africa and Australia

——— Atlantic route—world's busiest

——— Pacific route—latest route to develop

- - - Modern country borders

construction. In 1880, the French began work on the canal under the aegis of Ferdinand de Lesseps, but gave up in 1893, at which time the US took over the task, completing it in 1914. Until 1999, it was under US control, but is now run by the Panama Control Authority. It has had a dramatic impact on shipping, more than halving the distance it takes to sail around Cape Horn. Each year almost 15,000 ships pass through the canal, taking eight to 10 hours to do so.

OCEAN HIJACKS

Pirates continue to affect modern shipping worldwide. In the Strait of Malacca, between Malaysia and the Indonesian island of Sumatra, pirates on fishing boats replace their fishing gear with guns when a prospective target draws near. By contrast, well-organized Somali pirates use high-technology equipment on large vessels to carry out raids far from the African coast. They can only be deterred by concerted naval action.

LEFT A container ship with maximum load is manouvered out of port by tugs each side. Tugboats are still used to push and pull massive ships around within the confines of small harbors and busy ports.

Watery Waste Dump

The seas have long been under assault from humans, with many forms of pollution threatening the health of the oceans and their inhabitants. Around 80 percent of ocean pollution is caused by runoff from land-based activities. Some of this is natural as soil washes away in runoff, but the impacts of human dumping and other activities are increasingly endangering our seas and oceans.

ABOVE Oil spills are the ocean's great polluters, causing devastation along the coastlines and disease and death to birds and other marine life.

BELOW In 2006, the beach at Acapulco became more and more polluted when the garbage service was cancelled. Even with a garbage service, hundreds of tons of waste end up on Mexico's shores each year.

THE POLLUTION CHALLENGES

Much pollution is human garbage and waste that has been dumped directly into the sea. Headlines report that plastic products are killing marine life, needles wash up on the shores of New Jersey, masses of fish are poisoned in Indonesia, and so on. Other, hidden impacts may not capture headlines, but nonetheless create areas that poison the food chain. The phenomenon known as Harmful Algal Bloom, largely caused by chemical nutrients from fertilizers such as nitrogen and phosphorus, also wreaks havoc.

What is being dumped into the seas? Plastic in the form of bottles, wrappers, six-pack rings, cups, bags, fishing nets, and condoms are prime culprits, comprising around 80 percent of all marine debris. Plastic is a particularly serious pollutant because it does not readily biodegrade in sea water, lasting for decades. Many animals, mistaking it for food, eat plastic and starve to death. Others die from suffocation, or entanglement in plastic products.

COLLECTION POINTS

Prevailing winds and ocean currents have created immense garbage dumps in the oceans. In 1997, a massive garbage patch was discovered in the Pacific Ocean between Hawaii and California. It is still growing in size, as is the polluted area of the Sargasso Sea in the North Atlantic Ocean. Ninety percent of this pollution is plastic, 80 percent from land-based sources.

Other toxins pollute the seas, including agricultural runoff laced with fertilizers and pesticides. These are consumed by plankton, benthos (bottom-dwellers), and other tiny animals at the bottom of the food chain that have many predators.

Ships are also a prime source of pollution. Oil spills regularly poison myriad aquatic animals and birds, and are very difficult to clean up. Ships cast off waste from cargo holds, introducing further toxins and introducing species to new environments where they have no natural predators, thus damaging the balance of nature.

Marine pollution comes in another, less visible form. Seas are becoming more acidic as the ratio of carbon increases in the atmosphere and dissolves in the oceans, a side-effect of human burning of oil-based products or "fossil fuels." The consequences of this to the oceans are not fully-known as yet, but many scientists are predicting devastating consequences.

ATTEMPTS AT CLEAN UP

The only hope for the future wellbeing of our oceans is for us to reduce our consumption and pollution. The 1994 United Nations Convention on the Law of the Sea requires governments to prevent, reduce, and control marine pollution from land-based sources.

Other international agreements cover issues such as ocean dumping, ship pollution, and preservation of coral reefs. Many agreements are regional, designed to protect areas such as the Mediterranean, or the Arctic.

However, many nations refuse to sign such agreements, continuing to pollute as they have in the past. In addition, enforcing agreements is virtually impossible as patrolling the Earth's seas is a policing effort beyond our current capability, or will.

Education is perhaps the most important factor if we are to maintain and improve the quality of our marine environments, protect our marine animals, and preserve our ocean heritage.

ABOVE One of the worst oil spills in history was from the *Exxon Valdez*, which split apart near Green Island, Alaska, in 1989, spewing crude oil into the pristine sea for thousands of miles.

LEFT In 1990, near Galveston, Texas, the Norwegian tanker *Mega Borg* exploded and caught fire. The resulting pollution took months to clear.

Endangered Species

Anyone who enjoys seafood is keenly aware of a stark reality: prices have soared and the variety, availability, and quality of marine delicacies have sharply declined. So serious is the drop that many of today's seafood delicacies are raised under artificial conditions with an accompanying reduction in texture and taste. What has happened during the past half-century?

During the mid-twentieth century, the oceans were looked upon as the "coming abundance." The global sea was generally believed to be an unlimited store-house of food and countless other resources. But with a rapidly growing population and high demand for seafood, stocks have been over-harvested, resulting in some species being driven to the very brink of extinction. In other instances, environmental changes—both human- and nature-induced—have caused many species to become endangered.

FISHING

Ocean-facing countries have an Exclusive Economic Zone (EEZ) that is off limits to foreign fishing fleets. However, beyond this zone, which extends outward 200 nautical miles (370 km), lies the global sea—a fishing commons open to all. There, few incentives exist to limit harvests. When resources are free for the taking, conservation takes a second place to profit.

With contemporary technology, few commercially valuable marine species can escape detection. Sonar, remote imagery, and search planes are just some of the methods that are used to locate schools of fish. Huge fleets, with numerous fishing boats and huge cannery ships, stalk the oceans in search of commercial fish species. Many fishing nets and methods, including beam (bottom) trawling, do not discriminate. Bottom

BELOW Steller's sea lions are native to the northern Pacific. The depletion in their numbers is thought to be due to diminishing food sources, caused by the huge stocks of fish taken by commercial fishing operations.

The Biggest of Them All

The blue whale (*Balaenoptera musculus*) is the world's largest animal and is thought to be the largest animal ever to have existed on Earth, bigger even than the largest dinosaurs. The largest blue whale ever sighted measured over 108 ft (33 m) in length, although the average blue whale is about 85 ft (26 m) long. Their large size, however, also makes them more vulnerable to changes in their marine habitat. Threats to the blue whale include entanglement in fishing nets, the long-term effects of ocean pollution, and illegal whaling. Recent scientific estimates put blue whale numbers at less than 10,000 worldwide.

trawling has a very high level of "by-catch"—marine life that is discarded because it is too small or not of any economic value. Such methods are extremely destructive and can reduce once-productive fishing grounds to an oceanic wasteland.

As well as depleting fish stocks, large-scale fishing creates some other significant problems. Dolphins, seals, and other animals, such as turtles, drown when caught in discarded fishing nets or snagged by stray fishhooks; and fishing lines wrap around coral reefs slowly killing them. In addition, other marine populations, such as seabirds, lose their food source and become threatened species too.

OTHER THREATS TO MARINE WILDLIFE

Pollution is another serious threat to marine environments, just as it is to the rest of our planet. Rubbish can be found throughout the world's oceans. Seabirds choke on plastic materials, and corals suffer when mud or other sediment is dumped into the oceans from various coastal enterprises.

Offshore mining activities have a severe impact on the marine environment. Dredging not only destroys or shrinks many habitats, it also results in the deaths of untold numbers of sea creatures. Oil spills cause devastation to marine birds, turtles, fish, and vegetation. Ecosystems are destroyed and entire species vanish from our oceans.

For a number of species, including coral and coastal species such as clams, oysters, mussels, lobsters, and crabs, increased pollution and a recent warming climatic cycle have contributed to decline.

The introduction of non-native species in certain areas is another problem, threatening, among other

marine life, seabirds, which either become prey for the introduced species, or have to compete for the same dwindling food sources.

VANISHING SPECIES

During the past half-century, populations of numerous fish species have fallen by 90 percent or more. Cod, sharks, groupers, sailfish, and sea bass are threatened. So are bluefin tuna and marlins. Salmon populations have collapsed in the eastern Pacific Basin. Various species of whale have declined to near extinction. In 1930, 30,000 blue whales were taken from the waters of the Southern Ocean alone. Today, their population has dwindled to an estimated 10,000. Most whales are now protected, but like the massive blue whale, some populations are very slow to recover.

WHAT CAN BE DONE?

The world's oceanic fisheries face a massive challenge. If immediate action is not taken, many marine species will certainly be driven to extinction. Catch levels must be capped at sustainable levels. Spawning areas must be protected by rule of law. And pollution of the global sea must be greatly reduced.

Some Endangered Marine Species

Humpback whale (*Megaptera novaeangliae*)
Steller's sea lion (*Eumetopias jubatus*)
Saimaa seal (*Phoca hispida saimensis*)
Mediterranean monk seal (*Monachus monachus*)
Chinook salmon (*Oncorhynchus tshawytscha*)
Atlantic goliath grouper (*Epinephelus itajara*)
Loggerhead turtle (*Caretta caretta*)
Green turtle (*Chelonia mydas*)
Leatherback turtle (*Dermochelys coriacea*)
Hawksbill turtle (*Eretmochelys imbricata*)

ABOVE Although populations of humpback whales have slowly increased since international bans on commercial whaling, these marine mammals are still considered to be endangered.

LEFT The loggerhead turtle is often a victim of by-catch in nets and lines of commercial fishing fleets. One method that is helping to reduce turtle deaths in nets is the Turtle Excluder Device (TED), which allows the animals to escape the fine mesh. Unfortunately, loggerheads are often too large for the device to be effective.

Conservation of our Maritime Heritage

In our passage through the generations, we have saved a whole range of things—Chinese vases, Greek sculptures, Flemish paintings, Egyptian temples, to name but a few. We inherently recognize and glory in the work of the thousands of generations that have gone before us and learn from what they lived through and discovered before our time.

OPPOSITE Marine architects inspect the planks from the hull of an ancient Greek ship, *Kyrenia*. Underwater archeologists from the University of Pennsylvania raised the wreck in the mid-1960s.

Among the countless things we admire about the past is our seafaring heritage. The sea and ships have played an immensely important role in shaping our languages, literature, cultures, and commerce. Is it any wonder then that across the world people work to preserve and conserve all that is embodied in maritime heritage?

Securing the past comes in many different guises, from stately maritime museums and their national treasures, such as the National Maritime Museum at Greenwich in the UK, to the far smaller regional museums found in many countries, that display the artefacts and memories of their local seafarers.

Then there are those who preserve not just the artefacts from ships of the past, but the ships themselves—from indigenous rafts made from local materials for fishing or short distance travel, through the ocean-voyaging vessels of the Polynesians, to the dinghies, skiffs, and launches used for coastal commerce and recreation; and finally to the big ships that built nations from the sea, or fought their naval battles. Examples of all of these are preserved around the world.

SHIP PRESERVATION

The 1960s and 1970s were perhaps the turning point in the history of ship preservation.

ABOVE The painstakingly restored tea clipper *Cutty Sark* at Greenwich, UK. Launched in 1869, *Cutty Sark* carried cargo across the Atlantic and Pacific oceans before coming to rest at Greenwich in 1954.

In 1961, the raising of the Swedish warship *Wasa*, which sank in Stockholm harbor in 1628, caught the world's imagination. The astonishing salvage of the hulk of Isambard Kingdom Brunel's *Great Britain* from the Falkland Islands, and its tow from the South Atlantic to the dry dock in which it was built in Bristol, UK, was a feat of compelling drama. San Francisco's waterfront was enlivened with the majestic square-rigger *Balclutha*; New York created the South Street Seaport, a mix of early port buildings and ships, such as *Wavertree* and *Peking*; San Diego brought back to life the tall ship *Star of India*; and Galveston became home to another square-rigger, *Elissa*. The two latter ships are still sailing today. Perhaps the most famous ship of them all—*Cutty Sark*—was carefully restored and brought ashore at Greenwich, UK, for all to see.

In Australia, the tall ship *Polly Woodside* was restored and went on display in Melbourne. Sydney embarked on a 30-year project to restore the 1874 barque *James Craig*, salvaged from a beach in southern Tasmania. Today, *James Craig* is fully operational and regularly carries passengers on pleasure trips.

It should come as no surprise that sailing ships dominate the world's preserved "big ships." All the world loves a sailing ship, a statement that is amply supported today wherever the world's tall ships gather, be it during the annual European Tall Ship Races, or the gatherings of America's tall ships, or when a lone ship, perhaps on a world voyage, puts into port.

American Peter Stanford, one of the men who did so much to lead the ship preservation movement of the twentieth century, eloquently explained the wide appeal in these words: "A sailing ship built for ocean voyaging is an artefact of compelling power. She is an expression of purpose, will and work in which men invested more than we generally invest in our lives—how much more! That is what hits and staggers the bored suburbanite, or the child who comes to such a ship. It doesn't hit people with words, it comes with the mute testimony of the thing itself."

PRESERVING STEAMERS

It would be wrong to suggest that only sailing ships create a passion for preservation. The generation of ships that followed sail—the steamers—also have their devotees. Around the world there are many examples of preserved steamers, but due to modern safety standards and the particular skills required to restore and maintain steam machinery, few of them are still operational. Australia stands out here. Along with the restored and operational barque *James Craig*, the Sydney Heritage Fleet boasts two centenarian steamers not just operational, but in commercial survey—the elegant steam launch *Lady Hopetoun* and the workmanlike tug, *Waratah*. A third steamer, 1927 coastal steamship *John Oxley*, is also being restored to operational condition in the Fleet's own shipyard.

In his poem "Ships," English poet John Masefield (1878–1967), wrote:

"… *They mark our passage as a race of men—
Earth will not see such ships as those again*."

However, the memories, the artefacts, the time-honored traditions—and some of the ships—survive.

Saving our Oceans

During the mid-1900s, explorer–scientist Jacques Cousteau sought to learn more about the ecology and marine life of the Sargasso Sea. He was astounded to find that the drag nets deployed in the mid-Atlantic gyre became fouled with oil blobs, styrofoam, plastic, and other trash. So disturbing was this discovery to Cousteau, that he pioneered marine conservation, a mission that occupied the remainder of his life.

Until a half-century ago, the oceans were believed to be so vast that they could never possibly become polluted. Yet today, we know that they constitute an extremely fragile and threatened ecosystem.

THE THREATENED MARINE ENVIRONMENT

Today, the global sea is under siege. During recent decades, the public has become increasingly aware of its many threats. Environmentally devastating spills from huge oil tankers have become all too common. Many marine species are endangered. The populations of many fish and various other commercial marine organisms have collapsed. Elsewhere, invasive species have wrought havoc on marine ecosystems. Coral reefs are seriously threatened. Many beaches are littered with trash, polluted and off-limits to swimming, or have been made unsafe by exploding populations of jellyfish. The world's largest garbage dumps are not on land—rather, they are found in the mid-Pacific and Atlantic oceans. These, and many other problems threaten the marine environment.

Red tides, caused by algal blooms, can produce natural toxins that are responsible for the deaths of many coastal and marine species including shellfish, crustaceans, fish, birds, marine mammals, and other organisms. Some occur naturally, but many are the result of pollution caused by human activity. They are increasing in number, area covered, and toxicity.

In the 1970s, oceanographers recognized that large near-shore areas of the world's oceans were void of life. In 2004, the UN reported about 150 such "dead zones" worldwide, some small, but others spread over more than 25,000 square miles (65,000 km^2). These lifeless areas are caused by hypoxia, a lack of oxygen. By 2008, their number had increased to over 400, affecting coastal waters throughout much of the world.

During the 1980s, scientists began to recognize that the Pacific and Atlantic oceans had areas that had become vast garbage dumps. The largest—the North Pacific Garbage Patch—is believed to cover an area

ABOVE LEFT Oceans have long been a dumping ground for all manner of human garbage, including these toilets. The negative effects of pollution on marine ecosystems are now recognized.

LEFT Harmful algal blooms cause the phenomenon known as a red tide. These algae produce toxins that can have a detrimental effect on marine life and interfere with the food chain.

larger than the United States and contain more than 100 million tons (91 million tonnes) of debris. Similar, although smaller, garbage patches exist in the South Pacific and both the North and South Atlantic. Trash accumulates within huge gyres created by prevailing winds and resulting ocean currents. Once debris enters a gyre, it is unable to leave.

Coastal zones are also threatened. In the tropics and subtropics, stands of mangroves are threatened in many locations. In addition to protecting shores from erosion, mangroves create a habitat in which many marine organisms spawn and/or live. Coastal pollution threatens oyster, crab, shrimp, and lobster populations, and can be toxic to those who eat them.

SOURCE OF POLLUTANTS

The great majority of oceanic pollutants—including solid trash, liquid wastes, and other materials—come from land-based sources. A small amount, perhaps less than 10 percent, comes from ships and boats.

Many municipalities, particularly in the developing world, use the sea to dispose of sewage and garbage. Industrial wastes pour into rivers and make their way into the global sea. So, too, does agricultural run-off, including animal wastes, and chemical fertilizers, herbicides, and pesticides.

CONSERVING THE MARINE ENVIRONMENT

Only recently have scientists and others realized that the ocean is a fragile, imperiled environment. Most initiatives to save the sea are in their infancy. Today, a considerable number of agencies, including the United Nations, the (US) National Oceanic and Atmospheric Administration (NOAA), and the World Resources Institute, are deeply involved in initiatives designed to protect and restore the marine environment.

Worldwide, more than 5,000 Marine Protected Areas (MPAs) have been established to help protect critical ecosystems and habitats and to restore threatened marine life. Red tides and dead zones can be reduced in number and size in several ways. Use of fertilizers can be adjusted to limit excess run-off of nutrients from farmland. Animal wastes can be better controlled. Industries can be encouraged to reduce the discharge of pollutants including nutrients, organic matter, and chemicals into the sea. And sewage can be better treated and otherwise handled in many places.

In what may be the most ambitious oceanic restoration plan, an organization—the Environmental Cleanup Coalition—has formed to clean up the North Pacific Garbage Patch. The plan involves a fleet of ships that will clear the area of debris and use it to create a floating laboratory called Gyre Island.

ABOVE Indonesian children plant mangrove trees at a conservation area in Jakarta. The project was undertaken to try to restore mangrove forests destroyed by industrial development of the twentieth century.

ABOVE A male elephant seal basks on the beach beneath a sign for a protected wildlife area at Año Nuevo State Reserve in California, USA.

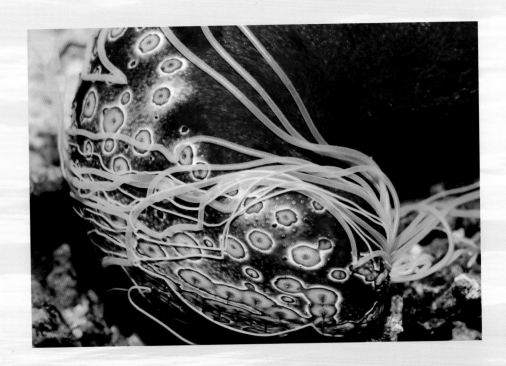

ABOVE Pigmy seahorse *(Hippocampus bargabanti)*.

TOP Sea cucumber *(Bohadschia argus)*.

RIGHT Red harp gorgonian *(Ctenocella pectinata)*.

PREVIOUS PAGE King penguins *(Aptenodytes patagonicus)* confront seal.

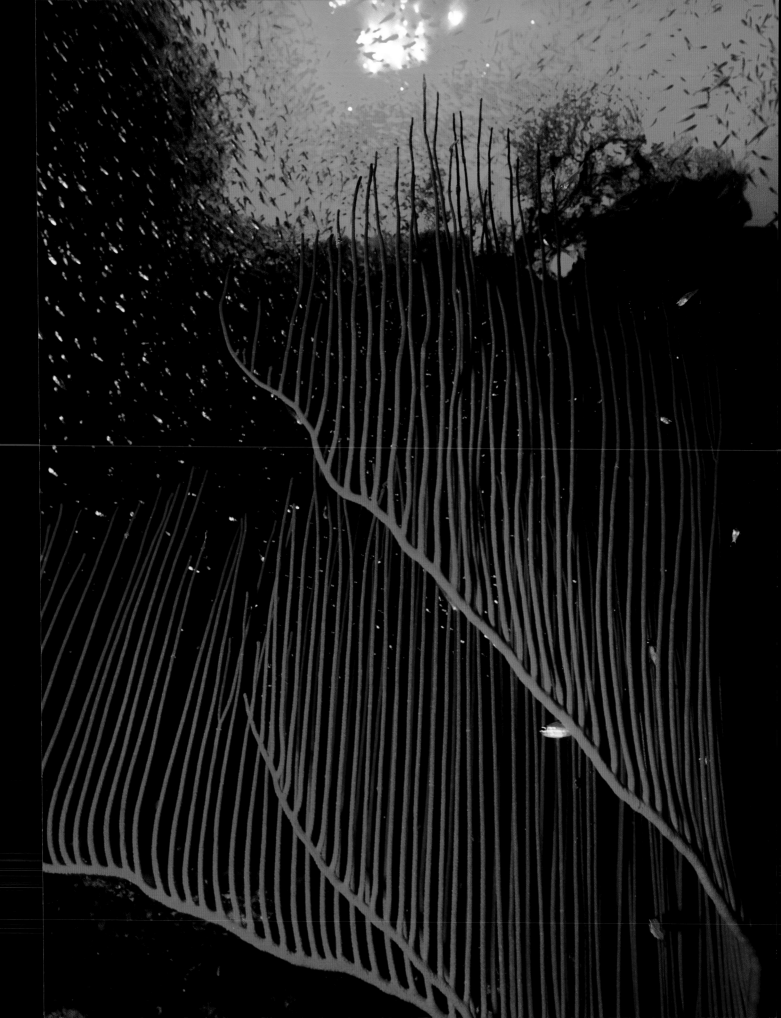

ABOVE Mantis shrimp *(Odontodactylus scyllarus).*

TOP Prawn crawling on rock.

LEFT Clown fish *(Amphiprion ocellaris).*

FOLLOWING PAGES Seabird flying over melting tabular iceberg

ABOVE Humpback whale *(Megaptera novaeangliae).*

TOP Weddell seal *(Leptonychotes weddellii)* and pup.

RIGHT Polar bear *(Ursus maritimus)* and cubs.

FOLLOWING PAGES Sea otters *(Enhydra lutris).*

ABOVE Spiral-gilled worms, also called Christmas tree worms *(Spriobranchus* sp.*)*.

TOP Pajama cardinal fish *(Sphaeramia nematoptera)*.

RIGHT Variety of tropical fish.

FOLLOWING PAGES Eyes of queen conch *(Strombus gigas)*.

50
R.de los Estrechos
el Trabaios
Tuchano
Quino
QVIVIRA.
Quiura
Sierra nevada
Rio Grande
Bade los Primeros
TOLM.
40
Cicuic
Axa
Chucho
Tiguas rio.
TOTO-
Jotom teac
TEAC.
Tiguex
MARATA.
Snala mon
Abacus, nunc
Granata
CVLIACAN,
Sardinas
P.de S. Clara
del papagaio
 Lauconian
Marata
Guaimal rio.
ASTATLAN
TERLICHIC
Y.del Primero
Cazanes insl.
Coana
Astatlan
Cerlatan
Ometlan
HISPANIA NOV
XALISCO
Chicil-
tiscalo
Cuchillo
Coana
Culua
Vacatya
Insl. Cedri
Chianet
Petatlan
TOPIRA
Los Alamant
Baia de la
trinidad
Gunxaca
Caraconi
Los volcanes
Las dos hermanos
Malabrigo
La farsana
Y.de Paxaros
Tala
Calchuichi
La Vezina
O Cali-
fornia
Insl.de
Xalisco
MECHVACAN
ARCHIPELAGO DI
Lo Monjes
Y.de Algreman
Rocha
partida
S. Thomas
SAN LAZARO.
La Anubr
ada
Restinga de ladrones
Zamal
Insl. de los corales
Y.de S.y
20
Insl. de S.Steuan
OCCIDENS
Los iardines
Insl.de los reys
MAR DEL
SVR, quod
210
220
230
Circulus Æquinoctialis
240
250
260
Barbuda
Caimana
Nombre de Iesu
Los Bol
canos
Isola Adreguada
et PACIFICVM.
Peru
Isabella
Aduah a
P.Efton
Las Marias
Tierra
baxa
Amastra
de la X.
B.S.Benito
Botad.
S.Catalina
S.Ana
S. Nicolas
Naio
Vezern.
NOVA GVINEA. Andre-
as Corsalus Florent. videtur eam
sub nomine Terræ Piceunnacoli
designare.
Tuberones
20
Insulæ Salomonis
S. Petri
TERRA AVSTRA-
LIS, SIVE
MAGELLA-
30
NICA HAC-
TENVS IN-
COGNITA.
40
50

AMERICAE SIVE
NOVI ORBIS, NO-
VA DESCRIPTIO.

OCEANS

Key to Oceans Text

☐ Surface Area (approx.)

▽ Deepest Point (approx.)

♡ Length of Coastline (approx.)

⅜ Bordering Continents

Atlantic Ocean

☐ 29,637,974 square miles (76,762,000 km²)

▽ 28,232 ft (8,605 m)

♡ 69,510 miles (111,866 km)

⅜ Africa, Europe, North America, South America

Arctic Ocean

☐ 5,428,000 square miles (14,060 million km²)

▽ 18,050 ft (5,502 m)

♡ 28,204 miles (45,389 km)

⅜ Asia, Europe, North America

PREVIOUS PAGES Old map from *Theatrum Orbis Terrarum* by Abraham Ortelius, 1592, showing North and South America with Pacific and Atlantic oceans.

Indian Ocean

- ☐ 26,000,000 miles (67,500,000 km²)
- ▽ 23,812 ft (7,258 m)
- ♡ 41,300 miles (66,500 km)
- ⅊ Africa, Asia, Australia, Europe

Pacific Ocean

- ☐ 60,000,000 square miles (155,400 million km²)
- ▽ 35,800 ft (10,911 m)
- ♡ 84,297 miles (135,663 km)
- ⅊ Australia, Asia, North America, South America

Southern Ocean

- ☐ 780,000 square miles (20,000,000 km²)
- ▽ 23,736 ft (7,235 m)
- ♡ 11,164 miles (17,968 km)
- ⅊ Antarctica

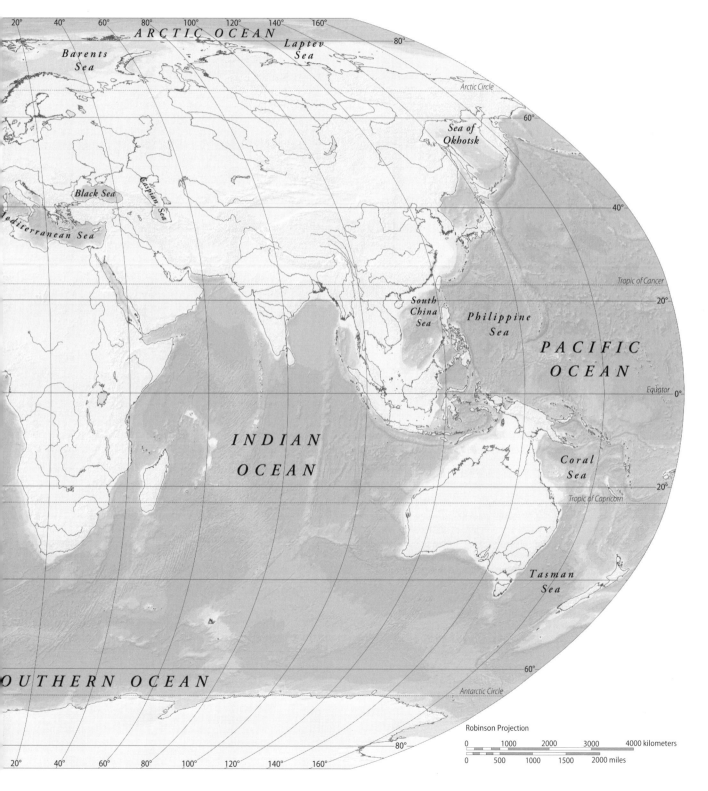

SEAS

Key to Seas Text

⬚ Surface Area (approx.) ○ Main Coastal Cities

≈ Water Temperature ↯ Bordering Countries

▽ Deepest Point (approx.) ≈ Main Waters Flowing From

◇ Notable Feature ＞ Endangered Fish Species

Adriatic Sea

⬚ 50,590 square miles (131,050 km²)

≈ 50°F (10°C)–75°F (24°C)

▽ 4,265 ft (1,300 m)

◇ canals of Venice

○ Naples, Roma, Venice

↯ Albania, Croatia, Italy, Montenengro, Slovenia

≈ Po River, Strait of Otranto

＞ carpione del garda *(Salmo carpio)*, chondrostoma soetta *(Chondrostoma soetta)*, Maltese ray *(Leucoraja melitensis)*, romanogobio benacensis *(Romanogobio benacensis)*, scardinius scardafa *(Scardinius scardafa)*, squalius lucumonis *(Squalius lucumoni)*

Aegean Sea

⬚ 83,000 square miles (214,000 km²)

≈ 50°F (10°C)–75°F (24°C)

▽ 11,627 ft (3,543 m)

◇ over 1,400 islands

○ Athens

↯ Greece, Turkey

≈ Black Sea

＞ Aegean minnow *(Phoxinus strymonicus)*, almiri toothcarp *(Aphanius almiriensis)*, alosa vistonica *(Alosa vistonica)*, cobitis hellenica *(Cobitis hellenica)*, cobitis arachthosensis *(Cobitis arachthosensis)*, cobitis trichonica *(Cobitis trichonica)*, cobitis stephanidisi *(Cobitis stephanidisi)*, Corfu toothcarp *(Valencia letourneuxi)*, doiran bleak *(Alburnus macedonicus)*, ellinopygosteos *(Pungitius hellenicus)*, Greek brook lamprey *(Eudontomyzon hellenicus)*, Greek rudd *(Scardinius graecus)*, knipowitschia thessala *(Knipowitschia thessala)*, knipowitschia milleri *(Knipowitschia milleri)*, nanogovios *(Economidichthys trichonis)*, pelasgus laconicus *(Pelasgus laconicus)*, pelasgus epiroticus *(Pelasgus epiroticus)*, etropsaro *(Barbus euboicus)*, rutilus ylikiensis *(Rutilus ylikiensis)*, rutilus meidingeri *(Rutilus meidingeri)*, salaria economidisi *(Salaria economidisi)*, squalius sp. nov. 'Evia' *(Squalius sp. nov. 'Evia')*, squalius moreoticus *(Squalius moreoticus)*, squalius keadicus *(Squalius keadicus)*, telestes beoticus *(Telestes beoticus)*, vistonis shemaja *(Alburnus vistonicus)*, yalartza *(Alburnus volviticus)*

Andaman Sea

☐ 308,000 square miles (797,000 km²)

≈ over 68°F (20°C) all year

▽ 12,392 ft (3,777 m)

◇ Strait of Malacca

○ Medan, Yangon

⇄ Indonesia, Malaysia, Myanmar (Burma), Thailand

≈ Irrawaddy River delta, Salween River

> Asian bonytongue *(Scleropages formosus)*, banggai cardinalfish *(Pterapogon kauderni)*, Boeseman's rainbowfish *(Melanotaenia boesemani)*, double lipspot mouthbrooder *(Betta spilotogena)*, duck-billed buntingi *(Adrianichthys kruyti)*, egg-carrying buntingi *(Xenopoecilus oophorus)*, Encheloclarias kelioides *(Encheloclarias kelioides)*, Java stingaree *(Urolophus javanicus)*, Popta's buntingi *(Xenopoecilus poptae)*, poso bungu *(Weberogobius amadi)*, sarasins minnow *(Xenopoecilus sarasinorum)*, sentani rainbowfish *(Chilatherina sentaniensis)*, sharp-jawed buntingi *(Oryzias orthognathus)*, silver shark *(Balantiocheilos melanopterus)*

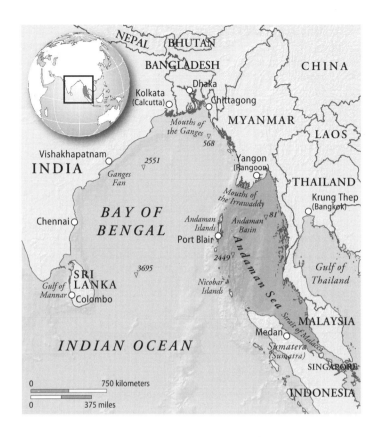

Arabian Sea

☐ 1,491,130 square miles (3,862,009 km²)

≈ over 68°F (20°C) all year

▽ 15,262 ft (4,652 m)

◇ trade route between Europe and Asia

○ Karachi, Mumbai, Porbandar

⇄ India, Iran, Oman, Pakistan

≈ Indus River

> knifetooth sawfish *(Anoxypristis cuspidate)*, longheaded eagle ray *(Aetobatus flagellum)*, narrowsnout sawfish *(Pristis zijsron)*, pondicherry shark *(Carcharhinus hemiodon)*

Arafura Sea

- ☐ 250,000 square miles (650,000 km²)
- ≃ around 88°F (31°C) all year
- ▽ 12,000 ft (3,600 m)
- ◇ underwater gas reserves
- ○ Kladar
- ⮃ Australia, Indonesia, Papua New Guinea, Timor-Leste (East Timor)
- ≈ Timor Current
- ➤ glass blue-eye *(Kiunga ballochi)*, knifetooth sawfish *(Anoxypristis cuspidate)*, Lake Wanam rainbowfish *(Glossolepis wanamensis)*, speartooth shark *(Glyphis glyphis)*

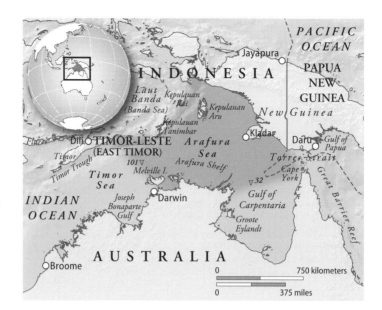

Baltic Sea

- ☐ 145,560 square miles (377,000 km²)
- ≃ 35°F (2°C)–57°F (14°C)
- ▽ 1,506 ft (459 m)
- ◇ Kiel Canal
- ○ Copenhagen, Stockholm
- ⮃ Denmark, Estonia, Finland, Germany, Latvia, Lithuania, Poland, Russian Federation, Sweden
- ≈ North Sea
- ➤ European eel *(Anguilla anguilla)*

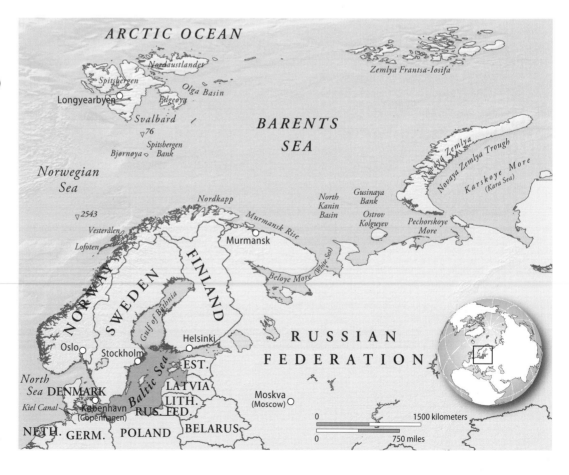

Barents Sea

- ☐ 542,000 square miles (1,405,000 km²)
- ≃ 37°F (3°C)–57°F (14°C)
- ▽ 2,000 ft (600 m)
- ◇ extensive fishing grounds
- ○ Murmansk
- ⇄ Norway, Russian Federation
- ≈ North Atlantic Drift
- ⟩ European eel *(Anguilla anguilla)*

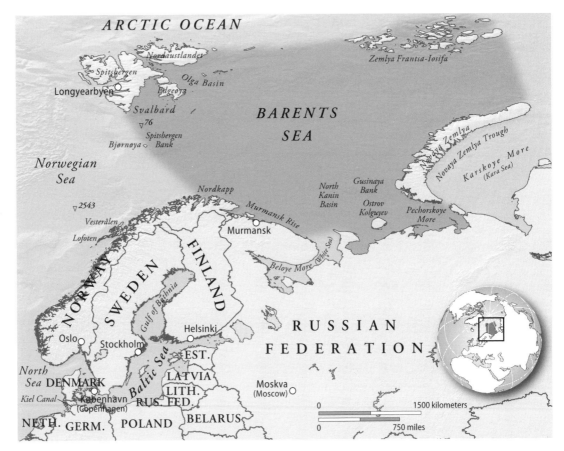

Bering Sea

- ☐ 890,000 square miles (2,304,000 km²)
- ≃ 32°F (0°C)–38°F (3°C)
- ▽ 13,442 ft (4,100 m)
- ◇ Bering Strait
- ○ Anadyr, Togiak, Ust'-Kamchatsk
- ⇄ Russian Federation, USA
- ≈ Kamchatka Current, Transverse Current
- ⟩ no endangered fish species

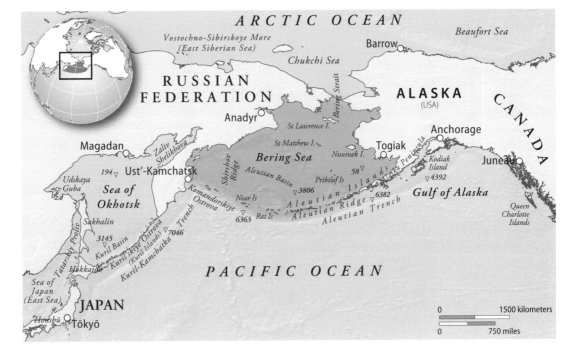

Bismarck Sea

☐ 15,000 square miles (40,000 km²)

≋ 77°F (25°C)–84°F (29°C)

▽ 8,200 ft (2,500 m)

◇ Admiralty Islands

○ Kokopo

↯ Papua New Guinea

≈ New Guinea Coastal Current

❯ glass blue-eye (*Kiunga ballochi*), knifetooth sawfish (*Anoxypristis cuspidate*), Lake Wanam rainbowfish (*Glossolepis wanamensis*), speartooth shark (*Glyphis glyphis*)

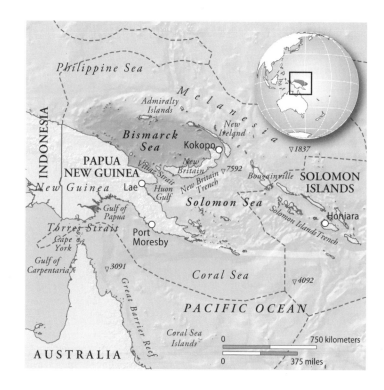

Caribbean Sea

☐ 1,063,000 square miles (2,753,000 km²)

≋ 70°F (21°C)–85°F (29°C)

▽ 24,500 ft (7,500 m)

◇ coral reef

○ Cancún, Caracas, Kingston

↯ Belize, Colombia, Costa Rica, Cuba, Dominican Republic, Haiti, Honduras, Jamaica, Mexico, Nicaragua, Panama, Trinidad and Tobago, Venezuela

≈ Caribbean Current

❯ no endangered fish species

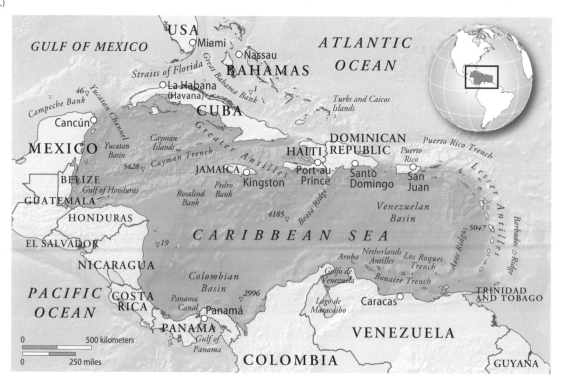

Coral Sea

- ☐ 1,615,262 square miles (4,183,510 km²)
- ≈ 75°F (24°C)–82°F (28°C)
- ▽ 30,079 ft (9,165 m)
- ◇ Great Barrier Reef
- ○ Bundaberg, Cairns, Mackay, Nouméa, Port Moresby, Rockhampton, Townsville
- ⇵ Australia, Papua New Guinea, Solomon Islands, Vanuatu
- ≈ South Equatorial Current
- ⟩ ornate eagle ray (*Aetomylaeus vespertilio*), purple eagle ray (*Myliobatis hamlyni*), red-finned blue-eye (*Scaturiginichthys vermeilipinnis*)

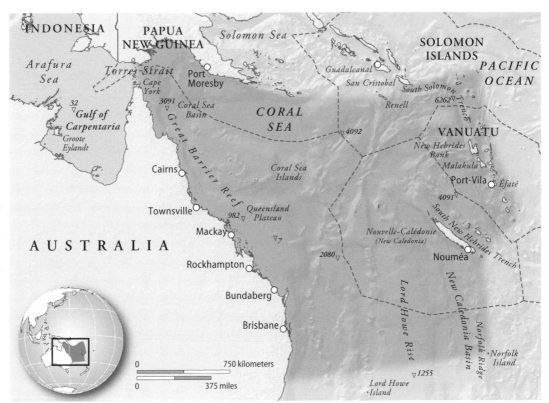

East China Sea

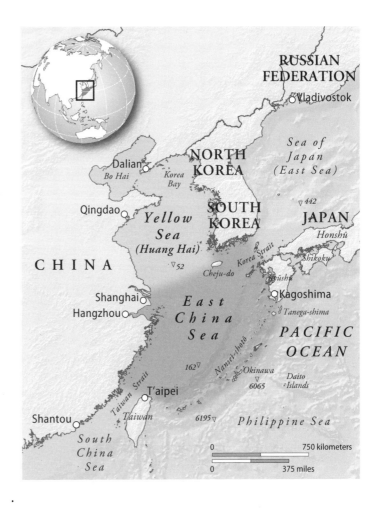

- ☐ 480,000 square miles (1,243,200 km²)
- ≈ 70°F (21°C)–85°F (29°C)
- ▽ 9,126 ft (2,782 m)
- ◇ Yangtze River delta
- ○ Hangzhou, Kagoshima, Shanghai
- ⇵ China, Japan, South Korea
- ≈ Yangtze River, Philippine Sea, South China Sea
- ⟩ big white fish (*Anabarilius polylepis*), Chinese paddlefish (*Psephurus gladius*), Chinese sturgeon (*Acipenser sinensis*), Dabry's sturgeon (*Acipenser dabryanus*), dianchi bullhead (*Pseudobagrus medianalis*), dianchi carp (*Cyprinus micristius*), elongate bitterling (*Acheilognathus elongates*), golden line fish (*Sinocyclocheilus grahami*), kaluga (*Huso dauricus*), king's bullhead (*Liobagrus kingi*), kunming nase (*Xenocypris yunnanensis*), kunming snout trout (*Schizothorax grahami*), kunming-lake catfish (*Silurus mento*), liobagrus nigricauda (*Liobagrus nigricauda*), schizothorax lepidothorax (*Schizothorax lepidothorax*), silvery white fish (*Anabarilius alburnops*), sphaerophysa dianchiensis (*Sphaerophysa dianchiensis*), tor yunnanensis (*Tor yunnanensis*), yunnanilus nigromaculatus (*Yunnanilus nigromaculatus*), yunnanilus discoloris (*Yunnanilus discoloris*)

Greenland Sea

- ☐ 465,000 square miles (1,205,000 km²)
- ≈ 32°F (0°C)–42°F (6°C)
- ▽ 16,000 ft (4,800 m)
- ◇ drifting Arctic icebergs
- ○ Longyearbyen
- ⅂ Greenland
- ≈ Arctic Ocean, East Greenland Current
- ＞ redfish (Sebastes fasciatus)

Irish Sea

- ☐ 38,610 square miles (100,000 km²)
- ≈ 46°F (8°C)–57°F (14°C)
- ▽ 576 ft (175 m)
- ◇ natural gas and oil
- ○ Dublin
- ⅂ Ireland, United Kingdom
- ≈ Dee, Mersey, and Ribble estuaries, Firth of Clyde, Belfast Lough
- ＞ goureen (Alosa killarnensis), pollan (Coregonus pollan), salvelinus obtusus (Salvelinus obtusus), Salvelinus grayi (Salvelinus grayi)

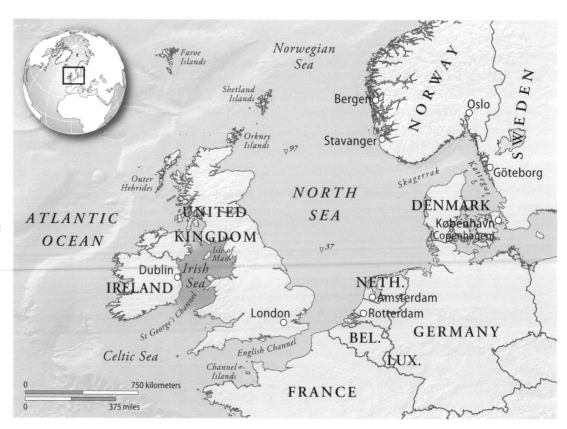

Laccadive Sea

☐ Maldives—34, 750 square miles
(90,000 km^2)

≋ 71°F (22°C)—82°F (28°C)

▽ 15,535 ft (4,735 m)

◇ Maldives

○ Colombo, Male

⇄ India, Maldives, Sri Lanka

≈ Indian Ocean

＞ giant wrasse (Cheilinus undulates),
ornate eagle ray (Aetomylaeus vespertilio)

Mediterranean Sea

☐ 970,000 square miles (2,510,000 km^2)

≋ 41°F (5°C) Gulf of Trieste—88°F (31°C) Gulf of Sidra

▽ 16,000 ft (4,900 m)

◇ almost no tides

○ Alger, Athina, Barcelona, Marseille, Roma, Tarābulus, Tunis

⇄ Albania, Algeria, Croatia, Egypt, France, Greece, Israel, Italy,
Jordan, Lebanon, Libya, Montenengro, Morrocco, Spain,
Syria, Turkey

≈ Atlantic Ocean

＞ European eel (Anguilla anguilla), see also Adriatic and
Aegean seas

North Sea

☐ 290,000 square miles
(750,000 km²)

≈ 43°F (6°C)—63°F
(17°C)

▽ 2,500 ft (750 m)

◇ kelp forests

○ Amsterdam, Bergen,
Rotterdam,
Stavanger

⇅ Belgium, Denmark,
France, Germany,
Netherlands, Norway,
United Kingdom

≈ Atlantic Ocean,
English Channel

❯ Atlantic halibut
(*Hippoglossus
hippoglossus*),
European eel
(*Anguilla anguilla*)

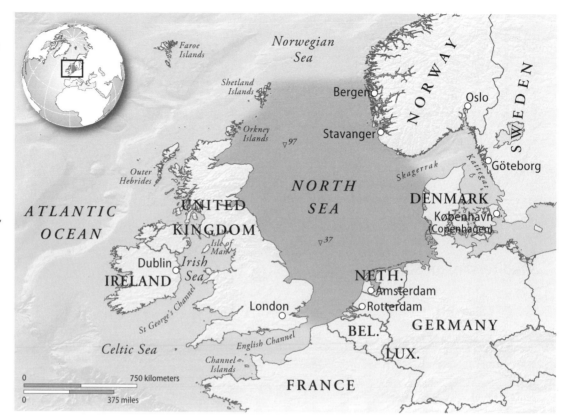

Norwegian Sea

☐ 533,000 square miles
(1,380,000 km²)

≈ 32°F (0°C)–42°F (6°C)

▽ 13,202 ft (3,970 m)

◇ fjords

○ Tórshavn

⇅ Iceland, Norway

≈ Norwegian Current

❯ European eel
(*Anguilla anguilla*)

Philippine Sea

- ☐ 380,000 square miles (1,000,000 km²)
- ≈ around 84°F (28.9°C) all year
- ▽ 35,796 ft (10,911 m)—world's deepest point
- ◇ Mariana Trench
- ○ Davao, Manila
- ↯ Japan, Micronesia, Palau, Philippines, Yap
- ≈ South China Sea
- ❯ bagangan (*Puntius clemensi*), baolan (*Puntius baoulan*), bitungu (*Ospatulus truncates*), cephalakompsus pachycheilus (*Cephalakompsus pachycheilus*), disa (*Puntius disa*), dwarf pygmy goby (*Pandaka pygmaea*), hampala lopezi (*Hampala lopezi*), kandar (*Puntius lanaoensis*), katapa-tapa (*Puntius flavifuscus*), katolo (*Puntius katalo*), kanalak (*Puntius manala*), mandibularca resinus (*Mandibularca resinus*), ospatulus palaemophagus (*Ospatulus palaemophagus*), pait (*Puntius amarus*), palata (*Spratellicypris palata*), puntius herrei (*Puntius herrei*), tras (*Puntius tras*), whitefin tope shark (*Hemitriakis leucoperiptera*)

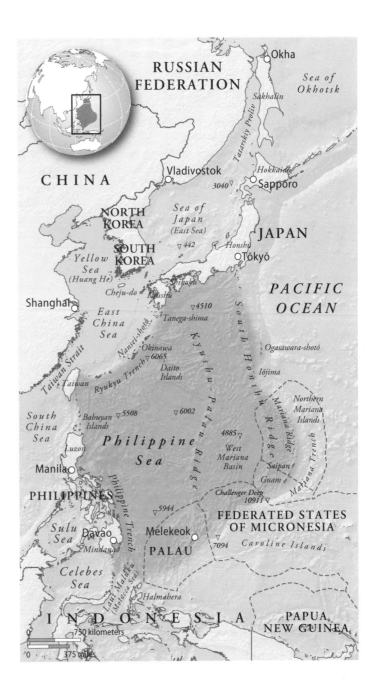

Red Sea

☐ 169,100 square miles (440,000 km²)

≋ 68°F (20°C)–86°F (30°C)

▽ 10,029 ft (3,039 m)

◇ Suez Canal

○ Jiddah

⇄ Eritrea, Egypt, Saudi Arabia, Sudan, Yemen

≈ Gulf of Aden

❯ angel shark *(Squatina squatina)*, blackchin guitarfish *(Rhinobatos cemiculus)*, common guitarfish *(Rhinobatos rhinobatos)*, dusky grouper *(Epinephelus marginatus)*, giant devilray *(Mobula mobular)*, giant wrasse *(Cheilinus undulates)*, hammerhead shark *(Sphyrna mokarran)*, red porgy *(Pagrus pagrus)*

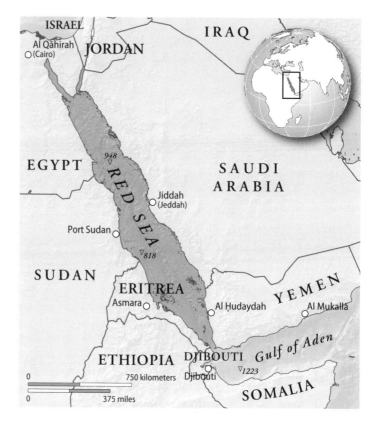

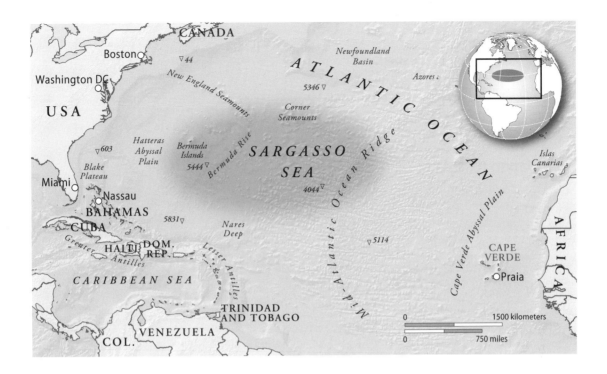

Sargasso Sea

- ☐ 1.5 million square miles (3,900,000 km²)
- ≈ around 80°F (27°C) all year
- ▽ 17,860 ft (5,444 m)
- ◇ collects waste from Atlantic
- ○ no coastline
- ⇅ international waters
- ≈ Gulf Stream
- ➤ no endangered fish species

Scotia Sea

- ☐ 350,000 square miles (900,000 km²)
- ≈ 42°F (6°F)–62°F (17°C)
- ▽ 26,900 ft (8,200 m)
- ◇ Drake Passage
- ○ none
- ⇅ Argentina, Chile
- ≈ Antarctic Circumpolar Current, Weddell Sea Deep Water Current
- ➤ graytail skate (Bathyraja griseocauda), tollo (Diplomystes chilensis)

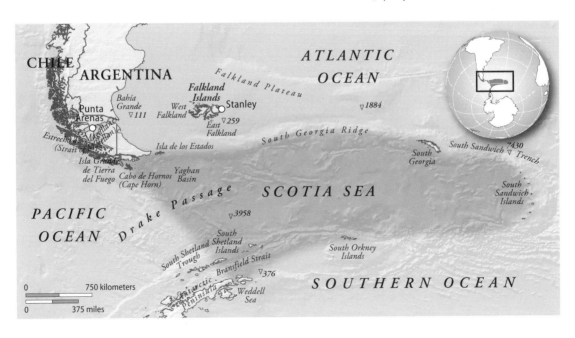

Sea of Japan (East Sea)

- ☐ 378,000 square miles (978,000 km²)
- ≊ 51°F (11°C)–62°F (17°C)
- ▽ 12,277 ft (3,742 m)
- ◇ almost no tides
- ○ Vladivostok
- ⇄ Japan, North Korea, South Korea, Russian Federation
- ≈ Tsushima Warm Current, Liman Cold Current
- ⟩ ayumodoki *(Leptobotia curta)*, Chinese sturgeon *(Acipenser sinensis)*, Hong Kong grouper *(Epinephelus akaara)*, ito *(Hucho perryi)*, kirikuchi char *(Salvelinus japonicus)*, miyako tango *(Tanakia tanago)*, nekogigi catfish *(Coreobagrus ichikawai)*, satsukimasu salmon *(Oncorhynchus ishikawai)*

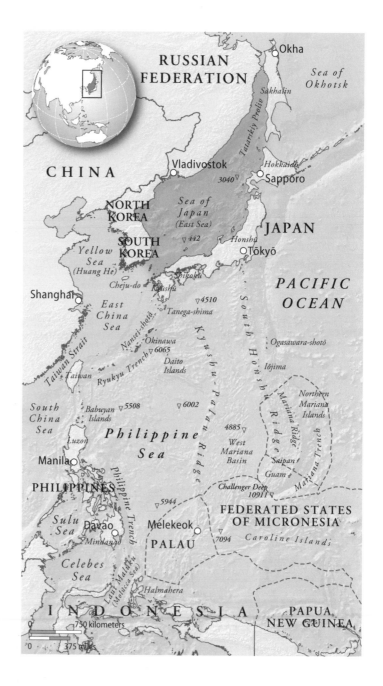

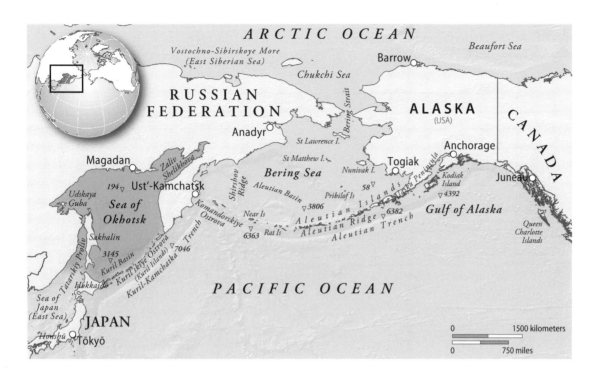

Sea of Okhost

- ☐ 611,000 square miles (1,580,000 km²)
- ≋ 32°F (0°C)–38°F (3°C)
- ▽ 8,200 ft (2,500 m)
- ◇ sea ice
- ○ Magadan
- ⇄ Japan, Russian Federation
- ≈ La Perouse Strait, Pacific Ocean, Sea of Japan
- ❭ amur sturgeon (*Acipenser schrenckii*), clupeonella abrau (*Clupeonella abrau*), ito (*Hucho perryi*), kezenoi-am trout (*Salmo ezenami*), sakhalin sturgeon (*Acipenser mikadoi*), shortspine thornyhead (*Sebastolobus alascanus*)

Solomon Sea

- ☐ 280,000 square miles (720,000 km²)
- ≋ around 86°F (30°C) all year
- ▽ 30,000 ft (9,140 m)
- ◇ some of the warmest waters in the world
- ○ Honiara
- ⇄ Papua New Guinea, Solomon Islands
- ≈ Bismarck Sea, Coral Sea
- ❭ giant wrasse (*Cheilinus undulates*)

South China Sea

- ☐ 1,390,000 square miles (3,600,000 km²)
- ≈ 70°F (21°C)–82°F (28°C)
- ▽ 18,000 ft (5,490 m)
- ◇ Gulf of Tonkin
- ○ Hong Kong, Manila
- ⁊ Brunei, China, Malaysia, Philippines, Vietnam
- ≈ Red, Mikong, Min, Jiulong, Rajang, Pasig, and Pahang rivers
- ⟩ Hong Kong grouper (*Epinephelus akaara*), knifetooth sawfish (*Anoxypristis cuspidate*), mottled eagle ray (*Aetomylaeus maculates*), oncorhynchus formosanus (*Oncorhynchus formosanus*), onychostoma alticorpus (*Onychostoma alticorpus*), ornate eagle ray (*Aetomylaeus vespertilio*)

Tasman Sea

- ☐ 900,000 square miles (2,300,000 km2)
- ≈ 44°F (7°C)–55°F (13°C)
- ▽ 17,000 ft (5,090 m)
- ◇ Cook Strait
- ○ Auckland, Hobart, Sydney, Wellington
- ⁊ Australia, New Zealand
- ≈ East Australian Current
- ⟩ Southern bluefin tuna (*Thunnus maccoyii*)

Timor Sea

- ☐ 235,000 square miles (610,000 km²)
- ≋ around 82°F (28°C) all year
- ▽ 10,800 ft (3,300 m)
- ◇ natural gas reserves
- ○ Darwin, Dili
- ⇄ Australia, Timor-Leste
- ≈ Indian Ocean
- ❯ giant wrasse (*Cheilinus undulates*)

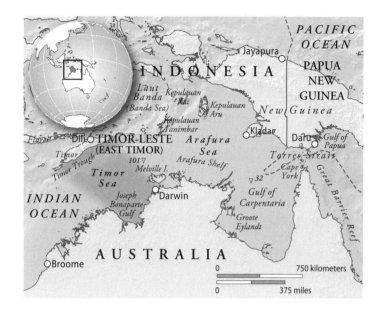

Yellow Sea

- ☐ 156,000 square miles (404,000 km²)
- ≋ 51°F (11°C)–75°F (24°C)
- ▽ 500 ft (152 m)
- ◇ heavy sediment and high tidal ranges
- ○ Qingdao, Dal
- ⇄ China, North Korea, South Korea
- ≈ Huang He (Yellow River)
- ❯ Borneo shark (*Carcharhinus borneensis*), Chinese paddlefish (*Psephurus gladius*), Chinese sturgeon (*Acipenser sinensis*), Dabry's sturgeon (*Acipenser dabryanus*), golden line fish (*Sinocyclocheilus grahami*), Hong Kong grouper (*Epinephelus akaara*), King's bullhead (*Liobagrus kingi*), kunming nase (*Xenocypris yunnanensis*), kunming snout trout (*Schizothorax grahami*), kunming-lake catfish (*Silurus mento*), liobagrus nigricauda (*Liobagrus nigricauda*), oncorhynchus formosanus (*Oncorhynchus formosanus*), onychostoma alticorpus (*Onychostoma alticorpus*), schizothorax lepidothorax (*Schizothorax lepidothorax*), sphaerophysa dianchiensis (*Sphaerophysa dianchiensis*)

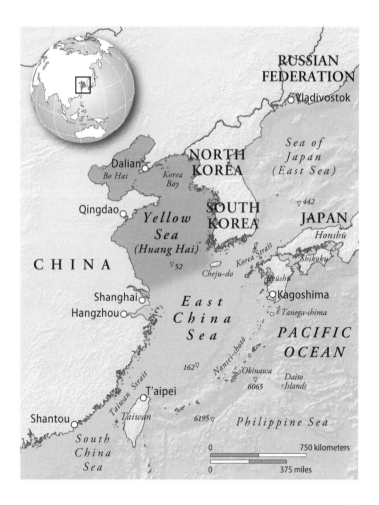

GULFS

Key to Gulfs Text

□ Surface Area (approx.)   ⅀ Bordering Countries

≈ Water Temperature   ═ Adjoins

◇ Notable Feature   ＞ Endangered Fish Species

○ Main Coastal Cities

The Gulf

□ 92,500 square miles (240,500 km²)

≈ around 82°F (28°C) all year

◇ Strait of Hormuz

○ Abū Ẓabī, Al Kuwayt, Bandar 'Abbās, Bandar-e Ganāveh

⅀ Bahrain, Iran, Iraq, Kuwait, Qatar, U.A.E.

═ Gulf of Oman

＞ hammerhead shark (Sphyrna mokarran)

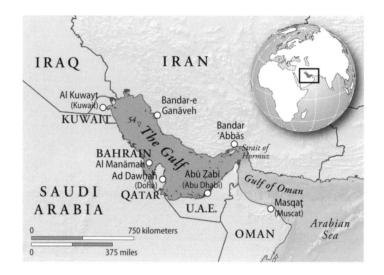

Gulf of Aden

□ 205,000 square miles (533,000 km²)

≈ around 77°F (25°C) all year

◇ one of the world's major shipping routes

○ Al Mukalla, Djibouti

⅀ Somalia, Yemen

═ Red Sea, Indian Ocean

＞ giant wrasse (Cheilinus undulates), hammerhead shark (Sphyrna mokarran)

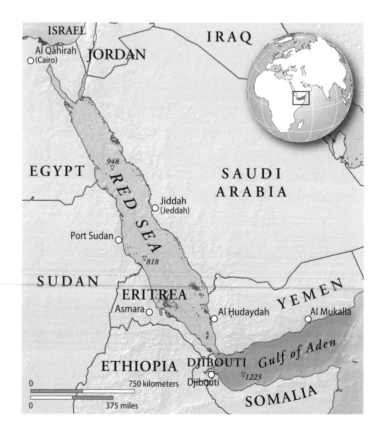

PREVIOUS PAGES Aerial view of Clearwater, Florida, on the Gulf of Mexico. Extensive reclamation has created luxury housing estates and anchorages.

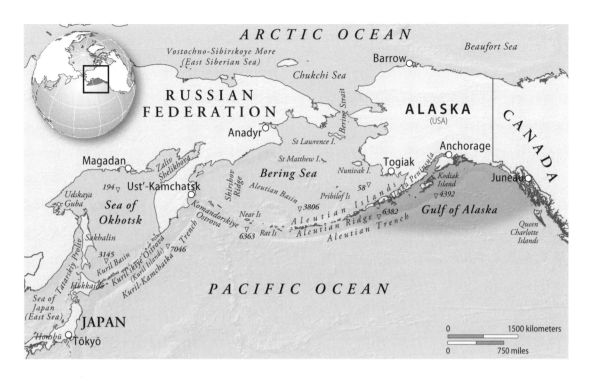

Gulf of Alaska

- ☐ 592,000 square miles (1,533,000 km²)
- ≈ 41°F (5°C)–59°F (15°C)
- ◇ major storms
- ○ Anchorage, Juneau
- ⇄ Canada, USA
- ═ Bering Sea, Pacific Ocean
- ❯ Atlantic halibut *(Hippoglossus hippoglossus)*, shortspine thornyhead *(Sebastolobus alascanus)*

Gulf of California

- ☐ 60,000 square miles (155,000 km²)
- ≈ 65°F (18°C)–71°F (22°C)
- ◇ host to many migratory marine species
- ○ Guaymas, La Paz
- ⇄ Mexico
- ═ Pacific Ocean
- ❯ Black Sea bass *(Stereolepis gigas)*, bocaccio rockfish *(Sebastes paucispinus)*, common sawfish *(Pristis pristis)*, desert pupfish *(Cyprinodon macularius)*, gulf grouper *(Mycteroperca jordani)*, razorback sucker *(Xyrauchen texanus)*, totoaba seatrout *(Cynoscion macdonaldi)*

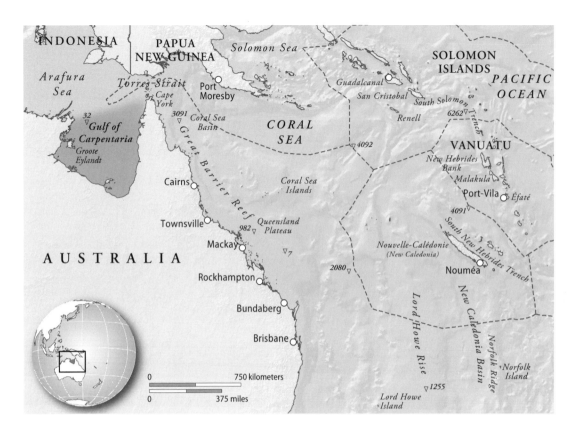

Gulf of Carpentaria

▢ 116,000 square miles (300,000 km²)

≈ around 80°F (27°C) all year

◇ relatively unspoiled

○ none

⇅ Australia

= Arafura Sea

> ornate eagle ray (*Aetomylaeus vespertilio*)

Gulf of Guinea

▢ Cameroon Line Islands—450 miles (724 km) long

≈ around 80°F (27°C) all year

◇ crude oil deposits

○ Accra, Lagos, Lomé, Malabo, Porto Novo, São Tomé

⇅ Benin, Cameroon, Côte d'Ivoire, Equatorial Guinea, Gabon, Ghana, Nigeria, Togo

= Atlantic Ocean

> African wedgefish (*Rhynchobatus luebberti*), bottlenose skate (*Rostroraja alba*), sawback angelshark (*Squatina aculeate*)

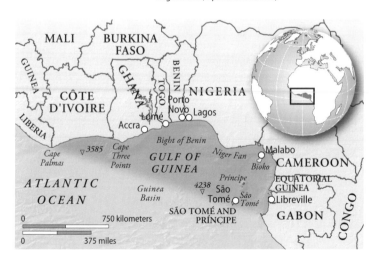

Gulf of Mexico

- ☐ 600,000 square miles (1,550,000 km²)
- ≈ around 82°F (28°C) all year
- ◇ deep sea coral reefs
- ○ Campeche, Corpus Christi, New Orleans, Tampa, Veracruz
- ⇄ Cuba, Mexico, USA
- ═ Caribbean Sea
- ❯ Anguila ciega (Ophisternon infernale), balsas splitfin (Ilyodon whitei), blackfin pupfish (Cyprinodon beltrani), bluntnose shiner (Notropis simus), boxer pupfish (Cyprinod), cachorrito cabezon (Cyprinodon pachycephalus), cachorrito de charco azul (Cyprinodon veronicae), cachorrito de dorsal larga (Cyprinodon verecundus), cachorrito de mezquital (Cyprinodon meeki), cachorrito enano de potosi (Megupsilon aporus), calico grouper (Epinephelus drummondhayi), carbonera pupfish (Cyprinodon fontinalis), charal de alchichica (Poblana alchichica), charal de la preciosa (Poblana letholepis), charal de quechulac (Poblana squamata), charalito chihuahua (Gila nigrescens), charalito saltillo (Gila modesta), checkered pup fish (Cualac tessellates), conchos shiner (Cyprinella panarcys), cuatro cienegas shiner (Cyprinella xanthicara), goodeid (Ameca splendens), guayacon bocon (Gambusia eurystoma), highland splitfin (Hubbsina turneri), La Palma pupfish (Cyprinodon longidorsalis), largescale pupfish (Cyprinodon macrolepis), maya pupfish (Cyprinodon maya), mexclapique (Girardinichthys viviparous), Mexican blindcat (Prietella phreatophila), mojarra (Cichlasoma labridens), molly del tamesi (Poecilia latipunctata), molly del teapa (Poecilia sulphuraria), Monterrey platyfish (Xiphophorus couchianus), Monterrey Spanish mackerel (Scomberomorus concolor), opal goodeid (Allotoca maculata), platy cuatro cienegas (Xiphophorus gordoni), platy de muzquiz (Xiphophorus meyeri), potosi pupfish (Cyprinodon alvarezi), rainbow goodeid (Characodon lateralis), Rio Grande silvery minnow (Hybognathus amarus), sardinilla cuatro cienegas (Lucania interioris), sardinita bocagrande (Cyprinella bocagrande), sardinita de tepelmene (Notropis moralesi), sardinita quijarrona (Dionda mandibularis), solo goodeido (Xenoophorus captivus), striped goodeid (Ataeniobius toweri), tepehuan shiner (Cyprinella alvarezdelvillari), thicklip pupfish (Cyprinodon labiosus), tiro (Skiffia francesae)

Gulf of Oman

- ☐ approximately 78,000 square miles (202,000 km²)
- ≈ around 82°F (28°C) all year
- ◇ Strait of Hormuz
- ○ Masqat
- ⇄ Iran, Oman, U.A.E.
- ═ The Gulf, Arabian Sea
- ❯ hammerhead shark (Sphyrna mokarran)

Gulf of Panama

- □ 900 square miles (2,300 km²)
- ≋ around 82°F (28°C) all year
- ◇ Panama Canal
- ○ Panama
- ⇄ Panama
- 〃 Pacific Ocean
- ➤ brownstriped grunt (*Anisotremus moricandi*), common sawfish (*Pristis pristis*), hammerhead shark (*Sphyrna mokarran*), Nassau grouper (*Epinephelus striatus*), red porgy (*Pagrus pagrus*)

Gulf of Thailand

- □ 123,500 square miles (320,000 km²)
- ≋ around 84°F (29°C) all year
- ◇ coral reefs
- ○ Bangkok
- ⇄ Cambodia, Malaysia, Thailand, Vietnam
- 〃 South China Sea
- ➤ Asian bonytongue (*Scleropages formosus*), bluetail glass barb (*Chela caeruleostigmata*), dwarf loach (*Botia sidthimunki*), giant pangasius (*Pangasius sanitwongsei*), Jullien's golden carp (*Probarbus jullieni*), knifetooth sawfish (*Anoxypristis cuspidate*), Laotian shad (*Tenualosa thibaudeaui*), marbled freshwater stingray (*Himantura oxyrhyncha*), mottled eagle ray (*Aetomylaeus maculates*), red-tailed sharkminnow (*Epalzeorhynchos bicolor*), silver shark (*Balantiocheilos melanopterus*), Thailand giant catfish (*Pangasianodon gigas*)

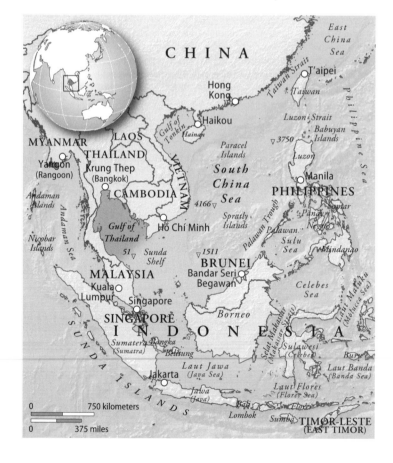

BAYS

Key to Bays Text

▢ Surface Area ⇄ Bordering Countries

≈ Water Temperature ═ Adjoins

◇ Notable Feature ＞ Endangered Fish Species

○ Main Coastal Cities

Bay of Bengal

▢ 889,000 square miles (2,172,000 km²)

≈ around 82°F (28°C) all year

◇ large deltas

○ Chennai, Chittagong, Dhaka, Kolkata

⇄ Bangladesh, India, Indonesia, Myanmar (Burma), Sri Lanka

═ Indian Ocean

＞ knifetooth sawfish (Anoxypristis cuspidate)

Hudson Bay

▢ 316 square miles (819,000 km²)

≈ 32°F (0°C)–46°F (8°C)

◇ longest bay shoreline in the world

○ Akulivik, Chesterfield Inlet, Churchill, Chisasibi, Fort Severn

⇄ Canada

═ Foxe Basin, Labrador Sea

＞ barndoor winter skate (Dipturus laevis), shortnose sturgeon (Acipenser brevirostrum), shortspine thornyhead (Sebastolobus alascanus), white sturgeon (Acipenser transmontanus)

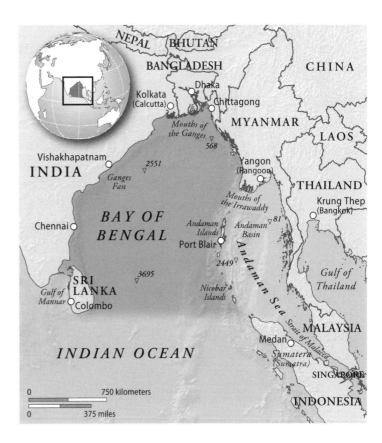

Great Australian Bight

▢ 7,488 square miles (19,395 km²)

≈ around 59°F (15°C) all year

◇ steep rugged cliffs

○ none

⇄ Australia

═ Indian Ocean

＞ no endangered species

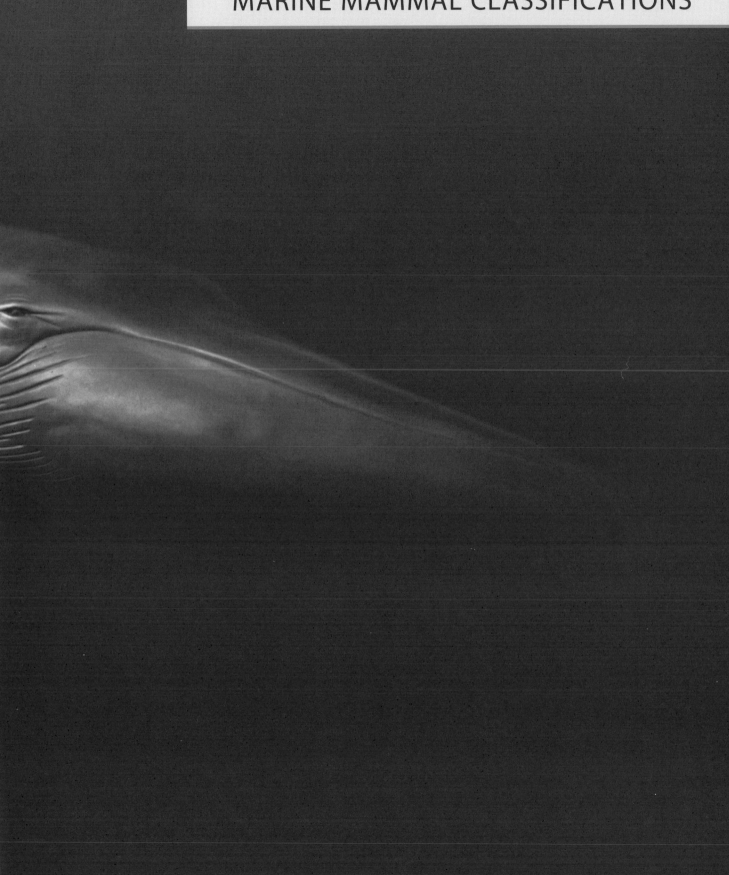

Dolphins, Porpoises, and Whales — ORDER: CETACEA: dolphins, porpoises, and whales

SUBORDER	FAMILY	GENUS	SPECIES

MYSTICETI: baleen whales

- **BALAENIDAE: bowhead whales and right whales**
  - *Balaena* (bowhead whale) — *Balaena mysticetus* (bowhead)
  - *Eubalaena* (right whale)
    - *Eubalaena australis* (southern right whale)
    - *Eubalaena glacialis* (North Atlantic right whale)
    - *Eubalaena japonica* (North Pacific right whale)

- **BALAENOPTERIDAE: rorquals**
  - *Balaenoptera* (rorquals)
    - *Balaenoptera acutorostrata* (common minke whale)
    - *Balaenoptera bonaerensis* (Antarctic minke whale)
    - *Balaenoptera borealis* (sei whale)
    - *Balaenoptera brydei* (Bryde's whale)
    - *Balaenoptera musculus* (blue whale)
    - *Balaenoptera physalus* (fin whale)
  - *Megaptera* (humpback whale) — *Megaptera novaeangliae* (humpback whale)

- **ESCHRICHTIIDAE: gray whale**
  - *Eschrichtius* (gray whale) — *Eschrichtius robustus* (gray whale)

- **NEOBALAENIDAE: pygmy right whale**
  - *Caperea* (pygmy right whale) — *Caperea marginata* (pygmy right whale)

ODONTOCETI: toothed whales
(continued on opposite page)

- **DELPHINIDAE: dolphins, killer whales, pilot whales, and relatives**
  - *Cephalorhynchus* (black dolphin, Commerson's dolphin, Heaviside's dolphin, and Hector's dolphin)
    - *Cephalorhynchus commersonii* (Commerson's dolphin)
    - *Cephalorhynchus eutropia* (black dolphin)
    - *Cephalorhynchus heavisidii* (Heaviside's dolphin)
    - *Cephalorhynchus hectori* (Hector's dolphin)
  - *Delphinus* (saddleback dolphin)
    - *Delphinus capensis* (long-beaked common dolphin)
    - *Delphinus delphis* (short-beaked saddleback dolphin)
  - *Feresa* (pygmy killer whale) — *Feresa attenuata* (pygmy killer whale)
  - *Globicephala* (pilot whales)
    - *Globicephala macrorhyncus* (short-finned pilot whale)
    - *Globicephala melas* (long-finned pilot whale)
  - *Grampus* (Risso's dolphin) — *Grampus griseus* (Risso's dolphin)
  - *Lagenodelphis* (Fraser's dolphin) — *Lagenodelphis hosei* (Fraser's dolphin)
  - *Lagenorhynchus* (white-beaked dolphins, white-sided dolphins, and relatives)
    - *Lagenorhynchus acutus* (Atlantic white-sided dolphin)
    - *Lagenorhynchus albirostris* (white-beaked dolphin)
    - *Lagenorhynchus australis* (Peale's dolphin)
    - *Lagenorhynchus cruciger* (hourglass dolphin)
    - *Lagenorhynchus obliquidens* (Pacific white-sided dolphin)
    - *Lagenorhynchus obscurus* (dusky dolphin)
  - *Lissodelphis* (right whale dolphins)
    - *Lissodelphis borealis* (northern right whale dolphin)
    - *Lissodelphis peronii* (southern right whale dolphin)
  - *Orcaella* (Irrawaddy dolphin) — *Orcaella brevirostris* (Irrawaddy dolphin)
  - *Orcinus* (killer whale and orca) — *Orcinus orca* (killer whale)
  - *Peponocephala* (melon-headed whale) — *Peponocephala electra* (melon-headed whale)
  - *Pseudorca* (false killer whale) — *Pseudorca crassidens* (false killer whale)
  - *Sotalia* (tucuxi) — *Sotalia fluviatilis* (gray dolphin)
  - *Sousa* (humpbacked dolphins)
    - *Sousa chinensis* (Indo-Pacific humpbacked dolphin)
    - *Sousa teuszii* (Atlantic humpbacked dolphin)
  - *Stenella* (spinner dolphins, spotted dolphins, and striped dolphins)
    - *Stenella attenuata* (pantropical spotted dolphin)
    - *Stenella clymene* (clymene dolphin)
    - *Stenella coeruleoalba* (striped dolphin)
    - *Stenella frontalis* (Atlantic spotted dolphin)
    - *Stenella longirostris* (spinner dolphin)
  - *Steno* (rough-toothed dolphin) — *Steno bredanensis* (rough-toothed dolphin)
  - *Tursiops* (bottlenose dolphin)
    - *Tursiops aduncus* (Indo-Pacific bottlenose dolphin)
    - *Tursiops truncates* (bottlenosed dolphin)

ABOVE Atlantic spotted dolphin *(Stenella frontalis)*.

PREVIOUS PAGES The largest creature on Earth, the blue whale *(Balaenoptera musculus)*, is also the loudest, with whale songs measured at 188 decibels. They live mainly on krill.

Dolphins, Porpoises, and Whales (continued) — ORDER: CETACEA: dolphins, porpoises, and whales

SUBORDER	FAMILY	GENUS	SPECIES
	INIIDAE: river dolphins	*Inia* (Amazon river dolphin)	*Inia geoffrensis* (Amazon river dolphin)
		Lipotes (baiji)	*Lipotes vexillifer* (baiji)
		Pontoporia (franciscana)	*Pontoporia blainvillei* (franciscana)
	MONODONTIDAE: beluga and narwhal	*Delphinapterus* (beluga)	*Delphinapterus leucas* (beluga)
		Monodon (narwhal)	*Monodon monoceros* (narwhal)
	PHOCOENIDAE: porpoises	*Neophocaena* (finless porpoise)	*Neophocaena phocaenoides* (finless porpoise)
		Phocoena (common porpoises)	*Phocoena dioptrica* (spectacled porpoise) *Phocoena phocaena* (harbor porpoise) *Phocoena sinus* (vaquita) *Phocoena spinipinnis* (Burmeister's porpoise)
		Phocoenoides (Dall's porpoise)	*Phocoenoides dalli* (Dall's porpoise)
ODONTOCETI: toothed whales (continued from previous page)	PHYSETERIDAE: sperm whales	*Kogia* (pygmy sperm whales)	*Kogia breviceps* (pygmy sperm whale) *Kogia sima* (dwarf sperm whale)
		Physeter (sperm whale)	*Physeter catodon* (sperm whale)
	PLATANISTIDAE: Indian river dolphins	*Platanista* (Indian river dolphins)	*Platanista gangetica* (Ganges dolphins and Indus dolphins)
	ZIPHIDAE: beaked whales	*Berardius* (giant beaked whales)	*Berardius arnuxii* (Arnoux's beaked whale) *Berardius bairdii* (Baird's beaked whale)
		Hyperoodon (bottlenose whales)	*Hyperoodon ampullatus* (northern bottlenose whale) *Hyperoodon planifrons* (southern bottlenose whale)
		Indopacetus (Longman's beaked whale)	*Indopacetus pacificus* (Longman's beaked whale)
		Mesoplodon, beaked whale	*Mesoplodon bidens* (Sowerby's beaked whale) *Mesoplodon bowdoini* (Andrews' beaked whale) *Mesoplodon carlhubbsi* (Hubbs' beaked whale) *Mesoplodon densirostris* (Blainville's beaked whale) *Mesoplodon europaeus* (Gervais's beaked whale) *Mesoplodon ginkgodens* (ginkgo-toothed beaked whale) *Mesoplodon grayi* (Gray's beaked whale) *Mesoplodon hectori* (Hector's beaked whale) *Mesoplodon layardii* (Layard's beaked whale) *Mesoplodon mirus* (True's beaked whale) *Mesoplodon perrini* (Perrin's beaked whale) *Mesoplodon peruvianus* (pygmy beaked whale) *Mesoplodon stejnegeri* (Stejneger's beaked whale) *Mesoplodon traversii* (spade-toothed whale)
		Tasmacetus (Shepherd's beaked whale)	*Tasmacetus shepherdi* (Shepherd's beaked whale)
		Ziphius (Cuvier's beaked whale)	*Ziphius cavirostris* (Cuvier's beaked whale)

LEFT Beluga whale *(Delphinapterus leucas)*.

Walruses, Sea lions, and Seals — ORDER: CARNIVORA: carnivores

SUBORDER	FAMILY	GENUS	SPECIES
	ODOBENIDAE: walruses	*Odobenus* (walruses)	*Odobenus rosmarus* (walrus)
		Arctocephalus (southern fur seals)	*Arctocephalus australis* (South American fur seal) *Arctocephalus forsteri* (New Zealand fur seal) *Arctocephalus galapagoensis* (Galápagos fur seal) *Arctocephalus gazella* (Antarctic fur seal) *Arctocephalus philippii* (Juan Fernandez fur seal) *Arctocephalus pusillus* (South African fur seal) *Arctocephalus townsendi* (Guadalupe fur seal) *Arctocephalus tropicalis* (Subantarctic fur seal)
	OTARIIDAE: fur seals and sea lions	*Callorhinus* (northern fur seal)	*Callorhinus ursinus* (northern fur seal)
		Eumetopias (Steller's sea lion)	*Eumetopias jubatus* (Steller's sea lion)
		Neophoca (Australian sea lion)	*Neophoca cinerea* (Australian sea lion)
		Otaria (South American sea lion)	*Otaria flavescens* (South American sea lion)
		Phocarctos (New Zealand sea lion)	*Phocarctos hookeri* (New Zealand sea lion)
CANIFORMIA: caniform carnivores		*Zalophus* (California sea lion)	*Zalophus californianus* (California sea lion) *Zalophus japonicus* (Japanese sea lion) *Zalophus wollebaeki* (Galápagos sea lion)
		Cystophora (hooded seal)	*Cystophora cristata* (hooded seal)
		Erignathus (bearded seal)	*Erignathus barbatus* (bearded seal)
		Halichoerus (gray seal)	*Halichoerus grypus* (gray seal)
		Histriophoca (ribbon seal)	*Histriophoca fasciata* (ribbon seal)
		Hydrurga (leopard seal)	*Hydrurga leptonyx* (leopard seal)
		Leptonychotes (Weddell seal)	*Leptonychotes weddellii* (Weddell seal)
		Lobodon (crabeater seal)	*Lobodon carcinophaga* (crabeater seal)
	PHOCIDAE: seals	*Mirounga* (elephant seals)	*Mirounga angustirostris* (northern elephant seal) *Mirounga leonina* (southern elephant seal)
		Monachus (monk seals)	*Monachus monachus* (Mediterranean monk seal) *Monachus schauinslandi* (Hawaiian monk seal) *Monachus tropicalis* (West Indian monk seal)
		Ommatophoca (Ross seal)	*Ommatophoca rossii* (Ross seal)
		Pagophilus (harp seal)	*Pagophilus groenlandicus* (harp seal)
		Phoca (harbor seals)	*Phoca largha* (spotted seal) *Phoca vitulina* (harbor seal)
		Pusa (ringed, Baikal, and Caspian seals)	*Pusa caspica* (Caspian seal) *Pusa hispida* (ringed seal) *Pusa sibirica* (Baikal seal)

LEFT Southern elephant seal *(Mirounga leonina)*.

Penguins — ORDER: SPHENISCIFORMES: penguins

FAMILY	GENUS	SPECIES

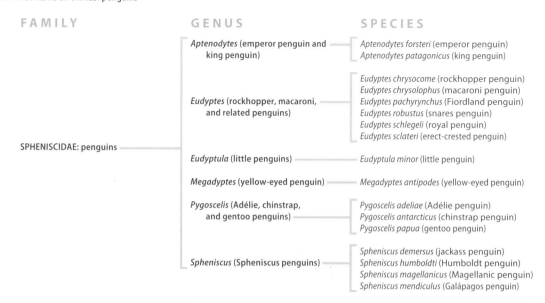

SPHENISCIDAE: penguins

Aptenodytes (emperor penguin and king penguin)
- *Aptenodytes forsteri* (emperor penguin)
- *Aptenodytes patagonicus* (king penguin)

Eudyptes (rockhopper, macaroni, and related penguins)
- *Eudyptes chrysocome* (rockhopper penguin)
- *Eudyptes chrysolophus* (macaroni penguin)
- *Eudyptes pachyrynchus* (Fiordland penguin)
- *Eudyptes robustus* (snares penguin)
- *Eudyptes schlegeli* (royal penguin)
- *Eudyptes sclateri* (erect-crested penguin)

Eudyptula (little penguins)
- *Eudyptula minor* (little penguin)

Megadyptes (yellow-eyed penguin)
- *Megadyptes antipodes* (yellow-eyed penguin)

Pygoscelis (Adélie, chinstrap, and gentoo penguins)
- *Pygoscelis adeliae* (Adélie penguin)
- *Pygoscelis antarcticus* (chinstrap penguin)
- *Pygoscelis papua* (gentoo penguin)

Spheniscus (Spheniscus penguins)
- *Spheniscus demersus* (jackass penguin)
- *Spheniscus humboldti* (Humboldt penguin)
- *Spheniscus magellanicus* (Magellanic penguin)
- *Spheniscus mendiculus* (Galápagos penguin)

BELOW King penguins *(Aptenodytes patagonicus)*.

Dugongs, Manatees, and Sea cows — ORDER: SIRENIA: dugongs, manatees, and sea cows

FAMILY	SUBFAMILY	GENUS	SPECIES
DUGONGIDAE: dugong and sea cow	DUGONGINAE	*Dugong* (dugong)	*Dugong dugon* (dugong)
	HYDRODAMALINAE	*Hydrodamalis* (sea cow)	*Hydrodamalis gigas* (Steller's sea cow)
TRICHECHIDAE: manatees		*Trichechus* (manatees)	*Trichechus inunguis* (Amazonian manatee)
			Trichechus manatus (West Indian manatee)
			Trichechus senegalensis (African manatee)

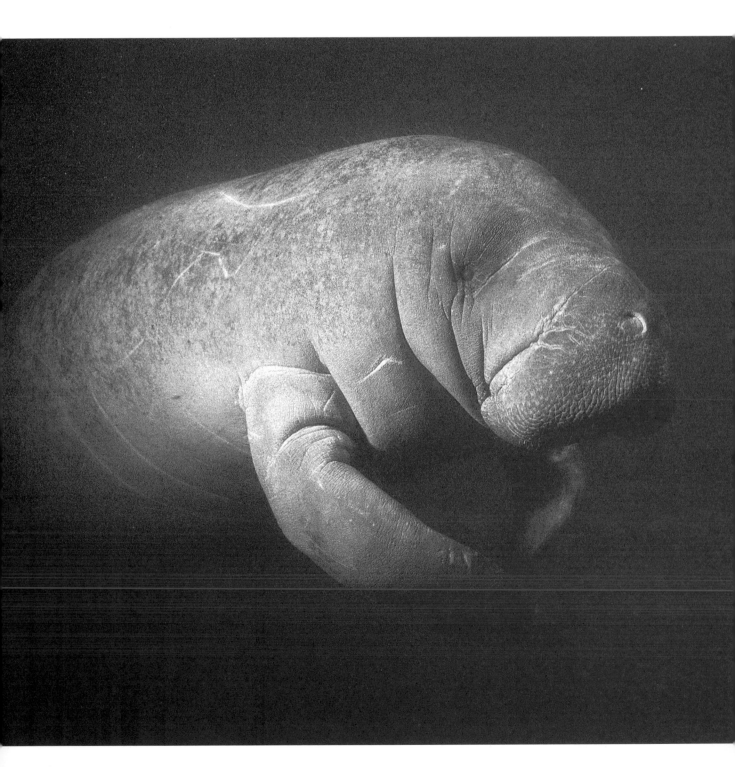

Polar Bears — ORDER: CARNIVORA: carnivores

SUBORDER	FAMILY	GENUS	SPECIES
CANIFORMA: caniform carnivores	URSIDAE: bears	*Ursus* (black bears, brown bear, and polar bear)	*Ursus maritimus* (polar bear)

RIGHT Polar bear *(Ursus maritimus)* and cubs.

LEFT Amazonian manatee *(Trichechus inunguis).*

Otters — ORDER: CARNIVORA: carnivores — SUBORDER: CANIFORMIA: caniform carnivores

FAMILY	SUBFAMILY	GENUS	SPECIES
MUSTELIDAE: badgers, otters, weasels, and relatives	LUTRINAE: otters	*Aonyx* (clawless otters)	*Aonyx capensis* (African clawless otter) *Aonyx cinerea* (Oriental small-clawed otter)
		Enhydra (sea otter)	*Enhydra lutris* (sea otter)
		Hydrictis (spotted-necked otter)	*Hydrictis maculicollis* (spotted-necked otter)
		Lontra (American river otters)	*Lontra canadensis* (northern river otter) *Lontra felina* (marine otter) *Lontra longicaudis* (neotropical river otter) *Lontra provocax* (southern river otter)
		Lutra (Old World river otters)	*Lutra lutra* (European otter) *Lutra nippon* (Japanese otter) *Lutra sumatrana* (hairy-nosed otter)
		Lutrogale (smooth-coated otter)	*Lutrogale perspicillata* (smooth-coated otter)
		Pteronura (giant otter)	*Pteronura brasiliensis* (giant otter)

LEFT Sea otter *(Enhydra lutris).*

1840 (previous pages)
James Clark Ross explores the Antarctic and takes
the first ocean sounding by lowering hemp rope.
HMS Erebus and *Terror* both become stuck in pack ice.

480 BCE
A Greek triere (trireme)
—a state-of-the-art battleship—is able to cover long
distances under oar and sail.

◀ 480 BCE   *c.*150 BCE ▶

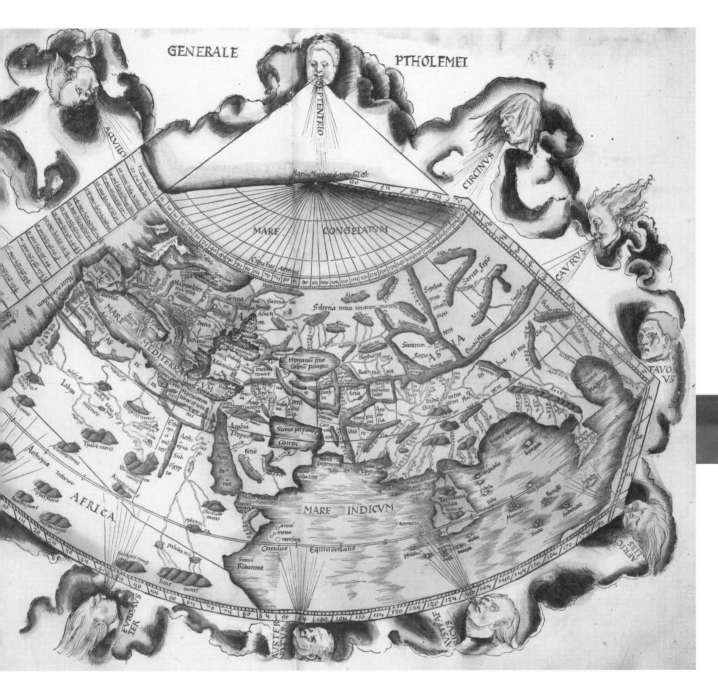

***c.* 150 BCE**
Ptolemy's map of the world shows early
shapes of continents, winds, and oceans.

***c.* 285 BCE (left)**
Pharos—a light tower to guide
ships into the harbor—is built at
Alexandria, Egypt.

1000 CE
Leif Ericson, the Norse explorer, lands in North America.

1000 CE

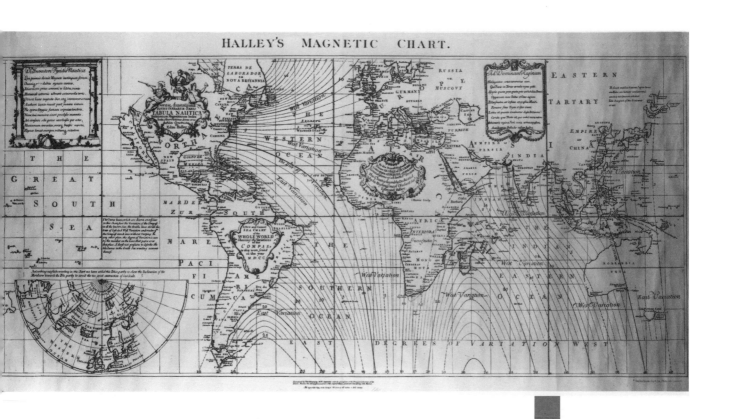

HALLEY'S MAGNETIC CHART.

1702

1702 (above)
Isogenic chart by Edmund Halley shows lines of equal magnetic variation across the oceans.

1492 (left)
Christopher Columbus (1451–1506) with his ships *Nina*, *Pinta*, and the *Santa Maria* approach America.

1520
Ferdinand Magellan (1480–1521) and his fleet discover a passage from the Atlantic to the Pacific Ocean—named the Strait of Magellan.

489

1770

After a mammoth voyage across the oceans, Captain James
Cook lands at Botany Bay and claims Australia for England.

1857
Submarine-type diving bell,
the *Nautilis*, is designed by
Samuel Hallett and the Count
of Rottermunde.

⬅ **1770**   **1843** ➡

1837–1843
HMS *Beagle* on a five-year
expedition with Charles Darwin,
arrives in the Strait of Magellan.

1883

1912
RMS *Titanic* sinks in
the Atlantic after
hitting an iceberg.

1925
Duke Kahanamoku popularizes
the sport of surfing, as well as
developing the long board.

1943
Jacques-Yves
Cousteau—pictured
on board *Calypso* in
1960—develops the
aqua-lung (scuba)
with engineer
Emile Gagnan.

1883 (left)
The volcanic eruption on Krakatoa,
Indonesia, which was the most
violent in history, became world
news headlines.

1946 ▶

1946
An atomic bomb
explodes on
Bikini Atoll in the
South Pacific.

1947
Norwegian explorer, Thor Heyerdahl, carries out an expedition on the raft *Kon-Tiki*, proving the possibility of the migration of Pacific islanders from South America.

1959 (below)
The US Navy bathyscaphe *Trieste* descends to the Mariana Trench.

 1947

2001
The oil rig, P-36,
begins to sink off
Brazil, following a
series of explosions.

2001 ➡

1966
Francis Chichester is the
first solo round-the-world
sailor in *Gipsy Moth IV*.

2004
The most devastating tsunami in history washes across Asia.

2004 **2009**

2009
The Whale Shark Expedition observes and identifies whale sharks *(Rhincodon typus)* in the Gulf of Tadjourah, as part of the Cousteau research program, Divers Aware of Sharks.

2009
Recovery of the black box is attempted after Air France Flight 447 disappears in the "Horse Latitudes" of the Atlantic Ocean with the loss of 228 persons.

A Brief Glossary of Terms

Abyssal plains: Extensive flat regions of the ocean floor, which are usually located at the base of a continental rise.

Algae (sing. **alga**): The term "algae" refers to a diversity of marine plants that produce organic compounds from carbon dioxide by photosynthesis, releasing oxygen as a byproduct. They include seaweeds, which range from slippery, turf-like filaments to dense underwater forests of tough, leathery fronds of kelp.

Archipelago: A clustered group of islands, or an elongate island chain.

Atoll: A circular coral reef that grows at, or near, the surface of the sea.

Barrier reefs: These develop along the edges of continental shelves and are separated from the mainland by open water. They do not necessarily form as a continuous strip; instead spurs, channels, and canyons may break them into composites of smaller reefs. A barrier reef usually grows on older reefs that were left stranded by a lowering of sea level and then re-submerged with an increase in sea level.

Bathypelagic zone: The deep-sea habitat below 3,280 ft (1,000 m). In this zone there is a total lack of sunlight penetration.

Beaufort scale: A 12-point scale used to measure wind speed, based on observation of the wind's effects; below 1 is "calm" and 12 is a hurricane.

Bight: An extensive curve in a coastline that forms a bay that is open to the sea.

Bioluminescence: The chemical emission of light from living creatures, such as some marine animals living in the ocean's depths.

Bireme: Battleship used in ancient times. It had two rows of oarsmen on either side of the vessel. A trireme had three rows of oarsmen.

Black smokers: Hydrothermal vents that appear as chimneys along the deep seafloor near spreading zones or centers that eject hot water, hydrogen sulfide, and other gases. The hydrogen sulfide forms sulfide precipitates, making the vents appear to exhale black smoke.

Carley float: An invertible life raft.

Celestial navigation: Using the stars and other celestial bodies to determine one's position. Used by sailors in times long past to cross the seas.

Channel: *see* Strait.

Circum–Pacific geothermal zone: More commonly know as the Pacific Ring of Fire, the Circum–Pacific geothermal zone is a large area known for volcanic activity that manifests itself in the form of frequent earthquakes and volcanic eruptions encircling the basin of the Pacific Ocean. It is also sometimes called the Circum–Pacific seismic belt or more simply the Circum–Pacific belt.

Coriolis effect: An apparent deflection of a freely moving object caused by Earth's rotation. In the Northern Hemisphere, objects are deflected to the right (clockwise direction) and in the Southern Hemisphere, objects are deflected to the left (counter-clockwise direction). The deflecting force of the Coriolis effect is greater at high latitudes and influences ocean currents.

Crest: The crest is the highest point on a wave. The trough, or valley between two crests, is the lowest point.

Dreadnought: A twentieth-century battleship carrying heavy guns, all of the same caliber.

Ekman spiral: This occurs when the combined influences of wind and the Coriolis effect cause ocean currents to move at an angle to the prevailing wind direction.

El Niño: A climate perturbation characterized by the warming of the equatorial waters in the Pacific Ocean by at least 0.9°F (0.5°C), which changes normal wind and current movements. It has far-reaching and often disastrous effects on the world's weather, notably bringing rain to South America and drought to Australia. It occurs on average every four or five years.

Epipelagic zone: The surface part of the ocean where enough sunlight penetrates for photosynthesis to occur.

Estuary: Estuaries are found at the mouths of rivers or streams as they flow into the ocean, in areas where the land is low, such that the fresh water does not drop steeply into the ocean.

Eustatic changes: Worldwide changes in sea level that affect all the oceans. They are generally caused in more recent times by removal and melting of ice from the frozen polar regions.

Foreshore: Also called the intertidal or littoral zone, the foreshore is the part of a beach submerged by high tides and exposed by low tides.

Galleass: Large galley with sails and oars.

Galleys: Small vessels propelled by oars.

Glacier: A large to very large mass of ice surviving year to year, and formed over time through the compaction and recrystallization of snow. A glacier moves down-slope very slowly by creep, due to the stress of its own immense weight.

Groin, groyne: A low structure, usually made of wood, built across the beach and into the sea to help reduce the effects of erosion.

Guyot: Flat-topped submarine mountains, usually volcanic in origin, that lie more than 660 ft (200 m) below sea level. They receive their flattened summits from wave action, sea level changes, or tectonic movements.

Gyre: A large-scale circular surface ocean current driven by the wind.

Horse latitudes: Zones of oceanic calms characterized by warmth and dryness that correspond with the subtropical highs at about 30° to 35°N and S.

Hydrothermal vents: *see* Black smokers.

Island: The internationally accepted definition of an island is "a naturally formed area of land, surrounded by water, which is above water at high tide."

La Niña: Opposite of El Niño; characterized by a cooling of the equatorial waters in the Pacific Ocean by at least 0.9°F (0.5°C); brings drought to South America and rain to Australia.

Longshore current: A current usually confined to the surface zone, which results when waves approach the shoreline or the coast at an angle.

Mangrove: A tropical evergreen tree or shrub with tangled, stilt-like roots forming dense clumps along tidal shores.

Marine deposit: Coastal alluvial deposits along the shore of an ocean, and extending outward to the edge of the continental shelf.

Marine erosion notch: A notch-like coastal structure formed mainly by the marine erosion.

Mesopelagic zone: The deep-sea habitat from approximately 656 to 3,280 ft (200 to 1,000 m) deep.

Mid-Atlantic Ridge: Part of a system of mid-ocean ridges that form the world's longest mountain range; it stretches approximately 10,000 miles (16,000 km) from north to south.

Mid-oceanic rift: The deep central fault trough or cleft in the crest of a mountainous mid-oceanic ridge, which may also be called a rift valley.

Neap tides: Small tides that occur during Quarter Moons. They produce the smallest tidal range.

Nearshore: A description of submerged land extending seaward or lakeward for a generally short although undefined distance from the shoreline.

Oceanic basins: Areas of the abyssal plain that are bounded by ridges, trenches, or continents.

Offshore: Description of any feature that is situated at an undefined distance from the shore.

Pacific "Ring of Fire": *see* Circum–Pacific geothermal zone. Also known as the Pacific "Rim of Fire."

Pangea: Also spelled Pangaea, this is the so-called supercontinent that existed during the Paleozoic and Mesozoic eras approximately 300 to 200 million years ago before each of the component continents was separated through the process of continental drift and formed their current configuration.

Passage: *see* Strait.

Pelagic zone: The upper layers of the waters of the open sea.

Phytoplankton: Microscopic single-celled plants and other simple algae that float in the upper layer of the ocean.

Plankton: Microscopic organisms floating in the ocean, made up of various tiny crustaceans, algae, diatoms, some protozoans, and eggs of other marine organisms. Plankton is an important food source for many marine creatures.

Rhumb line: A straight line followed by a ship from an initial bearing without changing true direction (not magnetic direction). A rhumb line crosses all meridians of longitude at the same angle.

Seamount: An underwater mountain that does not break the ocean's surface.

Sextant: A navigational device used to measure the angle between the horizon and a heavenly body, and thus determine latitude and longitude.

Spring tides: The largest tides; these occur when Earth, Sun, and Moon are in alignment.

Strait: A narrow strip of water between two or more areas of land. Also known as a channel or a passage.

Submarine canyons: Completely submerged, V-profiled, steep-sided canyons that extend down the slope of the continental shelf.

Tectonic plates: Sections of Earth's crust and uppermost mantle, together composing the lithosphere. Tectonic plates are around 60 miles (100 km) in thickness and consist mainly of oceanic crust and continental crust. The oceanic crust is mainly composed of basaltic rocks while continental crust consists principally of lower density rocks of granitic composition.

Tidal flats: Extensive in area and nearly horizontal in their topography, tidal flats are marshy or barren tracts of land that are alternately covered and uncovered by high and low tides.

Tidal inlets: Inlets through which water flows inward onto land at high tide and then retreats outward as the tide goes out.

Tidal surge: A massive surge in the tide, driven by a storm.

Tsunami: An ocean wave produced by a submarine earthquake, landslide, or volcanic eruption. It is often incorrectly called a tidal wave. These waves may reach enormous dimensions and have sufficient energy to travel across entire oceans. Their speed averages approximately 450 miles per hour (725 km/h).

Upwelling: The relatively quiet eruption of volcanic gases and lava without much force driving it.

Index

Page numbers in **bold** print refer to main entries. Page numbers in *italics* refer to photographs and illustrations

Credits and Acknowledgements

The Publisher would like to thank the following picture libraries and other copyright owners for permission to reproduce these images.

KEY: (t) top of page; (b) bottom of page; (l) left side of page; (r) right side of page; (c) center of page

Cover main image: Bridgeman Art Library/Thomas Luny/Getty Images

Cover inset images (from left to right): Copyright Corbis Australia; Bridgeman Art Library/George Carter/Getty Images; Visuals Unlimited/Brandon Cole/Getty Images; Bridgeman Art Library/Abraham Ortelius/Getty Images; WireImage/Getty Images

1 Copyright Corbis Australia; 2–3 White Images/Scala, Florence; 4–5 Paul Nicklen/National Geographic/Getty Images; 6–7 Copyright Corbis Australia; 8–9 Copyright Corbis Australia; 12–13 Copyright Corbis Australia; 14(tc) Copyright Corbis Australia; 14–15(b) Jeff Rotman/Iconica/Getty Images; 15(tl) Copyright Corbis Australia; 15(tr) Gary Bell/Taxi/Getty Images; 16(bl) Copyright Corbis Australia; 16(tr) Copyright Corbis Australia; 17(t) USGS National Center for EROS and NASA Landsat Project Science Office; 18(bc) Copyright Corbis Australia; 18(tl) Copyright Corbis Australia; 19(br) The Art Archive; 19(t) uniquedimension.com-Edimedia; 20–21 NASA/Goddard Space Flight Center Scientific Visualization Studio; 22–23(b) Millennium House; 23(tc) Copyright Corbis Australia; 24(b) Copyright Corbis Australia; 24(tl) Copyright Corbis Australia; 25(bc) NASA; Jacques Descloitres, MODIS Land Rapid Response Team, NASA/GSFC; 25(t) NASA; NASA Goddard Space Flight Center; 28–29 Yannick Le Gal/Getty Images; 30(c) NASA Johnson Space Center; 30–31(b) Eric Meola/The Image Bank/Getty Images; 31(cr) Copyright Corbis Australia; 31(tl) Copyright Corbis Australia; 31(tr) Copyright Corbis Australia; 32(bc) uniquedimension.com-World History Archive; 32(bc) uniquedimension.com-World History Archive; 32(cl) Copyright Corbis Australia; 33(t) Copyright Corbis Australia; 34(bc) Copyright Corbis Australia; 34(tl) Copyright Corbis Australia; 34(tr) NASA; NASA Visible Earth/Jacques Descloitres, MODIS Land Science Team; 35 Copyright Corbis Australia; 36(b) Copyright Corbis Australia; 37(c) Copyright Corbis Australia; 37(tr) Millennium House; 38(tl) uniquedimension.com-World History Archive; 38(tl) uniquedimension.com-World History Archive; 38–39(t) Copyright Corbis Australia; 40(bl) Copyright Corbis Australia; 40(cl) Copyright Corbis Australia; 41(tr) uniquedimension.com-World History Archive;/NOAA/NASA; 42(tl) NASA/GSFC/MITI/ERSDAC/JAROS, and U.S./Japan ASTER Science Team; 43(br) Copyright Corbis Australia; 43(tc) Copyright Corbis Australia; 44–45 Copyright Corbis Australia; 46(tc) Copyright Corbis Australia; 46–47(b) Darrell Gulin/Getty Images; 47(c) Copyright Corbis Australia; 47(tr) Copyright Corbis Australia; 48(bl) Copyright Corbis Australia; 48(tl) NASA Visible Earth/Jeff Schmaltz, MODIS Rapid Response Team, NASA/GSFC; 49(bc) Copyright Corbis Australia; 49(t) Copyright Corbis Australia; 52 Copyright Corbis Australia; 52–53(t) Tim Laman/Getty Images; 56(bl) Copyright Corbis Australia; 57(cr) Copyright Corbis Australia; 57(tl) Copyright Corbis Australia; 60(bl) Copyright Corbis Australia; 60(tl) Copyright Corbis Australia; 61(t) Copyright Corbis Australia; 64(b) Copyright Corbis Australia; 65(cr) Copyright Corbis Australia; 65(tl) Copyright Corbis Australia; 69(b) Copyright Corbis Australia; 69(b) Copyright Corbis Australia; 69(tl) Copyright Corbis Australia; 69(tl) Copyright Corbis Australia; 69(tr) Copyright Corbis Australia; 69(tr) Copyright Corbis Australia; 70(b) Copyright Corbis Australia; 71(cr) Copyright Corbis Australia; 72(tl) Copyright Corbis Australia; 73 Copyright Corbis Australia; 74(tl) Copyright Corbis Australia; 75(br) Jacques Descloitres, MODIS Rapid Response Team, NASA/GSFC; 75(t) Copyright Corbis Australia; 76(b) Copyright Corbis Australia; 77(bl) Copyright Corbis Australia; 77(br) Copyright Corbis Australia; 78(b) NASA; SeaWiFS Project, NASA/Goddard Space Flight Center, and ORBIMAGE; 79(bc) Copyright Corbis Australia; 79(cr) uniquedimension.com-World History Archive; 80(c) Copyright Corbis Australia; 80(cl) Copyright Corbis Australia; 81(t) uniquedimension.com-World History Archive; 82(b) Copyright Corbis Australia; 82(tl) Copyright Corbis Australia; 83(br) Copyright Corbis Australia; 83(tl) NASA; SeaWiFS Project, NASA/Goddard Space Flight Center, and ORBIMAGE; 84(tl) Copyright Corbis Australia; 84(tr) Copyright Corbis Australia; 85(b) Copyright Corbis Australia; 85(tr) Copyright Corbis Australia; 86(tl) Copyright Corbis Australia; 86(tr) Copyright Corbis Australia; 87(b) Copyright Corbis Australia; 87(tr) Copyright Corbis Australia; 88(br) Copyright Corbis Australia; 88(cl) Copyright Corbis Australia; 89(bl) Copyright Corbis Australia; 89(tr) Copyright Corbis Australia; 90(bl) Copyright Corbis Australia; 90(tl) NASA; Jacques Descloitres, MODIS Land Science Team; 91(t) Copyright Corbis Australia; 92(bl) NASA; Robert Simmon, NASA's Earth Observatory, based on data copyright Space Imaging; 92(tl) Copyright Corbis Australia; 93(b) Copyright Corbis Australia; 93(tr) Copyright Corbis Australia; 94(b) Copyright Corbis Australia; 95(cr) Copyright Corbis Australia; 95(tl) Copyright Corbis Australia; 96(bl) Copyright Corbis Australia; 96(cl) Copyright Corbis Australia; 97(t) NASA; Jacques Descloitres, MODIS Land Rapid Response Team, NASA/GSFC; 98(cl) Copyright Corbis Australia; 98(tc) Copyright Corbis Australia; 99(c) NASA/GSFC/METI/ERSDAC/JAROS, and U.S./Japan ASTER Science Team; 99(cr) Copyright Corbis Australia; 99(tl) Copyright Corbis Australia; 100(cl) Copyright Corbis Australia; 100(tr) Copyright Corbis Australia; 101(r) Copyright Corbis Australia; 101(tl) Copyright Corbis Australia; 102(bc) Copyright Corbis Australia; 102(t) Copyright Corbis Australia; 103(bc) NASA; Jacques Descloitres, MODIS Land Rapid Response Team, NASA/GSFC; 103(tr) Copyright Corbis Australia; 104(br) Copyright Corbis Australia; 104(cl) Copyright Corbis Australia; 105(br) NASA; SeaWiFS Project, NASA/Goddard Space Flight Center, and ORBIMAGE; 105(tr) Copyright Corbis Australia; 106(l) Copyright Corbis Australia; 107(tr) Copyright Corbis Australia; 108(cl) Copyright Corbis Australia; 108(tl) Copyright Corbis Australia; 109(t) Copyright Corbis Australia; 110(bl) Copyright Corbis Australia; 110(tr) Copyright Corbis Australia; 111(b) Copyright Corbis Australia; 111(tr) Copyright Corbis Australia; 112(b) Copyright Corbis Australia; 112(tl) Copyright Corbis Australia; 113(r) Copyright Corbis Australia; 114(bl) NASA; 114(br) Copyright Corbis Australia; 115(bl) Copyright Corbis Australia; 115(cr) Copyright Corbis Australia; 116(t) Copyright Corbis Australia; 117(cr) Copyright Corbis Australia; 117(tl) Copyright Corbis Australia; 118(b) Copyright Corbis Australia; 118(tc) Copyright Corbis Australia; 119(tr) Copyright Corbis Australia; 120(cl) Copyright Corbis Australia; 121(br) Copyright Corbis Australia; 121(t) Copyright Corbis Australia; 122(tl) Copyright Corbis Australia; 122–123(t) Copyright Corbis Australia; 124(tl) Copyright Corbis Australia; 125(bl) Copyright Corbis Australia; 125(t)(t) Copyright Corbis Australia; 126(bl) Copyright Corbis Australia; 126(cl) Copyright Corbis Australia; 126(tl) Copyright Corbis Australia; 127 Copyright Corbis Australia; 127(bl) Copyright Corbis Australia; 127(t) Copyright Corbis Australia; 130(tl) Copyright Corbis Australia; 131(t) Copyright Corbis Australia; 132(bl) Copyright Corbis Australia; 132(tl) Copyright Corbis Australia; 133(br) Copyright Corbis Australia; 133(t) Copyright Corbis Australia; 134(bl) Copyright Corbis Australia; 134(c) Copyright Corbis Australia; 134(tl) Copyright Corbis Australia; 135(t) Copyright Corbis Australia; 136(bl) Copyright Corbis Australia; 136(cl) Copyright Corbis Australia; 137 Copyright Corbis Australia; 138–139 Pete Atkinson/Getty Images; 140(bl) Copyright Corbis Australia; 140(tc) Copyright Corbis Australia; 140–141(background) Copyright Corbis Australia; 141(tc) Copyright Corbis Australia; 142(bl) Copyright Corbis Australia; 143 Copyright Corbis Australia; 146(br) Copyright Corbis Australia; 147(t) Copyright Corbis Australia; 148(br) Copyright Corbis Australia; 148(cr) NASA; 149(t) Copyright Corbis Australia; 150(cl) Copyright Corbis Australia; 151(br) Copyright Corbis Australia; 151(t) Copyright Corbis Australia; 152(br) Copyright Corbis Australia; 152(t) Copyright Corbis Australia; 153(br) The Art Archive/Bibliothèque des Arts Décoratifs Paris/Alfredo Dagli Orti; 153(tr) Copyright Corbis Australia; 154–155 Copyright Corbis Australia; 156(tc) Copyright Corbis Australia; 156(tr) Copyright Corbis Australia; 157(cr) Copyright Corbis Australia; 157(tr) Copyright Corbis Australia; 158(b) Copyright Corbis Australia; 159(bl) Copyright Corbis Australia; 159(tr) Copyright Corbis Australia; 160(cl) Copyright Corbis Australia; 160(tr) Copyright Corbis Australia; 161 Copyright Corbis Australia; 162(cl) Copyright Corbis Australia; 162(tr) Copyright Corbis Australia; 163 Copyright Corbis Australia; 164(b) Copyright Corbis Australia; 165(br) Copyright Corbis Australia; 165(tl) Copyright Corbis Australia; 165(tr) Copyright Corbis Australia; 166(bl) Copyright Corbis Australia; 166(tr) Copyright Corbis Australia; 167(t) Copyright Corbis Australia; 168(b) Copyright Corbis Australia; 169(br) Copyright Corbis Australia; 169(c) Copyright Corbis Australia; 169(tc) Copyright Corbis Australia; 170(bc) Copyright Corbis Australia; 170(cl) uniquedimension.com-World History Archive; 171(bc) Copyright Corbis Australia; 171(t) Copyright Corbis Australia; 172(cl) Copyright Corbis Australia; 173(br) Copyright Corbis Australia; 173(tl) Copyright Corbis Australia; 174(bl) Copyright Corbis Australia; 174(tl) Copyright Corbis Australia; 175(t) Copyright Corbis Australia; 176(cl) Copyright Corbis Australia; 176(tl) Copyright Corbis Australia; 177(t) Copyright Corbis Australia; 178(bc) Copyright Corbis Australia; 178(cl) Copyright Corbis Australia; 179(bc) Copyright Corbis Australia; 179(t) Copyright Corbis Australia; 180(t) Copyright Corbis Australia; 180(b) Copyright Corbis Australia; 181 Copyright Corbis Australia; 182–183(t) Copyright Corbis Australia; 183(bl) Copyright Corbis Australia; 183(br) Copyright Corbis Australia; 183(cr) Copyright Corbis Australia; 183(tr) Copyright Corbis Australia; 184(bl) uniquedimension.com-World History Archive/Drow; 184(c) Copyright Corbis Australia; 185(br) Copyright Corbis Australia; 185(t) uniquedimension.com-World History Archive/Jon Hanson; 186(cl) Copyright Corbis Australia; 187 DEA Picture Library/Getty Images; 188(bl) Copyright Corbis Australia; 189 Copyright Corbis Australia; 190(bl) Copyright Corbis Australia; 190(tl) Copyright Corbis Australia; 190(tr) Copyright Corbis Australia; 191(t) Copyright Corbis Australia; 192(b) Copyright Corbis Australia; 193(br) Copyright Corbis Australia; 193(tc) Copyright Corbis Australia; 194(bl) Copyright Corbis Australia; 194(c) Copyright Corbis Australia; 195(br) Peter David/Getty Images; 195(tl) Copyright Corbis Australia; 196(bl) Copyright Corbis Australia; 196(tr) Bill Curtsinger/National Geographic/Getty Images; 197(br) David Wrobel/Getty Images; 197(t) Copyright Corbis Australia; 198(b) Copyright Corbis Australia; 199(br) Copyright Corbis Australia; 199(tr) Copyright Corbis Australia; 200(br) Copyright Corbis Australia; 200(tl) Copyright Corbis Australia; 201(br) Copyright Corbis Australia; 201(t) Copyright Corbis Australia; 202–203(b) Copyright Corbis Australia; 203(br) Copyright Corbis Australia; 203(cr) Copyright Corbis Australia; 203(tl) Copyright Corbis Australia; 204(cl) Copyright Corbis Australia; 205(bl) Copyright Corbis Australia; 205(t) Copyright Corbis Australia; 206–207(t) Copyright Corbis Australia; 207(cr) Copyright Corbis Australia; 207(tr) Copyright Corbis Australia; 208(bl) Copyright Corbis Australia; 208–209(t) Copyright Corbis Australia; 209(br) Copyright Corbis Australia; 210(cl) Copyright Corbis Australia; 210–211(b) Copyright Corbis Australia; 211(br) Copyright Corbis Australia; 212(cl) Copyright Corbis Australia; 212(tl) Copyright Corbis Australia; 213(bc) Copyright Corbis Australia; 213(t) Copyright Corbis Australia; 214(bl) Copyright Corbis Australia; 214–215(t) Copyright Corbis Australia; 215(br) Copyright Corbis Australia; 216(bl) Copyright Corbis Australia; 217 Copyright Corbis Australia; 218–219(t) Copyright Corbis Australia; 219(bl) Copyright Corbis Australia; 219(br) Copyright Corbis Australia; 219(cr) Copyright Corbis Australia; 219(tr) Copyright Corbis Australia; 220(cl) Copyright Corbis Australia; 221(b) Copyright Corbis Australia; 221(tl) Copyright Corbis Australia; 222(bl) Copyright Corbis Australia; 222(cl) Copyright Corbis Australia; 223(br) Copyright Corbis Australia; 223(t) Copyright Corbis Australia; 224(bl) Copyright Corbis Australia; 225 Copyright Corbis Australia; 226–227 George Carter/Getty Images; 228(t) Copyright Corbis Australia; 229(tc) Copyright Corbis Australia; 229(tr) Copyright Corbis Australia; 230(bl) uniquedimension.com-World History Archive; 231(cr) Photo Scala Florence/HIP; 231(t) uniquedimension.com-World History Archive/Museum für Antike Schiffahrt (Museum for Ancient Navigation) in Mainz; 232(bl) uniquedimension.com-World History Archive; 232(tr) The Art Archive/Museo Storico Navale Venice/Gianni Dagli Orti; 233 The Art Archive/Science Academy Lisbon/Gianni Dagli Orti; 234(tl) Copyright Corbis

The publisher also wishes to thank Alexander Goldberg and Jason Newman of uniquedimension.com for their assistance with photo research.